Algrove Publishing Limited
1090 Morrison Drive
Ottawa, Ontario
Canada K2H 1C2

Canadian Cataloguing in Publication Data

Main entry under title:

Popular mechanics shop notes for ...

(Classic reprint series)
Includes indexes.
Originally published: Chicago : Popular Mechanics Co., 1905-
"Compiled from the "Shop notes" department of Popular mechanics magazine, and "Written so you can understand it;" tells easy ways to do hard things" --Added t.p., v. 1.
Cover title.
Contents: v. 20. 1924.
ISBN 1-894572-26-2 (v. 20)

1. Do-it-yourself work. 2. Industrial arts. 3. Bricolage. 4. Métiers. I. Title: Shop notes for ... . II. Series: Classic reprint series (Ottawa, Ont.)

TJ1160.P66 1999 600 C99-900763-7

Printed in Canada
#10101

Publisher's Note

Virtually every woodworking magazine in the English-speaking world has a shop notes section and has published an accumulation of them in book form. This was all started in 1905 with the first annual issue of *Popular Mechanics Shop Notes*, a compilation of advice on jigs, fixtures, methods of work, processes and projects. The earlier issues focussed primarily on metalworking, but with tips for a variety of other trades liberally sprinkled throughout. As years went by, the contents shifted more and more to woodworking and handyman projects. Each book is profusely illustrated. The line drawings of the earlier issues were supplanted by superb engravings until photographs started to creep in during the 1920s. Each year has its charm but all issues share the attribute of being clear, concise and widely informative.

Leonard G. Lee, Publisher
Ottawa
September, 1999

WARNING

This is a reprint of a book compiled in the early 1900s. The book describes what was recommended to be done in accordance with the knowledge of the day.

It would be advisable to treat all corrosive, explosive and toxic materials with much greater caution than is indicated here, particularly any materials that come in contact with the body.

Similarly, some of the recommended projects were dangerous then and remain so now. All of this material should be regarded with a judicious eye and necessary precautions taken.

POPULAR MECHANICS

SHOP NOTES

FOR

1924

EASY WAYS TO DO HARD THINGS

OF DAILY USE
TO EVERY MECHANIC

PUBLISHED BY
POPULAR MECHANICS PRESS
CHICAGO, ILLINOIS, U. S. A.

PRINTED IN U. S. A.

A Rural Mail-Box Post of Concrete

BY A. J. R. CURTIS

PROGRESSIVE farmers and villagers all over the country are discarding the old makeshift wooden mail-box post, and substituting for it the modern concrete post, which is attractive in appearance, and is neither affected by frost, attacked by rot, nor likely to be destroyed by fire.

Any farmer with a little time to spare can make the post described in this article at home. It is so simple in construction that it is suggested as an excellent manual-training exercise for rural-school students.

The accompanying drawings show how the post is constructed. The form is built up on a floor having a level and regular surface, or on a pallet or mat of boards, 8 ft. long and at least 30 in. wide. If a floor is used, a strip of building, or other heavy, paper should be used as a covering. The form consists simply of a few wooden strips (dressed on all surfaces to be touched by the concrete), held in position by cleats lightly nailed to the floor or pallet. The post is cast on its side. Prepare first two pieces of 1-in. board, 7 ft. 4 in. long, 6 in. wide at one end, and tapering to a width of 4 in. at the other. Finish and sandpaper the opposite faces of each. One of these strips serves as a form for the straight, plain side of the post. The other serves as a form for the opposite side of the post, being cut as required, and joined to smaller pieces, of similar material, to make the entire outline of the bracket and shelf. The form for the interior triangle is best made from a block with a small amount of taper, so that it can be withdrawn upward. This piece in particular must be well greased and sandpapered, and screweyes should be inserted in the top to make its removal easier.

The longitudinal strips are held apart by square blocks inserted between them at the lower and upper ends. Triangular blocks, inserted at the upper end, form the upper corners of the post, as shown.

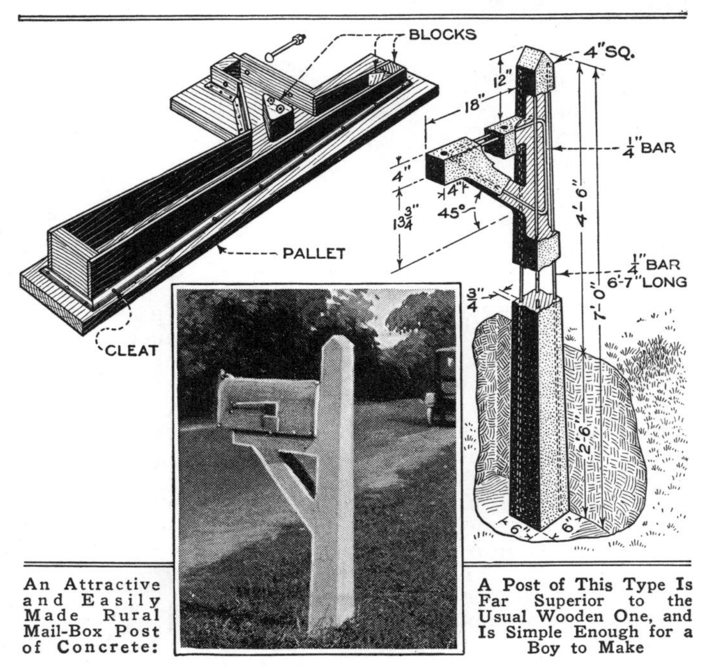

An Attractive and Easily Made Rural Mail-Box Post of Concrete: A Post of This Type Is Far Superior to the Usual Wooden One, and Is Simple Enough for a Boy to Make

The reinforcing in the post consists of four 1/4-in. round bars, 6 ft. 9 in. long, placed symmetrically at the four corners of the post, 3/4 in. in from the surfaces. The bracket and shelf are reinforced with two triangles made of 1/4-in. bars, bent as shown, and inserted in the mold one above the other, 1 in. away from all outer surfaces. The bolts to which the mail box is attached are placed through the molds before the concrete is deposited.

The concrete for the post is mixed in the proportions of 1 part Portland cement to 3 parts well-graded sand, under ¼ in. in size, or 1 part Portland cement to 2½ parts sand and 1 to 2 parts of crushed stone, or pebbles, from ¼ in. to ½ in. in size. The mixture must be made just wet enough to flow freely to all parts of the mold. The mold is well greased before the concrete is poured.

In moderate weather, allow the post to remain at least three days before attempting to raise or remove it. In cool weather, wait four or five days. At the end of that time move it only with great care, as posts that later become very strong and hard are easily injured by careless handling while "green."

As soon as the mold is removed, brush and scrape off fins and other blemishes, and fill up holes and hollows with the same mixture as used in the post. Then paint the surfaces with a creamy mixture of cement and water, and store the post where it will not be exposed to sun, wind, or frost, or subject to strain.

A Simple Drip Can

The drip can shown in the illustration has been used for a considerable time for

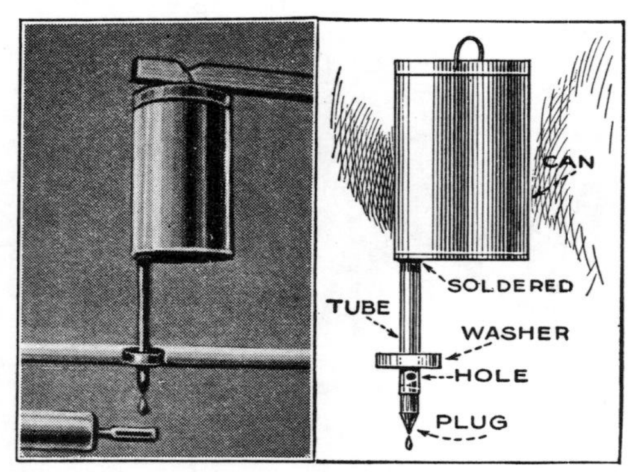

Simple Drip Can for Supplying Oil and Cutting Compounds to Taps in a Tapping Machine, Using Improvised Supply-Regulating Valve

supplying oil and cutting compounds to taps used in a tapping machine, and has been found to give as much satisfaction as any device on the market.

It is made by piercing a hole in the bottom of a tin can and soldering a short length of copper tubing into this hole. A wooden plug, pointed at one end, is driven securely into the lower end of the tube, and a small hole is drilled in the tube just above the plug. The amount of liquid flowing out of this hole is controlled by covering the hole more or less with a leather or rubber washer that slides snugly on the tube.

Steel Rivets Damage Brake Drums

It is a very poor policy to substitute common steel rivets for copper and brass ones where the latter are used for a special reason, as, for instance, in relining brake and transmission bands. Here such substitution will entail considerable unforeseen expense. This was the case when, in making repairs on a light car, it was found that the brake, slow-speed, and reverse drums were deeply grooved by the steel rivets used in lining the bands, making it necessary to remove the motor in order to replace these parts. Copper or brass rivets should be used under all circumstances when relining bands, and one should make sure that they are not copper-coated steel rivets by cutting one in two. Before substituting one material for another, in repair work of any kind, it should be ascertained that the substitution will not be harmful.

Scale Holder for Lathe Use

Much lathe work requires to be turned with a shoulder a definite distance from the end. When facing a shoulder to length, it is necessary to stop the lathe repeatedly in order to measure the distance, as while the machine is in motion, the scale cannot be applied with any degree of accuracy, apart from the danger involved due to the tendency of the scale to catch the work. With the holder shown, however, the user can measure the work without stopping the lathe at all, saving a good deal of time and trouble where much work of this kind is done. The construction is very simple; a piece of $\frac{3}{16}$-in. stock, 1 in. wide, is bent to form a "V," and then doubled over, as shown, to fit the scale. The side of the holder that bears against the shoulder is finished square with the V and the scale

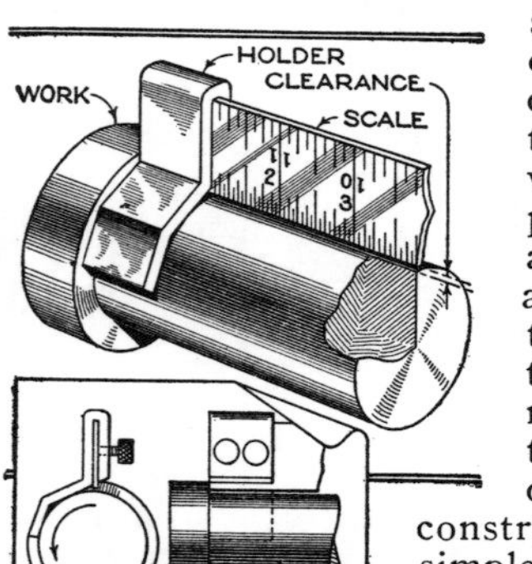

slot. Two knurled screws are used to hold the scale in place. When attaching the holder to the scale, it should be laid on the work, close to the shoulder, whereupon the scale, with its bottom just clear of the work, is pushed in to touch the shoulder lightly, and the two screws are tightened. Any number of pieces can then be turned and measured with the lathe in motion, the scale being held exactly in line with the work, insuring accurate results. The holder, of course, should be casehardened.

Clearing Sand from Loading Tracks to Prevent Derailment

Derailment of cars, due to an excessive amount of sand and gravel on the loading tracks at material yards, is not an uncommon occurrence. An inexpensive method of keeping the tracks clean was devised by a large building-material concern, and is shown in the drawing. A narrow concrete pit or trough was built on one side of the tracks; this drained into a waste basin. After a car had been loaded, the tracks were flushed by means of a stream of water, directed from a monitor nozzle set on the outer side of the track. The water and sand run into the concrete trough and to the waste basin.

Imitation Ice for Window Displays

Imitation ice adds to the effect of window displays that advertise skates and other outdoor winter goods. It is usually made with pieces of plate glass, to which a "frosty" effect is given by sprinkling fine flakes of mica on the glass, after it has been painted with a thin solution of glue and water.

In order to make this imitation ice look as real as possible, the plate glass should be given a bluish hue by mounting it on light-blue crêpe paper, stretched tightly under the glass to eliminate the wrinkles.—H. Webster, Winnipeg, Can.

Automatic Ventilator for Poultry Houses

Most poultrymen today acknowledge the value of good ventilation in the winter laying pens. But ventilation without objectionable drafts is often hard to accomplish, especially where snowstorms and blizzards are of frequent occurrence. The open-air type of henhouse, which is in general use, is not entirely satisfactory because snow and rain can enter. Even if a muslin curtain is provided to prevent this, it is necessary to adjust this curtain according to weather conditions, and this is very often neglected. To overcome these difficulties, and to make the ventilation entirely automatic, a Wisconsin poultryman devised the shutter arrangement shown in the illustration.

A Shutter for the Poultry House That, While Providing Ample Ventilation, Eliminates Draft, as It Closes Automatically in a Wind

It consists of a frame projecting from the side of the poultry house as shown, about 6 ft. long and 4 ft. high, roofed over with tar paper. Seven 6-in. boards are suspended within this frame, with enough space between them to insure proper ventilation at all times, and arranged in such a manner that they swing easily upon pivot nails driven through the frame at each end.

In fair weather the shutters hang vertically, but when gusts of wind, with rain or snow, beat against them, they close automatically. To prevent the fowls from scratching litter into the openings, which would interfere with the movement of the shutters, sparrow netting is tacked across the frame, on the inside of the house.—G. E. Hendrickson, Argyle, Wis.

Combination Farmyard Gate

A farmyard gate that answers a twofold purpose is shown in the illustration. One

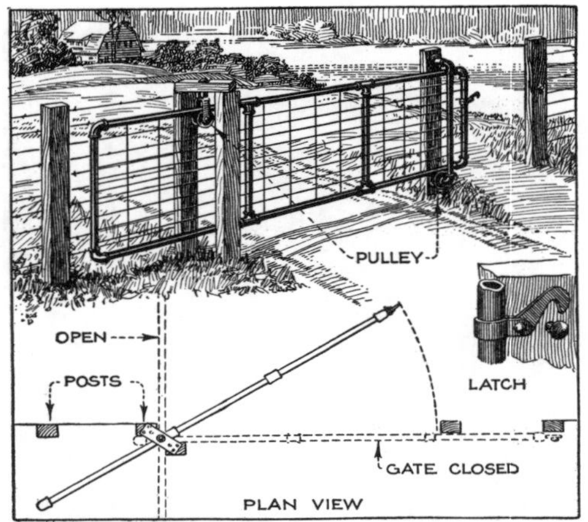

Sliding and Swinging Farmyard Gate That Serves Both Pedestrians and Cattle, or Vehicles

part is designed for pedestrians, and the other for cattle and farm vehicles.

To allow persons to pass through the gate, the latch is released and the gate pushed open; it is set on an incline so that it will close of its own weight. When it is desired to open the entire gate to permit cattle to pass through, it is pushed off the bottom pulley and swung around, which can be done very easily, as the other end of the gate is suspended from a swivel pulley, hung between two posts.

Vacuum Gauge Made from Pressure Gauge

While experimenting with a small ice machine, it was desired to know whether the compressor reduced the pressure sufficiently on the suction side. Two pressure gauges were available, but no vacuum gauge, and accordingly it was decided to try to convert one of these to register the amount of vacuum, if the curved rack that engaged the gear on the indicator pinion was long enough. By removing the glass, indicator hand, and dial, it was easily ascertained that this was so. Satisfied on that point, the pin opposite the zero mark on the dial was removed. Then, as the marking was regular from zero to 250, the dividers were set to indicate 5-lb. pressures and the graduations continued to 15 below zero. The dial was replaced, and, with the outlet open to the atmosphere, the pointer on the spindle was forced to stand at the zero mark. After this the glass cover was put back. On connecting the converted pressure gauge to the suction side of the compressor, the hand barely left the zero mark. The valves were then taken out of the machine and reground, after which everything operated as it should. The marking in this instance was made 15, because it was close enough for the purpose, as the machine functioned perfectly at the 5 mark.

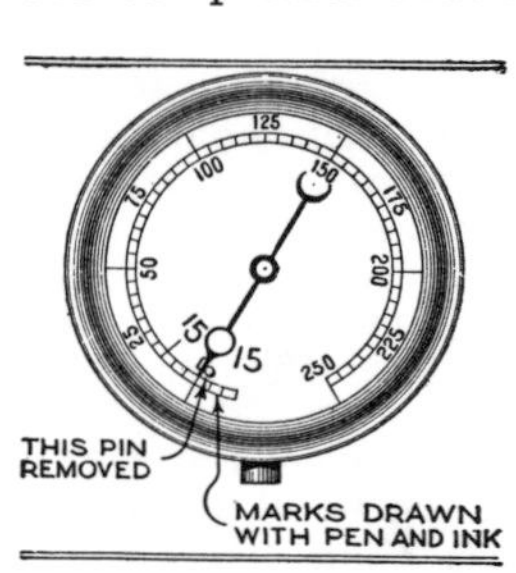

Setting Pipe in Concrete

In the construction of a reinforced-concrete and steel factory building, it was specified that, wherever conduit or other pipe was to pass through a floor, a short piece of pipe having an internal diameter large enough to accommodate the conduit or pipe, should be set. The short pieces of pipe were to be flush with the ceiling on the underside and project about 2 in. beyond the floor above. In most locations, it was difficult to secure these short lengths of pipe so that they would stay exactly where they were placed, and in the majority of cases, it was found that, after the concrete had set, and the forms had been removed, the sleeves had shifted a little, or had risen enough to allow the semiliquid concrete to enter and partly fill the pipe. After a number of faults of this kind had been discovered, the method illustrated was devised and used with excellent results. A block of wood was neatly rounded to slip inside one of the pipes, the other end of the plug being whittled down to fit into an auger hole drilled through the wooden form. A hammer and smaller piece of pipe were used to drive the plug into the hole tightly. It was found that the pipes set in this manner stayed in the exact position in which they were placed.—Leon D. Quick, Milesburg, Pa.

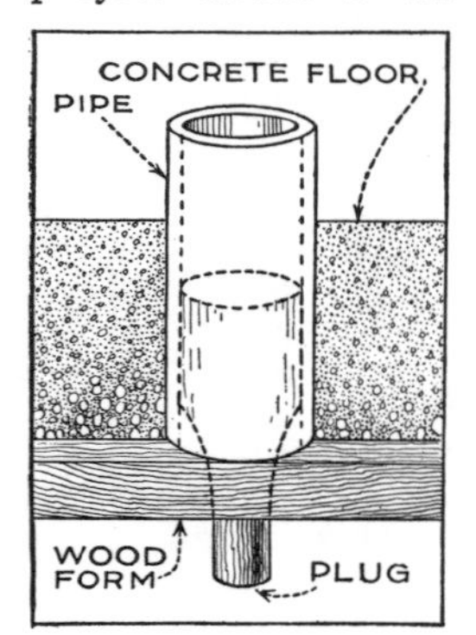

Pricker for Draftsmen

The pricker that is usually included in a set of drawing instruments is rather clumsy to handle, and does not prove very satisfactory to those who find it necessary to use this instrument frequently, as is the case with structural and topographical draftsmen. An extremely handy and serviceable pricker can be made very easily by purchasing a medium-size crochet hook at a dry-goods store, and grinding off the hook, to make a fine, round point. It should be finished on an oilstone to make a good job. This form of pricker will not tire nor cramp the hand. —E. D. Hay, Des Moines, Ia.

An Inclosure for the Garbage Cans

It is always desirable to place the garbage cans, and the rubbish that accumulates about the yard, in a part of the yard entirely out of sight from the house. As this was impossible, in one case, because

A Small Inclosure, Used for Garbage Cans and Rubbish, Keeps the Back Yard Neat and Clean

the back yard was so small, an inclosure, 4 ft. by 7 ft., was formed, as shown, inside of the fence that separated the back yard from the alley. The garbage collector need not enter the yard, and as the gate can be kept latched or locked, stray dogs, cats, and other undesirable visitors are kept out.

An inclosure of this type can also be used as a temporary storage place for wood or coal, in cities where it is not permissible to dump material of this kind in the alley.

Sawing Slots in Sleeves and Washers

It is very inconvenient to saw internal slots in washers, or sleeves, by means of a common hacksaw, as the blade must be removed from the frame, inserted through the hole, and again be fastened to the frame. A good holder, that makes this unnecessary, can be made from a short piece of broom handle, about 4 in. longer than the saw blade.

A groove is cut lengthwise in the holder, so that the blade can be inserted to

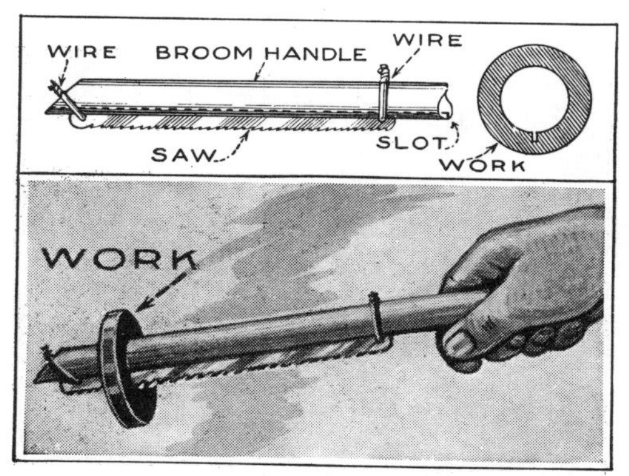

A Simple Tool for Sawing Internal Slots in Washers or Sleeves, Made from a Piece of Broomstick

about one-third of its depth. Soft wire is passed through the holes at each end of the blade and is twisted around the holder. The end of the holder is cut at an angle so that the wire, when twisted around this end, will pull the blade taut.

Spark-Plug Tester Protects Ignition Coil

Ignition coils are often injured while testing spark plugs. A plug with defective insulation will often spark under atmospheric pressure but fail to do so when under compression in the cylinder. Therefore, while testing it, a piece of mica is often placed between the points to increase the resistance and cause the spark to jump a gap of ¼ in. or more. Although this is an excellent method of testing spark plugs, the ignition coil is likely to be injured when the spark is caused to jump too far.

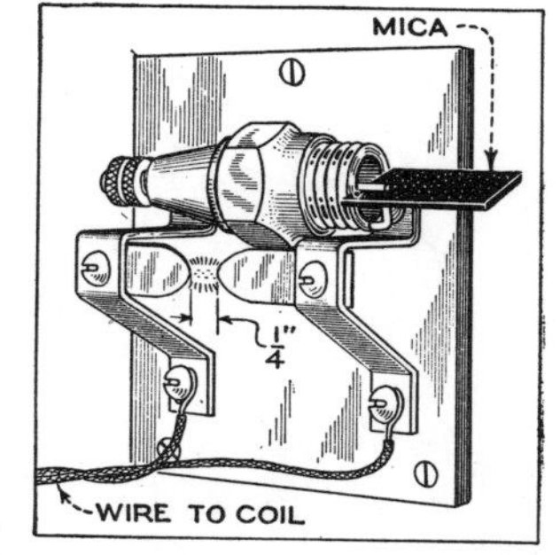

By using the simple arrangement shown in the illustration, the danger of coil breakdown is eliminated. The spark plug is placed across two brass brackets, which are mounted on an insulating base, and are fitted with points having a ¼-in. air gap between them. The spark will jump this gap as soon as the gap in the plug is over ¼ inch.

Concrete Wheel Ways Serve as Gutters

A plain dirt driveway, cut through a bank, was frequently ruined by washouts. As it was not desired to go to the ex-

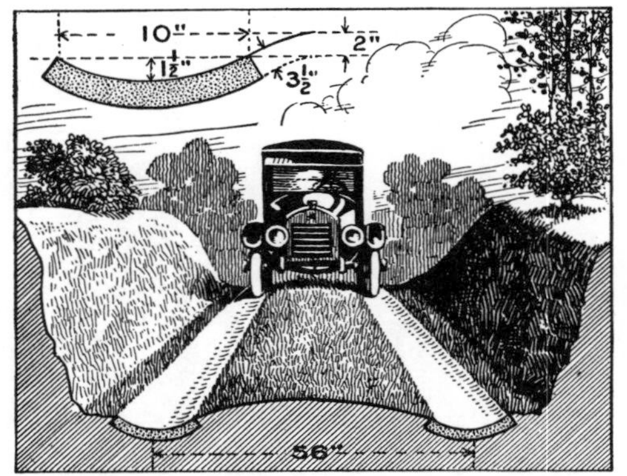

Concave Wheel Ways, That Also Serve as Gutters, Which were Built to Prevent Frequent Washouts That Ruined the Dirt Driveway

pense of building an entire cement driveway, two concave wheel ways, designed also to serve as gutters, were built, and no more trouble from washouts was experienced. These ways were 10 in. wide and about 3½ in. thick, and made of a circular-arc section, with the center about 1½ in. below the edges. The distance between the centers was 56 inches. The ground between the ways was crowned, so that all the water would be shed into them.—O. H. Hampsch, Nashville, Tenn.

Locating Arm for Faceplate Work

Sometimes it is a very difficult matter to bolt a job on the faceplate of a lathe while the former is on the spindle, and it often happens that it would be more convenient to lay the faceplate flat on a bench and bolt the work to it. When this is done, it generally requires much time and measuring to set the job near the right position. If much of this kind of work is done, a locating arm similar to the one shown in the drawing will soon pay for itself. The fixture consists of a cast-iron arm, screwed to the outer rim of the faceplate. The hole in the hub

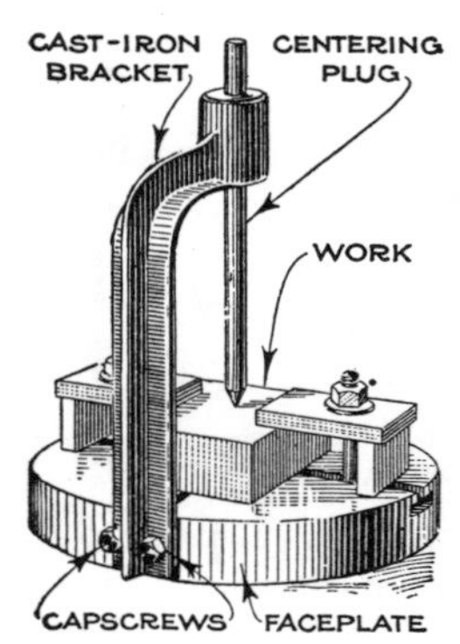

part is bored out while the arm is in this position, and a centering plug is fitted. The faceplate, after the hub is bored out, can be removed and the job bolted to it. After the work is properly located by the centering plug, the locating arm is taken off and put away. It can be accurately replaced at any time by bolting it to the same position on the faceplate.

Rough work is usually held to the faceplate by the tailstock center, but this device is better when it is desired to preserve the punch mark on work that has been laid out accurately, and when the plate is put back on the lathe and the center mark tested, it will be necessary to move the job only slightly in order to bring the center-punch mark dead true.—Chas. Homewood, Ontario, Calif.

Ladder Wedge Prevents Slipping

It is often necessary to place a ladder at such an angle to the wall that it has a tendency to slip. In such cases an assistant is usually required to hold the ladder firmly on the ground, which naturally increases the cost of the work. For this reason a builder improvised an excellent means of steadying the ladder so that it would not slip on the smoothest surfaces. Three lengths of 1-in. board, slightly less in width than the distance between the ladder rungs, are screwed together to form a U-shaped frame. The simple arrangement is slipped between the two lowest rungs, as shown, and prevents all danger of slipping.—Harry Moore, Montreal, Can.

Base for Mounting Maps

When maps are used with the colored push-pin system, as for sales purposes, a substantial base should be provided to prevent the walls or desks on which the maps are kept from being marred. A good base is made by mounting the map on two or three thicknesses of blotting paper pasted together, enough sheets being used to insure that the pins will not penetrate to the surface below.—C. I. Reid, Millersburg, Pa.

THE owners of large truck gardens will find that much trouble and hard manual labor can be saved by the use of a small garden tractor. Tractors of this type will run from four to eight hours on a gallon of gasoline, depending on the work, and will do all that can be done with a horse, or even more. Anyone with a little mechanical experience can build the tractors herein described.

The frame of the larger tractor is made of two 3-in. channel irons, 38½ in. long, with rear cross members of ½ by 3-in. iron or steel plate. The front frame members are made of ½ by 4-in. plate, cut out as shown. Either rivets or bolts may be used in assembling, bolts being perhaps the easier, and just as satisfactory, if used with lock washers. Two bolts should be used on each cross member. All the steel needed for the frame and other parts can be purchased for a few cents a pound from any structural-steel house, which will also do the necessary drilling and cutting, if desired, at a cost of a few dollars.

Front and Rear Views of Small Garden Tractor: This Is a Compact Little Machine That Is Capable of Hard Work

The axle, of 1¼-in. cold-rolled steel, is fastened to the frame by U-bolts. The wheels can be obtained from any farm-implement dealer, and should be of the ribbed-tread type shown. The drive gear should, of course, be cast on the wheel; it should not be less than 6-pitch, to insure its being strong enough for the work. Both wheels run free on the axle, and are held in place with cotter pins and washers, as indicated. They should be provided with grease or oil cups, and must be kept well lubricated. The drive-pinion shaft is journaled in two small pillow blocks, placed forward of the axle; its exact position is governed by the gearing. A little play should be allowed between pinion and gear, when assembling.

The speed of small garden tractors should be about 2½ miles per hour; this is attained, in the present instance, with an engine speed of 1,200 r.p.m. by using a speed reduction of 21 to 1, and 24-in. drive-wheels. About half of the speed reduction should be made in the gearing, and the remainder in the belt drive from engine to pinion shaft. Pinions of three to six teeth are now available, that function as well as those with 12 or more, and that enable a large reduction to be obtained at one step.

The mounting of the engine is the most important part of the assembly. It is fastened to the cross member nearest

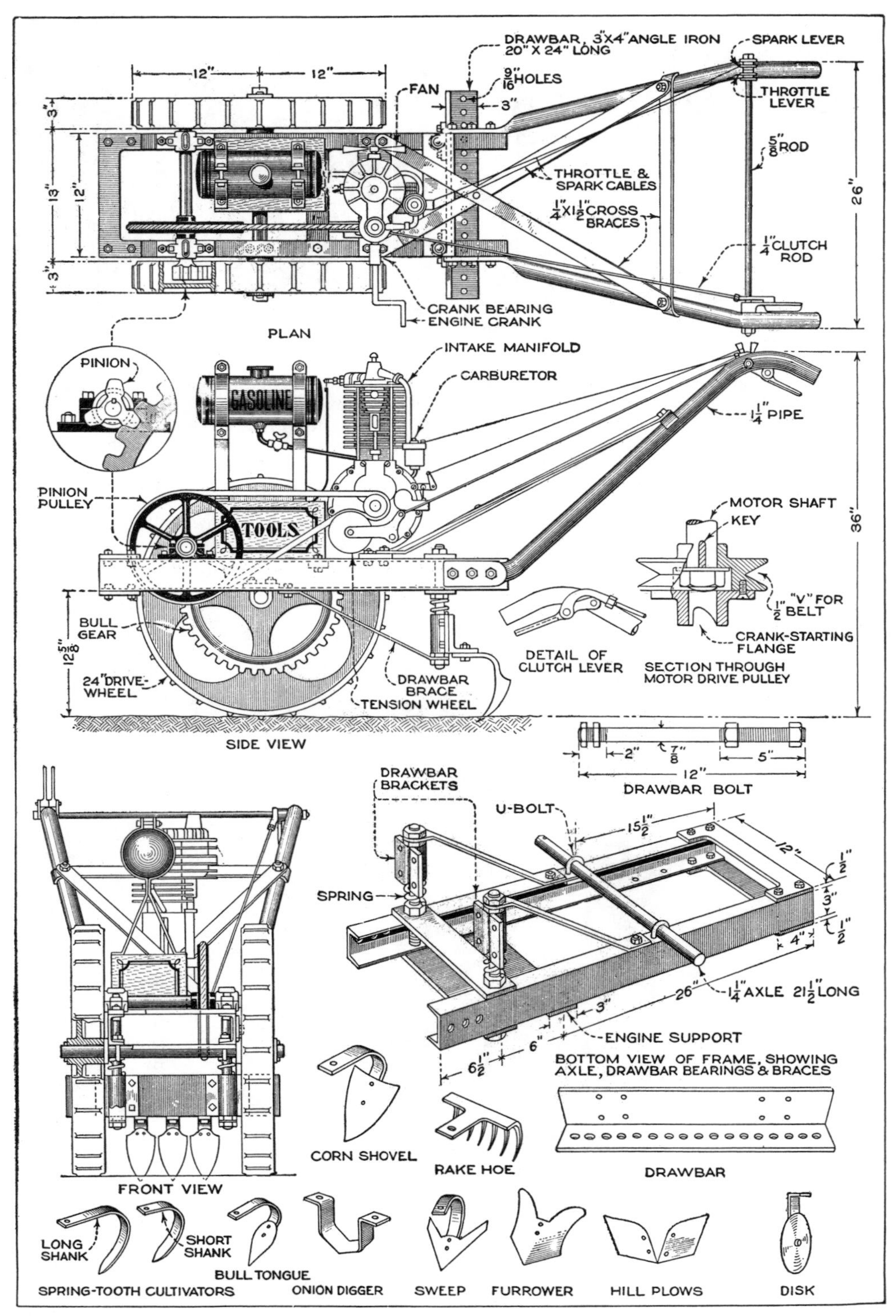

Full Details of the Larger Garden Tractor: This is Powered with a 2½-Horsepower Motorcycle Engine, and is Geared to Travel at the Rate of About 2½ Miles per Hour. The Left-Hand Wheel is Not Shown in the Side View of the Tractor, in Order to Make Clear the Engine and Drive Arrangement

the center, and must be bolted down tightly, and securely braced. An air-cooled, single-cylinder motorcycle engine, of about 2½ hp., running at 1,200 r.p.m., should be selected for the work. A four-bladed fan must be provided, to cool the engine, as the tractor travels so slowly. The fan is mounted opposite the cylinder, as indicated, and driven from the crankshaft. The sprocket is removed from the driving side of the crankshaft, and a flat pulley, or the V-grooved pulley shown, substituted. This pulley is recessed for the nut and washer that bind it to the shaft, and the flange for the starting crank is screwed to its outer side. As the starting crank must clear the drivewheel, the exact position of the engine must be determined with the crank in place. An auxiliary bearing, bolted to the frame, supports the crank.

If V-pulleys are fitted, a belt ½ to ⅝ in. in diameter should be used; if flat pulleys, the belt should be 1 in. wide. In either case, an idler pulley, or tension wheel, is used to tighten the belt, and serve the purpose of a clutch; it is mounted on the long arm of a bell crank, cut from steel plate, and the bell crank pivoted on a bracket bolted to the cross member, so that the pulley will aline with the belt. The short end of the crank is connected to the clutch lever on the left-hand handle by a length of ¼-in. rod, threaded at the upper end, screwed into a link pivoted to the clutch lever, and locked by a nut. When the clutch lever is depressed, the link passes over the pivot center of the lever, and keeps this position, holding the belt tight until the clutch lever is raised. The proportions of the bell-crank arms, and the position of the link, must be determined by experiment.

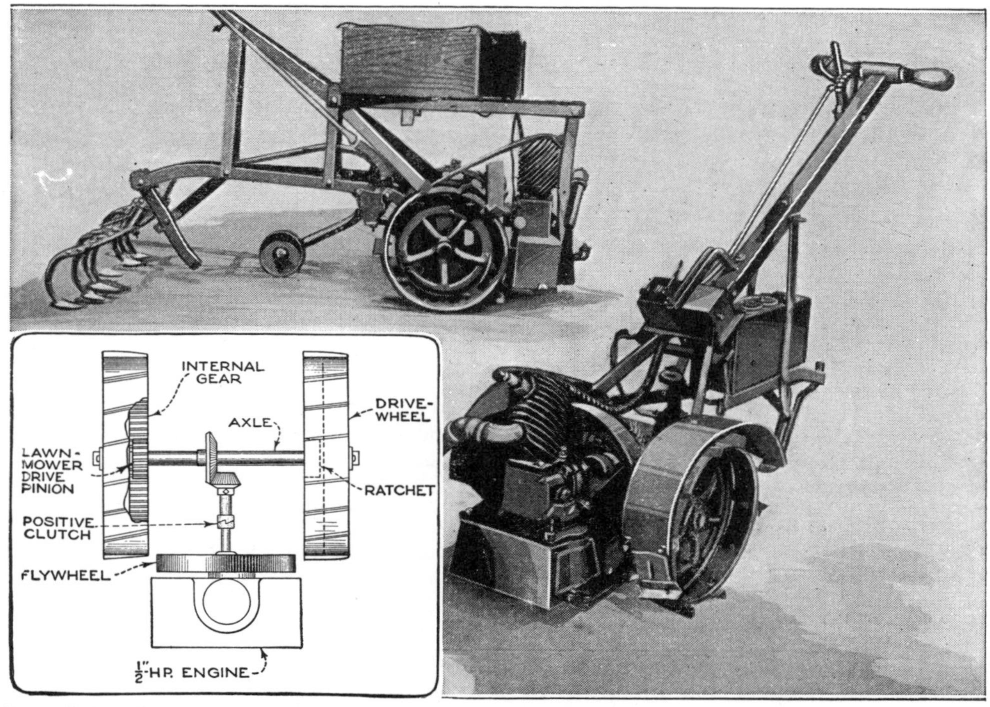

Upper Left: Side View of Small Tractor, Showing Present Arrangement of Battery Box, and Other Parts. Insert: Outline of Arrangement of Gearing. Right: Close-Up of Tractor, Showing Original Position of Box. The Lever on the Handle Controls the Operation of the Clutch

The tractor handles are made of 1¼-in. pipe, fastened to the frame, and braced as shown. On the right-hand handle, the spark and throttle controls should be mounted, and connected by wires to the engine.

The drawbar, or tool bar, is of prime importance, as upon its construction and position depend, to a large extent, the efficiency of the tractor, and the ease of its handling.

Two ⅞-in. drawbar bolts are fastened through holes drilled in the webs of the frame, and in the rear cross member.

They are braced by two 1/4 by 2-in. straps, as shown. Two 1/2 by 4-in. steel plates are bent to fit around the bolts, to form the drawbar brackets, and when the drawbar is bolted on, the whole assembly is free to move on the bolts. Short, heavy springs are placed between the upper nuts and the brackets, as shown, and make for easy action on rough or stony ground. The height of the drawbar from the ground is from 5 to 8 in., depending on the tools most used and on the choice of the maker.

The gasoline tank must be mounted high enough to provide a gravity feed to the carburetor; the brackets that hold it may be made of 3/8 by 1 1/4-in. steel. A box, set under the tank, contains the battery and ignition coil, and may also be used to carry tools, if desired.

Another type of small tractor is shown in the smaller illustrations. The basis of construction, in this case, is a large-sized lawnmower. Extension rims and cleats are riveted to the mower wheels, as shown, to provide traction, and the mower handle, raised to clear the gearing, etc., is used for steering. Power is furnished by a 1/2-hp. washing-machine engine, and the drive, shown in outline in the insert, is made up of gears taken from a grain binder. The ignition current is furnished by a dry battery, which was originally mounted on a bracket slung under the handle, the ignition coil being carried on another bracket at the bottom of the handle. This was later changed, as shown, and the battery and coils carried on one bracket, mounted above the gearing. A lever, mounted on the end of the handle, controls the operation of the clutch. The method of attaching the tools is shown quite clearly in the various photographs.

Implements for small tractors can be purchased from any dealer or made up, as desired. Old automobile springs, bent to shape, sharpened, and drilled, make excellent spring-tooth cultivators; they should be made in various lengths of shank, so that they can be "staggered" on the drawbar. Shovels, hoes, hillers, etc., can, however, be bought much cheaper than it is possible to make them. Light and shallow plowing can be done in open soil, but in plowing, too much should not be expected of the tractor. The larger tractor weighs from 250 to 300 lb.; if extra weight is desired, boards may be laid on the lower webs of the frame, and the frame filled in with cement. A caster wheel may be fitted to the drawbar, to relieve the arms of weight when running the tractor to and from the garden.

Remember always to use a good grade of oil in the engine, one especially adapted for air-cooled engines, if possible.

Dust, which is the greatest enemy of farm and garden machinery, can be excluded largely by covering the engine and gearing with a sheet-metal hood.

Vise for Holding Small Screws

The illustration shows a practical method of holding small headless screws while slotting or pointing them.

A machine-saw blade is bent to the shape shown, forming a sort of miniature vise, the space between the jaws being slightly larger than the diameter of the screw. A small hole is drilled and tapped in the top of the rear jaw to receive the screw. Another hole is drilled through the sides of the jaws to admit a stud that is driven into the bench; a thumbscrew is run on this stud. The lower end of the vise is fastened to the bench by means of a staple. After the screw is inserted in the hole the thumbscrew is turned so that the vise grips the screw tightly.

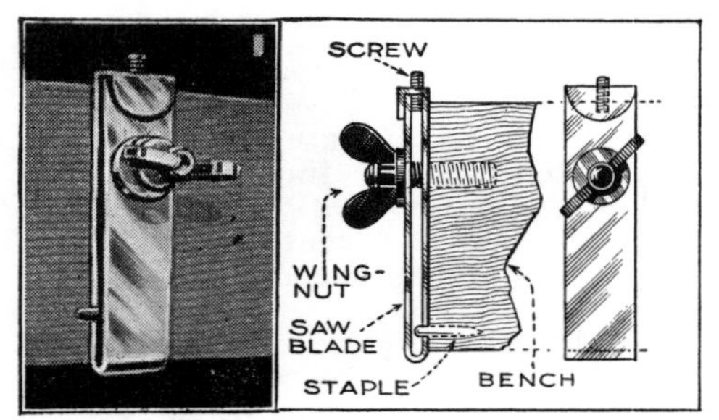

A Miniature Vise, Made from a Machine-Hacksaw Blade, for Holding Small Screws

Coloring Concrete

Mineral colors only should be used for coloring concrete. Other colors are affected by the cement and are therefore not permanent. The coloring matter should be incorporated in the top layer and distributed uniformly throughout the mass. In most cases this is best accomplished by mixing the color with the dry cement, and not with the sand, as the latter is usually wet and causes the coloring matter to lump. The color may also be dissolved in the water before it is added.

In order to determine the proportion

of color to use in producing a certain shade, a few sample batches should be mixed, with a different amount of color in each batch. These batches should then be allowed to dry thoroughly, as the color of concrete is very different when entirely dry and when just hardened. When the batch having the proper shade of color is found, the proportions used in mixing it must be accurately duplicated every time a quantity is made, so that the work will not appear spotty when finished. No more than 10 lb. of coloring should be used to each bag of cement.

Under no circumstances should dry color be sprinkled on fresh concrete and be troweled down in finishing, as this gives only a thin and uneven film of color, and at the same time makes the surface weak, and likely to dust. Color thus applied soon wears off, and the concrete will present a very spotty appearance.

Finger Guard for Circular Saws

To eliminate the danger of injuring the fingers, when working on a circular saw, a simple guard can be made of 5/8-in.

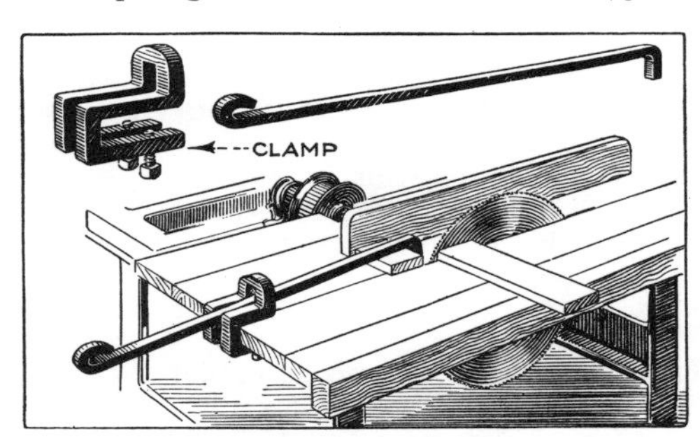

A Simple Safety Device for Protecting the Fingers of the Workman While Using a Circular Saw

square iron or steel. It consists of two pieces: a long bent arm and a clamp or guide. The latter is made so that it can be fastened on the edge of the table.

In operation, the regular work guide, on the top of the table, is set the required distance from the saw, and the clamp holding the arm is attached in a position centrally between the saw and regular work guide. The bent end of the long arm is then dropped over the work so that it will travel along as the piece is being cut. With the fingers of the left hand pressed against the work, between the arm and the guide, there is no possibility of a slip against the saw teeth. The long arm can also be used to draw back the cut stock, left between the guide and saw.

Homemade Implement Breaks Crusted Soil

Heavy rains often leave the surface of the soil so crusted that small grain has

A Homemade Device for Breaking the Surface of Crusted Soil, to Permit Small Plants to Come Up More Easily

difficulty in breaking through. The illustrations show a homemade implement that has been found very effective in breaking up crusted soil over small grain, or grass seed, without any danger of injuring the tiny plants, or of leaving a wide strip of unbroken ground.

The implement is constructed by fastening six pitchforks to a wooden crosspiece, 2 in. by 8 in. by 6 ft. in dimensions. The shanks of the forks are inserted into holes drilled 12 in. apart, and staples are used to hold them securely in position. The device can be attached to a cultivator, or other machine, by means of U-bolts.

The farmer who devised this had a tract of alfalfa, in an irrigated country, that was so crusted at the time the plants were ready to come through, that there seemed no way of saving the crop. By using this simple device, however, the ground was loosened up enough to permit

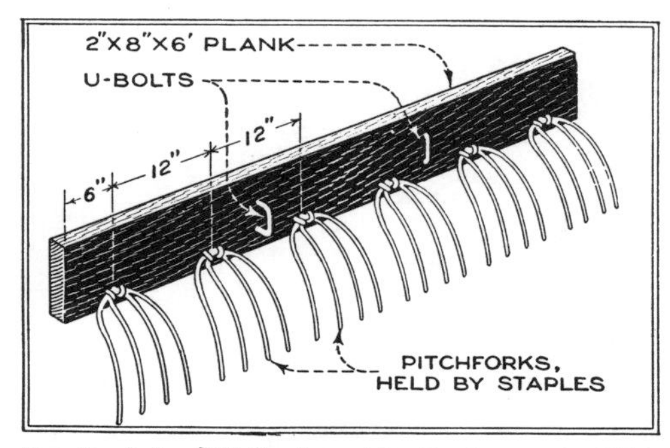

Details of the Soil Crusher: The Device can be Made in Half an Hour

the crop to come through and mature.—Mrs. R. D. Shultis, Grand Junction, Colo.

Heating and Drying Ingot Molds and Ladles

A handy and inexpensive way of drying out the lining of ladles and ingot molds, in which use is made of a ½-hp. motor directly connected to a blower, is shown at the right in the illustration. The air and gas are mixed by the blower, which delivers a blast of flame to the bottom of the molds or ladle. A sheet of metal, with a hole in the top, confines the heat while the fire-clay lining is baking.

Left: Arrangement of Heaters for Ingot Molds to Reduce Amount of Scrap Cut Off. Right: Air-Gas Blower Used to Dry the Ingot Molds and Ladles

The "pipe" in ingots was greatly reduced in the shop using a device, shown at the left, to heat the metal as it cooled. Previously it had been necessary to crop off about one-third of each ingot as scrap. This reduction in the amount of pipe was accomplished by using the hot top rings shown, and heating the outside and inside of the mold before and after pouring. These top rings are iron castings, 8 in. square and 8 in. long, lined with about 2 in. of molding sand, and baked on top of the electric furnace in which the metal is melted.

The gas burners are arranged in a rack, as shown, so that a blast of flame is directed to the bottom of the molds, until they are as hot as they can be made. At the same time, another set, not shown, is throwing flames against the outside. While the molds are being heated, the ladle is filled and the dross skimmed off. When everything is ready, the upper burners are extinguished, turned out of the way, and the ingots poured. The other burners continue to play against the outside of the molds until the ingots have become comparatively cold, so that the metal will not cool too quickly.

Soldering Vertical Seams

It is difficult and tedious work to solder vertical seams such as found in refrigerator interiors, tank linings, and in roofing work, because the solder has a tendency to run down from the underside of the soldering iron. To overcome this trouble, heat an iron to a dull red, draw it out to the shape shown, and cut a small groove, about 1/16 in. deep, in the upper face. This face only is filed and tinned. Starting at the top of the seam to be soldered, move the iron up and down, applying the solder, which will run through the groove to the point of the iron and into the seam, but not down the untinned sides.

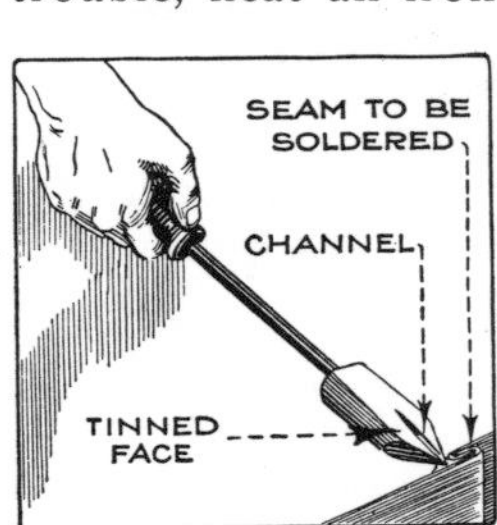

Attaching Brackets to Irregular Surfaces

A machinist in a small shop desired to put an automatic feed on a drill press. In doing so he met with the problem of attaching a bearing bracket firmly to the curved surface of the post, and it was therefore necessary to make a metal base that would fit this surface.

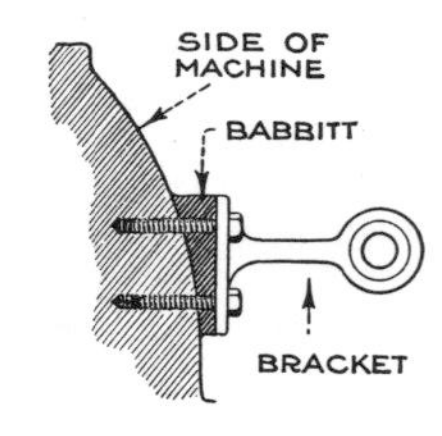

Four holes were drilled in the post, and tapped for studs, which were then screwed in. The bracket was put on the studs and the shaft was put in place so as to bring the bearing into accurate alinement. A clay mold was built around the space between bracket and post and filled with melted babbitt. When cool, this babbitt base was as solid and firm as could be desired.

Mending Tracings

To mend a badly worn tracing, so that the adhesive tape will not come off when the tracing is handled, make a few small holes on each edge of the tear and apply the gummed mending tape on each side. The holes permit the opposite strips of gummed tape to stick together, and as there is more adhesion between the strips of tape than there is between the tape and the tracing, the tape will not come off so easily.—Frank Harazim, New York City.

Handling Logs Easily

In building a log stable on a homestead in Manitoba, Can., a simple method was employed that made it possible for one man to raise the heavy pine logs into place. Two skid logs were set against each wall, the upper ends being flattened to prevent them from rolling. Holes were

Placing the Logs, Used in Constructing a Stable, by Means of Skid Poles, Enabled One Man to Do the Job Alone

bored in these skids, about 18 in. apart, to fit strong wooden pegs. It was then possible to raise the logs, one end at a time, and to keep them in position on the skids by means of the pegs. After a log had been raised to such a height that a man standing on the ground could no longer handle it, another set of pegs were used as footrests in climbing the skids.

Tool for Loosening Nuts

It is a very common practice, and a poor one, to use a hammer and chisel for removing nuts in positions where it is impossible to reach them with a wrench, or impossible to swing a wrench even if it can be placed on the nut. The chisel cuts and mars the edges so that they are very often unfit for further use. By using the simple tool shown in the photograph,

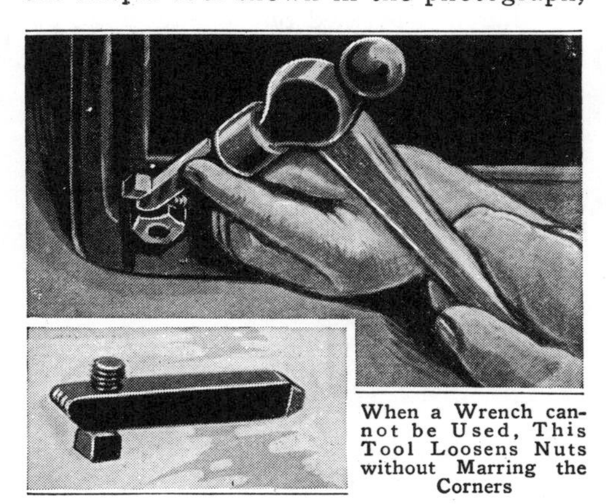

When a Wrench cannot be Used, This Tool Loosens Nuts without Marring the Corners

however, it is possible to remove the nuts without injuring them.

A piece of square stock, of suitable length, is rounded and checkered on one end with a file, and the other end is chamfered. About $\frac{1}{2}$ in. from the checkered end, a hole is drilled and tapped for a setscrew, and the point of the tool is then hardened and tempered. In using it, the checkered edge grips the nut securely, and the setscrew acts as a stop, preventing the tool from slipping. Only a slight mark will be left on the nut as evidence of the use of the tool.

Crimping Tool for Tinners

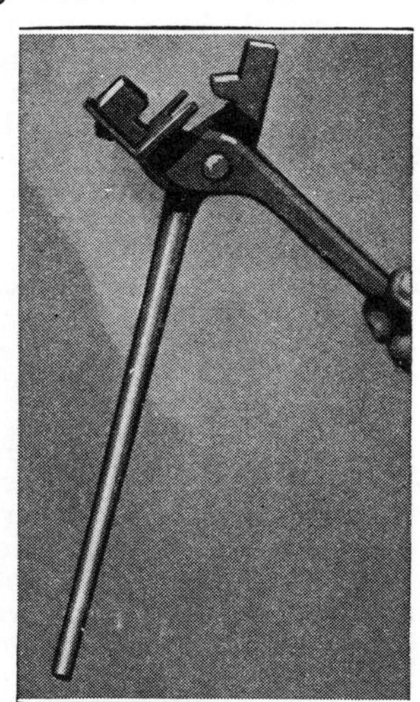

An excellent crimping tool for tinners can be made from an old pair of tongs, as shown in the illustration. The blocks that crimp the tin are best welded to the tong jaws. The upper lugs serve to give the tin the first bend, then the tin is inserted farther into the jaws,

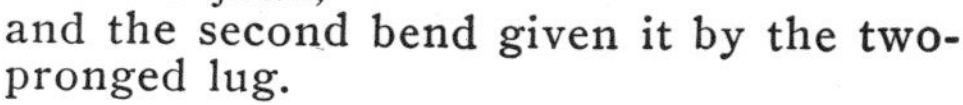

and the second bend given it by the two-pronged lug.

Pressing Off a Cracked Axle Housing

The drawing shows how a cracked axle housing was pressed out of the brake as-

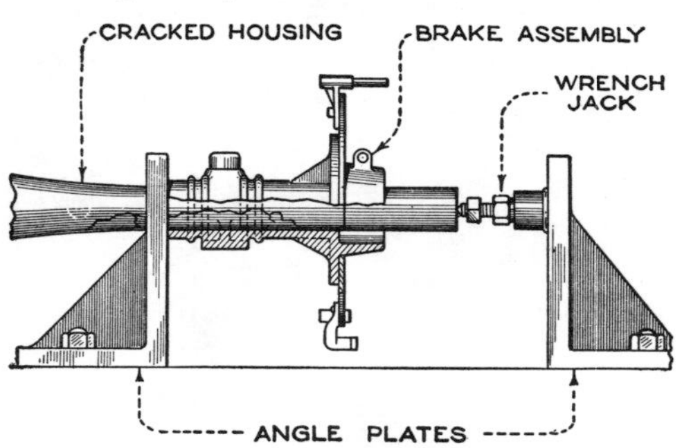

A Small Wrench Jack and Two Angle Plates Used to Force a Cracked Axle Housing from the Brake Assembly

sembly by means of a small wrench jack. The shoulder of the brake assembly was placed against the face of the left-hand angle plate, which had a V-slot cut in it. The jack was set against the other angle plate, and a piece of shafting placed between the jack and the end of the housing. This made it possible to exert a pressure of about 2,500 lb. on the housing, so that one man could do the job easily.—Daniel F. Smith, Jr., Pittsburg, Kan.

Improved Stud Tool

The two most common methods of setting studs are to use a stud tool that has a continuous thread through it, of the same size and hand as the stud, and to use locked nuts. Both of these methods require the use of two wrenches in releasing the tool from the stud, one wrench holding the tool or lower nut, while the other is used to loosen the upper nut or setscrew. An improved stud tool, that saves much time, is made as shown in the illustration. It is recessed in the center; one end is threaded to fit the stud, and a thread of the opposite hand is tapped in the other end, in which a setscrew is fitted. Simply turning the tool down on the stud, with the setscrew in place, locks the tool on the stud. By turning the upper setscrew in the same direction as the stud, the tool is unlocked. Only one wrench is required to lock or unlock it.

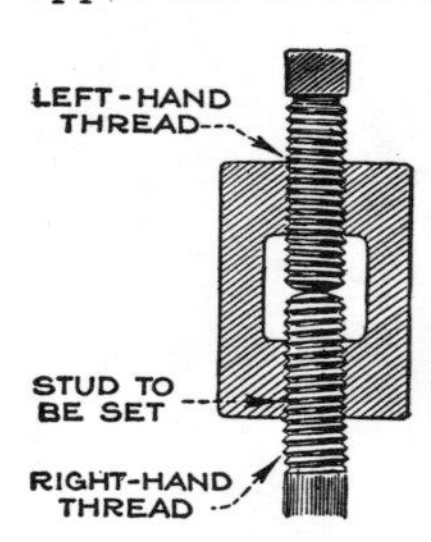

Removing Rear Wheels from Light Car

Rear wheels, that are forced on tapered axles, are often found so tight that a wheel puller will not remove them. It is, however, an easy matter to remove them by raising both rear wheels by means of a jack and starting the motor. When the wheels are revolving at a good speed, the clutch is released and the brake applied. By repeating this a few times the wheel will soon become so loose that it can easily be pulled from the axle.—Albert Chenicek, Chicago, Ill.

Straightening a Bent Reamer

A bent drill or reamer can be straightened easily without danger of breaking by placing it between the centers of a lathe, as shown. Reverse the regular toolholder and clamp it in the toolpost with the butt toward the tool being straightened. Play the flame of an ordinary blowtorch on the side of the shank opposite the toolholder. When the part is fairly hot, but not anything like red-hot, proceed to squeeze the butt end of the toolholder against the shank by means of the crossfeed screw. Occasionally the tool being straightened is tested to determine when it is straight.

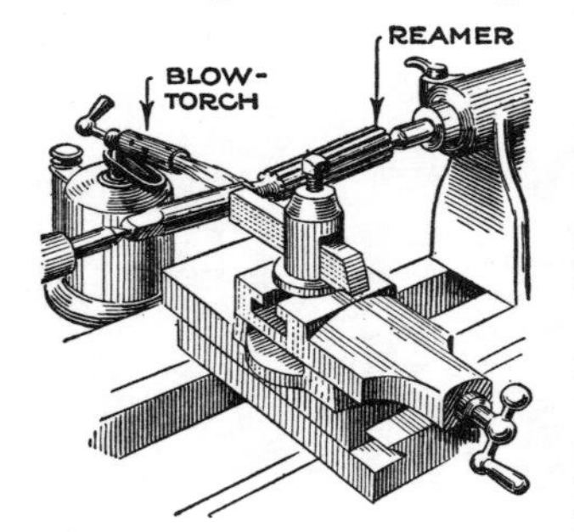

Protecting Plane Bit

After a plane bit is ground and honed, the edge is very often ruined while reinserting it in the plane, if the bit catches on the iron bottom instead of entering in the slot. By fastening a small wooden block between the sides of the plane, as indicated in the illustration, the bit will be properly guided into the slot. The block will not injure the edge should it be struck by the latter. The block is fastened by means of shellac.—M. E. Duggan, Kenosha, Wis.

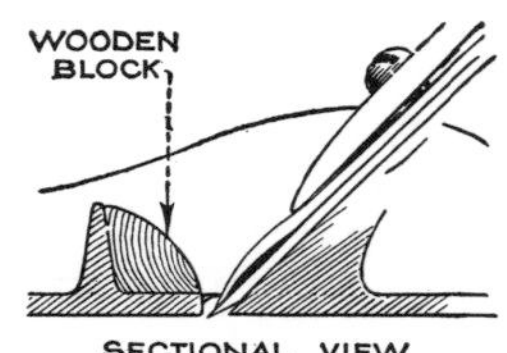

A Bench Shear for the Small Shop

By CLIFFORD A. BUTTERWORTH

THE bench shear described in this article can be made very easily, and will cut much heavier metal than can be cut with a pair of hand shears. It is designed to give a leverage of 30 to 1 on short cuts, and 10 to 1 at the end of a full stroke. As the blade is 6 in. long, and there is a clearance of 6 in. behind it, it is possible to cut metal that is 24 in. wide, by cutting from both sides.

The base is made of 2-in. stock, to the dimensions shown in the drawing. Two blocks, 2 by 3 in., are bolted to it, and the holes drilled for the bolts are counterbored on the underside of the base so that the heads of the bolts will be flush with the surface. Bolted on top of these blocks is a piece of ash, 2 by 4 by 15½ in., and a short piece of ¾-in. hardwood is attached to one end of this block with flat-head wood screws. This ¾-in. piece is faced on the outside with a ⅛-in. steel plate, in which the screw holes are countersunk, so that the screw heads will be flush. The shear lever is attached by means of a ¾-in steel stud passing through these pieces, and it is also faced with a ⅛-in. steel plate where the surface comes in contact with the plate on the ¾-in. block. A brass bushing is pressed into the blocks to serve as a bearing for the stud, which is a tight fit in the shear lever.

The hand lever and its supports are made of ⅞-in. ash. The lever works on a ½-in. bolt, and is also fitted with a bushing. One of the supports is fastened to the 2-in. ash block, while the other is screwed to the base. The links connecting the levers are made of ¼-in. iron or steel. Both the hand lever and the shear lever are fitted with bushings for the link bolts, which are made of ⅜-in. steel.

The shear blades are made of ⅜-in. tool steel, hardened, and the edges ground. The upper blade is 2 in. wide at the front, and 2⅞ in. at the back; it is held to the shear lever by means of bolts, while the lower blade is fastened to the base by flat-head screws, countersunk flush.

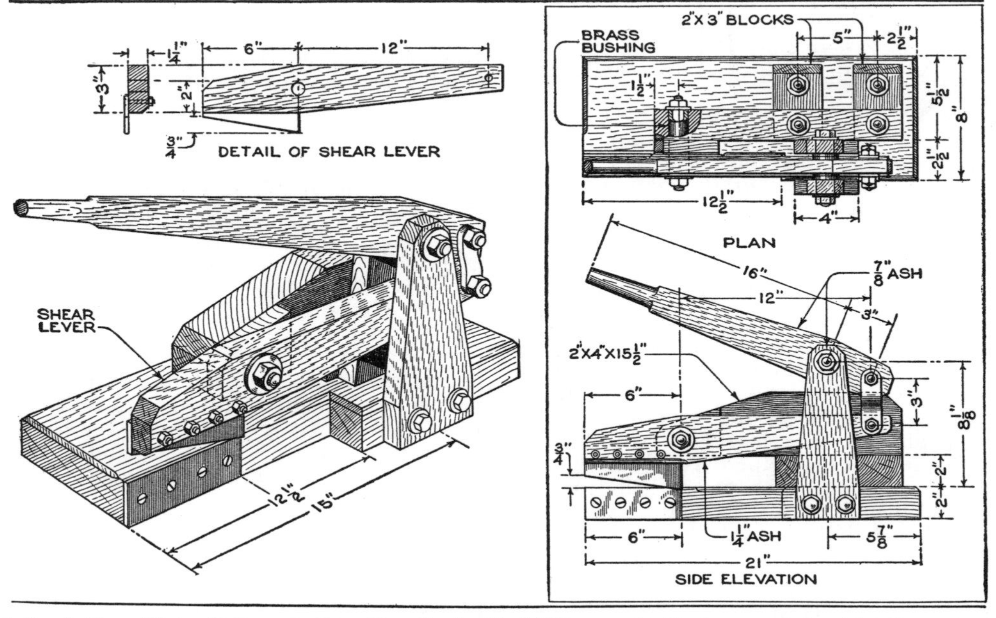

A Bench Shear That will Prove to Be a Very Serviceable Addition to the Equipment of Any Tin Shop: Due to Its Leverage, Much Thicker Metal can be Cut with It than with Any Ordinary Pair of Hand Shears. It is Made of Hardwood, with the Exception of the Links, Bolts, and Blades

Cross-Section Paper Aids in Making Diagrams

Considerable time is wasted by draftsmen in repeatedly picking up and laying aside the scale or dividers, when making wiring diagrams. This can be avoided by placing a sheet of cross-section paper under the tracing on which the diagram is to be drawn, and then scaling the diagram by means of the small squares.

Hooks on Terminal Tongs Lift Battery

The construction of many battery boxes, especially homemade ones, is such that the handles of the battery come below the edges of the box, and so close to the sides that it is almost impossible to remove the battery, without a special tool. A pair of terminal tongs, with the handle ends bent as shown in the illustration, will prove of considerable assistance. The hooks on the ends of the handles make it easy to lift heavy batteries from deep boxes.

Chuck for Threaded Work

The drawing shows a handy type of lathe chuck to be used when working on threaded parts. It is often necessary to use a threaded chuck, but if the work is held in a chuck of the usual type, it is very difficult to release the work. The application of a pipe wrench may mar the surface, and perhaps spoil the job if a good finish is desired. The chuck illustrated is threaded to suit the work, and the tapping size of the hole continued for about the same distance as the threads. A plunger is turned to a sliding fit in this hole, after which a hole is drilled through the center of the plunger, a drive fit for a pin. The body of the chuck has a slot cut through it as shown, and is threaded outside to fit a knurled ring, which has four "tommy" holes drilled in it. The chuck is operated as follows: The work is screwed in with the fingers, until it is a safe distance in the chuck, when the knurled ring is screwed up; this, bearing on the pin, pushes the plunger up tight against the face of the work. When removing the work, the ring is turned to the left, releasing the pressure of the plunger, so that the work can be unscrewed with the fingers. For light work, the chuck can be made with a taper shank to fit into the lathe spindle, but for heavy work it is best to thread the chuck to fit the spindle nose.

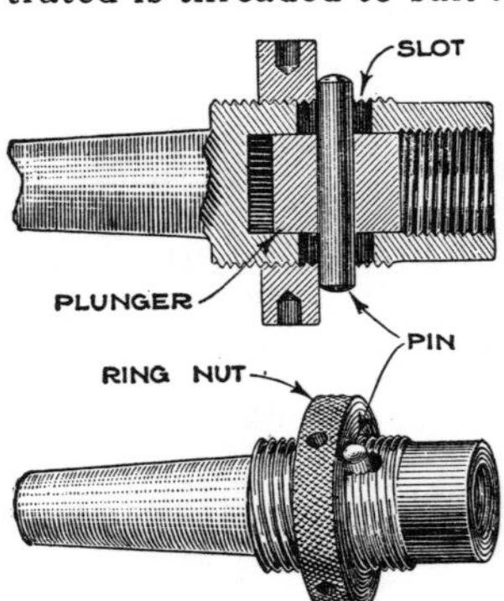

Tray under Vise Catches Small Pieces

When a vise is used for holding small pieces, it frequently happens that the work becomes loose, or slips through the fingers while being removed, and falls to the floor, where it is often lost in a crack. This can be prevented very easily by fitting a tray to the bench so that it extends under the vise, as shown in the drawing. The tray consists of a piece of sheet tin, bent at right angles, and with the sides turned up and fastened at the corners with small screws. A hole cut in the front fits over the vise screw, and the bottom of the tray slides underneath the bench between two lagscrews fitted with washers.

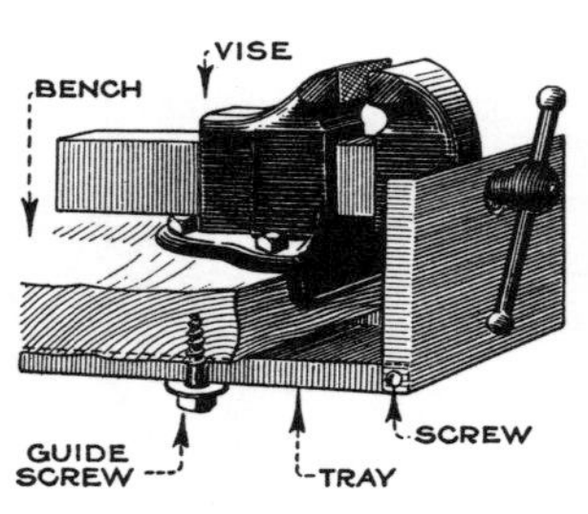

Small Soldering Bit Easily Made

A small soldering bit of the type illustrated can be made in a few minutes from a short length of 3/8-in. iron rod, some No. 6 copper wire, two small rivets, and a wooden file handle. The copper wire is doubled, sharpened to form the bit nose, and attached to the iron rod with the rivets; the rod is then driven into the handle. This bit has proved to be especially handy in soldering open circuits on small coils and rheostats.—G. C. Madison, West Haven, Conn.

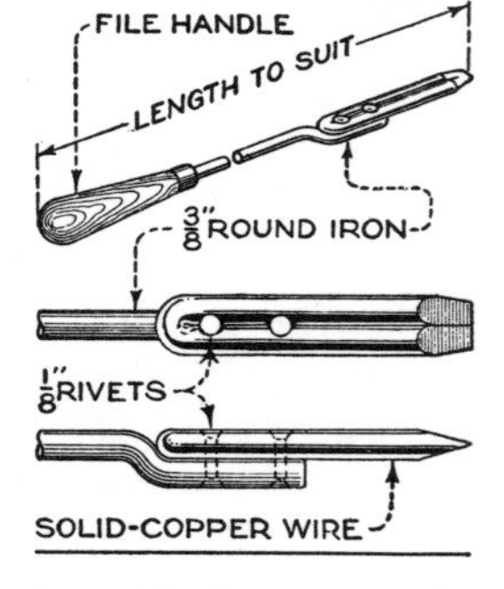

Gummed Business Cards

Business cards of machine repairmen are very often mislaid or lost, and this means that one must go to considerable trouble if the services of the same man are again desired. For this reason, the repairman will find it an excellent idea to use gummed small stickers, on which his name and address are printed, together with other advertising or recording data, as he may wish.

These stickers are made of a thin grade of tough paper, well covered with strong adhesive, so that they will stick for a long time. They should be pasted in a conspicuous place on the machine or fitting, where they may be accessible for constant reference, and at the same time present a neat appearance.

Grinder for Plug Cocks

The lever shown in the drawing makes the work of repairing leaky gas, water, or air cocks of the plug type a comparatively simple matter, and, as the tool will fit any valve handle of average size, is worth making where jobs of this kind must be done from time to time. The lever is made of a piece of pipe, bent to the shape shown, although, if preferred, it can be built up of nipples and elbows. In any case, the bottom end is threaded and a slot cut in it, so that, when the lever is slipped over the handle, it will be held upright; a nut screwed onto the threaded end prevents the tool from sliding off in use.

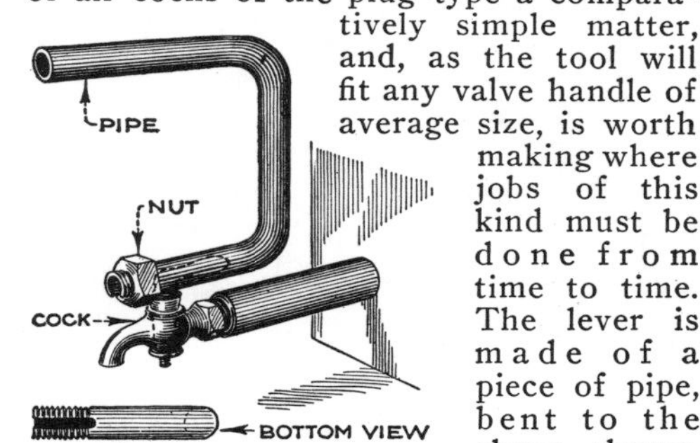

The correct way to repair a defective cock of this type is to apply a little grinding compound, at first only where the bearing marks or rings show and not over the whole length of the plug as is often done. The plug is rotated in semicircles by a back-and-forth movement of the handle. Using the lever shown, a good purchase is obtained and greater pressure applied to the plug than by using the valve handle alone, as the more pressure that can be applied, the quicker the plug can be made tight. When the bearing marks begin to show over the whole surface of the cock, the paste may be applied to the entire length.

Safe Sling for Heavy Bars

When handling heavy and slippery round bars with a crane, it is customary to pass the end of the sling around the bar once and then through the loop at the other end. This method is not a safe one, and it occasionally happens that an unbalanced bar slips out of the hitch. The illustration shows the front and rear views of a hitch that is safe, and at the same time self-tightening. The end of the sling is passed twice around the bar, instead of once, before being passed through the loop.—A. J. Denner, Brooklyn, N. Y.

Auto Tables Please Store Patrons

Stores catering to the trade of automobile parties can add greatly to the convenience of their customers by using small serving tables of the type illustrated, which can be made at very little expense.

The tables slip over the edges of the automobile doors, and can be put in place instantly. Each one is fitted with an adjustable brace consisting of two pieces. One piece is securely fastened to the underside of the table and has a slot cut lengthwise in it. The other piece has a hole drilled near the end. The pieces slide one upon the other, and are clamped together by a bolt and a wingnut. A strip of wood is attached to the end of the brace, and another strip nailed to the edge of the table, as shown. Felt, glued to the wood as indicated, is used to prevent the table from scratching the varnished surface of the car doors.—Tom Freeman, Beaumont, Tex.

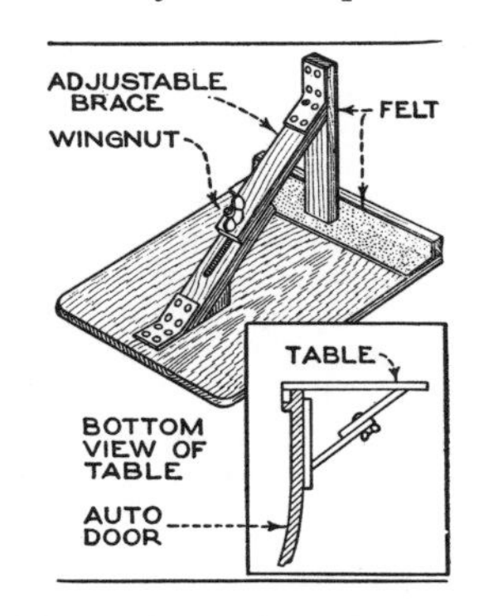

Reversing or Duplicating Tool

The interesting tool shown in the drawing was discovered in the shop of a sign

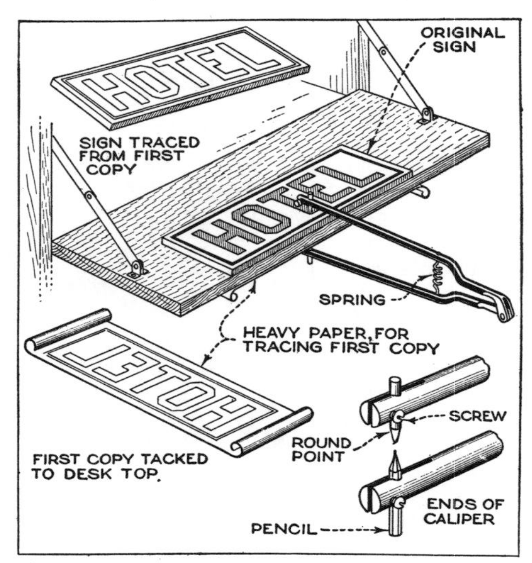

A Simple Tool That will Prove of Value to Sign Painters for Reversing or Duplicating Designs

painter, where it was used for making duplicate posters. Its uses are many; it will copy a picture, or transfer a drawing or design to the opposite "hand" without requiring any skill on the part of the person using it, so that a boy can do some work that ordinarily would require the time of a highly paid sign artist.

The tool consists simply of two rods, jointed as shown, drilled and slotted for a pencil and tracing point, and fitted with a spring. A buggy-top hinge would make a good tool of this kind.

As shown in the drawing, the original design is tacked to the top of a shelf, and a sheet of heavy tracing cloth, or paper, underneath. The design is then traced with the rounded point, producing a reversed copy on the paper underneath. If a duplicate of the original is required, the reverse is used, in the same manner, on top of the shelf.

The tracing point and the pencil should be exactly opposite each other, and be clamped tightly, as indicated, by means of round-head screws.

Preventing Tools from Rusting

Tools of all kinds soon become rusty when exposed continually to a damp atmosphere, or when used only occasionally. To prevent this, keep the tools in a box filled with oil-soaked sawdust. Oil that is drained from the crankcase of an automobile, and that is to be thrown away, will serve very well for this purpose. Sand may be substituted for the sawdust, in a box where shovels, spades, and similar large tools are kept. The sand will also serve as a scouring agent that will prove of great help in removing the rust already on the tools.

Stock-Oiling Device for Punch Presses

The drawing shows a method of oiling tin, or other metal, in sheet form, that is being formed or drawn on the punch press. An oil tank, similar to those used on milling machines, is supported on a bracket attached to one side of the punch-press frame. A steel ring is fastened to the side of the ram by a bracket, and a felt ring, a little larger in diameter on the outside than the blanking size of the die, or the diameter of the cup to be

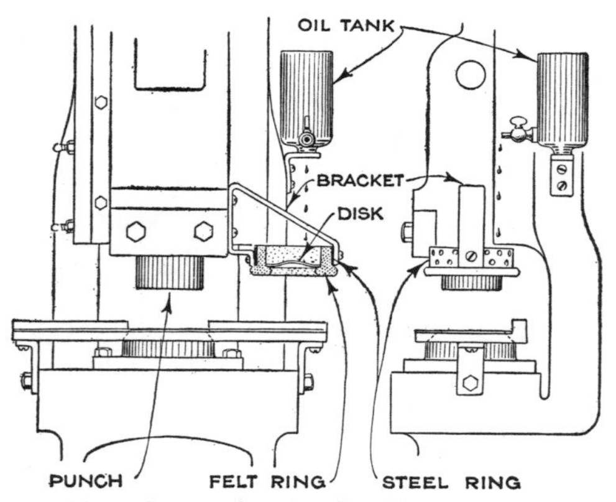

An Oiling Device for the Punching and Drawing Press, That Automatically Applies a Thin Film of Lubricant to the Face of the Stock at Each Downward Movement of the Ram

drawn, is forced into this ring, as shown. The felt ring is so located in relation to the punch that when the ram is in a "down" position, the pad will oil the stock as it rests on the platen, just where the punch will come on a later stroke. The oil drip is so arranged that the oil drops on a spring disk inside the felt pad, and the oil flow is regulated so that only a very light film of oil is left on the tin where it is needed in the drawing or blanking operation. This method, besides being economical in the amount of oil used, does away with the necessity of oiling as a separate operation, and on lithographed work, on which the lithographing tends to soften and scratch when left with a heavy coating of oil for a few hours, it is especially advantageous.

Alining Automobile Wheels

Alining the front wheels of an automobile alone is quite a job, and where work of this character is of frequent occurrence, as in the one-man garage, the alining device shown in the drawing will speedily prove its value.

Two pieces of 3/4-in. lumber, 3 in. wide and 8 or 9 ft. long, are planed true and fitted with ribs, glued and screwed to one side. The ribs are cut off and beveled, as shown, at the front ends of the "parallels," and cut off short about 1 ft. from the rear end. Two 3/4-in. pieces are then bolted to each rib and screwed to the parallel at the rear end, as shown. This forms a 3/4-in. slot, which is also cut through the bottom pieces, for the rear hook bolt. The front hook is inserted through a hole drilled a little forward of the center of the parallel, the rib being strengthened at this point. The bolts are made of 3/8-in. iron or steel rod, threaded on the upper end for wingnuts.

To use the device, the hooks are placed over the tire and rim on each wheel in such a manner that the straight edges are horizontal, then tightened. Then, by sighting over the projecting portions, they are made parallel. After making sure that both wheels are pointing straight ahead, the distance between the parallels is measured, close to the tires, as shown, then at the outer end of the parallels, and the two measurements are

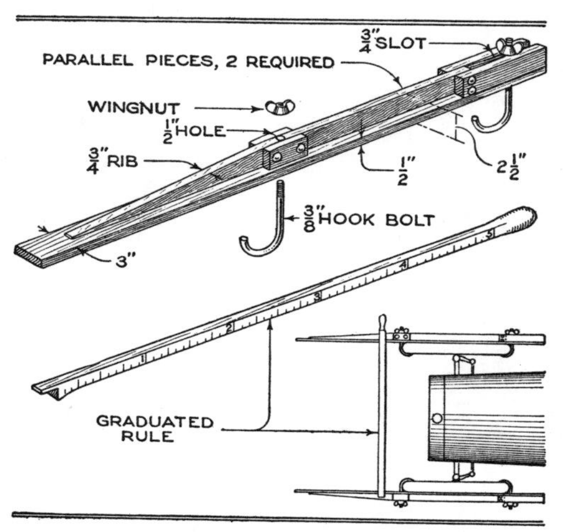

Truing Up the Front Wheels of an Automobile Is Not Usually a One-Man Job, but the Device Illustrated Above Makes It So

compared. The front wheels should "toe in" slightly, not less than 1/4 in. nor more than 3/8 inch.

Making Gouges of Steel Tubing

Gouges are tools that all woodworkers must use at times, but usually not often enough to necessitate the purchase of a

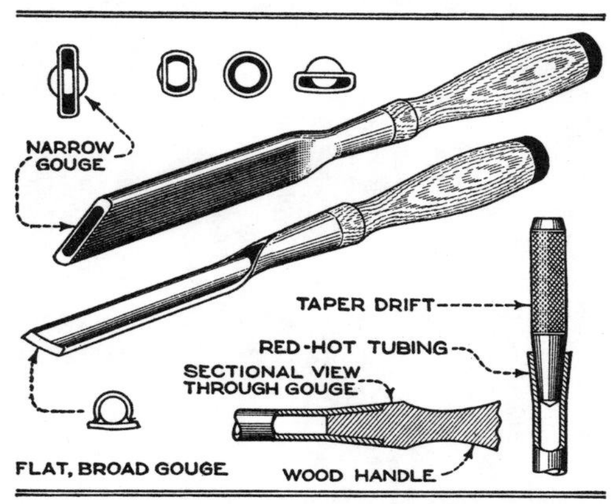

Steel Tubing, Used to Make Woodworkers' Gouges of Various Shapes and Sizes, and of Excellent Quality

complete set. Gouges made of seamless steel tubing, however, will answer excellently for the occasional user.

They are made from pieces of fairly heavy-gauge tubing, flared open at one end to receive a wooden handle. This is done by heating the tube until red and then driving a taper drift into it to expand it. For narrow gouges, the tubing is flattened as indicated, and beveled on the end to form the cutting edge. A medium-flat gouge can be made by flattening out the tubing a little less. By slitting the tube and spreading it open and almost flat, a broad gouge is formed.

To make the steel hold an edge, it is well to caseharden it slightly, which is done by dipping the red-hot steel in powdered cyanide of potassium and quenching in cold water. As these tools are always ground on their forward faces, the casehardening will not be ground away from the lower part of the cutting edge. In some cases it will be found that, if the tools are tempered after hardening, a better and longer-lasting edge will result. To those unaccustomed to using cyanide, a word of warning is necessary. Do not inhale the fumes, as cyanide of potassium is an active poison.

¶ When scraping carbon from automobile pistons, and from the face of the cylinder block, use short headless setscrews to keep the particles of carbon out of the cylinder-head bolt holes. This method is easy and quick.

Reflector Aids Motion-Picture Pianist

It is often a great strain for the organist or pianist in a moving-picture theater to glance up continually at the picture

This Arrangement of Two Adjustable Mirrors Enables the Moving-Picture Theater Pianist to Follow the Picture without Turning His Head

while playing, in order to make the music correspond to the action.

This trouble can be overcome very easily by using two adjustable mirrors, mounted on portable stands, as shown in the photograph. One of these mirrors is set at such an angle as to catch the picture on the screen and reflect it into the second mirror, which is placed close to the music rack, and in front of the musician.—H. F. Hess, Des Moines, Ia.

Action of Radio Switches Improved by Vaseline

While in a laboratory where radio-resistance measurements of great importance were being conducted, a visitor was much surprised to see one of the assistants apply a generous amount of vaseline to the points and blades of a rotary, or dial, switch. The action was slightly squeaky, and the lubricant was applied to overcome the scratchy effect and make the instrument operate smoothly and with good electrical contact. It was explained, that, paradoxical as it may seem, the use of vaseline on such switches had been found to improve not only the mechanical action but the constancy of the contact as well. This was discovered in an investigation where it was necessary to have a commutator operated with extraordinary definiteness and efficiency. Everything had failed until the worker drenched the part with oil. Much to his surprise, the experimenter found that this produced exactly the effect he sought. Since that time vaseline has been found to be equally effective, and cleaner and easier to apply than oil.

Making Center Testers Magnify Errors

A simple method of greatly magnifying the slightest movement at the point of a center-tester needle is to use a strong feather quill, about 1 ft. long, pressed on the end of the needle. The quill is very light and will not cause the needle to vibrate, which would be the case if an additional length of steel or even aluminum were used.—L. M. Steffen, Dayton, Ohio.

Rolling Oxygen Cylinders

Heavy oxygen cylinders are generally moved for short distances by tipping them slightly and rolling them on the edge in the same way as barrels. But owing to the small diameter, the height, and the weight of these cylinders, it is not an easy matter to roll them in this way. For this reason, the device shown in the drawing was made. It consists of a hardwood wheel, 6 or 7 in. larger in diameter than the cylinder, and fitting nicely over the bottom of the latter. A rope, knotted at the end, is passed through a hole drilled about halfway between the inner and outer edges of the wheel. After the rope is wound once or twice around the cylinder, it is caught in a ta-

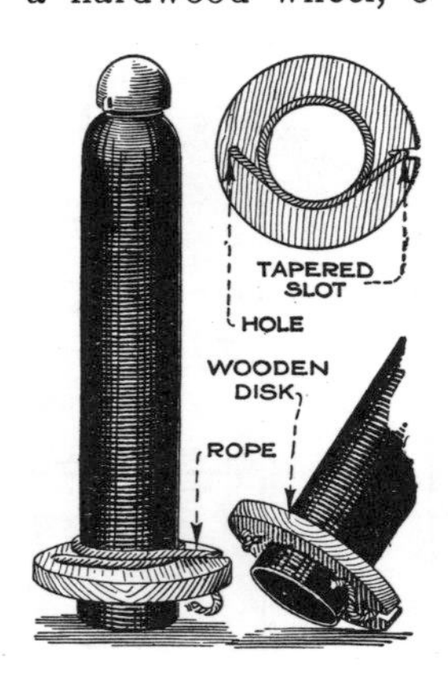

pered slot cut opposite the hole. By rolling the cylinder on the wheel in the direction opposite to that in which the rope is wound, the latter is tightened instantly. It can again be loosened by giving the wheel a slight twist in the same direction as the rope is wound.

An Inexpensive Farm Lime Spreader

By R. H. Moulton

ONE of the farmer's greatest problems is that of distributing lime or marl upon his land without great expense for equipment.

Prof. H. H. Musselman, of Michigan Agricultural College, has evolved a lime spreader that solves this problem, as it can be built at a cost of about $20. This will enable the farmer who wishes to use lime on his land, but who does not care to go to the expense of buying a commercial spreader, to make his own.

The spreader is designed to be attached to the rear end of a wagon box, and consists of a hopper, to which is fitted an agitating board, the latter being operated by a rocker arm dropping from pin to pin on a "disk" attached to one of the rear wheels of the wagon.

The hopper should be built of lumber at least ¾ in. thick, braced as shown, and hung from the wagon by ⅝ or ¾-in. hanger bolts. The agitator board is about 2 in. thick and is hung from the hopper by bolts, as indicated, lock washers being used between the nuts, to preserve the adjustment. It is beveled on each side ½ in. deep, and a piece of 1¾ by 4-in. stock, 18 in. long, is bolted to it. On this piece, the rocker arm, which is made of 2 by 6-in. oak, is bolted. A slot is cut in the arm, as indicated by the dotted lines, to fit the forward bolt.

Above: Close-Up of Hopper, Rocker Arm, and "Disk." Below: The Spreader in Action over Firm Ground, Drawn by a Small Tractor

The disk is made of a double thickness of ⅞ by 10-in. boards, the corners being cut off to fit inside the felloes. The pins are ½ by 6-in. bolts, passed through ½ by 4-in. pipes, as shown in the detail. The disk is fastened to the wheel by four bolts, passed through the disk and boards placed on the inner side of the wheel.

The wagon box should extend about 18 in. behind the rear axle, and the top of the hopper, when hung in position, should be from 24 to 30 in. above the axle. The rocker arm may be adjusted for different heights of boxes, but, when the spreader is to be used on two different wagons, it is preferable to have the boxes at the same height above and the same distance behind the axle.

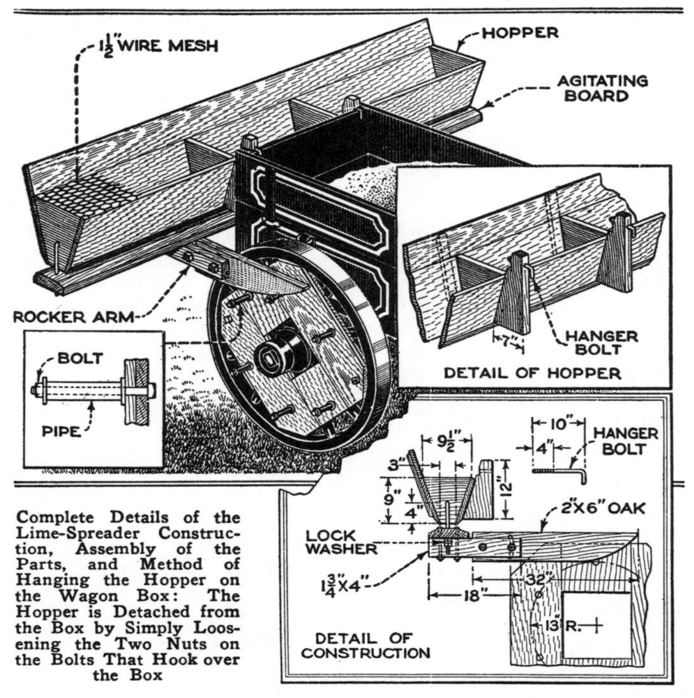

Complete Details of the Lime-Spreader Construction, Assembly of the Parts, and Method of Hanging the Hopper on the Wagon Box: The Hopper is Detached from the Box by Simply Loosening the Two Nuts on the Bolts That Hook over the Box

This spreader has been tested with pulverized limestone, both dry and damp, with excellent results. If lumpy material is to be used, it should be shoveled through a screen of poultry netting or 1½-in. wire mesh placed on top of the hopper. Lumps remaining on the screen can be broken up with the shovel, and brushed through.

Where the soil is firm enough to permit a load of lime to be drawn over it, the box may be hung on the loaded wagon and the lime spread by shoveling directly into the spreader. In case the spreading is to be done over plowed ground, it will be found impracticable to draw the full load. In this case, and where the lime is in storage, or piles, only enough is shoveled into the empty wagon carrying the spreader to go once around the field, or some other convenient distance. It will not be found practicable to spread pulverized lime in a high wind, although a moderate wind will not greatly affect the evenness of spread.

Refitting Piston Bushings

When fitting bushings in pistons, great care must be taken that the piston wall, which is made of thin metal, is not forced out of shape, as the piston will then score the cylinder.

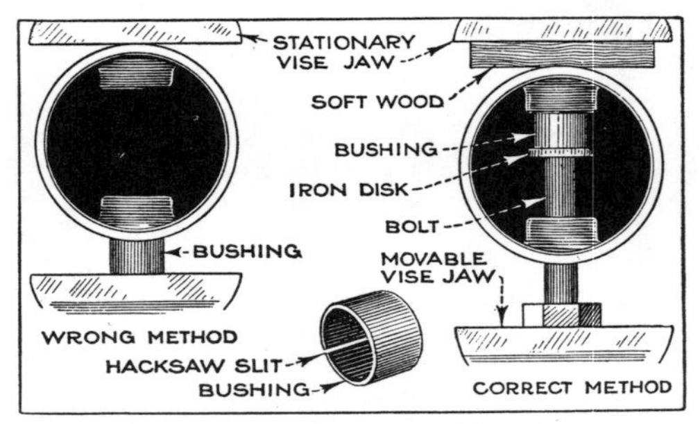

The Wrong and the Right Way to Fit New Bushings in Pistons: By Using the Correct Method the Cylinder will Not be Distorted

To remove the old bushings, first saw a slit in them; they can then be tapped out very easily. The new bushings should be .001 in. larger than the bearing holes. The illustration shows both the correct and the incorrect method of fitting bushings. The bushings should be forced in from the inside of the piston. An iron disk and a bolt, or piece of round steel, are placed between the bushing and the movable vise jaw; pressure is then applied by turning the vise screw. The bolt must be faced on both ends so that it will be square with the bushing. A block of soft wood is placed between the stationary vise jaw and the piston to prevent marring the latter.—E. J. Bachman, Fullerton, Pa.

¶Whenever a horizontal steam pipe is reduced in size, there should be a drip, to avoid partially filling the larger pipe with condensed water.

Gasoline Container for Tube Repairs

An empty shoe-polish bottle, of the common type that has a sponge swab attached to the stopper, is convenient for keeping gasoline in readiness for cleansing around a hole in an inner tube, preparatory to applying a patch. Another bottle and swab is of equal service for applying the cement.

Marking Scales on Machine Parts

It is often desirable to mark a scale on slide, spindles, and other parts of machinery where such graduations would facilitate operation. A marking tool for this purpose can be made quickly and at little expense, as shown in the photograph. It consists of two small, flat chisels and a sleeve. The chisels are ground flat on one side, so that, when the flat sides are put together, the edges will be in line. Both chisels, when fitted together in this way, slide snugly in the sleeve. The edge of the shorter chisel is placed on a division of a scale clamped on top of the piece to be graduated, and the long one is pushed

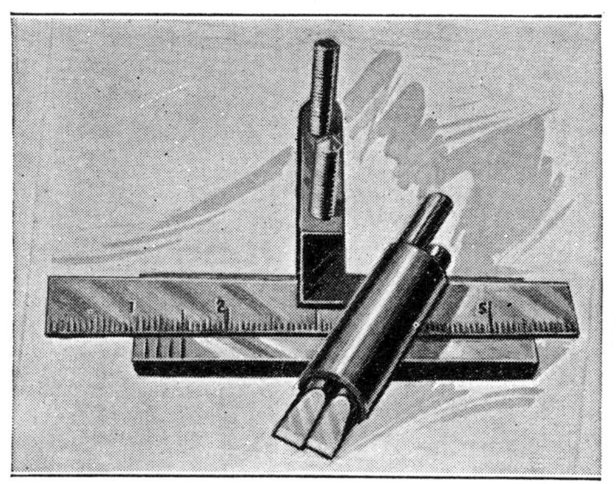

A Simple Tool, Consisting of Two Chisels and a Sleeve, Used to Mark Scale Graduations on Machine Slides or Spindles

down until it touches the work; it is then tapped with a hammer to make the impression.

Extension for Air-Hose Nozzles

The detachable extension to an air-hose nozzle, shown in the illustration, proves very convenient when blowing out dirt or chips from deep holes and slots, as it can be inserted into the hole, and the air pressure applied from the inside of the hole. When an ordinary nozzle is used, a sort of whirlpool action is set up, and much of the matter settles again when the pressure is shut off.

The extension consists of a piece of

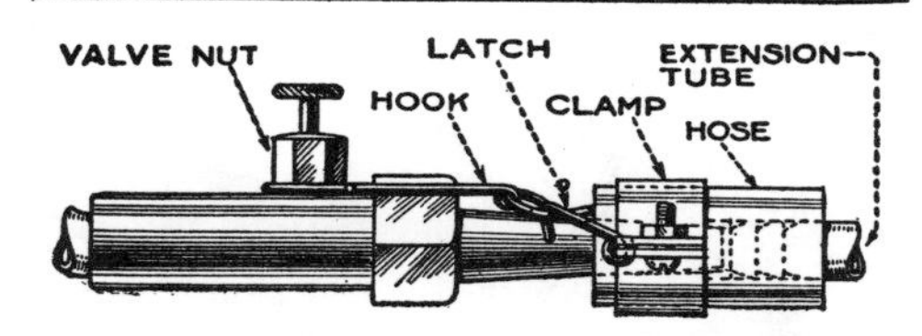

A Detachable Extension for an Air-Hose Nozzle That Facilitates Cleaning of Deep Holes and Slots: It can be Attached in a Moment

metal tubing, and a length of hose to fit over it, both being held to the nozzle by a clamp and a wire lock. The only work required on the tube is the cutting of a few hose steps. The clamp is made of two pieces of sheet metal, held together by two small stove bolts. A hole is drilled on each side for the wire lock. This consists of a latch on one side and a two-piece hook on the other. To attach the device, the hose is pressed tightly over the nozzle, the wire hook is placed around the valve nut, and is then drawn over so that the latch can be slipped into the ring. This attachment, although shown connected to a valve-operated air nozzle, can be used equally well on the spigot-operated type by placing the hook around the spigot instead of the valve nut.

Gold Color on Brass

A rich gold color can be imparted to brass articles by boiling them in a solution of 2 parts saltpeter, 1 part common salt, 1 part alum, 24 parts water, and 1 part hydrochloric acid, all by weight.

Another method of obtaining the same result consists in the application of a solution of 3 parts alum, 6 parts saltpeter, 3 parts sulphate of zinc, and 3 parts of common salt to the surface of the articles. After applying this solution, the articles are heated until they become black. They are then washed with water, rubbed with vinegar, and again washed with water and dried.

Detachable Beam Hook

The illustration shows a detachable beam hook that has been found to give

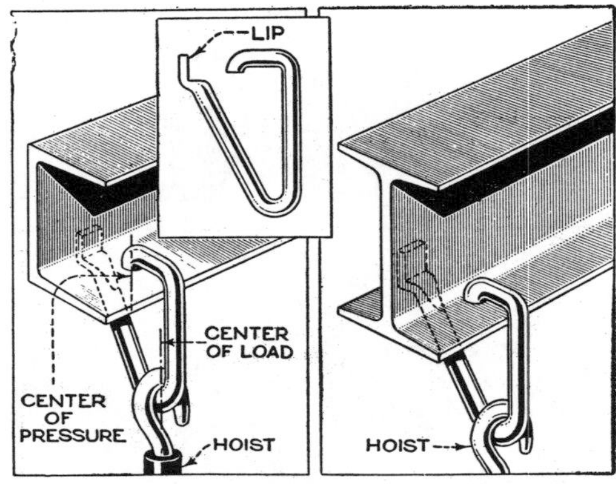

A Simple Beam Hook That Holds Heavy Loads Securely without Danger of Slipping, and That is Attached or Detached Instantly

excellent service in a machine shop for suspending loads on overhead channel and I-beams. The construction is very simple; the hook consists of only one length of iron rod, bent as indicated, and with a lip formed on one end. When attached to the beam, the load center is not in line with the center of pressure; this forces the lip against the beam, and keeps the hook rigidly in place. The hook must be made to fit the beam, but, as the beams of a shop are usually of uniform size, one size of hook may be found sufficient.

Relagging Pulleys

When relagging pulleys it is difficult to hold the leather tight enough, while riveting, so that it will not become loose after very short use. For this reason the method shown in the illustration was devised, and has been found to be entirely successful.

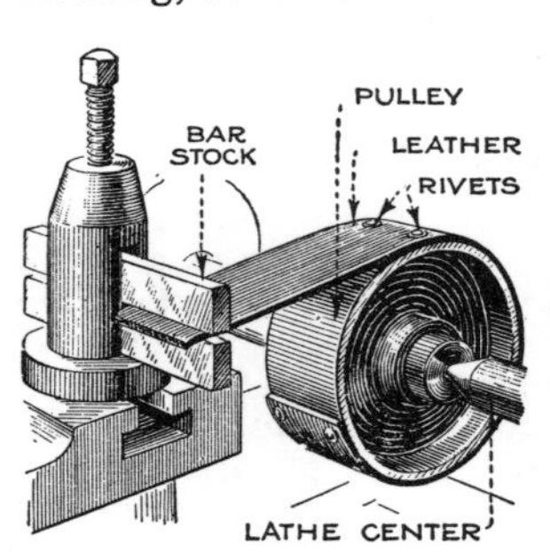

The pulley to be lagged is driven tightly on a mandrel and placed between centers in a lathe, the mandrel being dogged as usual. One end of the lagging is riveted to the pulley, and the pulley is then turned so that the next riveting point is uppermost. The lagging is gripped between two bars in the toolpost, as shown. The lathe is locked by placing it in back gear, and the lagging is tightened by means of the cross slide.

A Shield for Cloth Buffing Wheels

The shield for cloth buffing wheels shown in the drawing can be improvised in a few moments, and protects the worker's eyes and face from the rouge and particles of metal thrown off while the wheel is revolving, just as well as a much more elaborate one.

The shield is made of cardboard, cut out as shown, and provided with a slot to fit a 12 or 14-in. flat file. An ordinary rubber band is used to hold the shield to the file at any desired height over the wheel, the shield being bent and slipped over the file as shown. If the polishing spindle is attached to a wooden bench, the file tang is driven into the wood directly behind the wheel, but if the spindle is attached to a metal base, the file tang is driven into a box or wooden

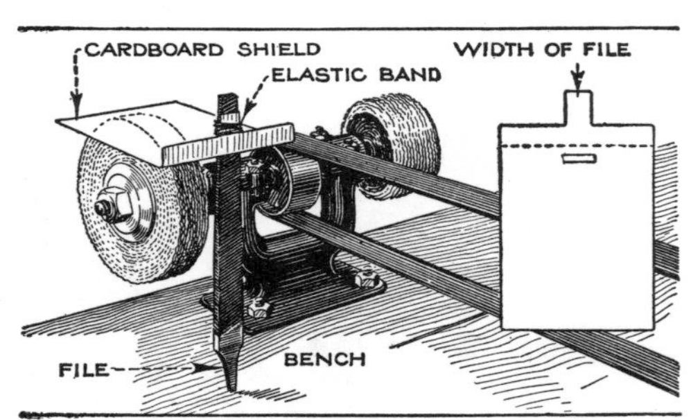

A Cardboard Shield, That can be Improvised in a Moment, Protects the Worker's Eyes from Particles Thrown off the Buffing Wheel

block of the same height, and this is placed behind the wheel.—Harry Moore, Montreal, Can.

Removing Stains from Concrete

Concrete and stucco houses are often discolored by stains, caused by dirty water dripping from window sills and cornices. These stains can be readily removed by scrubbing with water, using a heavy bristle or wire brush. Rust stains can be removed by scrubbing the spots with a solution of 1 part muriatic acid and 5 parts water. When using this, the hands should be well protected from the acid, as it is very strong, and will cause severe burns. After scrubbing the concrete, the acid must be well rinsed off with clean water.

Tool Tray for the Stepladder

Four pieces of quarter-round molding, nailed along the edges on the top step of a stepladder, form an excellent tray for holding tools. The molding is nailed with one flat side down and the other toward the center of the step. Electricians will find this tray of considerable assistance while hanging fixtures, as the tools, solder, and tape can be laid on the top without any danger of falling off, even while moving the ladder from one position to another.—W. Norman Fox, Atlantic City, N. J.

Shock Absorber for Door Glass

To prevent the glass panes in the door of his office from being broken when the door was slammed, a Wisconsin factory foreman fitted the glass to the door with rubber strips instead of wooden cleats. Rubber strips, 3 in. wide, are cemented to the edges of the glass on each side, and also across the center, as shown. When dry, the rubber-framed pane is placed in position in the door, and the rubber is tacked down. The strips are cut from a discarded inner tube. No glass has been broken since it was fitted in this manner.—G. E. Hendrickson, Argyle, Wis.

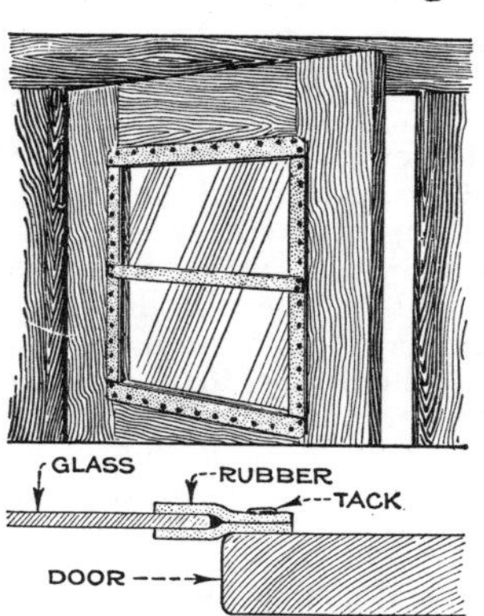

Seating Woodruff Keys

To tighten a Woodruff key in its seat, a slot is cut into the key, as shown in the illustration, and a small piece of sheet metal, slightly thicker than the slot, and tapered on one edge, is forced into the slot, to expand the key. The edges of the sheet metal are then trimmed off, and the key is filed to an exact fit in the seat.—L. R. Butcher, Des Moines, Ia.

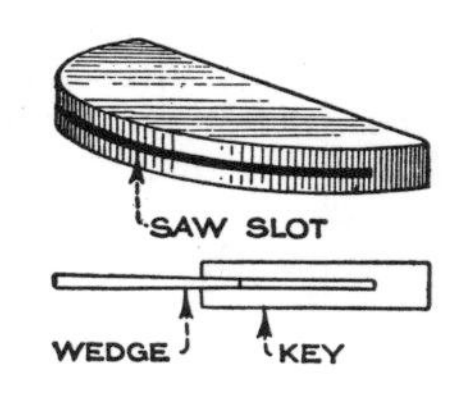

A Chamfering Tool

An excellent tool for chamfering wood, and one not as well known among woodworkers as it should be, can be made from a length of flat steel. A hole is drilled in each end and countersunk on opposite sides. The ends are bent to the shape shown in the illustration and are casehardened. The cutting edges of the holes are sharpened on an oilstone. The tool is held on the work at an angle, and the user may either draw it toward or push it away from his body.

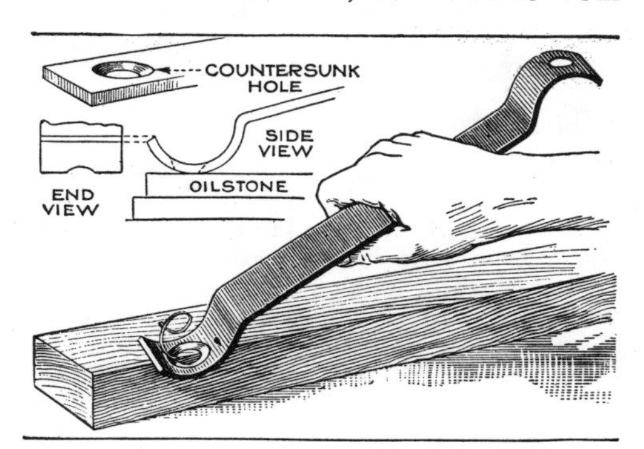

A Simple Chamfering Tool That can be Made in a Short Time from Flat-Bar Stock, and is Easily Sharpened

Bridging Joists with Wire

A novel method of bridging joists, using wire as a substitute for the diagonal wood bracing, has proved very successful in the construction of a frame building. Lengths of No. 8 gauge galvanized-iron wire are led under and over the adjacent joists as shown, and are securely fastened with heavy staples. Both wire and staples are driven down flush with the joists, so that the flooring boards can be laid without trouble. The usual form of stretcher for fence work is used to tighten the wire. The weight of the load places the wire in tension, instead of in compression, as with the wood bracing, and for this reason the wire must be stretched tightly and stapled securely, so that it cannot slip.

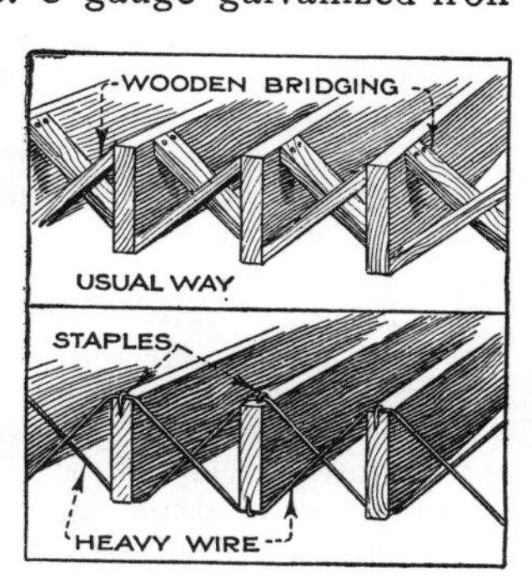

THE advantages of concrete watering troughs on the farm are obvious. Troughs made of wood and iron are short-lived, especially if they are not kept filled to a constant level, and they deteriorate even more rapidly if built below ground than if built above it. Besides, the rust and decay incident to the use of wooden or iron troughs foul the water they contain, while in concrete troughs, if kept clean, the water remains pure and sweet. Concrete troughs are, moreover, not only easy to build, but cost considerably less for maintenance than wooden or iron ones, as it is not necessary to drain and paint them periodically.

While this article specifically refers to watering troughs for stock, exactly the same procedure is employed in making tanks for storage of water, so that these remarks, and the following directions may be taken as applying to storage-tank construction as well.

Tanks may be made either round or rectangular. The round tank requires less material for a given capacity than a rectangular one, but is more difficult to construct, except when a concrete silo is being erected, when the same forms can be used in making the tank.

The construction of the rectangular tank will be taken up first.

The trenches for the foundation are dug well down below the frost line, and the pipe lines for inlet and overflow laid down at the same time. The trenches being finished and the pipes laid, the construction of the forms may be taken up. Forms for concrete work should be made of green lumber, as seasoned wood will warp and swell, owing to the moisture in the concrete. The boards used should be planed, and dressed on both edges, as a form made of planed boards is easily cleaned, and the dressed edges allow the form to be made "tight." This is a necessary feature, for, if any cracks or gaps are left in the form, the cement in the mixture will leak through, leaving a porous spot in the wall. If the forms are well soaked with water, after assembly, there will be little possibility of leakage. Tongued-and-grooved boards, while not essential, make the best form, and leave a good, smooth finish on the completed work.

Lumber 1 in. thick is used for the forms, and the braces are made of 2 by 4-in. stuff. The outside forms are braced to stakes, driven into the ground, as shown. The concrete used for the work is mixed in the proportion of 1 part cement to 2 of sand, and 4 of clean, broken stone. When the foundation has been poured and the outer forms erected, spread about 1 in. of concrete over the earth that carries the bottom of the tank proper, cut the lower piece of wire-mesh reinforcing to size, and lay it in place, carrying it up along the sides, as indicated. Lay about 1½ in. more concrete over the bottom, place the smaller section of mesh, and lay the remaining 1½ in. of concrete. The inner form, which must be ready before the pouring operation is started, is then hung in place, as shown, and the side walls poured; the concrete must be of a "quaky" consistency.

The forms must be liberally slushed with linseed or crude oil, before pouring, to prevent the concrete from sticking to the lumber.

The concrete, while pouring and afterward, must be thoroughly poked and rammed into all corners, and churned with a long iron rod, so that it will be homogeneous and waterproof. If this part of the work is done thoroughly, there will be no need of applying waterproofing compounds, but it is absolutely necessary that no porous or incompletely filled parts exist in the walls, and this can only be prevented by painstaking rodding. Tapping the forms all over lightly with a hammer will aid in giving the concrete a dense, smooth surface, eliminating subsequent troweling.

The inlet pipe for the tank should be flush with the bottom of the form, and may be temporarily plugged while pouring. The overflow pipe should be about 1 in. below the level of the walls. Reinforcing rods, ⅜ in. in diameter, are inserted around the tank in all four walls, near the top, although they are only

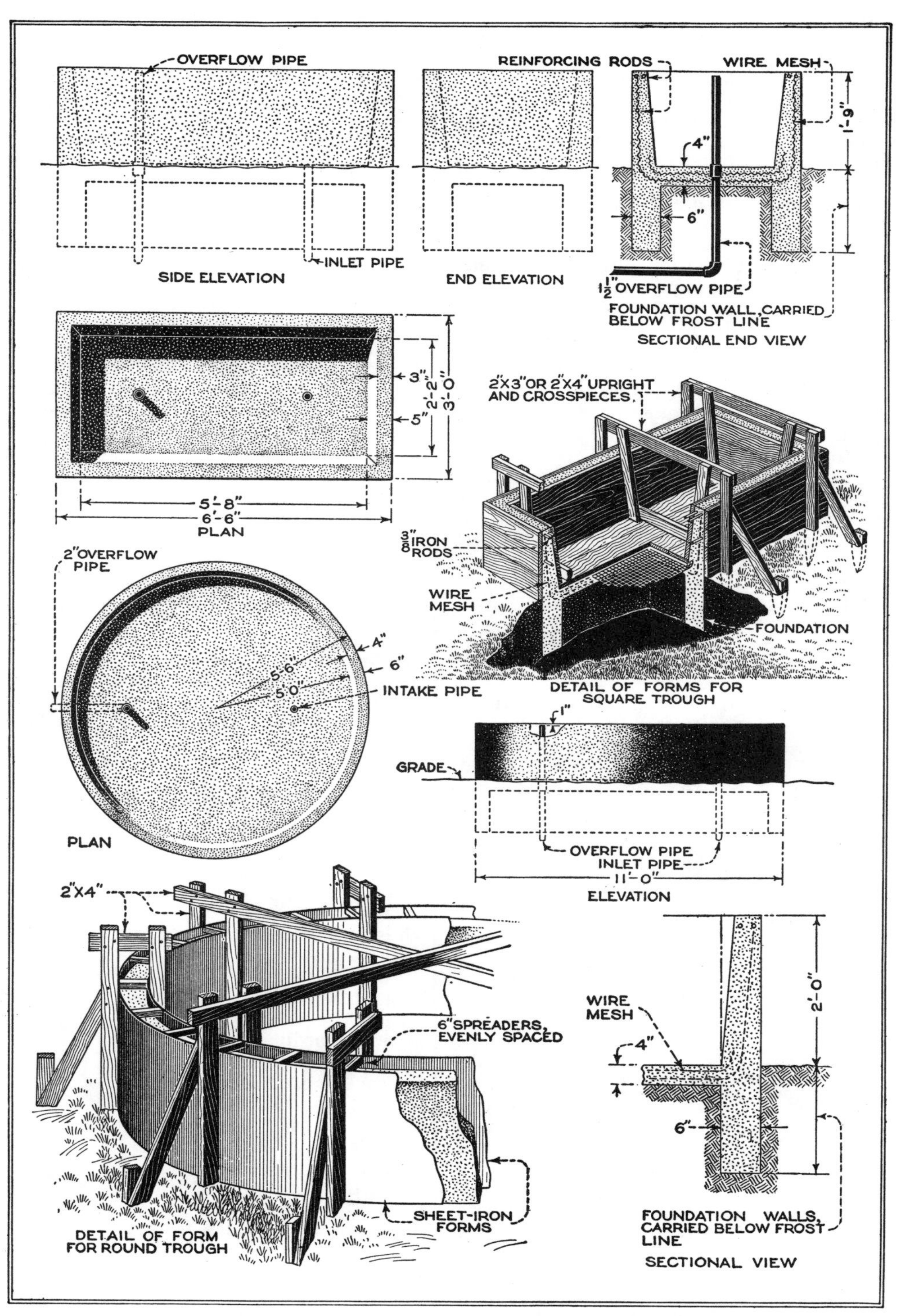

Construction of Concrete Watering Troughs: Above, Details of Forms and Dimensions for Rectangular Trough, Showing How Inner Form is Braced and Hung from Outer One; Below, Form Made of Sheet Iron for a Circular Trough, If Silo Forms Are Not at Hand. The Interior Taper is Formed by Hand, on the Circular Trough, After the Inner Form is Removed. The Edges of the Tanks may be Rounded, If Thought Necessary, While the Concrete Is Still "Green" and Easily Shaped

shown in two in the drawing. No stops should be made in the work once the foundation has been poured; the pouring should be as continuous as possible until the work is completed.

The inner forms can be removed in 24 hours, and the inside surface of the tank painted with a neat-cement wash. The tank should be soaked with water twice a day for two weeks, when the outer forms may be removed, and the tank put in service. The upper edges of the tank may be rounded while the cement is still soft, if desired. The material necessary for a tank of the dimensions shown is approximately 1.66 bbl. cement, .55 cu. yd. sand, 1.10 cu. yd. broken stone, 9 sq. yd. ½-in. square wire mesh, and 70 ft. ⅜-in. reinforcing rod.

If no silo forms are available, the circular tank may be constructed as shown in the lower illustrations, using heavy sheet iron to form the side walls.

The foundation is laid as for the rectangular tank, and the wire-mesh reinforcing placed in the same manner. The inner sheet-iron form must be securely braced, as shown, when hung from the outer one, and spaced from it by 6-in. wooden spreaders, which are moved upward as the concrete is deposited. The reinforcing rods are bent into hoops and placed in the concrete so that the joints come as far apart as possible. Three hoops are used, so the joints should be placed 120 degrees apart. The inlet and overflow pipes are placed as before.

The inner form should be removed as soon as possible, and the inner taper formed on the tank by troweling or cutting the cement as indicated by the dotted line in the sectional view. The inside taper on both tanks is important, as when ice forms on the water it tends to slip up the sides of the tank rather than exert pressure against them. After painting with a cement-water mixture, the tank is cured for two weeks.

The material required for the tank is 4.40 bbl. cement, 1.40 cu. ft. sand, 2.80 cu. yd. broken stone, 24 sq. ft. wire mesh, and 125 ft. ⅜-in. reinforcing rod.

Removing Crankshaft End Play

End play in the crankshaft of an automobile engine results in considerable wear on various parts. In a light car that has its magneto incorporated with the flywheel, such end play will not only vary the intensity of the light and the strength of the ignition, due to the varying distance between the magneto coils and magnets, but will often result in weakening of the magnets and breakdown of the coils, owing to the scraping of the magnets against the coil cores.

This trouble is usually remedied by fixing a shim to the end of the bearing cap with solder and pins. A better method, however, is to use a brass shim of the type shown in the illustration. It can be attached much more easily and is more satisfactory than the shim on each end of the cap. It is placed on the face of the bearing cap, and the ends are bent over as indicated.

A Cutter-Grinding Gauge

The cutting faces of side and face-milling cutters are apt to become out of parallel with the bore of the cutter, after being ground a few times. When this occurs, it is worth while to make the gauge shown in the drawing which is much better for testing the cutters than the ordinary square. A piece of stock is turned for a plug; this is made with a shoulder at one end, the body being a neat sliding fit in the bore of the cutter, and is drilled through its axis and tapped for a large fillister-head screw. A piece of ⅜-in. flat stock is then cut for the arm, shaped as shown, drilled and slotted for the screw and stud, and then ground on the side to be used against the cutter. This side should also be lapped, if possible.

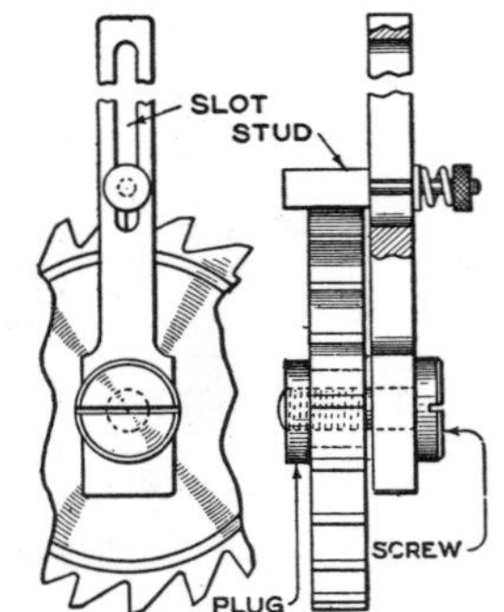

The stud, of tool steel, is turned and ground parallel, the smaller diameter being a good fit in the slot, and threaded on the end for a knurled nut. To hold the stud square and at the same time allow it to slide easily, a light spring is placed between washer and nut.

To use the gauge, insert the plug into the cutter bore, tighten the arm to the plug by means of the screw, then slide the stud down against the tooth. The clearance on the side of the tooth, and its parallelism, may be tested by holding the cutter up to the light.

Funnel for Pouring Melted Resin and Lead

The funnel shown in the illustration has been found very useful for pouring melted resin and lead into copper pipes, a customary operation before bending them, in order to prevent buckling.

The funnel is made of tin or sheet brass, shaped as shown. The wide end is cut off at an angle, to facilitate pouring when

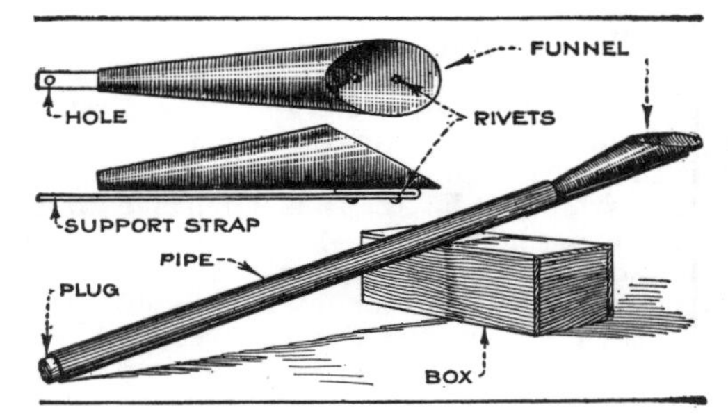

A Tin or Sheet-Brass Funnel That Facilitates the Pouring of Melted Resin or Lead into Pipes, before Bending Them, to Prevent Buckling

the pipe is in an inclined position. The narrow end of the funnel is inserted into the end of the pipe, and is held to it by means of a length of 1/4-in. strap iron, which is doubled and riveted to the funnel at the wide end, and extends a few inches beyond the narrow end. A small hole at the end of the strap permits the funnel to be hung on a nail when not in use.

Toolmaker's Magnifying Glass

A small magnifying glass can be made very easily by inserting a strong spectacle lens into the narrow end of a telephone mouthpiece. The glass is made round by grinding it on an emery wheel so that it fits exactly. Thick shellac is used to hold the glass in place.

Clamp for Rolled Material

A useful clamp, for holding down the end of rolled material that has a tendency to curl back when unrolled, is shown in

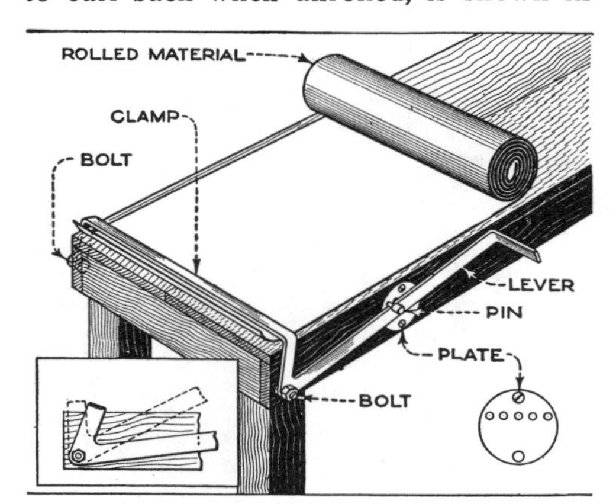

A Serviceable Clamp for Holding the End of Rolled Material Which Greatly Facilitates Marking Out, or Cutting It

the drawing. A length of 3/4 by 1/8-in. flat iron, bent as shown, to suit the width of the bench, is pivoted on two bolts driven into the bench. A circular plate is fastened to the side of the bench, under the center of the lever. A number of holes are drilled in a row through the plate to accommodate a pin, which is used to hold the lever down. By inserting the pin in different holes, the clamp is adjusted to various thicknesses of material.

A Quick-Acting Tap Holder

In addition to several turning jobs on hand for the lathe, there was one piece drilled, on the end, which required to be tapped. Being anxious to do this without changing the setting, the quick-acting tap holder shown in the drawing was devised. The square shank of the tap is held in a swinging piece, clamped to the tailstock center, so that, when in use, the center fits into the center hole in the tap shank. When the tap is in position for use, it is located accurately by the pin, which also prevents it from lifting. When the tapping operation is finished, it is only necessary to pull out the pin and swing the holder aside.

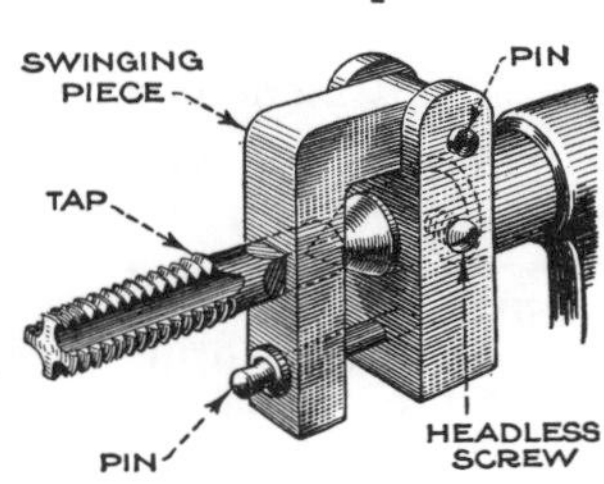

Cheap Gasoline-Storage Tank

The illustration shows the arrangement of a 550-gal. gasoline-storage tank, used by a service station. It was installed at far less expense than an ordinary single tank of similar capacity.

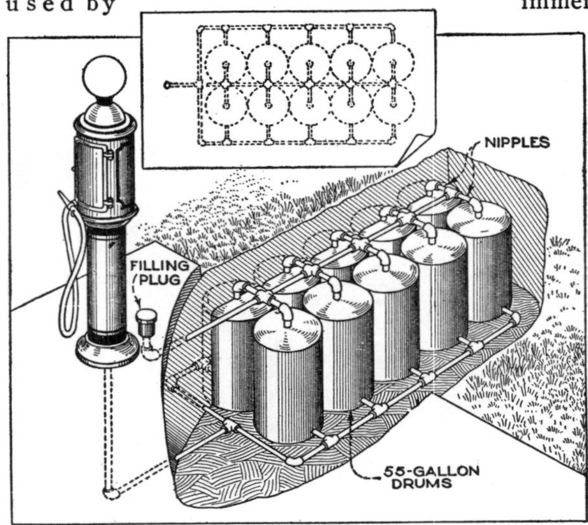

A Number of Steel Oil Drums, Combined to Make a 550-Gallon Storage Tank for Gasoline: The Cost Is Far Less than That of a Single Large Tank, and the Drums Are as Satisfactory

The reservoir is made from ten 55-gal. steel oil drums, arranged as shown, just below the surface of the ground. All the drums are connected, at the bottom, to each other and to the pump, with pipe and fittings; the small nipples that connect the fittings to the drums have a right and a left-hand thread, so that any one of the drums can be removed without much trouble. The tops are similarly connected to each other and to the filling pipe. By using this arrangement of drums, instead of a single large tank, an estimated saving of $400 was made.

Casehardening Bronze

The bronzes that possess the greatest hardness lack the requisite properties for chasing and sinking fine, intricate designs. It is, however, possible to obtain a hard face on bronze by a process similar to the casehardening of steel, and this is practiced with some bronze dies. The method is that of coating the surface of the die with pure tin and then heating to a low, red heat in order to alloy the tin with the surface of the bronze. Copper and tin unite in all proportions, and, when alloyed with from 20 to 30 per cent of tin, the bronze becomes comparatively hard. The surface of the die to be casehardened is cleansed of grease by soaking in a strong, hot potash solution, and then immersing in a pickle, or acid dip, to remove the oxide. A suitable pickle, which works more rapidly if hot, is made in the proportion of 1 part sulphuric acid to 5 parts of water. The die is allowed to soak several hours until clean; it is then taken out, brushed, and the surface coated with a strong solution of zinc chloride to act as a flux. The surface is then covered with pure, melted tin. The tin may be melted on the surface by a soldering iron, but the best method is to use a torch or a blowpipe. The tin is melted on the surface only, and as little as possible is put on, as the fine detail of the die must not be filled up. The die is then washed in water to remove the excess of flux, and the surface is examined. If there are any portions that are not covered with tin, the process is repeated.

The next operation is to heat the die to a red heat, preferably in a muffle, though a blowpipe or torch may be used if the work is small. To prevent the surface from oxidizing, it is advisable first to cover it with a strong solution of boracic acid. The boracic acid is dissolved in hot water and the solution brushed lightly over the surface. A light coat only is necessary. The die is placed on an iron plate, to keep it from breaking when heated, as tin-bronze becomes brittle at red heat, and it is heated to a low, red heat and allowed to remain in this condition from 10 to 15 minutes. The plate is then removed from the muffle and the die allowed to cool. The boracic acid is removed by soaking in hot water and afterward pickling, if necessary.

Dies hardened by this method can be used for stamping leather, soft metals, paper, and similar work, as they can be made originally soft enough for chasing or sinking with ease, and then hardened without destroying the design. The best results are obtained by using a rather soft bronze mixture with as little lead as possible. Such a bronze, high in copper, is not likely to give trouble by softening or cracking during the heating. A bronze mixture recommended for treatment by the method described is made in the proportion of 88 per cent copper, 8 tin, 2 zinc, and 2 lead.

Float for Boiler Gauge Glass

An indicator that plainly shows the water level in the glass gauge on a boiler can readily be improvised. Cut a thin slice from a small bottle cork, paint it bright red, and give it a few coats of shellac. Place this circular slice of cork inside the water glass, so that it will float in the water. The indicator enables one to read the gauge from a distance, even on dark days and in smoky boiler rooms, when it would otherwise be a considerable strain on the eyes to observe the water level in the glass.—John M. Pipp, Muncie, Ind.

Combination Harness Vise and Bench

The difficulty of sewing and mending harness without some convenient means for holding it firmly in place, led to the construction of the simple device shown in the drawing. After several methods had been tried, with slight satisfaction, it was found that by using this vise-and-bench combination, most of the difficulties were eliminated.

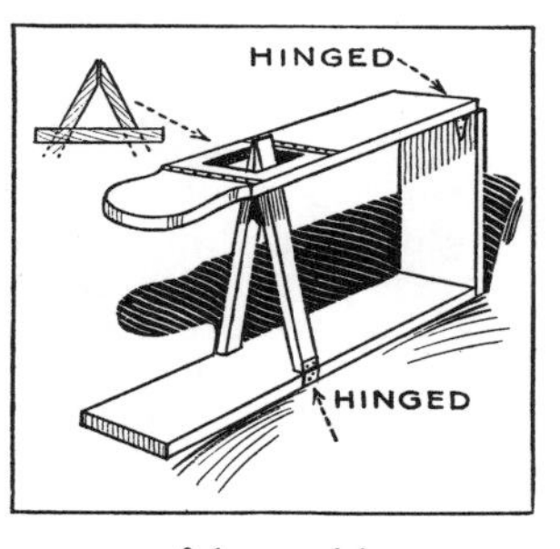

The base was made 4 ft. long, and an upright was nailed firmly to one end of it. A top, also 4 ft. long, was then fastened to the upright by means of large hinges, so that it could be raised and lowered. A square hole was cut near the other end of the top, to fit over two 2 by 4-in. uprights that were hinged to the base to form the vise. On two sides of this hole, pieces of strap iron were screwed, as indicated, to prevent the bench from being split. The end of the top was formed into a seat for the workman. His weight provided sufficient pressure on the vise to hold the work firmly at all times.—R. P. Lincoln, S. Minneapolis, Minn.

A Scraper for Glued Emery Wheels

When recoating glued emery wheels, the scraping device shown is very handy for removing the surplus abrasive, and is preferable to the usual hand scraper, which does not true the wheel surface.

The scraper is made by bending a length of iron rod to a U-shape, and hooking a strip of sheet metal across the legs. The strip of sheet metal swivels on one leg, so that it can be swung around to clear the wheel while pushing the rod through the hole in the center, and slides along the rod so that it can be used on wheels of various diameters.

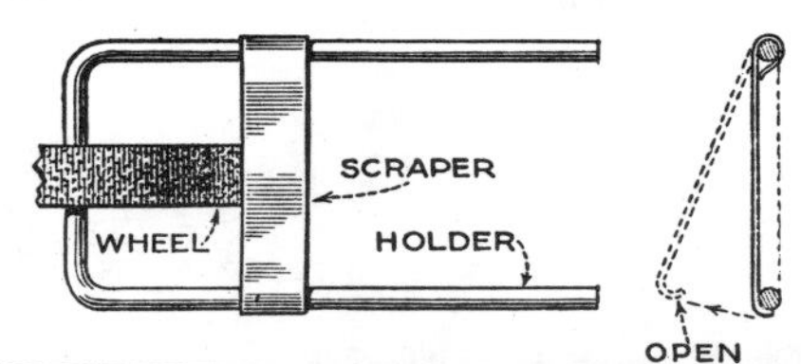

A Simple Scraper Used to Keep the Surface of Glued Emery Wheels True While Rolling Them in the Abrasive: Below: Method of Using

Keeping the Tire Gauge "at Home"

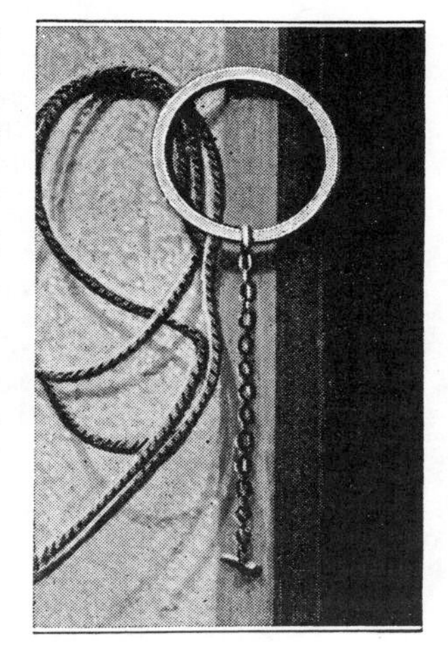

An excellent method of preventing the tire gauge from being lost or mislaid around a garage or service station, when it is not desired to attach it to the air-hose nozzle, is shown herewith. The gauge is brazed to one end of a length of towing chain, and an old steering-wheel rim is attached to the other end. No passing motorist can pocket this assembly.—S. A. Pease, Milwaukee, Wis.

Improvised Motor-Driven Washing Machine

An improvised washing machine, operated by a small spraying outfit, is shown

Above: A Spraying Outfit, Driven by a Gasoline Engine, Used to Operate Washing Machine. Below: Plunger Removed to Show Construction

in the illustration. A barrel, cut in half, provided two excellent tubs. A plunger, made to fit easily in one of these tubs, was attached by means of a long 2 by 3-in. stick, to the center of a 2 by 2-in. walking beam. One end of the beam was pivoted at the top of a fencepost, and the other was fastened to the pump arm of the spraying outfit. The clothes to be washed were tied loosely under the plunger, so that they would be partly lifted on each stroke of the plunger. By starting the engine of the spraying outfit, the apparatus was set in operation, and was found to wash the clothes thoroughly in a very short time.—W. L. Salvage, Beaumont, Calif.

Blue Stains on Wood

Blue stain is the most troublesome of the sap stains that discolor wood. It is caused by a fungus that germinates on the sapwood and penetrates its cells in search of starches and sugars. The action of the fungus causes no perceptible weakening of the wood, but the discoloration lessens the value of the lumber for many purposes, such as interior finish, flooring, and basket or box veneers. The stain at first may be no more than a bluish spot or streak on the surface, but later, as the fungus develops, the discoloration may involve all the sapwood and become too deep to be surfaced off. The blue-stain fungus can revive in timbers after long periods of inaction brought on by lack of moisture.

Warm weather and a comparatively high moisture content of the wood are the most favorable conditions for the growth of the fungus. Most of the infection occurs in green lumber that is piled without ample ventilation between the boards, in the mill yard or during shipment.

As yet no absolutely dependable means of preventing blue stain has been found other than kiln-drying the lumber. The ordinary kiln-drying process is entirely effective, but there are many cases in which this means of prevention is not feasible. Staining during air seasoning can be largely controlled by open piling. This affords free circulation of air and so hastens drying, but not always sufficiently under adverse weather conditions.

The treatment of the green lumber with antiseptic dips is the most effective method which is generally applicable at the present time. For this purpose the chemicals commonly used are soda ash and bicarbonate of soda. Neither, however, is a sovereign remedy under severe conditions, such as continuous rainy periods during the warm months, but will go far toward keeping the stock clean. In rainy seasons an eight-per-cent solution of sodium carbonate is desirable, but in drier weather, half this strength should suffice. When sodium bicarbonate is used, an 11-per-cent solution should be employed in wet weather and five to six per cent in dry weather. This chemical, when dry, should contain about 37 per cent of alkali.

In the use of these chemical dips, the following points should be kept in mind: The solutions should be carefully mixed, and the concentrations in the dipping tanks should be kept uniform by means of a hydrometer. The solutions should be heated when applied, the bicarbonate of soda solution not above 120° F., however, because it is broken down into the carbonate by excessive heating. The stock should be dipped as it comes from the saw. After dipping, it should be carefully piled so as to insure ample ventilation. Narrow, chemically treated cross strips are preferable to the wide untreated strips commonly employed, since treated "crossers" tend to eliminate stain at the point of contact.—U. S. Forest Products Laboratory, Madison, Wis.

Handling Roofing Paper

When applying prepared roofing paper, a great deal of time can be saved by using a pair of tin shears, instead of a knife, for cutting it, especially if the paper is coated with crushed slate or gravel.

The pitch used in cementing the laps, as well as the tar compounds in the paper, usually adhere to the hands while working. This can be removed very easily by means of kerosene.

Leaf for the Worktable

In a small printing shop, one of the benches is provided with a leaf at the end, as shown in the photograph, to prevent stacks of papers or booklets from falling off. The leaf is as wide as the table and about 20 in. long. It is hinged to the edge of the table, and, when raised, is held by means of a hasp fastener on each side. When not in use, the leaf is dropped down out of the way.

A Leaf Attached to the End of a Printing-Shop Workbench Serves to Keep Pamphlets and Papers from Falling Off the Bench

Safety Device for Punch Presses

On some makes of punch presses the manufacturers provide a number of holes in the flywheel, so that, by inserting a bar into the holes, the machine can be turned over by hand when setting and adjusting the dies. This makes a very handy arrangement, but, should the die setter forget or neglect to remove the bar, there is trouble as soon as the clutch is thrown in. Exactly such an occurrence caused a man to be struck by the flying bar, when the power was thrown on without the bar being removed. This accident resulted in the installation of the safety device shown in the photograph, which prevents the clutch from being thrown in while the bar is in the flywheel. As illustrated, the clutch lever operates a slide, to which a ring, running completely around the flywheel, is attached by means of a bracket. If the bar is not removed, the clutch cannot be operated because the ring comes up against the bar and prevents further movement of the clutch lever.—S. A. McDonald, Brooklyn, N. Y.

A Safety Device for Punch Presses That Prevents the Clutch from Engaging When a Handbar Remains in One of the Holes in the Flywheel

¶Oxygen and acetylene tanks should never be dropped or handled roughly, and should never be stood on end, unless fastened so as to prevent their falling over.

Shield Protects Worker Handling Dynamite

A large number of the accidents incident to the use of dynamite are directly traceable to the methods used for crimping fuses in caps. This operation is usually done by hand—very often, indeed,

A Shield, Made of Boiler Plate, That Reduces Materially the Number of Accidents Due to Explosions of Dynamite Caps While Crimping

by biting the end of the cap with the teeth, an exceedingly dangerous practice. Realizing these dangers, the head of a building-material company that does a great deal of blasting in its own quarries, devised the shield shown in the illustration for the protection of the workmen.

The shield is made of ½-in. boiler plate, curved at the top; an endpiece, made of the same material, is riveted to the left-hand side, as indicated by the dotted lines, and the whole fixture firmly fastened to a heavy base. In the front of the shield a slot is cut, large enough for the crimping pliers to work in, and a few inches above and to the left of this, a ¼-in. hole is drilled. A hole, large enough for the fuse, is drilled in the endpiece, level with the plier slot. The fuse is inserted through the hole in the endpiece, the cap slipped over it, and then, with the left hand holding the fuse, the pliers are pushed through the slot, and the cap crimped, the workman observing the operation through the ¼-in. hole.

Should the cap explode, the only harm done would be the "stinging" of the workman's fingers, due to the sudden opening of the pliers. A fine particle of an exploded cap might, of course, pass through the ¼-in. hole, but, in that case, it could, at most, injure only one eye, while, without the shield, the worker might lose both eyes, in addition to his fingers.

Familiarity with dynamite, as with many other potentially dangerous things, breeds, if not contempt, at least carelessness, and the company providing these shields has found it necessary to force the workmen to use them, by warning them that any workman crimping caps without using a shield not only does so at his own risk, but will be discharged immediately, if detected.

Backing Up Typewritten Copies for Blueprinting

When backing up typewritten copies with carbon paper, as is customary before blueprinting from them, the following method will be found very useful: The copies are usually made on thin bond paper, and it is found difficult to feed it through the typewriter without trouble, due to wrinkling of the carbon paper. To avoid this, wind the carbon paper, with the coated side exposed, tightly around the platen of the typewriter, taking care to get it perfectly smooth. Put a spot or two of paste on the free end and stick it down. The bond paper can then be inserted and run through without troubling about the carbon paper.

Holding a Surface Gauge

When a surface gauge is used on round work, it often happens that the gauge is forgotten on the work, with the result that it topples over and falls to the floor. As a precaution against this, a mechanic employed the method shown in the photograph. A pair of spring outside calipers were adjusted to grip the finger depressions on each side of the surface gauge, and a parallel clamp was fastened to the calipers to act as a counterweight.

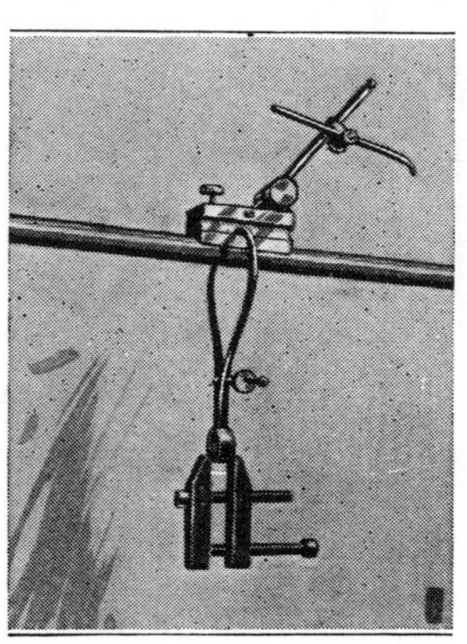

Making a Draftsman's Instrument Case

BY J. D. MCRAE

A SET of drawing instruments costs a considerable sum, if bought complete, and most draftsmen prefer to purchase the instruments as they are needed, especially topographical draftsmen, who use pens, etc., not found in the ordinary set. When the collection is complete, the draftsman thinks of a case for it, but soon discovers, upon consulting a catalog, that this is an expensive item.

The illustration shows a case that can be made for a negligible sum, and that, if the work is carefully done, will look as good as any commercial case. The instrument tray consists of two pieces of 3/16-in. soft wood, glued together and covered velvet. Where there is a cavity for a round lead box, saw slits around it at random. Cut a piece of velvet somewhat larger than the area of the tray. Apply glue sparingly to the bottom and sides of the cavities only. Lay the velvet over the tray and press the instrument that fits into a corner cavity in place. Then move on to the next cavity and press down the instrument that fits in it. Continue in this way, finishing an entire row before beginning with the next. Carefully force the gathered velvet, between the instruments, into the slits, with the blunt edge of a knife. This is all that there is to the tray-covering process. It

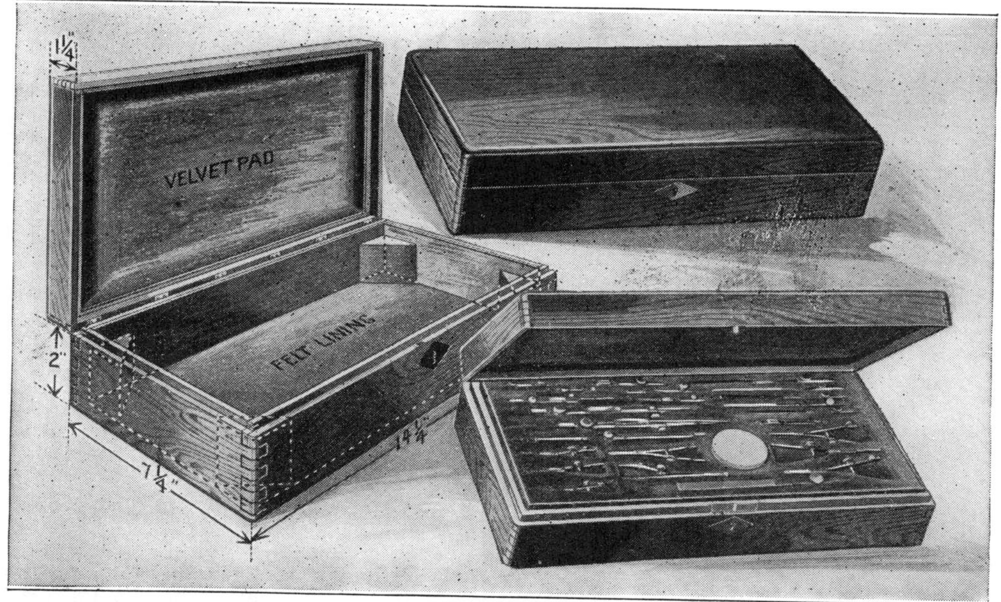

A Homemade Wooden Case for Mechanical Drawing Instruments That Compares Favorably with Manufactured Cases in Strength and Appearance: The Tray is Made to Suit Any Collection of Instruments Desired. The Space under the Tray can Also be Utilized for Pencils, Thumbtacks, Erasers, and Other Articles

ered with velvet. The length and width of the tray are determined by the number of instruments, and the arrangement desired. On one piece of wood, lay out the instruments in order and outline them in pencil. Cut these shapes through the wood, making the holes slightly larger than the outlines. Glue the perforated piece to the other piece, and place under pressure while drying. When dry, take a hacksaw blade and cut slits, 3/16 in. deep, from the ends of the instrument cavities to the ends of the tray, and also cut slits all around the edges, about 1/2 in. apart, as shown in the detail. These slits are to take up the surplus, or puckcan be done very easily if practiced first with a remnant of velvet and a scrap piece of wood. Bring the velvet over the edges of the tray 3/16 in., and cut off the surplus material. Also cover the underside of the tray with velvet, bringing the edges up 3/16 in. The seam along the edge is covered with a narrow strip of fiber or aluminum, fastened neatly with countersunk flat-head screws.

The case can then be made. It consists of two thicknesses of 3/16-in. wood, joined together with glue and screws, the latter being driven in from the inside, and countersunk. The double thickness prevents warping. Fit small blocks in the corners as shown, and drive screws through them to hold the dovetailed corners firmly together; the joints thus made are very strong and permanent. The blocks also serve as tray supports. Attach the cover with six hinges; these provide sufficient strength, and also stiffness, which eliminates the necessity of a stay hinge to hold the lid up. Fit a velvet pad inside of the cover to hold the drawing instruments in place when the case is closed and carried around. The pad consists of a piece of cardboard and several layers of cotton batting, covered with velvet, the edges of the velvet being sewed at the back of the cardboard.

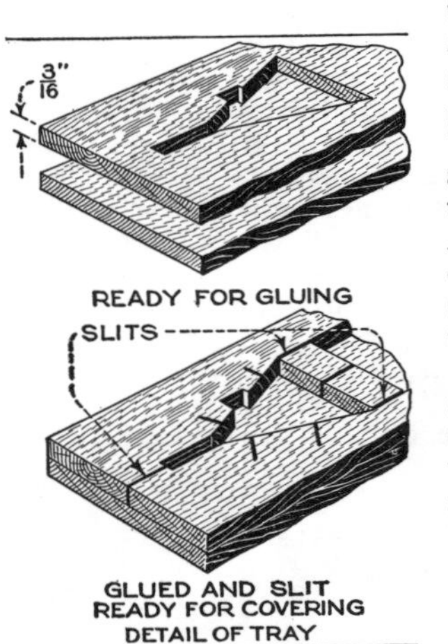

DETAIL OF TRAY

Line the inside of the lower part of the case with dark-colored felt, cut to fit, and glued to the bare wood. Stain the outside of the case and apply shellac. When dry, rub down with fine sandpaper and apply another coat of shellac. Repeat this process until the finish is satisfactory. Before varnishing, make a trimming for the keyhole by cutting a piece of drawing paper, colored black, to a diamond shape, and glue this over the keyhole.

Borax as Shellac Solvent

Borax has been found to be an excellent solvent for shellac, and an inexpensive substitute for alcohol. It is of special value in cases where it is necessary to avoid the fumes of alcohol. Another advantage of shellac dissolved in borax is that it does not dry so rapidly as shellac dissolved in alcohol, since the water evaporates much more slowly than alcohol.

An excellent shellac varnish of the proper consistency for brush work is prepared from 5 parts of borax, 15 parts of powdered shellac, and 100 parts of water, mixed well in a pail that is immersed in boiling water for a few hours. A very small quantity of glycerin adds pliability and toughness.

Stand for Gasoline Blowtorch

To hold a torch so that the flame is directed up against the underside of a lead or babbitt ladle, or against small tempering plates, the method shown in the illustration has been found to be much more convenient than the usual one of tilting it by means of blocks of wood, firebrick, or pieces of metal.

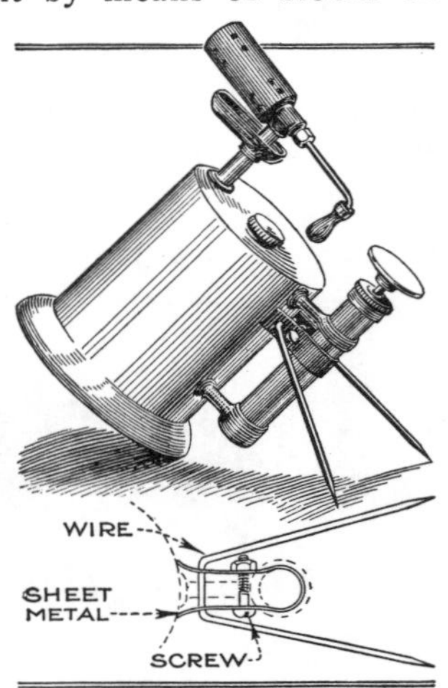

A strip of sheet iron is bent around the handle, the ends being long enough to reach the side of the torch so that they will be drawn against the latter when the bolt and nut are tightened. A piece of wire, shaped as indicated, and sharpened at each end, is pushed through holes drilled in the sheet-iron strip. This can be stuck into the bench to hold the torch in any position that is desired. This method of holding the torch is very neat and there is practically no danger of it falling over.

An Emergency Taper Gauge

When duplicating tapered pieces that are not standard, a simple gauge can be made to fit the taper. The sample piece is placed in a vertical position, approximately in the center of a piece of steel tubing, and the space between is filled with babbitt. Before pouring, the piece is given a thin coat of tallow, to prevent the babbitt from adhering to it. After pouring, it is tapped lightly to make it fit as perfectly as possible, then removed, and the rough ends of the gauge faced off. The pieces should all be rough-turned first, then the sample piece should be placed between centers, and indicated, setting over the

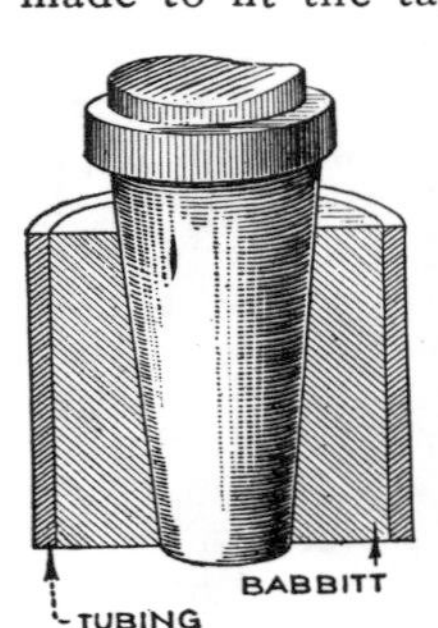

tailstock or adjusting the taper attachment until the indicator shows that it is set correctly. The sample may then be removed, and the pieces finish-turned.—E. N. Davey, Montreal, Can.

Sectional Rack for Welding Rods

It is an easy matter to keep welding rods in good order, so that the metal required for any particular job can be selected without any trouble, by making a rack equipped with removable steel containers.

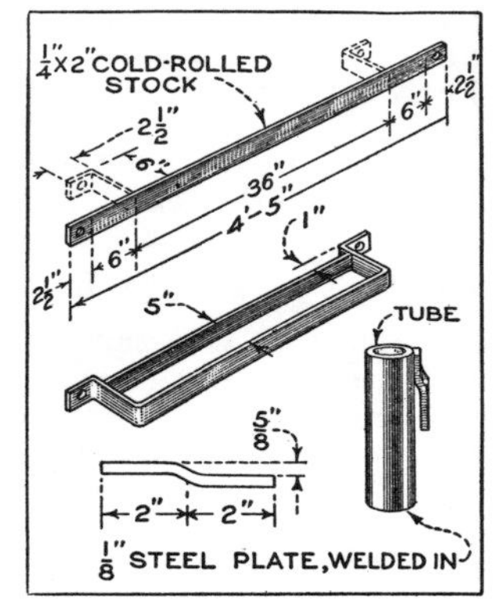

The rack is made of flat bar stock, welded together as shown in the drawing. The containers are made of steel tubing, a disk, made of 1/8-in. steel plate, being welded in one end of each length, to form a bottom, and a clip to the other end to serve as a hanger. These containers are made in two sizes, 12 in. and 25 in. in length, as the welding rods usually come in two general sizes. The steel, iron, and bronze rods are supplied in pieces about 3 ft. long, while the cast-iron, cast-aluminum, and other rods vary from 12 in. to 18 in. in length.—A. S. Jamieson, Springfield, Mass.

Spacer Aids Fitting of Caps

When fitting connecting-rod or main-bearing caps, spacers made of bushing stock or tubing have been found to facilitate the work and to save considerable time. By using spacers it is not necessary to turn the nut down until it touches the bearing cap, but only to turn it down three or four threads until it touches the spacer. Half a turn with a wrench will then tighten the cap. When the spacers are not used, a wrench must be used all the way.

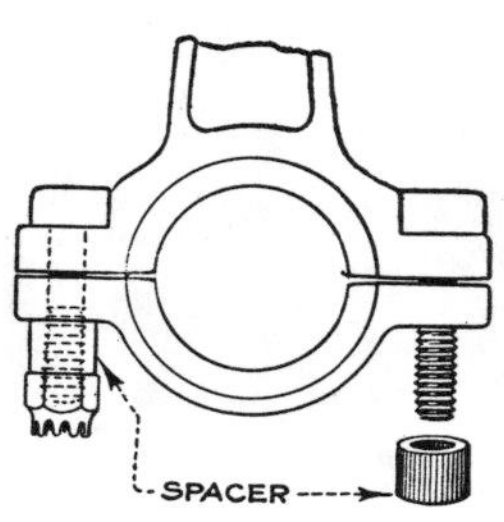

Countershaft Lock

A safety lock for countershafts is shown in the illustration. It is designed to prevent a machine operator from starting the machine while the clutches and pulleys are being oiled. The lock is simple to make. It consists of a piece of flat steel, 1/8 by 3/4 in., bent to U-shape, and bolted to the hanger so that it straddles the shifter-rod bearing, as shown. Two notches to fit the lock are filed in the shifter rod, while the belt is on the loose pulley. When the oiler desires to lock the countershaft, the device is swung down to catch in the notches. This prevents the shifting of the belt to the fast pulley.

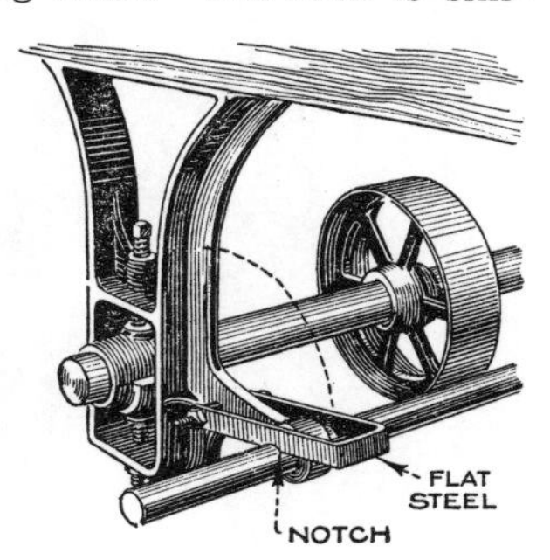

Tools for Cleaning and Polishing Shafts

The tool shown in the illustration is used for cleaning and polishing shafts without the aid of a ladder. A 2 by 4-in. hardwood block is cut out as shown. The upper part of the recess is lined with emery cloth, and a piece of flat steel is screwed to the block, as indicated. A hole is drilled in the bottom of the block to receive the 3/4-in. pipe that serves as a handle. A pin passes through both block and pipe to hold the pipe in place. The handle must be long enough to enable the operator to reach the shaft while standing on the floor below. The tool is pressed upward on the revolving shaft to scrape off hardened grease or oil, and pulled downward to polish it.

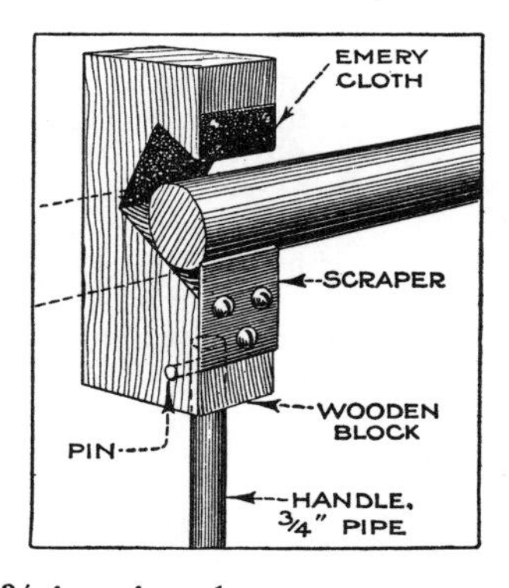

¶The best ratio of heating to grate surface is about 35 to 1, and grate area to draft area as eight to one.

Teeth on Cultivator Improve Efficiency

Teeth, fitted on the bottom of the shields of a cultivator, as shown, make them more effective in breaking crusted

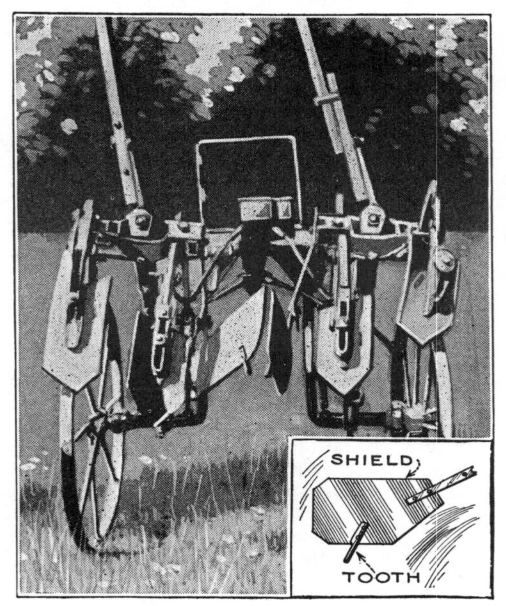

Small Teeth Attached to the Shields of a Cultivator Greatly Improve Its Efficiency in Breaking Crusted Soil and in Cultivating Listed Corn

soil, and are of special value when cultivating listed corn.

The teeth are 4 in. long and project 1½ in. below the edge of the shields. Each tooth consists of two pieces of ⅜-in. rod, flattened at one end and riveted to the rear part of a shield as shown, one piece on each side of the shield.—Mrs. Ruth Darling Shultis, Grand Junction, Colo.

Air-Dried Versus Kiln-Dried Wood

There is much difference of opinion as to whether air-dried or kiln-dried wood is the stronger. However, some 150,000 comparative strength tests, made by the Forest Products Laboratory, on kiln-dried and air-dried specimens of 28 common species of wood, show that good kiln-drying and good air-drying have the same effect upon the strength of the wood.

The belief that kiln-drying produces stronger wood than air-drying is usually the result of failure to consider the difference in the moisture contained in wood after being dried. The moisture contained in kiln-dried wood is generally from 2 to 6 per cent lower than that of thoroughly air-dried stock. As the strength of wood is increased with the elimination of moisture, kiln-dried wood is at first stronger than air-dried wood. However, the difference in strength is not permanent, because, in use, a piece of wood will come to practically the same moisture condition whether it is kiln-dried or air-dried.

The appearance of the dried wood is not a reliable index of its strength. Furthermore, the same kiln-drying process cannot be applied with equal results to all species. To insure uninjured kiln-dried material, a knowledge of the correct kiln conditions to use for stock of a given species, grade, and thickness, and a record showing that no more severe treatment has been employed, are necessary.

Novel Arrangement for Pumping Water

Finding it necessary to pump 3,200 gal. of water out of a cistern, a bicycle, electric motor, and small pump were arranged as shown in the photograph, and, although the arrangement presented a comical appearance while running, it proved to be very effective.

The bicycle was turned upside down and fastened to a wide board. Staples were used to fasten the handlebars, and a small wooden block to clamp the saddle. The tire was removed from the rear wheel and a small 1/16-hp. electric motor mounted on the board, behind the saddle, so that its pulley was in alinement with the rear wheel. A belt was made from a piece of ¼-in. cotton rope, with the ends spliced together, of such a length that,

A Novel Arrangement, Consisting of a Small Motor, Pump, and Part of a Bicycle, was Found Very Effective for Pumping Water from a Cistern

when it was put on the motor pulley and rear wheel, the coil springs of the saddle were slightly compressed, insuring a proper tension on the belt at all times. A 3-in. cistern pump was fastened to the board in front of the handlebars, the board set over the cistern, and a length of pipe run down to the bottom of the latter. A connecting rod was fitted from the handle of the pump to the bicycle pedal; the rod was made from an automobile brake rod.

The gear ratio is about 50 to 1. The pump operates at about 40 strokes per minute, and gives an output of 3 gal. per minute or 180 gal. per hour.—Dr. A. C. Griffin, Whitestone, L. I.

Machining Sheave Pulleys

The usual method employed to machine a large sheave pulley, by setting it on an arbor in a lathe, and turning it down first in the center and then on each side, is slow and laborious. A much quicker method, that has been found to be very successful, is to use a vertical milling machine and three cutters, two straight ones for the sides and a curved one for the center. All three cutters are in use at the same time, and a considerable saving in time is effected.

A Vertical Milling Machine, Equipped with Three Cutters, Finishes Sheave Pulleys Much Faster than They can be Finished in the Lathe

Truing a Universal Chuck

When operating on particular work with a three or four-jaw universal chuck that is out of true, the difficulty can be remedied without using shims, as follows: Place a piece of tubing, having an internal diameter suitable to the work, between the jaws, and tighten them up equally, so that the tubing is bent slightly out of round. Bore the tubing out to the size of the work. Then insert the work and tighten the jaws, and the work will run perfectly true. The tubing will not turn in the jaws.—J. Harger, Honolulu, Hawaiian Islands.

A Novel Gate

The photograph shows an original type of gate, built by a blacksmith and wheelwright to advertise his shop. It consists of a wagon wheel and a number of rims. A square frame is built around the wagon wheel, and rims of various sizes are attached to the spokes at equal distances from each other, as shown. A piece of sheet iron, cut in the form of an anvil, is fastened to the hub. The whole gate is painted red and black.—Mrs. M. F. Phillip, Caneadea, N. Y.

This Gate, Used to Advertise a Blacksmith and Wheelwright Shop, Is Quite Novel in Design and Attracts Considerable Attention from Passing Farmers

Tinning Black Iron

For tinning black-iron and steel objects, to prevent them from rusting, the following method has been found very satisfactory, leaving a thick deposit: The scale on the surface of the work to be tinned is first removed by immersing the object in raw muriatic acid until the metal turns white. The work is then put into cut muriatic acid; this is made by adding clippings of sheet zinc to raw muriatic acid, until it will dissolve no more. The cut acid leaves a zinc film deposited on the surface of the work, so that the molten tin will adhere better. After shaking off the surplus acid, the object is dipped into the molten tin, solder, or lead, as desired. If the coating is not satisfactory, dip the object into the cut acid and molten metal again.

Small pieces of bar solder that accumulate in shops, can be used for coating purposes; even the dross that is skimmed from the surface of molten solder and lead can often be used for this purpose.

Lathe Head Used as Variable-Speed Drive

An old lathe head has been found to give excellent service as a variable-speed

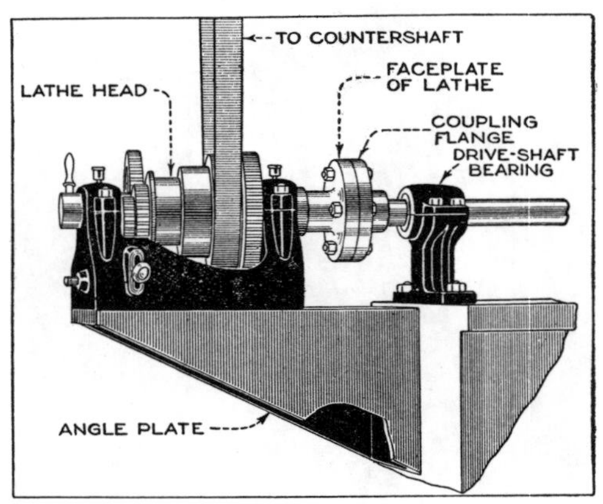

An Old Lathe Head Used as a Variable-Speed Drive Gives Six Speeds and has Proved Entirely Satisfactory on a Special Machine

drive for a machine tool. The head is mounted on an angle plate on the end of the machine bed. The spindle of the lathe is carefully alined with the drive shaft of the machine, and the two are coupled together by using the regular lathe faceplate as one half of the flanged coupling, and bolting it to a coupling on the end of the drive shaft. The lathe countershaft is fastened in place overhead and belted to the cone pulley. With this arrangement, it is possible to drive at six speeds. This drive saved considerable delay in one machine shop, on a special machine, where the choice of the drive was delayed until the machine was urgently needed.—J. V. Romig, Allentown, Pennsylvania.

Concrete Foundations for Engines

The concrete used in making foundations for engines that run without much vibration should be mixed in the proportion of 1 part cement, 2 parts clean, coarse sand, well graded from the finer particles to those just passing through a 1/4-in. screen, and 4 parts clean, hard pebbles, or hard crushed stone, ranging from 1/4 in. to 2 in. in size.

Foundations for all engines that produce considerable vibration should be made of concrete mixed in the proportion of 1 part cement, 1 1/2 parts sand, and 3 parts pebbles or stone, the sand and stone being graded as above. Care should be taken to mix the concrete thoroughly with sufficient water to make it of a quaky consistency, and to deposit the concrete in such a manner that a dense and compact mass will result.

Hacksaw Adjustable for Depth

As an ordinary hacksaw frame cannot be used for cutting in cramped places, because of its width, nor be set to cut to a certain depth, the frame shown in the drawing is of considerable advantage, because it can be adjusted for these purposes.

It can be made from two 3/8-in. tees, a length of 3/8-in. pipe, a short length of 1/2-in. round steel rod, and a piece of 5/8-in. square steel; the latter is turned and shaped as indicated, to fit the square screw and the tee. The pipe is cut and screwed so that the tees will be the correct distance apart for the saw; the tees are then screwed on, and drilled out to fit the 1/2-in. rods. A small hole is also drilled and tapped, opposite the side outlet in each tee, for the thumbscrews used for tightening the tees on the rods. The outer rod is shaped as shown, for holding the saw blade. The remaining parts can be taken from any common hacksaw, or made up, as desired.

When it is desired to saw to a certain depth, the pipe is fastened so that the distance from the teeth of the blade to the

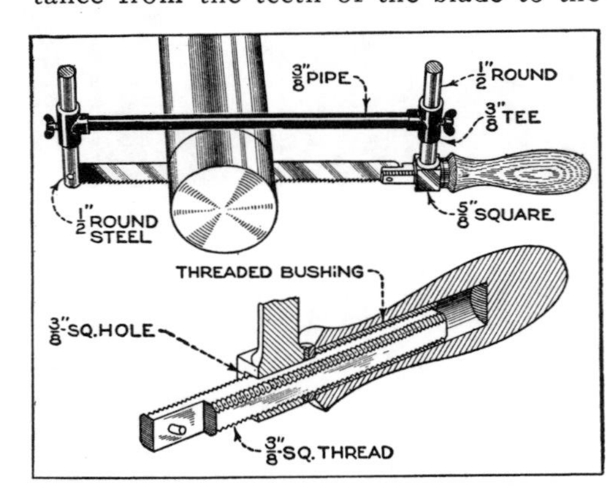

A Hacksaw Frame That can be Adjusted for Depth of Cut, and can be Used in Places Where a Common Hacksaw would Not Enter

pipe is equal to the depth desired; the saw will then stop cutting when the pipe touches the work. It is an easy matter to saw in narrow places by reducing the distance between the blade and pipe to the minimum. With this type of frame, the blade can be held very taut and rigid, and this prevents it from being broken easily.

Cheap Cistern Made of Vitrified Clay Pipe

BY LOUIS DAVIS

A SANITARY, substantial, and economical cistern can be constructed of 36-in. vitrified clay pipe, in the manner indicated in the drawing.

After the excavation is completed, a substantial base is made by laying a brick floor on the bottom and pouring a 6-in. layer of concrete over this. While the concrete is still soft, two units of 36-in. vitrified clay pipe, each with side outlet, are set into it and connected as shown. The connection is also covered with concrete to prevent any possible leakage. After the base has hardened, the other units of pipe are placed in position and cemented at the joints.

A filter is made by filling the lowest unit of one section with a mixture of fine and coarse gravel and charcoal. A wire strainer is inserted in the side outlet, and some coarse gravel and stones are placed around it, to hold it in position and to prevent the fine gravel and particles of charcoal from passing into the other section. The filter unit is covered with a circular piece of galvanized screen wire, held in place by bricks, as shown in the drawing.

The covers are made of 2-in. boards, nailed together to make a double thickness. A pump is fastened on the cover of the section containing the filtered water, and is fitted with a galvanized pipe extending to within an inch or two of the bottom.

A float gauge is attached to the other cover; this consists of a cedar ball and block connected by a length of No. 10 copper wire. The wire passes through a hole in the cover. When the water reaches the wooden block, it causes it to float and pushes up the ball, indicating that the well is full. A shut-off should, of course, be fitted in the downspout leading to the cistern, so that, when the latter is full, the water can be diverted to a drain.

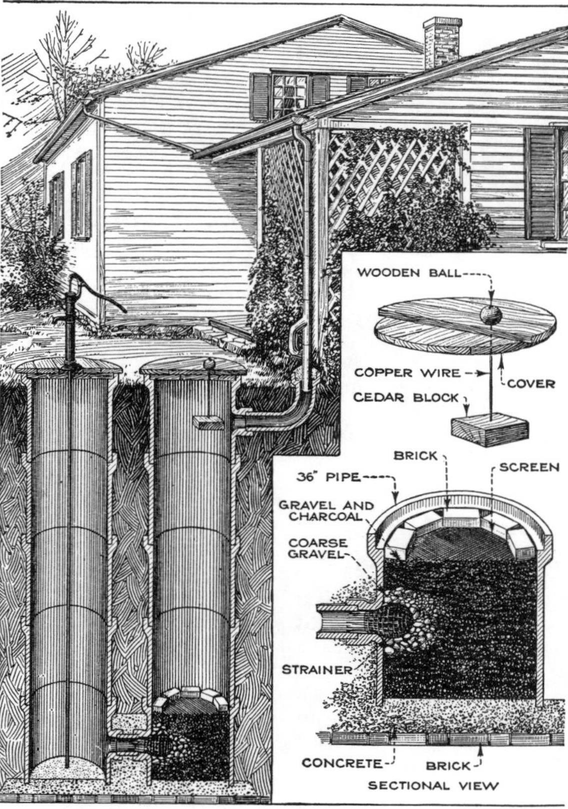

A Two-Section Farm Rain-Water Cistern Constructed of 36-Inch Vitrified Clay Pipe: It Is More Sanitary than Most Cisterns

A well of greater capacity can be made by adding sections, excavating deeper than is shown in the drawing.

This type of cistern is very sanitary, as it is immune from soil and rodent contamination, and there can be no seepage.

Furthermore, as the usual walling, bricking, and cement plastering are eliminated, considerable expense is avoided. A two-section cistern of this type can be built for approximately $100 and is virtually indestructible; it will not cave in, cannot be penetrated by tree roots, and is not affected by moisture.

Wrench for Turning Large Pipe

The wrench shown in the illustration can be made in a very short time, and is

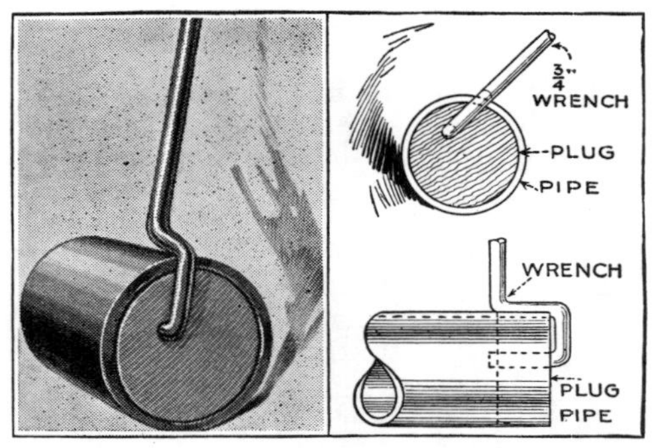

A Simple Wrench, Consisting of a Lever and a Wooden Disk, Makes a Good Substitute for a Large-Size Pipe Wrench

of great value when one is confronted with a job requiring the use of a large pipe wrench, a tool that is usually not carried in the mechanic's tool box.

It consists of a lever made of 3/4-in. bar stock, bent to the shape indicated, and a wooden disk that fits loosely in the end of the pipe and has a hole drilled through it, off center, to fit the end of the lever. The manner of using the tool is obvious from the illustration.

Drilling True Holes in Turret Lathe

The drill holder shown in the drawing will be found a very convenient means of drilling a hole true in the turret lathe. Any attempt at drilling a deep hole with a long drill, without previous preparation, will nearly always end in a "drunken" or untrue hole. A twist drill has a certain amount of spring, and if the hole is started slightly out of true, the error will increase with the depth of the hole. A short, stubby drill makes an ideal centering tool for starting a drill, but since the number of holes in the turret will not always allow the use of this, the same effect has been obtained by the use of this holder. The shank of the holder is turned to fit the turret, and left a little larger on the front end; a circle, the same diameter as that of the drill to be used, is scribed on the nose of the tool, and a punch mark made on the circumference of the circle. A hole, about 1/4 in. in diameter, is then drilled, parallel with the axis of the holder, from this mark; thus, when the holder is bored for the drill, a semicircular groove is left along the top of the hole. A 1/4-in. round-headed pin is driven into a hole drilled in the shank of the drill; this slides in the groove just mentioned. Near the rear of the holder, a hole, about twice the diameter of the pin in the drill, is drilled. The holder is then tapped for a knurled screw. This screw has a hole, the same size as the pin in the drill, drilled a short distance into the point. When in use, the screw is loosened and the drill pushed back until the pin enters the hole drilled in the back of the holder. The work is then centered and drilled part way; then the drill is pulled out until the pin touches the knurled screw, when the latter is tightened onto it and the work drilled to the proper depth.

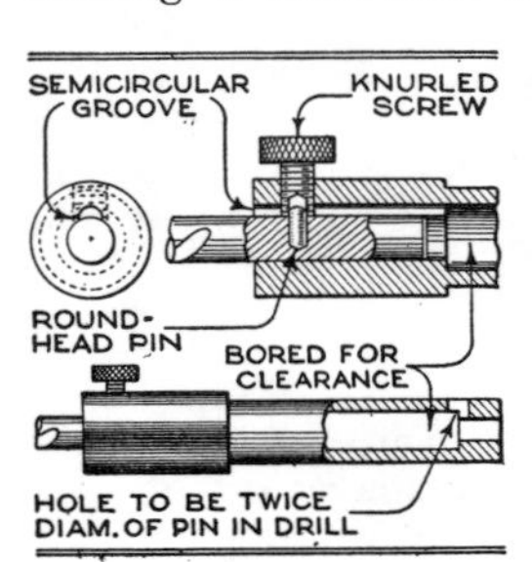

Setting Work in Power Hacksaw

Most power hacksaws have a length-gauge attachment of some sort to be used when cutting off a large number of pieces. To use this, however, when cutting off an occasional piece, requires too much time, and it is the usual practice to measure off the length wanted, file a mark, and set the saw to this. This method also takes time, as the saw frame must be lowered and lifted, and the piece adjusted in the vise, until the mark lines up with the saw. The drawing shows a simple fixture that is designed to be attached to the fixed jaw of the vise, so that the operator can set up a piece very quickly. The body of the fixture is screwed to the vise and has

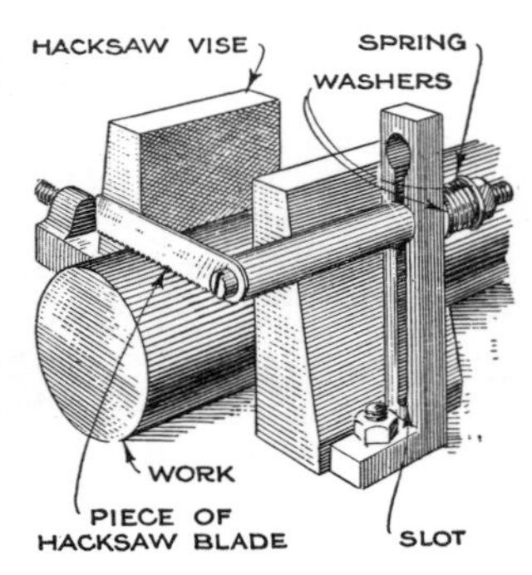

its upright part slotted, a hole about twice the width of the slot being drilled at the top. Next, a piece of cold-rolled steel is grooved so that the smaller diameter will fit into the slot, and the larger diameter easily into the hole at the top of the slot. This horizontal piece holds a piece of saw blade at one end and is threaded on its opposite end for a nut, which bears against a spring and washer. The fixture should be attached to the vise in a position that will bring the piece of saw blade into the exact position of the saw blade in the frame of the machine. After the work has been set, the horizontal arm is pulled up until it enters the hole, in which position it can be pushed out of the way.

Valve Wrench for Oxygen Tanks

Opening the valves of oxygen tanks, usually a more or less difficult job by hand, can be done very easily by means of the wrench shown in the illustration. It is made by cutting out a piece of 1/8 or 3/16-in. boiler plate with a cutting torch, to the shape shown, and then brazing or welding the shank or tang in a 6-in. length of 3/4-in pipe, flattened to fit the tang. Three 5/16-in. pins, 1 in. long, are welded to the face of the tool so that they will fit in the notches of the handwheel.—A. S. Jamieson, Springfield, Mass.

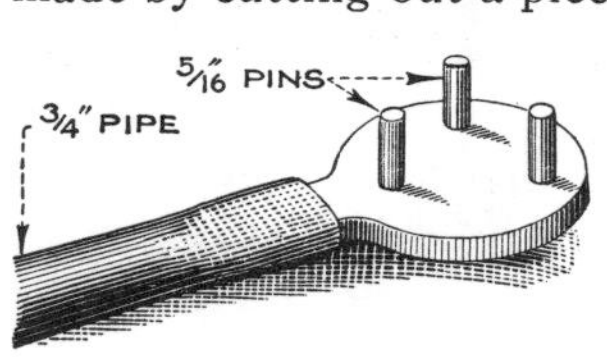

Making Rigid Crates

No method of joining the corner members of a crate is alone sufficient to give rigidity to a crate. Some kind of bracing across the faces is necessary.

Figure 1 shows a kind of bracing found in many crates sent to the U. S. Forest Products Laboratory for testing. Although this construction appears to be very strong, partly because of the amount of material used, it has been demonstrated by actual tests that crates so made are very weak when a diagonal strain is applied, and are therefore apt to "weave" and "skew" during transportation. Fig. 2 shows a crate with diagonal braces on six sides. This kind of bracing gives maximum strength for a minimum amount of lumber used. It has been found that crates so braced can withstand, with much less distortion, a diagonal strain twice as great as that applied to crates braced as shown in Fig. 1. Fig. 3 shows a combination of cross bracing

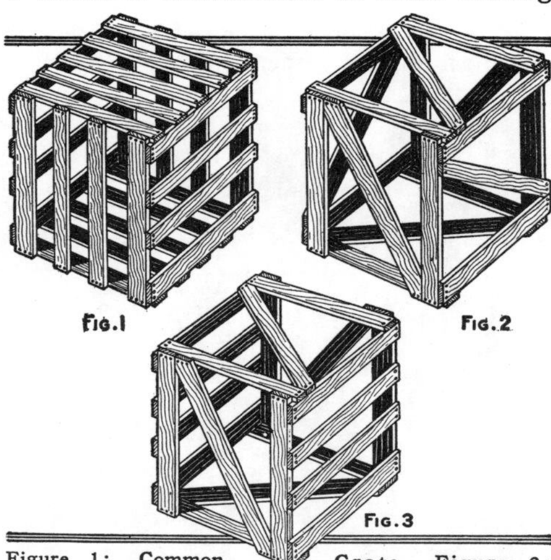

Figure 1: Common Crate. Figure 2: Bracing Giving Maximum Strength with Minimum Lumber. Figure 3: Type Recommended for Rigid Material

and diagonal bracing that is recommended for use with products that need protection on the sides, and that are rigid enough in themselves to withstand stresses in the direction in which the crate is weak.

Solid sheathing on all faces does not make a crate so rigid as diagonal bracing, except, perhaps, sheathing made of wide boards, with tighter joints than usually obtained. The crate with common sheathing might withstand as great a load, but the distortion caused by that load would be greater than in a crate with diagonal braces, and would, ordinarily, be great enough to cause damage to the contents.

Protector for Plow Handles

A flat-iron guard, bent and attached on the outside of a plow handle as shown in the illustration, protects the handle from being broken or splintered while dragging the plow on its side over the ground, the customary way of moving a plow for short distances.—J. Howard Hughes, Henriette, Tex.

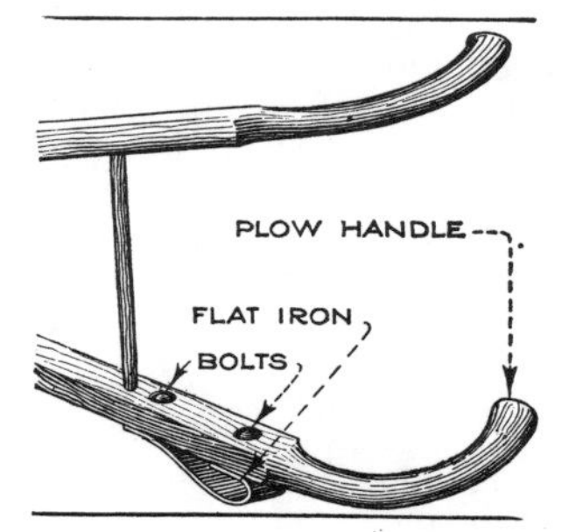

Rewinding Machine for Motion-Picture Films

A spring motor, taken from an old phonograph, has been used for several years in the laboratory of a western photographer for rewinding motion-picture films.

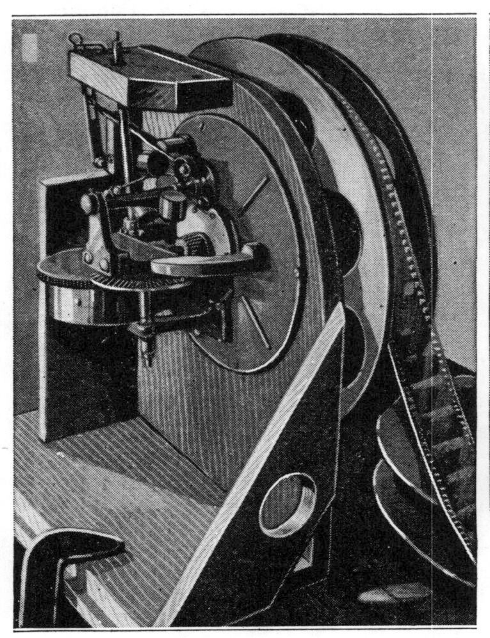

Left: Rear View of Film-Rewinding Machine, Showing How the Phonograph Motor is Attached. Right: Front View, Showing Reel in Place

The phonograph motor is mounted upon a wooden angle plate, as shown in the photograph, so that its shaft extends horizontally through the plate; this shaft is provided with an extension to hold the film reel. It is necessary to provide a dog on the shaft, with the tail fitting in one of the holes of the film reel for the purpose of driving it. The brake on the phonograph motor enables the operator to start or stop at will, to run slowly while examining the film, or fast while taking it up.—F. J. Hiscock, Cody, Wyo.

Drilling Out Broken Cylinder-Head Screws

A frequent job in the garage is that of drilling out broken cylinder-head screws. To do this, without the danger of spoiling the threads of the hole in the cylinder block, the drill should be guided by a bushing, fitted into the hole in the cylinder head. The bushing should fit snugly, so that light tapping is necessary to remove it. Its length should be equal to the depth of the hole in which it fits, and its inside diameter should be the same as the root diameter of the threaded end of the capscrew; this can be determined by consulting a table of tap and drill sizes.

The broken screw is chipped off flush with the surface of the cylinder block. The cylinder head is then put in place, and held by two or three screws. After the broken screw has been drilled out, the cylinder head is removed, and the hole is tapped to its original size, to clear it from the remainder of the screw. Care must be taken to back out the tap frequently to clean out the broken pieces. The bushing should be hardened to prevent it from wearing quickly. It can then be used indefinitely.—Fred H. Wadden, New Glasgow, Can.

Submerged and Exposed Concrete

Concrete laid under water will set much better than concrete laid in air. This is due to the fact that a far better hydration of the lime results in submerged work than in ordinary work, where the concrete dries out quickly. Work that is exposed to air, such as walks and driveways, should be kept covered for several days with old wet carpet or canvas, or even with moist earth, to prevent it from drying out too quickly.

Demagnetizing Watches

When a watch is brought within the magnetic field of a powerful generator or magnet, it frequently occurs that the hairspring becomes magnetized, and renders the watch useless.

To demagnetize it, pass a shoestring, or a similar cord, through the bow of the watch and bring the ends together. Suspend the watch by holding the doubled shoestring in one hand, and twist the string tightly by turning the watch with the other hand. Then place the watch close to the field magnets of the generator, or to the magnet, and allow the string to unwind, which will cause the watch to revolve. While the watch is revolving, gradually draw it away from the generator or magnet, so that when it stops revolving, it will be out of the magnetic field. The watch will thus be completely demagnetized. The explanation of this is that the revolving movement of an object in a magnetic field prevents its molecules from assuming any definite arrangement or relation to each other, as they do when the object is at rest in a magnetic field.

If one has no access to a strong magnet or generator, a magnetic field can be created by forming a hollow coil, 3 to 4 in. in diameter, of about 200 turns of No. 16 insulated copper wire. Connect a flatiron or incandescent lamp in series with the coil and pass the house current through the circuit, which will set up a strong magnetic field inside of and around the coil. Hold the watch suspended on a twisted shoestring inside of the coil and gradually draw it out, while it is revolving.—R. R. Spencer, Denver, Colo.

Enlarging Holes in Wood

To enlarge a hole with an ordinary wood bit, fit a wooden plug, about 1 in. long, with its grain running lengthwise, into the hole. Drill a small hole in the center of the plug to admit the screw end of the bit. Then drill as usual, as if the wood were solid. When the cutting edge of the bit strikes the plug, it will not cut it easily, as the grain runs lengthwise, and, as the plug does not fit tightly, it will be pushed through the hole, guiding the bit. The plug may be greased if the work permits, and can be used repeatedly for holes of the same size.—Adolph Rieter, Marinette, Wis.

Loading Pipe onto Trucks

By using the simple method shown in the photograph for loading pipe onto a truck, the work is accomplished in less than one-half the time otherwise required.

A Method of Loading Pipe onto a Truck That Enables the Work to be Accomplished in One-Half the Time Otherwise Required

A 6 by 6-in. beam is carried crosswise under the truck in specially made U-irons. When the truck is to be loaded, this beam is pulled out so as to project a few feet beyond the side. Then, by lifting one end of the pipe so that the center is rested on the beam, it is an easy matter to swing first one and then the other end onto the truck.

A Powder-Loading Tool

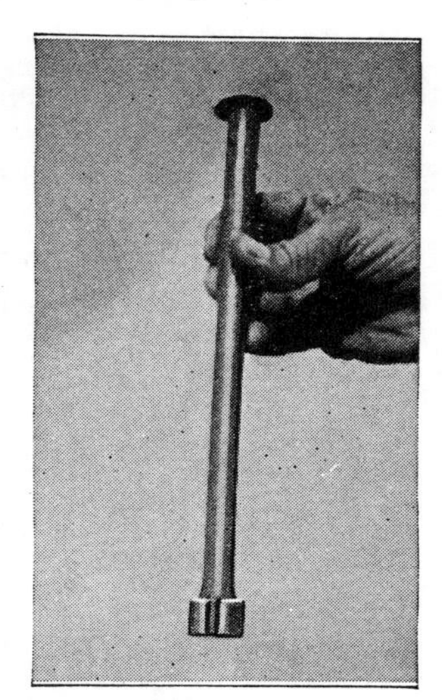

When tamping powder into a hole for blasting a large tree, or similar purposes, trouble is usually experienced in pressing the powder down firmly without damaging the fuse. To overcome this difficulty, a tool like that illustrated can be used. It is made from a long bolt, a ring of flat stock being welded around the end to form a boss the size of the hole. A groove is cut in this, as shown, so that the fuse will slide in this groove without being damaged, while the powder is being tamped.

Cutting Grooves on a Power Saw

The illustration shows how grooves of varying width and depth can be cut very quickly on a circular saw with a wooden table.

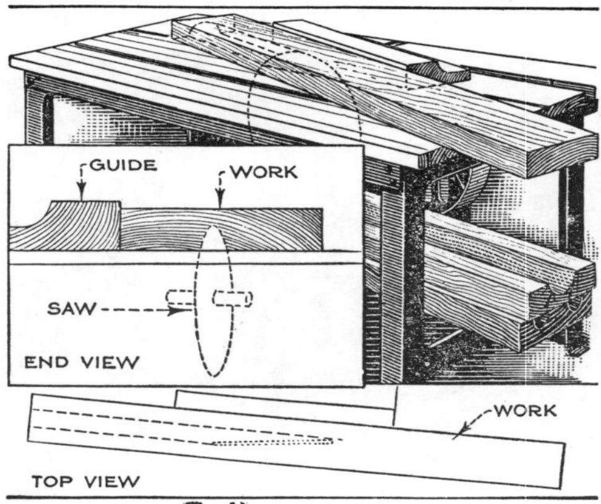

A Practical and Timesaving Method of Cutting Grooves of Varying Depth and Width in Wood, with a Power Saw

A wooden strip is tacked at an angle across the table; this angle determines the width of the groove. Tilting the table up and down determines the depth of the groove, and the work is pressed along the edge of the guide strip as usual.

A woodworker who specializes in dentists' tool cabinets and work of a similar nature, where it is necessary to cut a great number of grooves, finds this a very practical and timesaving method.

Clips Hold Connecting-Rod Shims

Small brass clips of the kind shown in the illustration have been found to be of considerable assistance for holding connecting-rod shims in place while replacing the caps. The shims on one bolt are held in place with a clip while other shims are being put on the opposite bolt, and these are also held by a clip while the cap is put in place and the nuts are turned on. The clips are pulled off just before the cap is tightened.

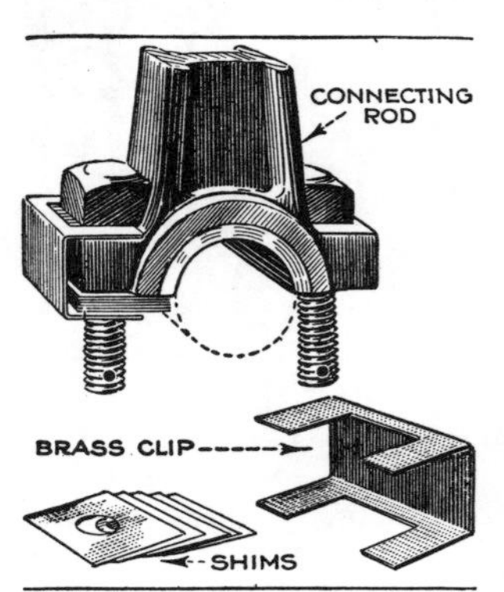

Simple Blower for Sawdust

After experiencing considerable trouble owing to accumulation of sawdust in a sawmill, the following scheme was devised to blow the sawdust away: The sawdust was led into a 15-ft. wooden pipe, and steam pressure was applied behind the sawdust to blow it through. The wooden pipe was made from four 1 by 4-in. boards nailed together. A ½-in. steam pipe was led to a point opposite the center of the end of the pipe, and about 3 in. away from it. The steam blast picked up the sawdust, forced it through the pipe and blew it to a point 40 ft. from the farther end.—E. C. Smith, Barney, Ga.

Tailstock Adapter for Standard Tapers

When there is frequent need of turning tapered work in the lathe, to standard or identical tapers, it is difficult to set over the tailstock every time, and always to obtain the correct amount of setover. The drawing shows an adapter that clamps to the end of the tailstock quill and carries an offset center, permanently set for turning a certain taper, such as that of the machine handle shown. The adapter body, of cast iron, is counterbored to a push fit over the quill, and the counterbore assures that it is set in the same position each time. A cast lug, bearing against the end of the tailstock, fixes the longitudinal position of the adapter, while it is prevented from rotating, as well as set for its angular position, by means of a setscrew, the end of which is turned down to fit into the quill keyway.

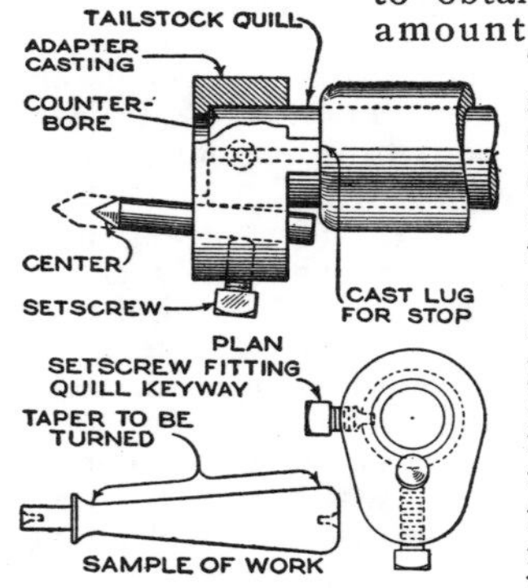

The offset dead center is made of drill rod, with the point hardened and tempered. It is set into the adapter body at an angle, so that it will line up with the center line of the work. This angular setting allows a slight adjustment of the amount of taper, by moving the center in or out and then clamping it in place by means of the heavy setscrew provided for the purpose.

For work having a very slight taper, the construction of the adapter body must be modified by extending it beyond the end of the quill, to allow room for the insertion of the dead center without interfering with the quill.—H. H. Parker, Oakland, Calif.

Tool Marks Circumference by Measuring Diameter

The tool illustrated is valuable to the sheet-metal worker, as it shows the circumference of a circle at once, by measuring its diameter, thus effecting a considerable saving in time, in making cylinders, and the like, and eliminating calculation.

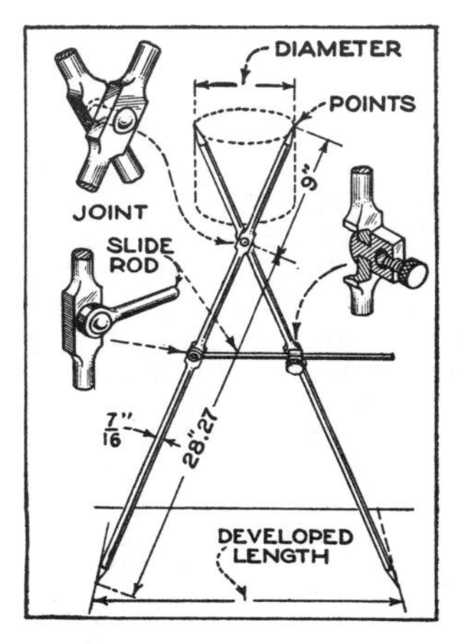

The construction of the tool is simple. It consists of two lengths of 7/16-in. iron rod, flattened at the joint and drilled for a snug-fitting rivet. The center of the joint is exactly 9 in. from one end and 28.27 in. from the other, which is the ratio of the diameter of a circle to its circumference. A slide rod, riveted to one leg, below the joint, so as to move freely, but without shake, and passing through a swivel on the other leg, locks the tool at any desired measurement. Measurements may be taken from a full-size drawing or from metal parts already made. While the dimensions given in the drawing cover a tool suitable for average work, it can be made as large or as small as desired, providing the proper ratio of leg lengths from joint to ends is maintained.

Marking Dismantled Machines

When dismantling machines for repair, it is always wise to place an identifying mark on various parts before removing them, so as to avoid mistakes in replacing them and to save time in reassembling. It is often difficult to distinguish the correct marks from other similar marks that have been made either accidentally during use, or purposely during previous repairs. A method that makes it easy to distinguish the correct marks is to punch a circle around them

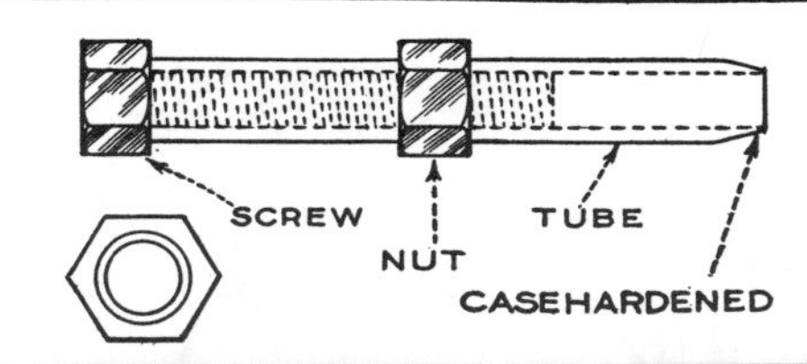

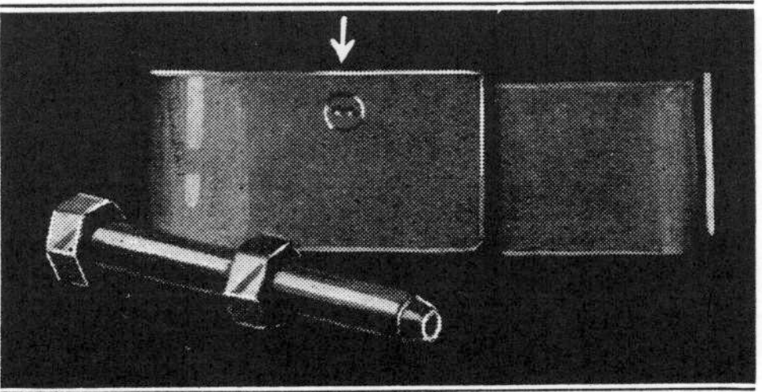

A Steel Die Stamp That Punches a Circle around Identifying Marks on Parts of Machinery Dismantled for Repair

with a steel die stamp of the kind shown in the illustration.

This stamp consists of two short pieces of steel tubing, a capscrew, and a nut. One piece of tubing is ground on the end to a cutting edge and this end is casehardened. The other end of this piece and the entire length of the other piece of tubing are tapped so that the capscrew can be screwed in to hold both pieces together. The nut is run onto the screw between the tubes. This makes the tool solid so that it will sustain the tapping of a hammer. The nut in the center makes it easier to press the cutting edge squarely on the work, and the hexagonal shape of the screw head and nut prevents the tool from rolling when laid down.—Harry Moore, Montreal, Can.

Turning Heavy Shafts

The method shown in the illustration makes it easy to turn a heavy shaft around. By placing the end of a crowbar under one of the nuts on a coupling and using the hub of the coupling as a fulcrum, sufficient leverage is obtained to turn the shaft around.

Board Supports Auto Body

The malleable castings, trussed by two rods that extend crosswise under the chassis, that support the running boards

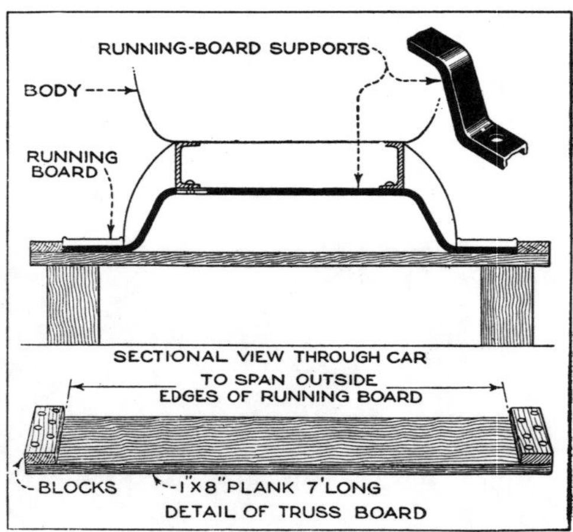

A Plank Support Prevents Running Boards and Dust Shields from being Bent by the Blocking Used during Repairs

of a light car, have been dispensed with on the latest models, and two supports, made of channel iron, bent to the shape indicated in the drawing, have been substituted for them. This change of construction necessitates a change in the method of supporting the body while removing the rear end for repair.

If the usual method is employed, of blocking under the running boards, the latter, and the dust shields, are bent and otherwise damaged. To prevent this, a strong plank with blocks of wood securely attached to the ends, as indicated, has been found very satisfactory. The blocks fit on the outer edges of the running boards as shown, and prevent them from spreading apart when the car is jacked up and blocks placed under the plank.

Emergency Index Plate

In the course of experimental work on a spring motor, it was found necessary to use a 24-pitch pinion having 11 teeth. As no index plate for this size of pinion was available, the following method was used to make the pinion:

The index plate was removed from the miller and shellacked to the center of a smooth piece of wrapping paper, 3 ft. square. A circle of 3-ft. diameter was drawn on the paper, concentric with the circumference of the index plate. With the dividers, the circumference of the 3-ft. circle was divided into 11 equal parts, and radii drawn with a sharp-pointed pencil to the center; this was, of course, done as accurately as possible. The paper was then trimmed off to the size of the index plate, after which the latter was replaced in the miller. A surface gauge was clamped to the machine so that its scriber touched one of the radii, near the circumference. The locating finger of the head, which was adjustable, was set in place in one of the notches. After a cut had been made in the pinion blank, the index plate was set with the scriber at the next radius line in the same way as before, the finger moved into another notch, and fastened, and a second cut made. In this way all 11 teeth were cut.—Dexter W. Allis, Whitman, Mass.

A Lathe Center-Hole Mandrel

For light turning in the lathe, a mandrel with a taper shank, fitting into the live-center hole, is a useful attachment, as no faceplate and dog are then needed, and the cutting tool can work up close to the end of the mandrel. If the live-center hole is true, the taper shank may be fitted and the mandrel body finish-turned and ground while in place. Under such conditions the mandrel should run true whenever replaced, but in any event, the best way is to scribe a line or make a chisel mark on the shank in line with a corresponding mark on the face of the nose. In replacing the mandrel, the two marks are made to register, and the mandrel should then run true, even if the hole is slightly "out."

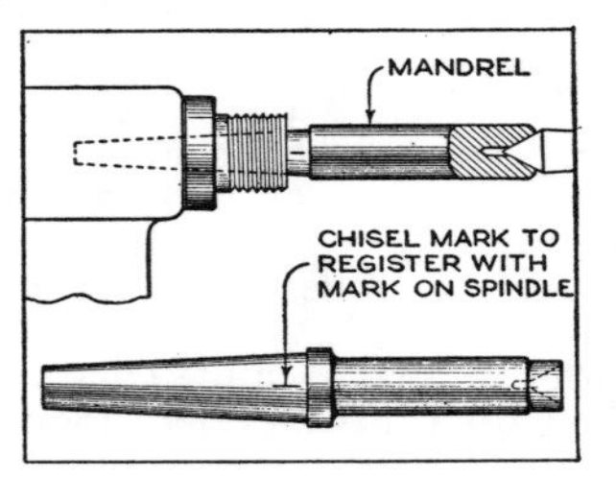

Several mandrels of different lengths and diameters, to suit the work at hand, may be made; they should be center-drilled for the tailstock center, though short pieces could be finish-turned, by taking light cuts at fairly high speed, without the use of the tailstock-center support. The mandrel body is preferably hardened and ground in place, but the temper of the shank should be drawn until soft enough to scrape; then Prussian blue is used for testing the fit in the center hole, and the shank is scraped until it fits accurately all over. It will hold tightly enough for all ordinary work.

Circular Yard Saves Brooder Chicks

In my first years of experience in raising brooder chicks I used an inclosed "yard," 10 ft. sq., that could be moved about to give the chicks a space of fresh grass occasionally. While watching the chicks one day, I noticed that several of them, that appeared to be suffering from the cold wind, would run along one side of the inclosure until they came to a corner, where they remained, huddled together as if they could go no farther. I picked them up, placed them in the brooder, and returned to watch the yard again. As soon as the cool breeze again swept over the yard, another dozen or more huddled together in one corner.

Satisfied that the corners were to blame, I placed all the chicks in the brooder, and rebuilt the yard in the form of a circle. The chicks were then released into this yard, and, when desirous of returning to the warmth of the brooder, simply followed the fence until they came to the open door. The result was that the loss of chicks due to chilling was greatly reduced.—G. E. Hendrickson, Argyle, Wis.

A Handy Auto-Cleaning Tool

A stiff scrubbing brush, such as commonly used about the house, with a piece of stiff sheet metal fastened to one end to serve as a scraper, makes a very convenient tool for cleaning the inaccessible parts of an automobile chassis. By mounting the brush on the end of a handle, as indicated in the drawing, almost any part of the machine, even the oil pan, can easily be freed of mud and dirt without the necessity of crawling underneath the car. The scraper will be found particularly convenient for removing accumulations of road tar, and dislodging clods of mud on the brake mechanism and frame, the brush being then used to clean the scraped surface.

Farm Tractor Used as Snowplow

Following a snowstorm that blockaded traffic in a Kansas town, a farm tractor was used to clear the streets. The blade of a road-grading machine was attached at an angle under the frame, as shown. A roadway, 20 feet wide, was cleared in two trips, the snow being pushed to both sides of the road. The work was accomplished by one man at the rate of three miles per hour.

A Tractor Used to Clear the Snow from the Streets in a Kansas Town after a Heavy Snowstorm: The Work was Accomplished by One Man at the Rate of Three Miles per Hour

Wagon-Wheel Rim Puller

During dry weather, wagon-wheel rims have a tendency to slip to one side or the other of the fellies, owing to the shrinking of the wood. Where this occurs, it is necessary to force them back into place, a job usually done with a heavy hammer. A better tool for the purpose, made from a ¾-in. iron or steel rod, is shown in the illustration. A 5-in. length of the same material is welded to the rod, near one end, and both arms are forged as shown. In use, the hooked arm is caught on the side of the rim, and the longer arm pressed against the felly.

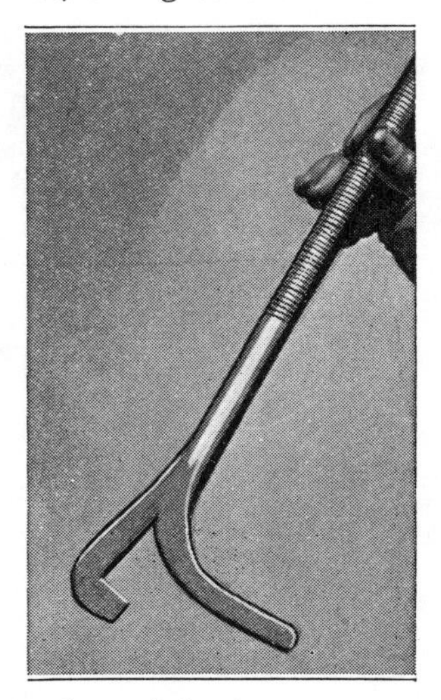

Tool for Removing Handles from Files

In shops where a box of files is carried around from one job to another, each one is not fitted with a handle, because of the space that this would require. Two or three handles are used, and these are usually knocked off and then fitted to other files, as required. Using the files themselves to do this, as is commonly done, is very injurious to the teeth, as both faces are scraped together, and furthermore, the files are frequently broken in this way. The photograph shows a simple tool for removing the handles. It is made of flat stock with a tapered slot cut in one end. By holding this tool in one hand, to grip the file, as shown, it is an easy matter to pull the handle off with the other hand.

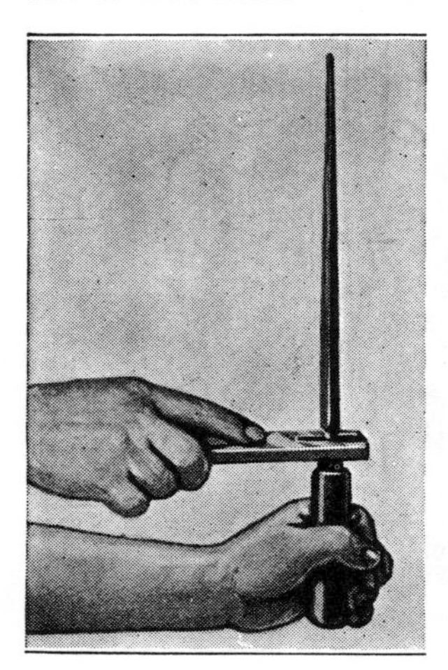

Ball-Bearing Guide Roller for the Band Saw

Anyone who has used the band saw as a woodworking tool is familiar with the troubles that result from a loose roller guide. The usual method of making these guides is to mount a hardened roller on a hardened pin, but, after a few months of operation, wear causes the roller to "wobble." This defect, however, is not found in the ball-bearing roller shown, which is practically everlasting, and, besides, is adjustable in three directions.

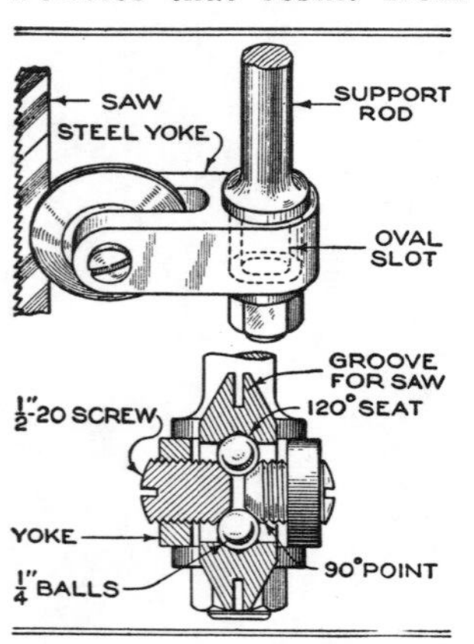

The roller is made of tool steel, machined with a groove around its circumference. The cold-rolled steel yoke is drilled and tapped for ½-20 screws, the points of which are ground to an included angle of 90°, as shown in the drawing. Quarter-inch steel balls are nested into the raceway with a liberal amount of grease, to make them stick until the roller is assembled. Adjustment for play and proper running fit is obtained by tightening the screws, which should be made of hardened tool steel, and be a tight fit in the yoke. When, after using, looseness develops in the guide roller, the slack can easily be taken up.

A Brace for Overhead Lagscrews

Much of the difficulty and danger connected with erecting or removing overhead line shafting is eliminated if the lagscrews are loosened or tightened with a brace of the type shown in the illustration.

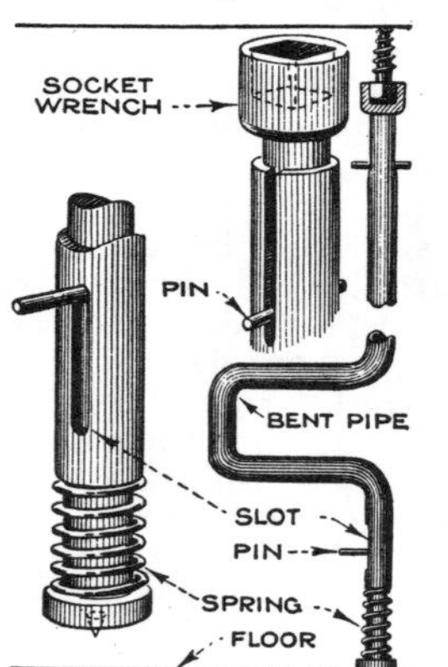

The brace is made of pipe, bent to the shape indicated, and extends from the floor to the ceiling. At the bottom end an extension leg fits loosely inside of the pipe; this leg has a coil spring around it, and a collar and small point are turned at its lower end. A pin, driven into the leg through a slot cut in the pipe, keeps the leg from falling out, and also allows the brace to adjust itself to suit the height of different line shafts. Two slots are cut opposite each other in the top end of the brace, to allow the insertion of a pin-driven socket wrench.—S. A. McDonald, Brooklyn, N. Y.

Labels Made of Adhesive Plaster

It is often difficult, and sometimes impossible, to stick gummed-paper labels to oily or rough surfaces. In such cases, a strip of adhesive plaster, properly lettered in ink, makes an excellent substitute, as it will stick to almost any surface. Adhesive plaster can also be used satisfactorily to fasten samples to the outside of boxes.—Thos. W. Benson, Philadelphia, Pa.

Friction Clutch Substitute for Ratchet

A friction clutch, of the type illustrated in the drawing, is used in place of a ratchet when it is not advisable, or possible, to use the latter. The clutch consists of two double-leaf springs, fastened to a hub block as indicated. Double-leaf springs are used, as they are stiffer than single-leaf springs and do not add to the friction when working in the reverse direction. There are several advantages gained by using this type of clutch. It is well balanced and therefore does not give a one-sided pull, which wears the shaft and bearings. Another feature is its reversibility; by simply turning the hub block over, the operation of the clutch is reversed.

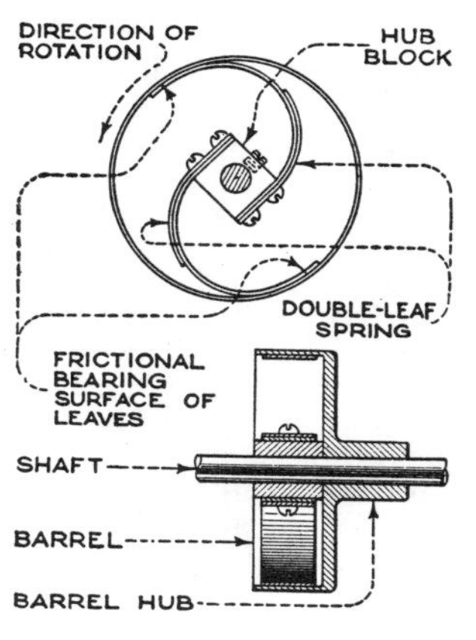

Measuring beyond Capacity of Micrometer

A shop kink that will enable the mechanic to get the micrometer measurement of large bushings and similar cylindrical work when only small micrometers are at hand, is shown in the drawing. The anvils of the two instruments are placed together and inserted inside the cylinder, with the spindles in contact against the outside wall. The correct measurement is the sum of the two readings.

Colored crayons are recommended instead of water colors for tinting drawings. The crayon should be rubbed on the drawing lightly and spread by means of a soft brush dipped in gasoline. The color does not readily rub off, although, unless the paper is very porous, it may be erased with a soft rubber.

Shortening Valve Stems

The illustration shows a simple method of shortening valve stems without removing them. Raise the valve high enough to allow the insertion of a flat file under the stem, as shown. The tension of the valve spring will hold the stem solidly against the file teeth. Turn the valve with the valve grinder; this will grind away the end of the stem in contact with the file. Remove the file occasionally and test with a feeler gauge to keep the clearance within the proper limits.

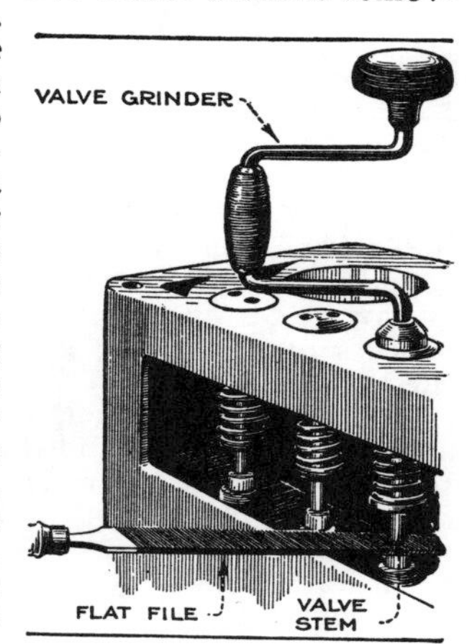

Simple Clamp Holds Timbers

The illustration shows a serviceable clamp for holding together the ends of timbers of uniform width while putting in bolts or screws, or accomplishing other work that requires the timbers to be held in position firmly. A clamp of this type has been used by a builder for holding 6 by 6-in. beams temporarily while bolting them together. A length of iron rod is bent to a U-shape, as shown, to straddle the beams. Both ends of the rod are turned over to form hooks to fit over the edge of the cam plate. The cam is cut from a piece of steel plate. Raising the handle to a vertical position tightens the clamp, and bringing the handle slightly over the center position locks it. The length and thickness of the iron rod, and also the thickness of the steel plate, depend on the work for which the clamp is to be used.—G. A. Luers, Washington, D. C.

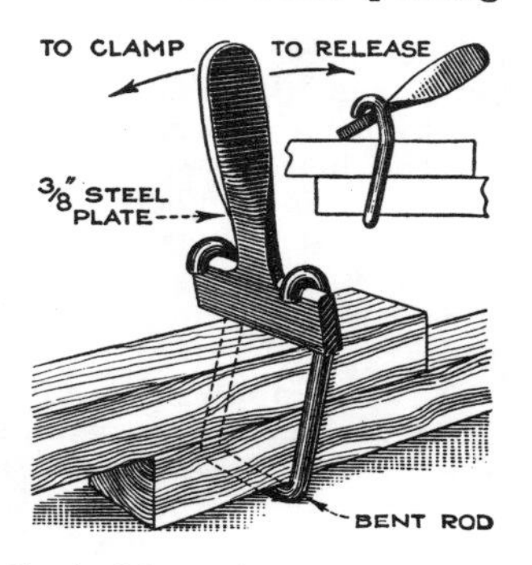

MAKING GLASS SIGNS BY SANDBLASTING

By JAMES TATE

COMPARATIVELY few persons, aside from the limited number engaged in the commercial side of the work, are aware of the possibilities latent in the process of decorating glass by means of the sandblast.

The process is a simple one, and with some artistic talent, and the proper facilities for the work, there is no reason why any reader could not build up a good business in this field.

The first necessity, of course, is some form of sandblast machine. These are made commercially in a wide variety of types, but the man starting on a small scale may use any of the homemade forms shown in Figs. 1 to 3 with perfect satisfaction. It is assumed, of course, that a supply of compressed air is available; for experimental work, this may be furnished by a small garage compressor, or even by a more simple apparatus, consisting of a tank capable of withstanding a pressure of about 60 lb. per square inch and a hand air pump.

The pressures used in sandblasting vary from 8 to 60 lb. per square inch; the higher the pressure, within these limits, the better, as, with a high pressure, the sand is projected against the work with greater force and velocity, and the abrasive action of the sand is heightened, thus lessening the time required for the work.

A word about the sand used will be pertinent here; any clean, sharp sand will answer for the purpose, although there are a number of dealers around the country who can supply special sand for the work. Sand of various grades of fineness should be kept in stock, as the texture of the "frosting" on the glass can be varied by their use. For example, with a coarse sand, the surface of the treated portions of the work will be quite rough to close inspection, while, if a very fine sand is used, the surface will be practically smooth. The sand used should be chosen with regard to the character of the work to be done, using very fine sand for such work as monogramming tableware and similar small pieces, and coarser sand for door panels, large signs, and the like. The use of the coarse sand for large work will also speed up the work considerably.

The equipment shown in Fig. 1 is made, for the most part, of pipe and fittings, with a few feet of rubber hose, and a hopper for the sand. The size of the latter, of course, may be varied to suit individual desires, space, or type of work. The sand is fed from the hopper by gravity, and the flow may be controlled by means of a sliding shut-off valve fitted in the bottom of the hopper, or by a butterfly valve in the ¾-in. pipe below it. This control valve has been omitted in the drawing, for the sake of simplicity.

The outfit shown in Fig. 2 has proved to be very practical for this work. The sand tank is made from an old range boiler, which is quite suitable for use with pressures not exceeding 20 lb. per square inch. If higher pressures are employed, it is recommended that a new range boiler be used; these are usually tested to 150 lb. per square inch, and will thus stand pressures up to 60 lb. with an ample margin of safety. Before using an old boiler it would be well to have it tested to about 75 lb., and thereafter use it for not more than 20 lb., using a gauge, as shown, to insure that this pressure will not be exceeded.

Practically all of the piping used is 1½ in., and it will be noted that the tank is not completely filled with sand, an air space being left at the top, and a connection from the air pipe made to this space. This puts the sand under pressure, and insures a steady flow. A cross may be used instead of the tee shown below the tank, and the lower outlet plugged; then, if the sand valve becomes choked, the plug may be unscrewed, and a wire run through the valve, to clear it. The pipe at the nozzle is reduced to ½ in., and a valve must be provided in the line between the sand and air tanks. When filling the tank, the sand should always be run through a fine sieve, to remove foreign matter and small pebbles, as the former might choke the valves or pipes, and the latter break the work, and the tank should not be filled higher than the level shown,

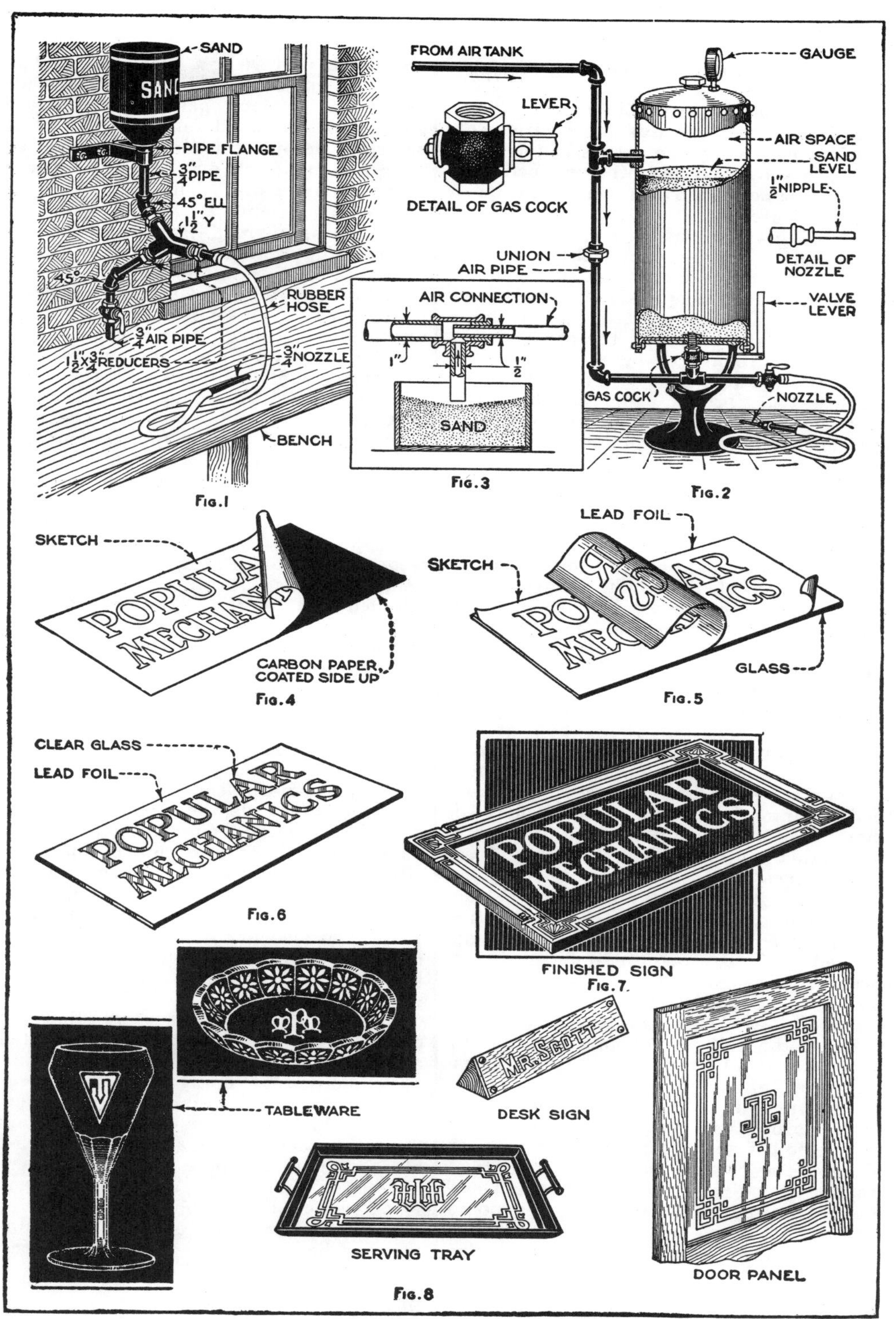

Figures 1 to 3: Simple Forms of Homemade Sandblast Machines, Made, for the Most Part, of Pipe and Fittings. Figures 4 to 7: The Various Steps in Making a Glass Sign by the Sandblast Process. Figure 8: A Few Examples Illustrative of the Wide Variety of Decorative Work to Which the Process may be Applied

to prevent sand from choking the air pipe.

The equipment shown in Fig. 3 is very simple, and may be used for a variety of small work. Only the details at the sand box are shown, as the other connections are the same as those shown in the preceding figures.

It is a peculiar quality of the sandblast that soft, yielding materials, such as paper, lead foil, etc., are not attacked or abraded nearly as quickly as hard ones like glass. This makes it possible to protect, by means of masks, the parts of the glass that are not to be acted upon by the sand. The masks are usually made of lead foil; brown paper can be used, but the foil is preferable. A supply of suitable foil can be obtained from any florist.

Figures 4 to 7 show the various steps in the work of making a plain sign; this example, while a simple one, completely illustrates the process.

The glass having been cut to the proper size, a pencil sketch of the lettering, the exact size of the work, is made on good paper. The sketch is laid on a piece of carbon paper, the coated side of the latter being up, as shown in Fig. 4, and the outline of the letters gone over again with a stylus or medium-hard pencil. This leaves a carbon impression of the lettering on the back of the sketch sheet.

The glass is now coated with melted beeswax, a sheet of foil placed on it, and rubbed into close contact with a piece of hard felt, or the rounded edge of a piece of leather belting. The glass should be kept warm while this is being done—by laying it on a radiator, for instance—so that the foil will adhere firmly to the wax. When this is done, the foil is also coated with wax. Both applications of wax may be made with an ordinary paintbrush. The sketch, with the carbon impression down, is laid on the waxed surface of the foil, in the proper position, and rubbed all over with the bottom of the bowl of a spoon, or a like article, then lifted off. This leaves the carbon lettering on the wax surface, as in Fig. 5.

The foil is then cut, along the lines of the lettering, with a mat knife, or photographer's etching knife, and the cut-out portions removed by inserting the point of the knife under the foil. The foil, when stripped, brings with it practically all the wax on the glass, and leaves the sign as shown in Fig. 6, ready for sandblasting.

If the work in hand is a sign that must be "printed" in reverse, the foregoing procedure is varied a little—no carbon paper is employed. The sketch is made with a soft, black pencil, placed, face down, on the waxed foil, and rubbed as described before; this leaves the reversed lettering, in pencil, on the wax, and the foil is cut as before. This makes a rather nice effect, after the work is done, as the lettering is read through the glass.

The sandblasting is simplicity itself, consisting in nothing more than directing the blast of sand and air against the exposed glass. The sandblast is capable of producing any effect from a light surface frosting to a very deep etching, or even to cutting completely through the glass. The method of handling the blast for best results depends upon several factors, and can best be learned by experience.

Any kind of glass can be used in the process, although, for signs and work of a similar character, plate glass is preferable. Particularly pleasing results, for some purposes, especially where a light is used behind the sign, are obtained by using what is known to the trade as "flashed" blue or ruby glass. In this, the color is only on, or rather a part of, the surface, and, when the letters are frosted as described, they stand out white against a sharply contrasting background.

The samples of work shown in Fig. 8 indicate but a few of the many uses to which this process may be put. Glass is not the only material that may be decorated by means of the sandblast; metals and woods may also be treated exactly as described. Wood, being softer than glass or metal, will require more time than either, but very elaborate effects can be produced in it, providing the design is deeply blasted, say, to a depth of about 3/16 in. In all work of this character, the result, of course, will depend almost entirely upon the artistic talent of the worker.

It is essential, in this work, that the eyes, nose, and throat be protected against flying particles of sand. The simplest method of doing this is to wear close-fitting goggles, and tie a moistened handkerchief or sponge over the nose and mouth. Special helmets may be obtained also, with an air hose that is led to a source of pure air. An old army gas mask, which is obtainable from any of the so-called army stores about the country, can be adapted to this purpose, and will make a very good helmet.

¶ A general principle in fastening members together with wood screws is to hammer them before final tightening.

An Invisible Tank Repair

An excellent method of repairing punctured gasoline tanks is shown in the illustration. After the repair is finished, it is practically invisible, and very strong.

A rectangular opening is cut at the spot where the puncture occurs, and two metal plates are cut to form a patch for this opening. One plate, which may be of any convenient thickness, is cut slightly larger than the opening, so that it laps about ½ in. over the edges. The other plate is cut to fit exactly in the opening, and its thickness must be the same as the thickness of the tank wall. A wire is soldered at right angles to the center of the larger plate, as shown, so that it can be held firmly against the inside of the opening. The edges of this plate are tinned with solder, and it is then slipped through, and drawn into place. The smaller plate has a hole drilled in its center to fit over the wire and is pushed down into the opening against the inner plate. Solder is applied between the plates along the edges, and a blowtorch is then used to sweat the two plates together. The wire is pulled out after melting the solder that holds it,

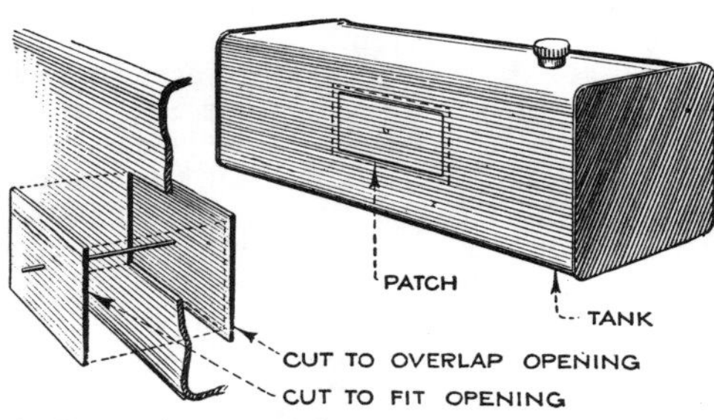

An Inconspicuous and Strong Repair for a Punctured Gasoline Tank Made by Sweating Two Plates Together

and the small hole in the outer plate is filled with solder.

Adjustable Wheelbarrow Handles

The difficulty of handling a wheelbarrow with a heavy load is eliminated by providing it with a set of adjustable handles. This enables the body to be lowered, to suit a high load, or, in other words, to lower the center of gravity. Although wheelbarrows differ in size and design, they can all be reconstructed along the lines shown in the drawing.

The original handles are cut off where the sideboards end. Two plow handles, straight style, are swung on a pivot rod fastened just underneath this point. This rod is run through small wooden blocks, A, fastened on each side of the body with

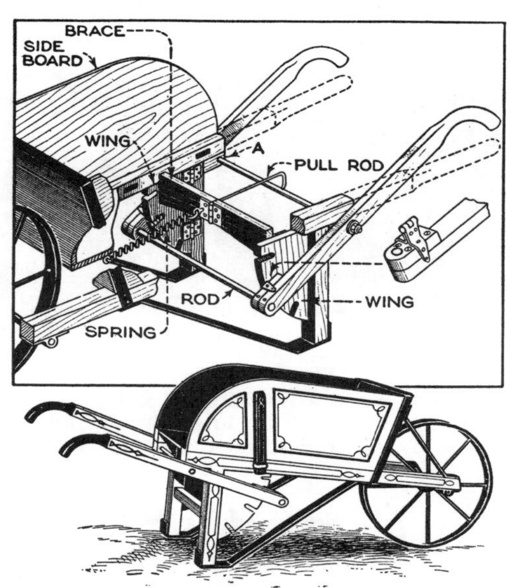

Wheelbarrow Handles That can be Raised or Lowered and Locked as Desired, Make It Easy to Handle Heavy Loads

3-in. wood screws. A quadrant-shaped wing is hinged on each leg to swing toward the inside; these are 1 in. thick, and 6 in. wide at the top. The curvature of the wings depends on the radius of the handle and can be marked off accurately, before sawing, by holding a pencil in the proper position, near the lower end of the handle, while moving it. Three or more slots are cut in the curved side of each wing in a radial line with the pivot on which the handle moves. Hinges, bent and mounted on blocks at the end of the handles as shown, fit into the slots in the wings. A wooden rod runs through the lower end of both handles. A two-piece brace is hinged to the inside of the wings in the position indicated. The two parts of this brace are connected by a hinge, which holds them together firmly, yet allows them to be pulled outward by means of the pull rod that is attached to the front side of one piece. When the pull rod is released, both pieces are instantly brought back into their end-to-end position by a coil spring, connected to the brace and to the underside of the wheelbarrow. To change the pitch of the handles, they are unlocked by pulling the pull rod; then, after moving the bent hinges to another slot, the handles are locked by releasing the pull rod.—R. B. Cutler, Springfield, Vt.

A Folding Horse

The photograph shows a folding horse that has been found to be of great con-

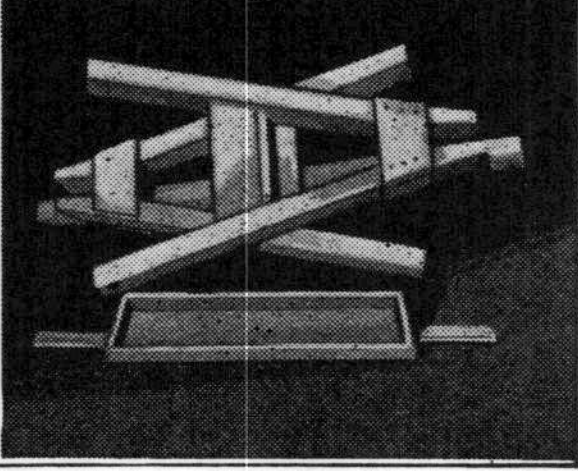

A Folding Horse, Consisting of Four Members, That Takes Little Space When Folded, and Proves Very Convenient around the Shop and Garage

venience around the shop or garage. The tray, attached to the lower cross rail, is used to hold tools and materials such as screws and nails; it is an added convenience, but can be omitted if desired.

The upper cross rail is fastened to the legs with hinges, so that the three members can be folded compactly, as shown. The hinges are attached to the underside of the rail, and to the braces nailed to the upper end of the legs, on the inside. The corresponding braces on the outside fit under the extending ends of the cross rail when the horse is set up, to prevent the legs from swinging out at more than 90° from the rail. The lower rail fits between the legs in notches cut for this purpose. When folded, this horse takes up very little space and may be carried from job to job in an automobile.—Donald W. Clark, Buffalo, N. Y.

Bench-Lathe Lap Operated with Rubber Bands

A simple but effective method of making an ordinary bench lathe work automatically is shown in the accompanying photograph. In this case the lathe happens to be used for lapping a small hole through a diamond wire-drawing die. The toolholder A moves back and forth while the work revolves. The movement is kept up by means of a cam, C, and rubber band, E. The cam C is driven by a

Lapping Diamond Wire-Drawing Dies in a Bench Lathe: The Toolholder is Reciprocated by Means of a Cam and Rubber Bands

belt, D, and bears against the vertical post B. At every half turn the cam pushes the toolholder away from the work. At the other half turn of the cam, the rubber band E pulls it back toward the work. The band E also holds the toolholder down in the V-pulley in front of the tailstock. A second rubber band, H, keeps the toolholder down in the rear V-pulley.

A common sewing needle, ground and lapped to the correct size, is used to lap the hole through the diamond. A thin paste, made of diamond dust and oil, is applied to the end of the needle and the hole. The movement of the lap in and out of the hole enables the paste to flow into the latter, and keeps the end of the lap covered. Once the lathe is arranged as shown, and started, it is only necessary to keep the lap well supplied with paste. In the shop where this method was employed, it required only one-third of one man's time, per day, to attend to 20 machines.—E. F. Lake, Detroit, Mich.

Proper Use of the Nipple Chuck

Many a good mechanic will spoil a perfectly good short nipple, after threading it in the chuck, by trying to unscrew it by means of a pipe wrench gripping the newly cut threads. The nipple, with threads cut on one end, is screwed into the nipple chuck, consisting of a piece of pipe of the same size as the nipple, and about a foot long, with an ordinary pipe sleeve or long coupling screwed on for about two-thirds of its length.

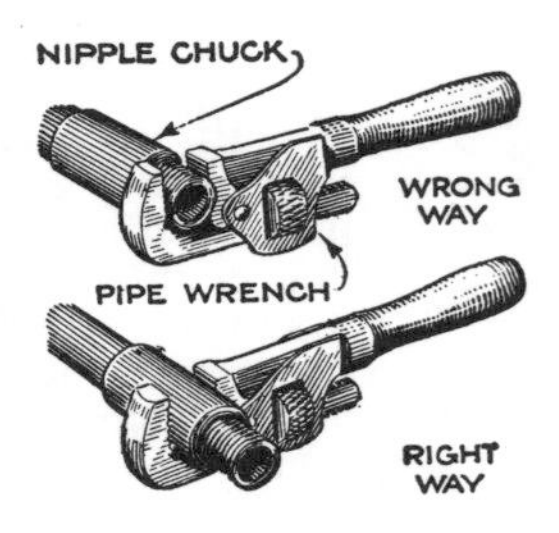

The nipple, having one end threaded,

will bottom against the pipe and prevent it from screwing too far into the sleeve when the die is rotated. All this is common practice; it is the removal of the completely threaded nipple without spoiling the thread that constitutes the trick. Instead of catching the threads with the pipe wrench and crushing them, the wrench is applied to the sleeve and turned far enough to separate the abutting ends of the pipe, where the nipple can easily be unscrewed by hand.—Edwin J. Bachman, Fullerton, Pa.

A Sphere-Turning Tool

The illustration shows a tool that will finish a ball in one operation, except for cutting off the work on either side of the shank. It consists of a tube made of solid steel. The inside diameter is drilled out to the measurement required. Two slots are cut opposite each other on the end where the drilling is finished, as this end is usually more true to size than the end where the drilling is begun. For greater accuracy, the hole should be ground to size. The width of the slots is equal to the diameter of the shank desired, and the depth about two-thirds greater than the diameter of the sphere to be turned.

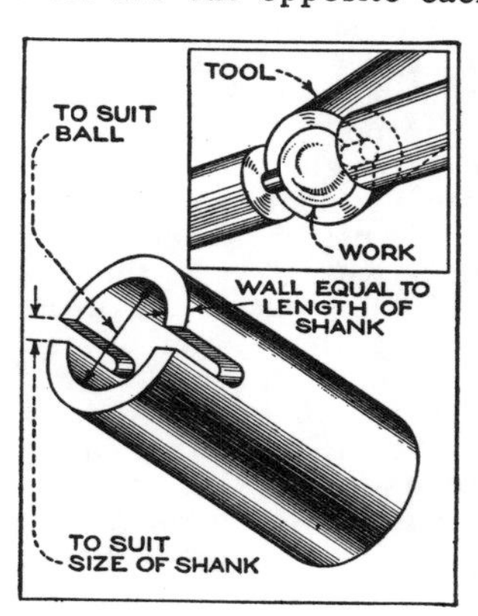

A handle may be made to hold the smaller sizes, as for model work, so that the tool can be held in the hand and steadied on the hand toolrest while pressing it against the stock as it turns. Small balls can be made in one operation. Work of larger size should first be roughed off in the ordinary way, as this is quicker and saves wear on the tool.

A tool of the above description was used for turning one hundred 2½-in. balls, with shanks, that had to be finished accurately to size. In this case the tool was tapered on the inside, from the rear, to give it a better cutting edge. It was held stationary on a V-block in the toolrest of the lathe, the end being held on a dead center also clamped to the toolrest.

Starting Nuts in Slots

The tool shown in the illustration has proved of considerable assistance in placing washers and starting nuts on bolts located in a hole, or slot, so deep that one cannot get at them with the fingers.

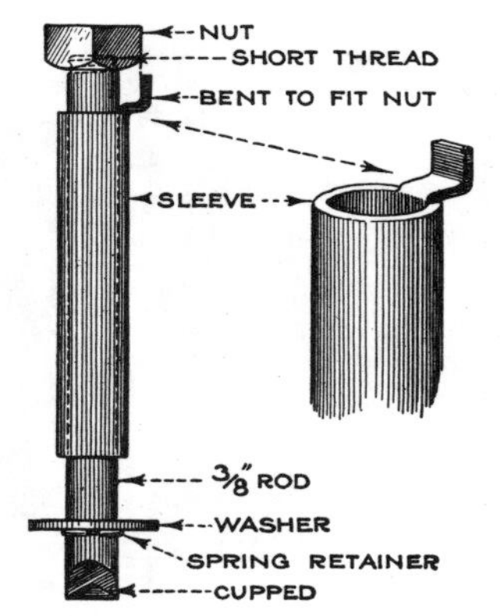

The tool is made of a short length of ⅜-in. steel rod of the same diameter as the bolt threads. A groove is cut around it near one end, to allow a spring-wire ring, or retainer, to be snapped in. This ring is cut so that it can be compressed in the groove, to allow a washer to be slipped over it. When released, the retainer will spread out and prevent the washer from slipping off. The end of the rod, near the retainer, is cupped so that it will fit on the round end of a bolt. The other end of the rod is threaded to the same pitch as the nut to be screwed in place; only a few threads are required. A sleeve, made of steel tubing, and fitting neatly on the rod, is cut and bent to grip the nut.

The tool is loaded for use by pushing a washer over the spring retainer, and screwing a nut on the threaded end. Then the cupped end of the tool is rested on the end of the bolt, and the sleeve is pushed down, forcing the washer over the retainer and onto the bolt. The other end of the tool is then placed in the slot, and the nut is screwed on the end of the bolt. While the threaded end of the tool is being unscrewed from the nut, the hook on the sleeve is held against it, to prevent it from being screwed off again.

Warming the Gas-Engine Lubricator

During cold weather, when oil thickens in the oil cup of a gas engine, preventing proper lubrication, place an old tin can upside down over the oil cup. Punch a hole in the bottom of the can to allow the feed-regulating lever to project. The heat and steam rising from the water hopper enter the tin can and keep the oil warm. The can also prevents chaff and dirt from sticking to the oil-cup glass.

Hydraulic Scale for Crane

The hydraulic scale shown in the illustration is a novel adaptation of hydraulic pressure as a means of weighing directly

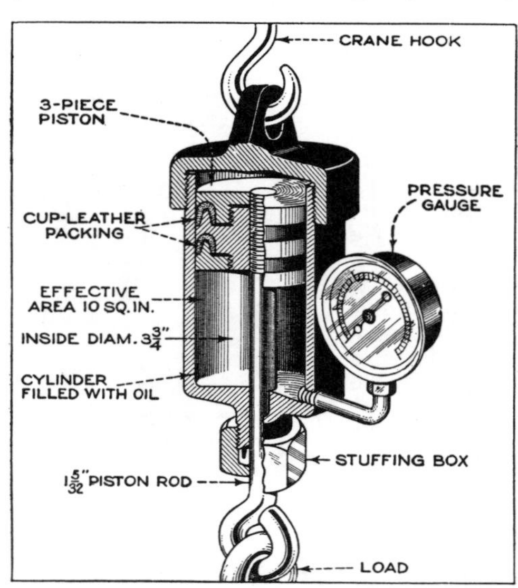

A Hydraulic Scale for Use on a Crane as a Safeguard against Overloading, Which can be Readily Detached

any machinery or parts lifted by a crane. It is not necessary for a workman to attend to this scale, as there are no sliding weights or springs needed. The entire scale weighs only about 30 lb., and is interposed between the load and crane hook so that it registers every load that the crane carries, and thus safeguards the equipment against overloads.

A cylinder, about 3¾ in. in inside diameter, is fitted with a piston provided with cup-leather packing, as shown. The piston rod is 1 5/32 in. in diameter, and the effective piston area is thus about 10 sq. in. The cylinder contains oil, and a pressure gauge, on which the pressure reading is shown in pounds per square inch, is connected to it. The weight of a load is obtained by multiplying the pressure-gauge reading by 10, which can be done mentally in an instant.

Facing Mixtures for Concrete Work

Many workers in concrete are more or less of the impression that the familiar, and frequently hideous, smooth, gray, monotonous, and uninteresting surface left by the forms is the only effect obtainable. However, a surface almost identical in appearance with granite or other pleasing stonework may be produced in a simple and inexpensive manner. This is accomplished by using a thin facing of cement mixed with small crystals of crushed quartz, or similar materials of different colors.

If the section is thin, say up to 4 in., it generally would not be too expensive to cast it entirely of the facing concrete, which is composed of 1 part of white cement to 2 parts of the crushed quartz. However, if the portion to be poured is more than 4 in., so that the expense of using the quartz particles for the entire thickness would be too great, a thickness of about 1½ in. of the finer materials will be found sufficient, and a less expensive and coarser mixture can be used for the rest of the piece. This is accomplished by placing a piece of expanded metal, of the smallest available mesh, inside the forms and about 1½ in. from the face. The facing mixture, prepared as previously explained, is then poured into this small outside space until it has piled up about a foot deep, when it is rammed down well with a rod. As the mixture begins to run through the expanded metal, the common concrete mixture, composed of the usual materials, is poured into the space between the expanded metal and the back of the form, until it has piled up to a point several inches below the facing mixture.

It is very important that the front, or facing concrete be always kept at a greater height than the backing concrete while the pouring is being done, so as to prevent any of the latter from running forward and getting into the front part of the mold, thus spoiling the effect. Also, the facing mixture should be mixed "dry," so that it will not flow too easily. A dry mix is one that uses just enough water to hydrate the cement.

A variety of finishes is possible. The form may be stripped while the concrete is still "green" or incompletely hardened, and the surface wire-brushed so as to show the quartz and produce a rough effect, or it may be ground down until absolutely smooth, when it will take the appearance of polished granite. Still another possible method is to bush-hammer it in lines, either narrow or wide.—Gilbert I. Stodola, New York City.

¶In grinding, a fast work speed will wear out the wheel faster than a slower work speed. The work speed should be adjusted so as to secure the longest life of wheels consistent with efficient production.

Concrete Curbs and Gutters

BY JAMES TATE

BUILDING a fine cement driveway or wide walk, without providing gutters, means the eventual formation of irregular and disfiguring natural gutters, with the attendant possibility that the driveway will be undermined. Where the driveway is belov grade, a curb is especially necessary and besides acting as a retaining wall for the higher grade, prevents vehicles from being driven accidentally over the edges of fine lawns.

The simple curbs shown in Figs. 1 and 2 serve excellently for edging gravel walks and drives, where gutters are either not thought necessary, or already provided. The method of making the forms for these curbs is quite clear from the drawings; 1 by 8-in. boards are used for the sides, 1 by 2-in. stuff for the cleats, and 2 by 2-in. for the stakes. When placing the concrete in the forms, the trowel or spade should be well worked up and down between concrete and form; this allows the moisture to run to the form, and is a great help in obtaining a smooth finish.

The curbs should not be made all in one piece, but the forms should be di-

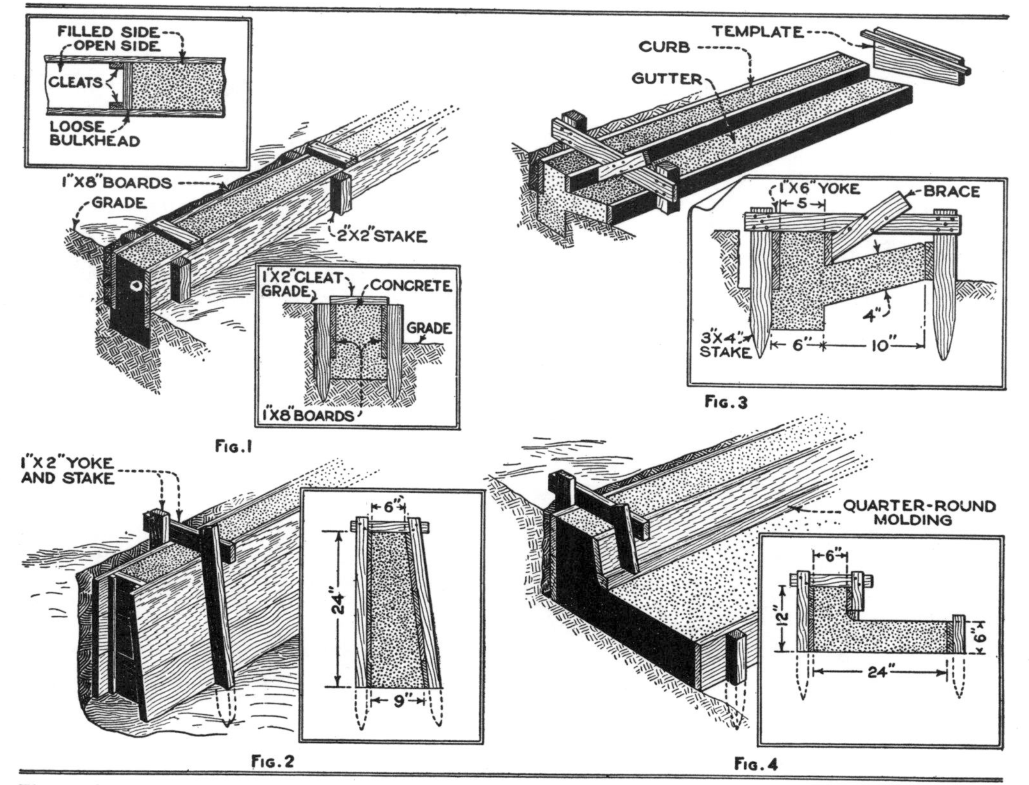

Figures 1 and 2: Simple Forms for Making Curbs without Gutters. Figure 3: Curb with Sloping Gutter Cast Integral with It. Figure 4: Another Form of Combined Curb and Gutter

vided into sections, each 7 or 8 ft. long, by means of loose bulkheads, as shown in the detail, Fig. 1. The concrete is placed in alternate sections, then, when it has just begun to set, the bulkheads are removed, and the remaining sections filled—first filling the joints between the sections with three thicknesses of tar paper, to allow for expansion.

The concrete used in all the work illustrated should be mixed in the proportion of 1 part Portland cement to 2 parts of sand and 4 parts of clean gravel or broken stone, mixed to a "mushy" consistency.

When building a new driveway or walk, the curbs and gutters shown in Figs. 3 and 4 should be used.

When making the form shown in Fig. 3, the facing board—that is, the board forming the face of the curb proper—should be beveled at the bottom to conform to the slope of the gutter, and should be braced securely, as shown, every 3 ft. A template, made as indicated, will aid in forming the gutter, after which it should be finished by troweling. The foundation should be carried below the driveway grade, to prevent undermining.

The curb and gutter shown in Fig. 4 may be built with a sloping face, as shown in perspective, or with a straight face, as in the detail. The advantage of the sloping face is that automobiles may be stopped quite close to the curb without danger to tires or rims. Even in the straight form, however, the faces of the form should be given a "batter," or taper of about ½ in. to enable the form to be removed easily. The outer corners, in all curbs, should be rounded, as a sharp edge is easily chipped, and may soon become unsightly.

Any rough or porous places in the work may be filled, when the forms are removed, with a mixture of 1 part cement and 1 part sand. The exposed surfaces should be finished with a wood float and a wide brush.

The forms should remain in place at least 24 hours—longer if possible—and, as soon as the concrete has set hard enough not to become pitted under sprinkling, it should be sprinkled, at frequent intervals, for at least two days. The more frequent and prolonged the sprinkling, the better; some authorities favor keeping the concrete wet for seven days.

Cleaning Drill Flutes

When drilling deep holes in metal, considerable trouble is encountered in keeping the flutes free from chips. The small hand brush usually used for this purpose is unsatisfactory, owing to the difficulty of holding it rigidly against the drill when the latter is revolving. To overcome this, the rigid brush holder shown in the illustration has been found satisfactory.

The handle of a stiff, round bristle brush is sawed off, leaving only the portion that holds the bristles. This portion is screwed into a pipe socket, and a short length of pipe is screwed into the other end of the socket. The pipe is slotted at the opposite end, to fit over a screweye in the drill-press column; a pin passing through both holds them together. To complete the job, a flat or round-wire spring is pushed through small holes or slots cut in the pipe a short distance from the end of the slot, as indicated.

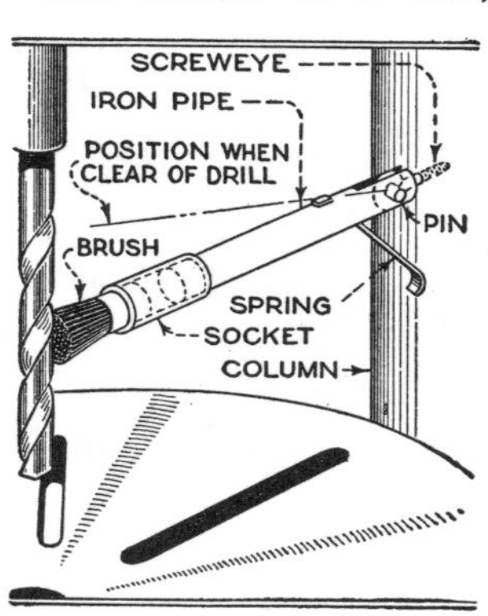

The length of the whole arrangement is such that it will force the brush to dig well into the flutes when the pipe is at right angles to the drill. When using, the operator presses lightly down on the pipe each time the drill is withdrawn from the hole. This forces the bristles into the flutes and clears them of chips. As soon as the pressure on the pipe is released, the spring forces the brush up and away from the drill. The brush can, of course, be screwed in and out as desired, to adjust for wear and for various sizes of drills.

Cutting Small Work with Welding Torch

Small iron work can be cut conveniently with an oxyacetylene welding torch when a regular cutting torch is not available, or when it is not desired to take time to make the change. To do so, play the flame along the line to be cut so that the metal is heated almost to the melting point; then, by shutting off the acetylene, slightly increasing the pressure of the oxygen, and going over the line again, the metal will be cut as nicely as it can be done with a regular torch.—Ralph M. Rausch, Milan, Mich.

Holding Castings While Painting Them

The illustration shows an easily made device for holding small hollow castings while painting them. This work is always found more or less "messy" in a shop not equipped for it, and the holder was devised to eliminate the necessity of handling the castings either during or after painting.

Ordinary round-steel rod is used for the two parts of the holder, which are bent as indicated. The stand fits into a hole in the bench. The other part, the spring holder, fits loosely in the eye formed at the top of the stand. Although the work shown in this particular example is an offset bend, it is obvious that the same device can be used for any shape of casting, provided there is a hole in it somewhere. In operation, the casting is slipped over the ends of the spring holder where it is securely held while being painted. The job can be turned around in any direction desired, and can be dropped into a box when finished by pressing the two branches of the holder together. Thus, at no time need the workman actually touch the work.—Harry Moore, Montreal, Can.

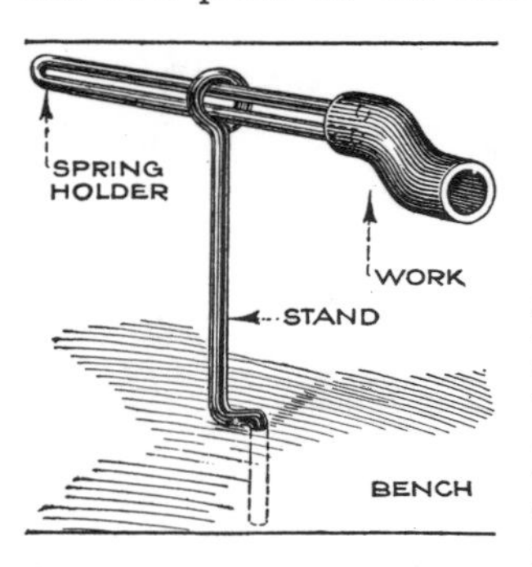

Improvement for Draftsman's Scale

By equipping his scale with a screw on each end, as shown, the draftsman will find that he can manipulate it much more easily, and that it brings the graduations closer to the line being scaled. Drill a hole in each end of the rule and insert the screws, tightening them in place with nuts on each side, as indicated. The heads of the screws are cut off and both ends rounded.—C. Bryan, Chicago, Ill.

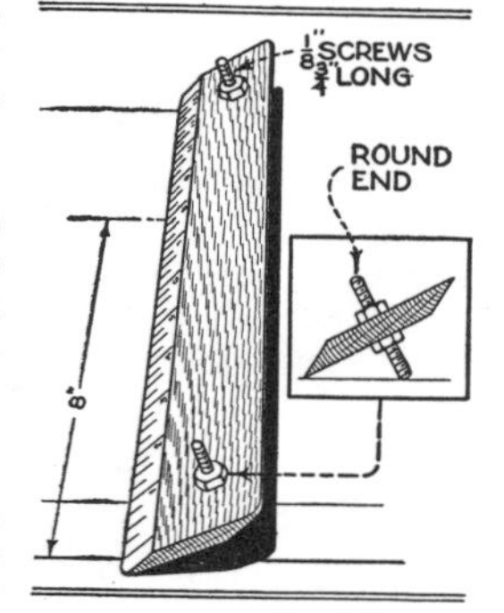

Saw-Filing Clamp and Vise

Using the ordinary wooden clamp to hold a saw while sharpening the teeth, one usually finds it difficult to keep the bars parallel while placing the clamp in the vise or filing stand. This objectionable feature is overcome by using a saw-filing clamp and vise of the type shown in the illustration. The bars are held parallel to each other at all times by means of 1/16-in. flat iron strips, bent to the shape indicated. Two beveled grooves are cut on each bar, to fit snugly into the vise, which consists simply of two 2 by 4-in. pieces, with the ends cut as shown, and securely braced.—F. M. Arthur, Bethune, South Carolina.

Making a Tractor Seat Comfortable

An excellent method of preventing "that tired feeling" with which the tractor operator is so familiar, is to equip the seat with a back taken from a discarded kitchen chair. A small hole is drilled through the lower end of each stile, and soft wire is used to fasten it to the seat. To prevent the back from working out of place, the lower end of each stile should be cut to fit against the curved rim of the seat. Care should be taken not to have the back too straight. —Dale R. Van Horn, Walton, Neb.

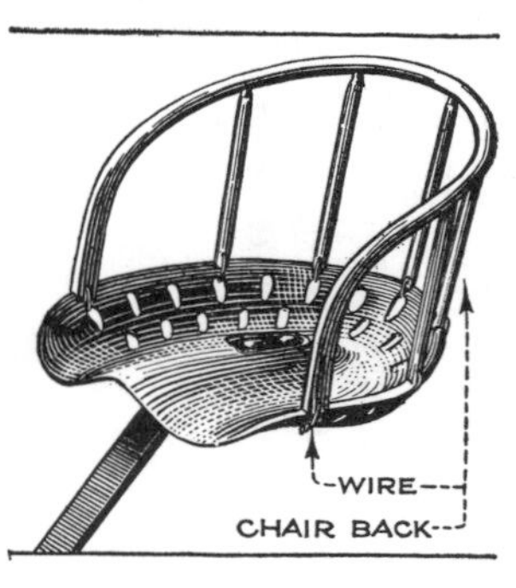

¶A new tube should be used in a new casing; an old tube is much more likely to give way than a new one, and when it does, the tire is usually run flat for some distance before the fact is discovered, which so reduces the life of the tire that a new tube is a paying investment.

Pliers Used as Reamer

Cutting edges formed on the nose of a pair of pliers are particularly useful to electricians and to pipe fitters, for the purpose of trimming off the burr from the inside edges of conduit and pipe. This is done, in conduit to avoid abrading the insulation of the conductors while pulling them through, and, in the case of pipe, to prevent material from catching on the burrs, and choking the pipe. The nose of the pliers is ground as shown in the illustration. For light burrs, the pliers can be turned by hand; for heavier cutting, more leverage can be obtained by using a screwdriver, placed between the plier handles as indicated.

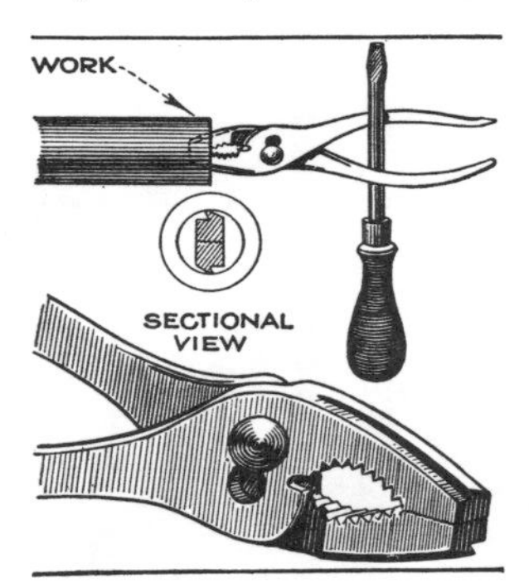

Lamp Shows When Current Is On

In laundries and elsewhere where electric irons and similar appliances are used, there is more or less danger of fire due to an overheated iron, as it is not always possible to tell whether or not the current is turned on or off, unless an indicating switch or lamp for each iron is used. Of these, the lamp is preferable, as it can be seen from a distance. A simple arrangement, used in a large laundry, consists of a 10-watt incandescent lamp, preferably of the carbon-filament type, shunted around the switch in parallel with the flatiron so that both are operated by the same switch. In a conduit installation, a two-gang body, fitted with a single-pole flush switch and a flush screw socket, as illustrated, presents a very neat appearance. The wiring diagram shows the method of connecting. If desired, the lamp can be protected from being accidentally broken by inclosing it in a perforated sheet-iron cylinder, fastened to the front plate by means of small angle irons.

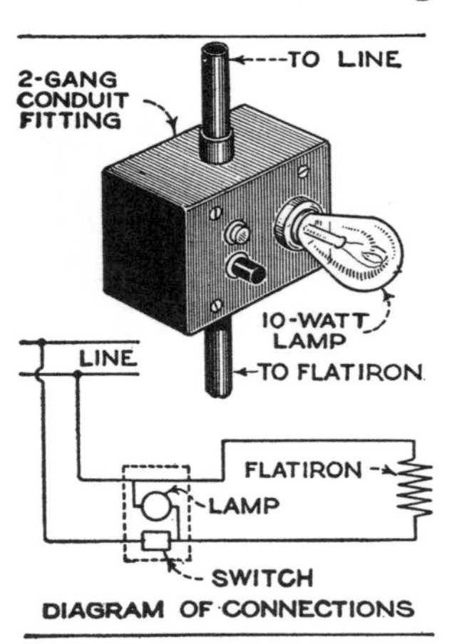

Placing Screws in Deep Slots

In the final assembly of a machine used in the printing trade, it was necessary to screw a number of round-head screws into the bottom of slots where the hand could not reach. To do the job, the special screwdriver illustrated was used. A loose sleeve, of square stock, was drilled lengthwise to fit the shank of the screwdriver. At right angles to this hole, near the bottom of the sleeve, a hole large enough to fit the heads of the screws was drilled, and a slot, breaking into the hole, cut across the bottom of the sleeve. A slot is also milled halfway down the sleeve, running into the lengthwise hole, as indicated. A pin, driven into the shank, fits in this slot, and keeps the blade of the screwdriver in line with the slot in the bottom of the sleeve.

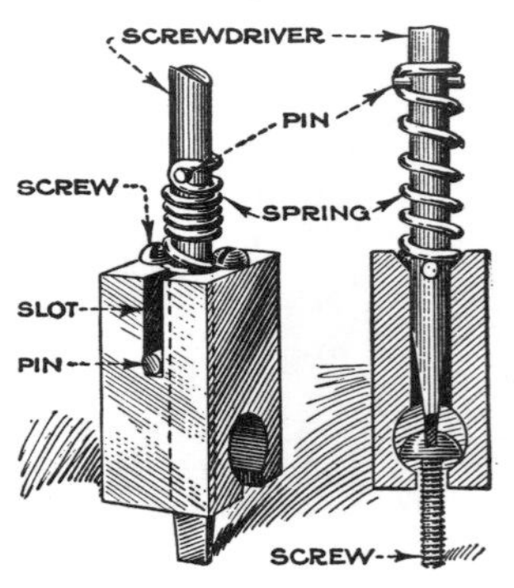

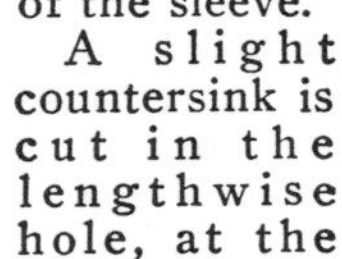

A slight countersink is cut in the lengthwise hole, at the top, to accommodate the bottom coil of the tension spring shown; this coil is held down in the countersink by two small round-head screws, and the other end of the spring is looped around a pin driven through the shank.

Normally, the blade of the screwdriver projects as shown at the left; when it is necessary to place a screw in a slot, the sleeve is pulled down and a screw slipped into it, as at the right, the tension of the spring holding it tightly. When the screw has been started in its hole, a slight side pressure slips the sleeve off, and the screw is then driven home as with any ordinary screwdriver.

¶Use the smallest milling cutter possible—the cost is lower and less power is needed.

DESIGNING SOLENOIDS

By Curtis Ralston

[This article was written in response to a number of requests from our readers. The author has endeavored to present the subject in as simple and understandable a manner as possible, and we hope that the article will prove of value to the large number of readers interested in the subject.—Editor.]

ONE of the simplest of electromagnetic devices is the solenoid. Almost every experimenter in electricity has occasion, early in his experience, to build some kind of solenoid or electromagnet, and, while it is no trick to make "some kind of a coil," there is considerable science involved in getting just the right coil for a particular purpose.

By a solenoid, or "plunger magnet," we mean a coil of wire, nearly always used with a plunger of iron which moves lengthwise inside the coil. The difference between a solenoid and a common or "lever" electromagnet is that in the electromagnet the moving part of the iron circuit is somewhere outside of the coil, as shown in Figs. 1 and 2, while the solenoid has the moving part inside the winding, as in Fig. 3. The solenoid may have an almost complete iron magnetic circuit, as in the "ironclad" type shown in Fig. 4, but as long as the air gap is inside the coil, and the core itself is movable, it is, properly speaking, a solenoid.

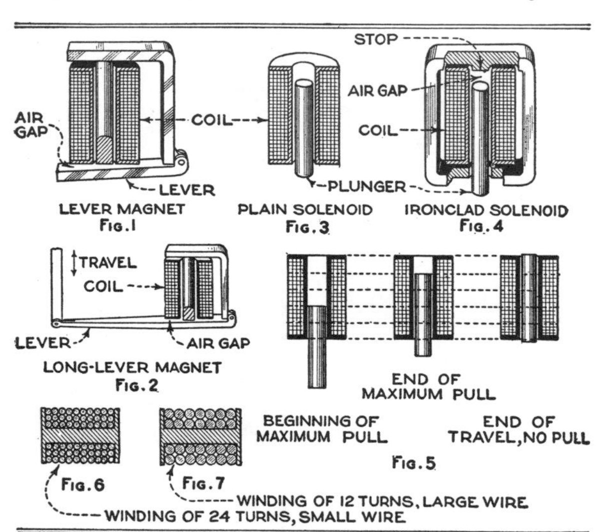

Figures 1 and 2: Common Types of Lever Magnets. Figure 3 Shows a Plain, and Figure 4, an Ironclad Solenoid. Figure 5 Illustrates the Action of the Solenoid on the Plunger, and Figures 6 and 7, the Relation between Coils of the Same Size, but of Different Windings

The first thing to know about solenoids is when they should be used, rather than lever magnets. This depends chiefly on the distance it is necessary to move the part actuated by the plunger. If only a small movement is necessary, as in a relay or electric bell, the lever magnet is better, but whenever more than a small fraction of an inch of movement is necessary, the solenoid becomes useful. This does not mean that more work is obtainable from the solenoid than from the lever magnet, because, with the longer travel, it is found that the number of pounds pull is lower. That is, with the solenoid the same effect is obtained as if a lever magnet with a long lever, like Fig. 2, were used—only the awkwardness of the long lever is avoided.

Before the solenoid is designed, then, it is necessary to know two things: how far the plunger must be pulled (in inches), and how hard it must be pulled (in pounds). Knowing these things, the proper coil for the work can be designed.

The question of distance is much the simpler of the two, and may be answered by this rule: Any "plain" solenoid (one having no iron in its construction but the straight plunger) will exert its greatest pull on the plunger as soon as the latter has entered to a distance of two-fifths of the length of the coil, as shown at the left in Fig. 5. It will keep on pulling, just as hard, until the plunger has entered a distance of about four-fifths, as in the center, Fig. 5. By this time the plunger is beginning to reach its "goal," and its pull gradually weakens, until it is all the way in, as at the right, when it ceases to pull at all. So that, in general, a coil should be made about twice as long as the distance the plunger is to be pulled. The plunger should be at least as long as the coil, but making it any longer will not give any more pull.

Taking up, next, the question of how to get the necessary amount of pull, we shall consider for the present only the plain solenoid; the possibilities of the ironclad type will be explained later. Just as the travel of the plunger is governed entirely by the length of the coil, so the pull is governed by the cross-sectional area of the iron plunger, and by the ampere-turns supplied per inch of coil length.

So far as the size of the plunger is concerned, it may be readily understood that the pull varies directly as the area of its cross section. If the diameter of the plunger could be doubled, without changing the coil, four times the pull would be obtained; this cannot be done, of course, as any increase in the size of the plunger increases the length of wire necessary to go around it. But care can be taken to use a plunger big enough to fill the hole through the coil, leaving just enough clearance for a "sliding fit"; if this is not done, current is wasted.

It can be said, then, that there is a certain pull for each square inch of area in the iron; the intensity of this pull, or the number of pounds per square inch of force exerted, is governed entirely by the "ampere-turns per inch." Providing the right ampere-turns per inch, by the cheapest winding that is safe, is the main problem in solenoid design. To determine it accurately by ordinary calculations involves a good deal of "cut-and-try" figuring, but by making a few assumptions which simplify the conditions, it is possible to bring the design of solenoids down to a fairly simple basis.

It will be noted, in the above introduction, that nothing has been said about voltage, current, or resistance. The reason for this is something the reader should get firmly fixed in his mind: The strength of any magnet coil does not depend on the voltage or the current applied, except so far as these change the ampere-turns per inch. Solenoids can be wound with any size of wire, to operate on any desired voltage. Let us consider, in order to make these relations clear, two coils of exactly the same size, but wound with different sizes of wire, Figs. 6 and 7. Fig. 6, having a certain size of wire, can stand a certain voltage applied to it without becoming hot enough to endanger the insulation. Fig. 7 is wound with wire just twice as large in cross-sectional area; it thus has half the length of wire of the first coil, and one-fourth the resistance. But it will carry twice as many amperes, so that the proper voltage to apply to it for the same heating effect, is one-half the voltage required for the first coil. The power in watts, being the product of volts and amperes, will be the same in each case. The second coil will have half as many turns of wire as the first, so that the ampere-turns will be the same for both. It may be seen from this comparison that any two coils of the same size, but wound with different sizes of wire, will use the same power and give the same ampere-turns, provided they carry the same amount of current per square inch of cross section of wire. That is to say, when we know how high a "current density" (or amperes per square inch) we can use, we can tell how many ampere-turns a given size of coil will require—and without as yet considering the actual volts, amperes, or size of wire to be used.

Current densities in the field windings of large dynamos seldom run over 1,000 amperes per square inch, but since the small coils we are dealing with here have relatively a great deal more radiating surface, we can safely run up to 2,000 and even 3,000 amperes per square inch for very small coils. The figures given in the table for the various coil diameters are computed by allowing about .6 watt for each square inch of cylindrical surface on the coil.

Knowing the current density, and having assumed, for simplicity, that a winding depth equal to the plunger diameter will provide a high enough flux density for the purpose, one can proceed to calculate the magnetizing force in ampere-turns per inch, and, from this, the amount of pull which the solenoid will give at the current density used in it. This "solenoid pull" is the magnetic attraction between the wires of the coil and the plunger, and is the only force present in a simple solenoid like Fig. 3. However, commercial plunger magnets are usually made with an iron shell, as shown simply in Fig. 4. Here there is not only the solenoid pull, but in addition the pull developed between the two magnetic poles formed in the iron, at the stop and at the end of the plunger. This "end pull" depends on the length of the coil and the air gap, so, in order to show about how much it amounts to, we assume, in the table, that the coil is twice as long as its outside diameter, and that the air gap is equal to the plunger diameter, as in Fig. 4. Examining the figures in the table, on the line showing the end pull, it can readily be seen that, even with this short air gap, the increase in pull by adding the iron shell, at these low flux densities, hardly pays for the additional complication, so that the "best bet" for the amateur builder is the plain solenoid.

Going on to the actual winding data, the first thing to know is the watts of power that will be consumed in each inch of length, at the current density used. From this we find a very useful figure which is called, in the table, "circ. mils for 1-in. coil, at 1 volt," or M. This number is really not very reliable for coils shorter than their diameter, but its importance lies in the fact that from it we can find very quickly the wire size to use in a coil of any length, for any voltage. To do this, simply multiply the number M by the length of the coil, in inches, and divide by the volts to be used, as indicated in the note. The answer is our wire size in circular mils; to find the nearest wire-gauge number, consult a table of B. & S. (or A. W. G.) wire sizes.

In selecting a wire size, remember that using too small a wire will cut down the strength of the magnet; using too large a wire, while giving greater strength, will cause more heating. However, in cases where accurate design is not as important as the possibility of using a size of wire one happens to have on hand, it is well to remember that a smaller wire can be used with less weakening effect if the wire length (or winding depth) is also decreased, though overheating must be guarded against. Similarly, it is possible to use a larger size of wire than that indicated by calculation, but a larger quantity of wire is then required to keep the current consumption down, making a heavier, bulkier coil.

The above discussion refers, of course, particularly to direct current. Alternating current is not so satisfactory for any kind of magnet, and, particularly for the plain solenoid, it is very hard to arrive at any general winding rules. The note below the table gives suggested windings for the common 60-cycle alternating-current voltages, but they are to be taken only as very rough approximations. Much depends on the length, the quality of iron, and the thickness of the laminations, for in order to get a satisfactory a.-c. magnet for continuous operation, it is necessary to use a "laminated" plunger, such as one made of a bundle of fine iron wires, insulated from each other by dipping in varnish. It will also be found that the a.-c. solenoid is rather noisy.

The results obtained by the use of the table apply to coils that are to carry current steadily. If the pull is to be applied only occasionally, and especially if the solenoid is wired so as to break its own circuit as the travel is completed, then considerably higher current densities may be used, with corresponding increase of pull. If, for instance, one wants a plunger to pull 5 oz. a distance of 1½ in., with an automatic instant break in the circuit, it is pretty safe to use a ¼-in. plunger and to increase the current density to 6,000 amperes per square inch instead of 3,000. This should give .34 lb. of pull instead of .17, and the watts required will increase in proportion to the

WINDING DEPTH EQUAL TO PLUNGER DIAMETER

DESIGNING DATA	HOW FOUND	ALL LINEAR DIMENSIONS IN INCHES				
PLUNGER DIAMETER = WINDING DEPTH	T (ASSUMED)	.250	.375	.5	.750	1
PLUNGER AREA	$A = .7854\ T^2$	.049	.110	.196	.442	.785
OUTSIDE DIAMETER OF COIL	$D = 3\ T$	.75	1.125	1.5	2.25	3.00
LENGTH OF AVERAGE TURN	$L = 6.28\ T$	1.57	2.36	3.14	4.72	6.28
CURRENT DENSITY, (AMPS. PER SQ. IN.)	$d = 1{,}600\sqrt{\frac{1}{T}}$	3,200	2,610	2,260	1,850	1,600
CURRENT DENSITY, REDUCED FOR SAFETY	d	3,000	2,400	2,000	1,600	1,400
AMPERE-TURNS PER INCH OF LENGTH	$ni = .6\ Td$	450	540	600	720	840
SOLENOID PULL IN POUNDS	$P = .006\ T^2 m$	.17	.46	.90	2.43	5.04
END PULL IN POUNDS (ASSUMED COIL)	$p = A\left(\frac{2\ Dni}{2660\ T}\right)^2$	.05	.16	.36	1.16	2.81
% INCREASE DUE TO IRON SHELL	$\% = \frac{p}{P}$	29%	35%	40%	48%	56%
WATTS REQUIRED PER INCH OF LENGTH	$W = .00000256\ T^2 d^2$	1.44	2.08	2.56	3.68	5.01
CIRC. MILS FOR 1-IN. COIL AT 1 VOLT	$M = 1{,}273{,}000\ \frac{W}{d}$	610	1,100	1,630	2,930	4,550
WIRE REQUIRED PER IN. OF LENGTH	$LB. = .21\ T\ L$	.082	.186	.33	.75	1.32

To find the circular mils required for any desired length of coil, and for a certain voltage: Multiply the length by the figure opposite M in the table, and divide by the voltage.
For 6 volts a.c., use next size larger than for 6 volts d.c.
For 110 volts a.c., use three sizes larger than for 110 volts d.c.

Winding Data and Formulas Used in the Design of Experimental Solenoids: It must be Remembered That the Table is Intended to Serve Only as a Guide, and the Figures Given in It are Intended for the "Average" Coil, Making a Certain Amount of Calculation Necessary in Each Special Case

square of the current density, giving 5.76 watts per inch instead of 1.44. For 1½ in. of travel we shall need a coil about 3 in. long, so that our total power requirement will be 17.3 watts. The actual change to be made in finding the size of wire is simply that, instead of using 610 for M as in the table, we use 1,220. Multiplying this by the length (3) and dividing by 32 (if we are designing for a 32-volt farm-lighting system) gives 114 as the number of circular mils in the size of wire we shall require. The nearest wire size is No. 29, with 127 circ. mils; it would hardly do to use No. 30 (100 circ. mils), especially on account of "space-factor" considerations.

This space factor is something we have said nothing about so far; it means the proportion of the cubic inches of winding space which is actually occupied by copper, rather than by air or insulation. For simplicity, we have assumed throughout these calculations that the space factor will be about .6, though it really runs a little higher for the larger wires and down to .4 for No. 30 wire. The weights of wire given in the table are all figured for a factor of .6; the consequence is, that when one tries to wind the specified amount of wire onto the spool, it will be found, if the wire is small, that the coil diameter grows larger than the table shows. This should be allowed for in preparing the spool, and there will also be some weakening of pull if the wire is small, due to extra space occupied by insulation. But it is better to allow a little for this than to complicate the calculations.

Little need be said as to the spool for winding a solenoid, except that the tube on which the wire is wound must not be of iron, steel, or "tin." Thin brass tubing or paper makes a good spool, with ends of fiber or cardboard; wooden spools will do, but are not very efficient because of their thickness. The most important thing in winding any coil is to maintain an even tension, so as to get the turns perfectly "bedded." If they are not wound evenly and closely, a weaker pull will result.

It is well to remember that smaller wire can be used instead of larger by connecting several lengths in parallel. For instance, a ½-in.-plunger solenoid, 4 in. long, for 2 volts, would take a large wire according to the table: 1,630 times 4 divided by 2 gives 3,260 circ. mils, or No. 15 wire. Instead of winding 4 times .33 or 1.32 lb. of No. 15 wire, two windings, each containing .66 lb. of No. 18 wire (1,624 circ. mils), can be used, connected in parallel. It makes no difference how the two windings are placed on the coil, so long as they are connected to help, and not "buck" each other.

Too great accuracy is not to be expected at any point in the design process here outlined, as a number of approximations are involved, and the thickness of the spool between coil and plunger is neglected. But the table should enable any amateur to design a solenoid to fit his needs with sufficient exactness.

A Lathe-Chuck Remover

Various clumsy makeshift methods and devices are used to remove lathe chucks from the spindle, such as pounding with a soft hammer, or using a block of wood held beneath one of the jaws, which is brought down against the block sharply. It is obvious that any such treatment to one jaw will very quickly throw the whole chuck out of line and weaken the jaws besides. The drawing illustrates a chuck-removing device that has the merit of being simple and yet highly effective. It consists of a steel ring, the outer diameter of which is almost as large as the chuck body. The inside of the ring is slotted to fit over the chuck jaws, and its outside is cut away to form a tooth on the edge of the remover.

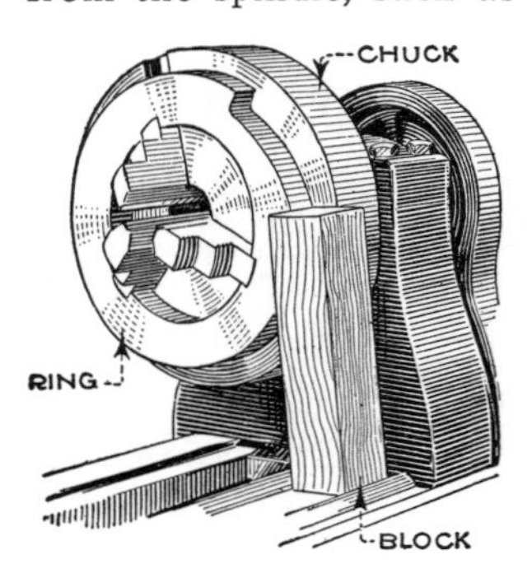

It will be seen from the drawing that the device sits back against the face of the chuck, making it a solid fixture, while the large diameter of the ring gives it a good leverage. When it is desired to remove the chuck, the ring is slipped into place, and the jaws are screwed outward tightly into the equally spaced slots. Then, with a piece of hardwood resting on the lathe bed in a slightly inclined position so that its end rests against the edge of the ring, the lathe is reversed, causing the tooth to come into contact with the wood. In this manner all three jaws of the chuck take the strain and it is not so likely to be injured.

Board Substituted for Workbench

In a hardware store where it was necessary to use all the floor space available,

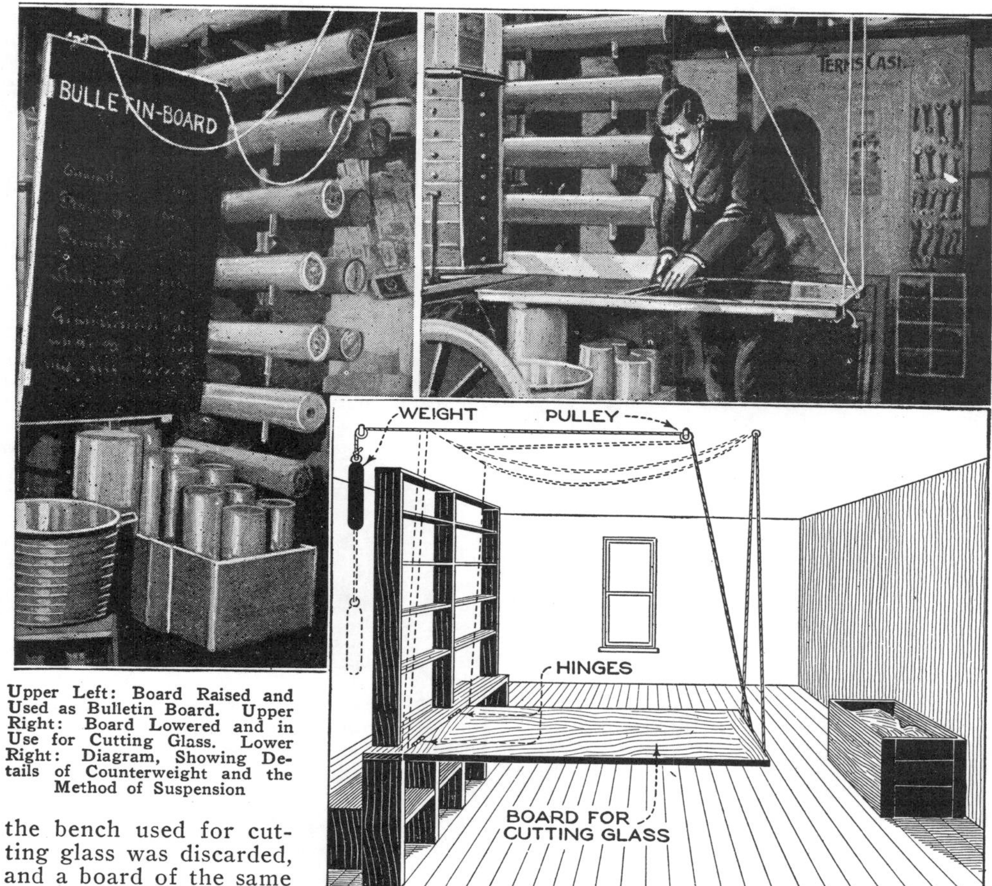

Upper Left: Board Raised and Used as Bulletin Board. Upper Right: Board Lowered and in Use for Cutting Glass. Lower Right: Diagram, Showing Details of Counterweight and the Method of Suspension

the bench used for cutting glass was discarded, and a board of the same width was substituted, which, when not in use, could be raised to a vertical position, and the exposed side used as a bulletin board. One end of the board was attached to the edge of a shelf by means of hinges. The other end was counterbalanced by a sash weight, suspended as indicated. The strain of cutting, and any weight on the board, was taken by two stout ropes attached to the outer corners of the board, and to a screweye in the ceiling.—K. W. Williams, Rochester, N. Y.

A short chalk line, held taut with both hands over a glass or metal surface in which it is impossible to drive a nail or tack, can be snapped very easily by the teeth, if a short length of string is attached to the center of the line.

Keeping Cable Clamps from Slipping

Considerable difficulty was experienced in keeping a cable from pulling out of the clamps that held it to a clamshell bucket, the trouble not being due to the weight of the bucket, but rather to the "yanking" it received. After several fruitless attempts, the problem was finally solved in the following way:

The end of the cable was bent around the shackle pin, and the clamps were attached as usual and screwed up as tightly as possible. A piece of tin was wrapped around the clamps, to form a mold, and the space inside was filled with melted babbitt, after one end had been closed with asbestos. A small piece of resin was dropped into the mold before pouring.

No stronger joint than this could be desired; the clamps are still immovable after six months' use.—A. S. Jamieson, Springfield, Mass.

Tool Makes Solder Shavings

It is possible to do a much neater job on small and sweated work if solder shav-

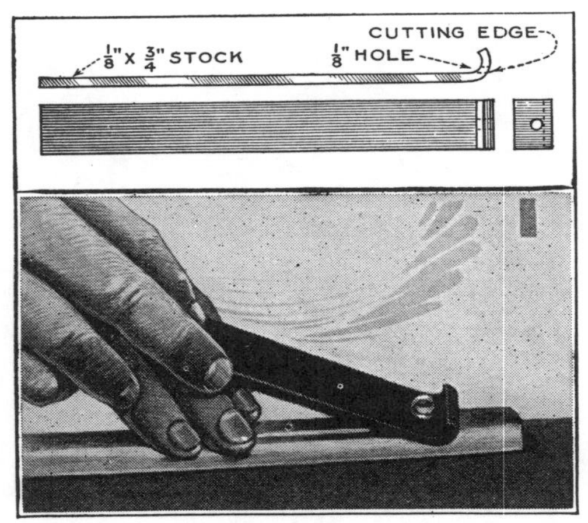

Above: Tool for Cutting Small Shavings from Solder. Below: Tool in Use, Showing How It is Held

ings are used instead of large pieces, because the correct amount of solder necessary for a successful joint can be more readily determined. If lumps of solder are used, there is danger of getting too much solder on the work, as one lump too much makes a considerable difference, which is not the case with shavings.

The illustration shows a simple tool used to make solder shavings quickly. It is made from an old flat file, or from a short length of steel, about 1/8 by 3/4 in. One end is heated and bent over as indicated. A hole is drilled in this end so that its lower edge is in line with the upper face of the tool. When the tool is held at an angle, as shown in the drawing, and pushed over a stick of solder, a thin shaving is cut.

Sign for Office-Building Window Washer

The sign shown in the illustration is used in a large Chicago skyscraper to indicate the whereabouts of the window washer. The sign is hung on the outside of the corridor door of the room in which the washer is working. To locate the window washer, it is not necessary to go into every office on the floor, but merely to glance along the corridor.—E. M. Scott, Chicago, Ill.

Adjusting Clutch on Light Car

When adjusting the three clutch fingers on the high-speed clutch of a light automobile, it is necessary to turn the motor over to bring the fingers to the top where they are accessible. As it is difficult, when using the crank, to determine when these points are reached, the following method will prove of considerable assistance:

Jack up one of the rear wheels and release the hand brake, thereby throwing in the clutch. The latter can now be turned over by stepping on the spokes of the wheel, until the proper position is reached.—E. T. Gunderson, Humboldt, Ia.

Leveler for Concrete

Efficient work in leveling concrete can be done with the homemade implement shown in the drawing. The workman is not obliged to walk in the wet concrete to manipulate this tool, as is the case with the levelers usually employed; hence it is particularly desirable for the worker not having a pair of rubber boots. The tool is made from pieces of wide board nailed together as illustrated. The length of the handle is, of course, determined by the area to be leveled.

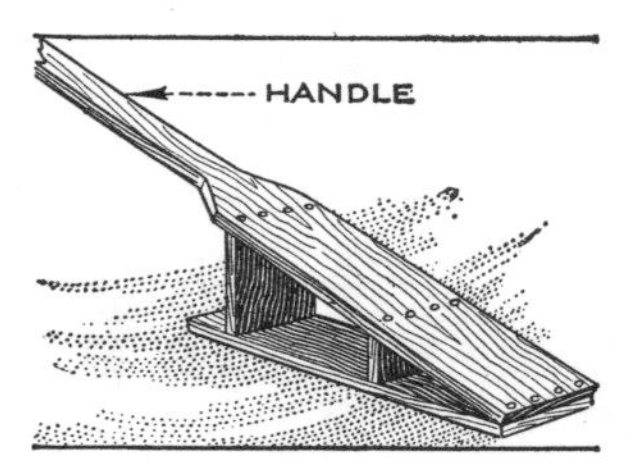

A Simple Torch

A simple torch that is very serviceable for many purposes can be made in a short time from a length of pipe, bent to the shape indicated. The pipe is threaded on one end, and is fitted with a cap that can be unscrewed to fill the torch with fuel. A cotton wick, about half as long as the pipe, is twisted into the other end. The circular form of the torch prevents it from upsetting and allowing the oil to run out.

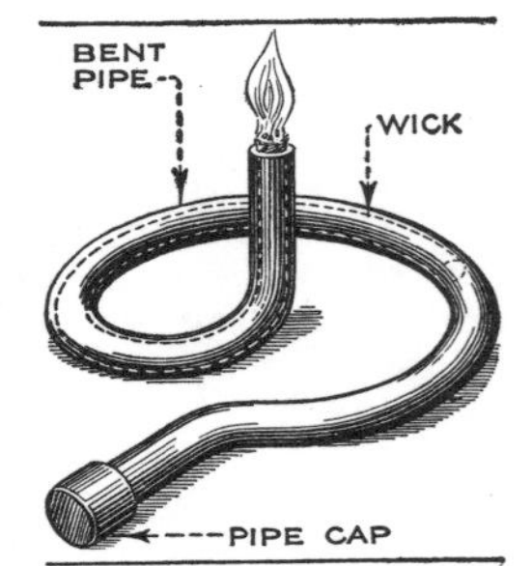

Novel Method of Bending Small Moldings

A simple, but very effective method of permanently bending small moldings to any desired curvature is illustrated in the drawing and photograph. By this method the work can be accomplished without using steam, and without kerfing or cutting the molding.

From a piece of hardwood, preferably of the same thickness as the height of the molding, the block A is cut. A curved portion is sawed out along the same radius as the desired curvature on the outside of the molding. Then, by placing a piece of the molding against this edge, and using a bevel, it can easily be determined at what radius and bevel to cut the block B, which is of the same thickness as A. The beveled edge is necessary in case of triangular molding, to prevent it from becoming twisted in the form. Both blocks are then firmly fastened to a wooden base, care being taken to set them the proper distance apart. It is desirable to use screws in attaching the block B to the base, since the pressure of the molding will have a tendency to raise the edge. The screws, however, should not be put too close to the edge, as a slight projection will block the passage and ruin the molding.

The form now being ready for use, the molding to be bent should be soaked thoroughly, preferably in hot water, to make it pliable. After beveling the end, so that it will not catch, the molding is slowly forced into the form by tapping it lightly with a hammer. It will be rather difficult to drive the molding the first quarter or third of the way, but by using care and patience, a good job will be sure to result.

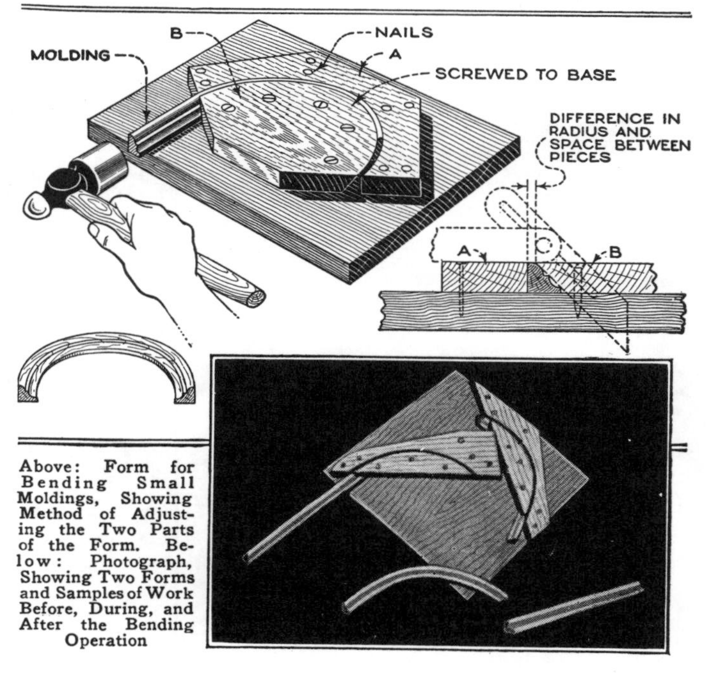

Above: Form for Bending Small Moldings, Showing Method of Adjusting the Two Parts of the Form. Below: Photograph, Showing Two Forms and Samples of Work Before, During, and After the Bending Operation

After the molding has dried thoroughly in the form, it can be removed by loosening the block B, and it will be found to have been distorted very little, or not at all.—Francis Wilkin, Pittsburgh, Pa.

Correcting "Second-Gear" Trouble

One of the most frequent sources of trouble experienced by owners and drivers of a certain six-cylinder car, is the stripping of the teeth on the "second gear." This trouble is always attended by the bending of the spline shaft, and although the car can be run on low and high gear, the operation is unsatisfactory.

One man, after experiencing trouble of this kind several times, made an investigation to determine the cause. He found that the gear box, which in this make of car is bolted to the rear-axle housing, was fitted with soft-metal bushings, which soon wore away when the lubricating oil ran too low. This allowed too much play in the shaft on which the second gear was mounted. As the gears are all made with the stub-form tooth, this excessive play caused one gear to crawl up on its mating gear, so that eventually the gears rode on the tooth tops, with the result that the shaft was bent and the gear stripped.

To correct this, all the bearing holes of the shaft were bushed with the best grade of bronze bushings procurable, and thereafter the gear box was kept well filled with lubricant at all times.

Substantial Loading Skid

The loading skid shown in the illustration has been specially designed for loading barrels, and is free from the objec-

A Substantial Skid, Especially Convenient for Loading or Unloading Barrels: As the Barrels Rest on Two Points, They Tend to Roll Straight

tionable features found in most types of skids. It is made of lengths of 1-in. wrought-iron pipe and four elbows, and is substantial enough to bear a weight of 350 lb. without bending permanently. One of the advantages of this type of skid is that a man can stand between the two runners to push the load up. Another advantage is that there are two bearing points for the barrels, which makes the task of guiding them much easier. The lower ends of the skid are fitted with nipples, beveled to a point; these prevent the skid from slipping or spreading. The skid is comparatively light, and can be placed in position quickly.

Aluminum Hones

Cast-aluminum hones are now being used in a western shop to take the place of the ordinary hones, as aluminum has an abrasive quality of particular usefulness for fine work. These hones are better in many ways than the ordinary hones, owing to the fact that no lather, oil, or compound is needed to make the aluminum "take hold" of the steel. The tool is merely rubbed on the bare metal in the usual manner.

Aluminum hones may be made in any shop by melting the aluminum in a babbitt ladle and pouring it into a plaster or sand mold with a cavity 2 in. wide, 5 in. long, and ½ in. deep. When the metal is cold, it is polished on a grindstone, or on a grinding disk covered with medium-grade sandpaper. If desired, a hone can be made by cutting a square or rectangular piece out of a discarded aluminum crankcase, or other cast-aluminum article that has a flat surface. The aluminum can also be cast in the form of a common whetstone or a heavy butcher's steel, for use in sharpening kitchen knives and other tools.—David Baxter, Hutchinson, Kansas.

Small High-Pressure Fittings

The use of standard fittings is out of the question for hydraulic or ammonia work as they will burst under the pressures to which they are subjected. It is advisable, therefore, for the experimenter to make special fittings of steel, of which a few examples are shown in the illustration.

Flange unions, consisting of a male and a female flange, are made in sets and are bolted together with 5/16-in. bolts. They are tongued and grooved as indicated, a little play being allowed to facilitate assembling. In the bottom of the groove is placed a thin lead washer that will squeeze and spread tight when the bolts are drawn up. These flanges are made of 1 by ⅝-in. flat steel, drilled and tapped as required.

Elbows are readily made from a cubical piece of 1-in. stock. The inside corner is beveled, and the outer one rounded, as

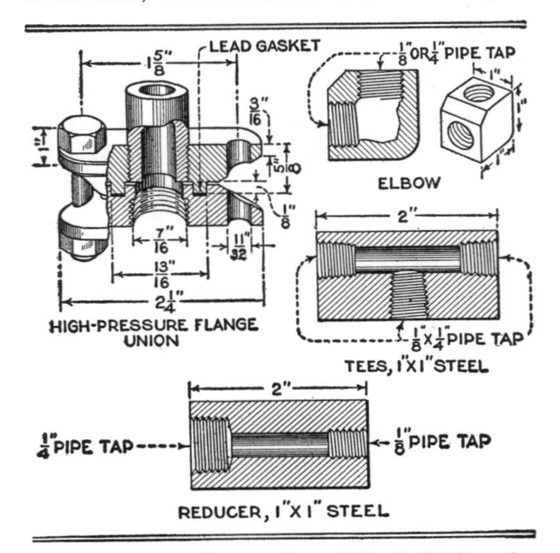

Details Showing Construction of Small Fittings for Hydraulic or Ammonia Work: Owing to the Pressures Involved, Standard Pipe Fittings cannot be Used

shown. Holes are then drilled at right angles to each other, and are tapped to the size required.

Tees are made of 1-in. square stock,

2 in. long, the through hole being drilled a little out of center, which will allow a longer thread in the short hole at right angles to it. These tees are very strong and at the same time appear neat.

Reducing sleeves are made of 1-in. round or square stock, drilled and tapped as shown. With the above four kinds of fittings, almost any pipe line for hydraulic or ammonia work can be built up.

Indicator for Bandsaw Table

When using a bandsaw on accurate work, it is very provoking to the operator to find, after he has finished his sawing and the damage has been done, that the "other fellow," who used the saw before him, left the saw table tilted a few degrees, the result being that the work is not cut at right angles to its surface. A table that is tilted so little will not attract the attention of the workman unless it is provided with some sort of indicator to show the angle of the table.

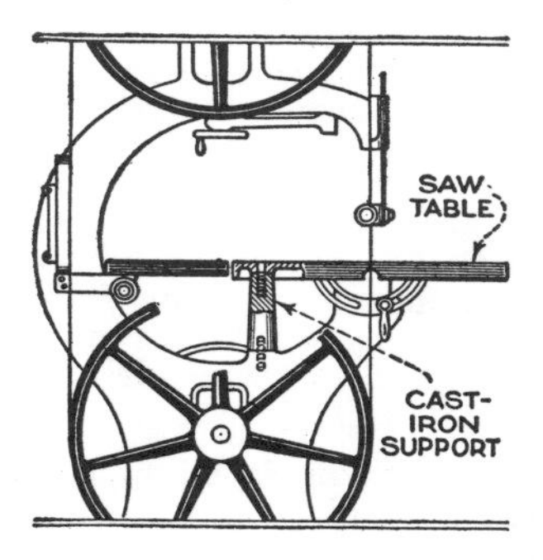

A simple indicator for this purpose, that never fails to keep the workman informed, is a ½-in. stud, fitted in the cast-iron table support and through the table, as shown in the illustration, so that its end is perfectly flush with the surface of the table when the latter is horizontal, but is below the surface when the table is tilted in the slightest degree.—M. E. Duggan, Kenosha, Wis.

Convenient Radiator-Repair Stand

The greatest loss of time in the repair of automobile radiators is not usually encountered in the application of the solder, but in moving the radiator and fastening it in the best position for work. For this purpose an adjustable stand, made of 2 by 4-in. and 1 by 3-in. lumber, is very handy. The frame that holds the radiator is pivoted to the uprights, and has two slotted braces, provided with clamp screws, so that the frame may be locked rigidly when set. The radiator is clamped to the frame by means of ordinary C-clamps, in any position desired, as the movable frame may be set at any angle from vertical to horizontal. If the base is provided with swivel casters, the convenience of the stand may be further increased.—G. A. Luers, Washington, District of Columbia.

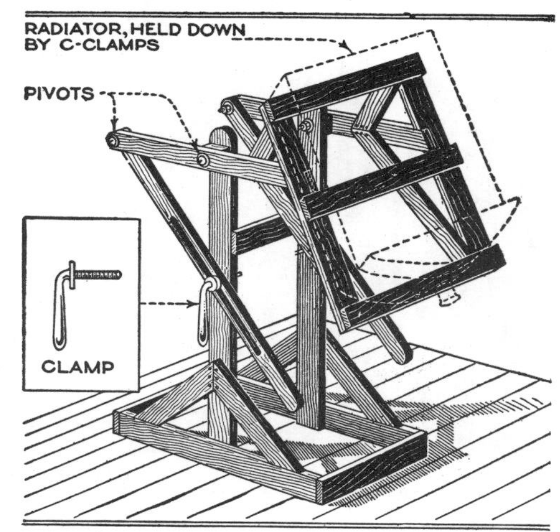

A Repair Stand Used in Soldering Radiators: It can be Adjusted to Any Angle That Is Most Convenient for the Workman

Attachment for Washing Machine

Cylindrical washing machines, in commercial or private laundries, are equipped with sheet-metal covers that must be loosened and raised each time a small quantity of water or washing compound is added, or when it is desired to look at the clothes. As the attendant is required to lift the heavy covers innumerable times during a day's work, the total energy wasted in this way is quite considerable.

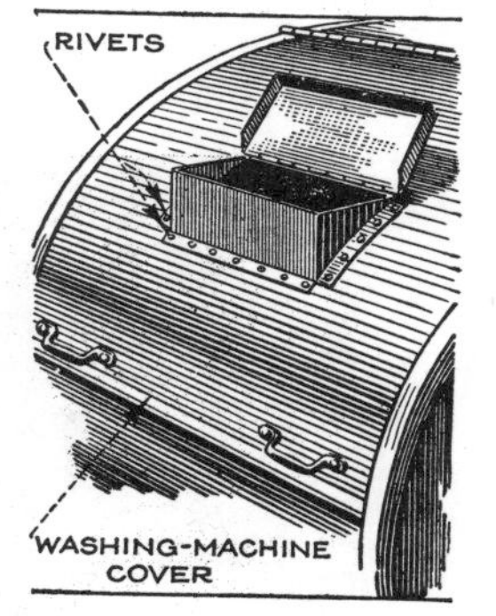

To eliminate this unnecessary labor, a large laundry fitted small "doors" on the covers of the machines, as shown in the illustration. A rectangular hole was cut in the center of the cover, and a hopper-shaped box, equipped with a lid, was riveted over the hole. This arrangement permits a full view of the interior by merely lifting the lid, and allows water and washing compound to be poured through the door.

Sling Support for Pouring Babbitt

When pouring babbitt with a ladle, much of the metal is splashed around before the workman succeeds in directing it squarely into the hole. This is usually due to the fact that the ladle handle is grasped at the extreme end as a precaution against burns. By supporting the ladle with a sling, it has been found possible to pour the babbitt without splashing, and to maintain a steady flow, with a consequent smooth finish in the work. The arrangement shown in the illustration makes a very satisfactory support.

A Sling Support for the Babbitt-Pouring Ladle Eliminates Much Waste Due to Splashing, and Also Helps the Workman to Maintain a Steady Flow

A rope is slung over a pulley, or staple, above the babbitting bench; one end is knotted, and a hook is attached to the other to support the ladle. If a hook is not available, one can easily be made from an ordinary 1½-in. washer, by cutting away part of it, making a cut through half the width, and bending the two ears thus formed around the knotted rope, as shown. A piece of spring wire is wound into a few small coils, of such a diameter that they will grip the doubled rope securely, to keep it from sliding, and the spring is placed on the rope. When the ends of the spring wire are pressed, the grip is released, allowing the rope to be adjusted for height. If the rope is fixed near the center of the table, any position can be reached by swinging the rope around.

Kerosene Tank for the Grocery Truck

A gasoline tank, taken from an old or wrecked car, is just the thing for carrying kerosene on a grocery truck, as shown in the illustration. A petcock is soldered at one end, preferably at the right side, as the truck usually stops at the right side of the road, and this end of the tank is therefore low. By using such a tank, the necessity of carrying several small cans in the truck, with the possibility of spoiling the groceries by spilling kerosene on them, is eliminated. If desired, another tank can be fitted for carrying gasoline, or the one tank can be divided into two sections by means of a partition, and another petcock soldered onto the new section thus formed.

A Gasoline Tank from an Old Automobile Serves to Carry Kerosene on a Grocer's Truck, Thus Eliminating the Possibility of Spoiling Groceries

Remedies for Dusting Concrete Floors

Boiled linseed oil and a sodium-silicate (water-glass) solution are two simple remedies that can be used, at small expense and without much trouble and time, to prevent the dusting of concrete floors. The linseed oil is applied in one or two coats. It penetrates the concrete and tends to bind the loose particles together. It also prevents water or other fluids from being absorbed.

The sodium-silicate solution has been successfully used in many instances. The preparation consists of one part of 40° Baume sodium silicate mixed in 3 or 4 parts of water. The more porous the floor the less water is necessary. Before applying this mixture, the floor must be thoroughly cleaned with a scrubbing brush and clean water. As soon as the floor is dry, the solution is evenly applied over the surface with a whitewash brush. When dry, the floor is again washed with clean water and a mop, and after this, another application of sodium silicate is given as before. A third coat is given the floor in the same manner.

It is better, however, to prevent concrete floors from dusting by laying them correctly than to apply remedies later. A dusty concrete floor is caused by too lean a mixture in making it; by using too little water in the mixture; by troweling too much over the surface, or by permitting the surface to dry out too quickly.

For the best kind of floor, use a mixture consisting of 1 part cement, 2 parts sand, 4 parts pebbles or broken stone, and enough water to make a "quaky" mixture. After laying the floor, trowel the surface just enough to smooth it. If the water stands on top, do not use either sand or cement to dry it up, but allow it to evaporate. The floor should be allowed to dry for a week; no draft should be allowed to touch it, and the temperature should be kept as constant as possible.

A Swivel Picket Pin

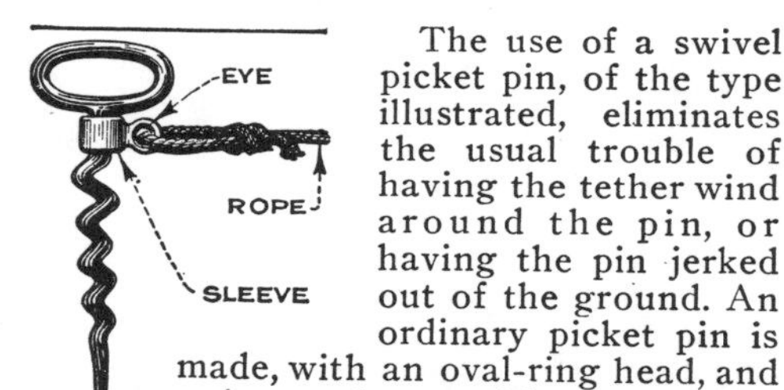

The use of a swivel picket pin, of the type illustrated, eliminates the usual trouble of having the tether wind around the pin, or having the pin jerked out of the ground. An ordinary picket pin is made, with an oval-ring head, and a loose sleeve with an eye for the rope welded to it, is placed around the pin just below the head; the body of the pin is then forged like an auger. This permits one to screw the pin into the ground without any difficulty, and makes the use of a hammer unnecessary.—C. M. Brown, Marion, Ia.

Shop Ventilators Driven from Line Shaft

An effective ventilation system is of vital importance in any shop, to provide healthful working conditions for the employes, which in the end means increase in production. Instead of purchasing and installing an electrically driven exhaust system, a similar system, just as dependable, can readily be made in the small shop, and run in connection with the line shaft at a very small cost. The only equipment necessary is the sheet-metal hooded ventilators on the roof, sheet-metal pipes leading down to the cast-iron housings in which the fans are located, and, of course, the fans themselves, which are made of heavy sheet steel, and the housings. The fan casings are cast in two parts, as shown. The fans are also made in sections, and bolted together to facilitate assembling on the shaft. There are

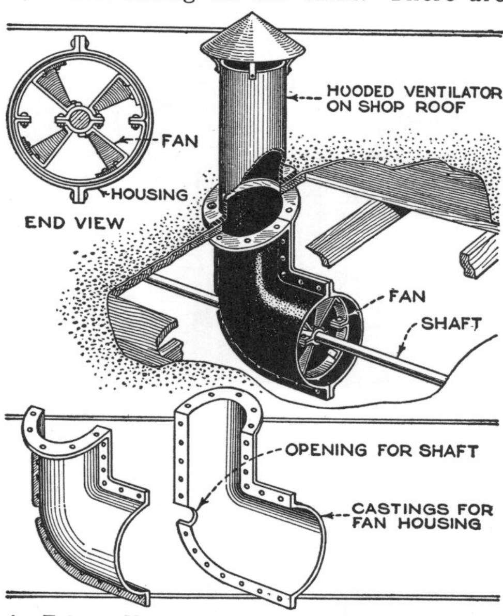

An Exhaust Ventilation System Driven by the Shaft: The Equipment Expense Is Small, and the Upkeep does Not Add to Shop Production Costs

no bearings or hangers required with this arrangement, and therefore, no particular care or attention is needed. As the system is operated on the shafting, the upkeep does not add to production costs.

Emergency Connection on Battery Terminals

When one of the soldered connectors on a storage battery breaks at the shoulder of the terminal, an emergency repair can easily be made. The insulation of the wire is cut off for a distance of about 2 in. behind the broken terminal, as indicated. The twisted wire is then separated into two strands and forced over the battery terminal, after which the nut is tightened solidly as before. While such a connection is not as secure mechanically as it should be, it will serve satisfactorily until a permanent repair can be made.

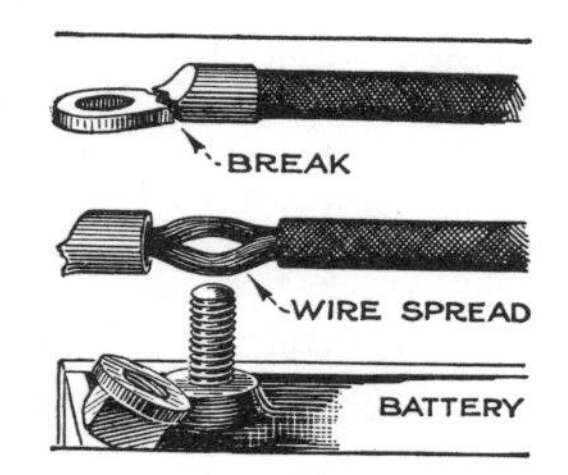

Substitute for Drawers in Small-Parts Cabinet

Anyone who has ever attempted to make a small-parts cabinet, knows how

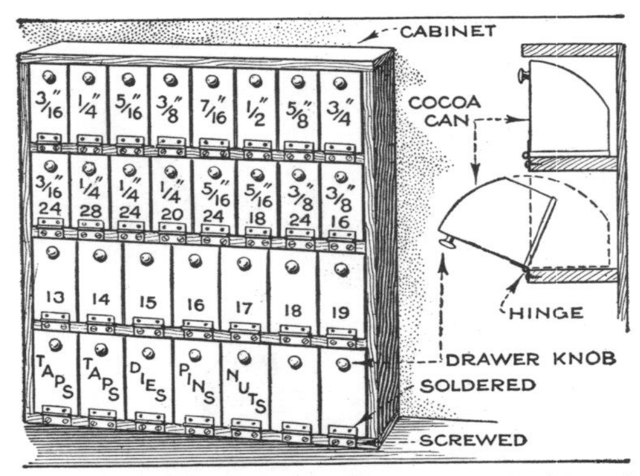

A Small-Parts Cabinet Made from ¼ and ½-Pound Cocoa Cans: It Holds Considerable Material and Looks Neat

tedious is the job of making the drawers. In order to eliminate the drawer problem, one mechanic has fitted up his small-parts cabinet with tin-can bins, which are, in a way, better than drawers.

The frame of the cabinet is made of wood, and is fitted with four shelves. Common cocoa cans, of ¼ and ½-lb. sizes, are cut as indicated, and small brass hinges are soldered to the lower front edges of the cans, and screwed to the shelves. Small knobs are fastened to the tops of the cans. A space of ¼ in. is left between the cans, so that, when pulled out, they will not rub against each other.

The feature of such a cabinet is the fact that one can get an article out of the cans much more quickly and easily than by digging into drawers with the fingers. While containing a large quantity of material, the cans take up very little space, as the slides that are necessary with drawers are eliminated. The cabinet as a whole presents a neat appearance, if arranged symmetrically and constructed correctly. The cans may be labeled in any manner desired.

Rounding Off Square Corners on Cement Work

If no beading tool is at hand, a bead may be put on cement work with the hollow half of an ordinary curling iron, which may be purchased at any 5 and 10-cent store. The two halves of the curling iron are separated, and the slight shoulder on the hollow half, through which the rivet passes, is snipped or ground off, or the iron may be bent at this point, to prevent the shoulder from scraping the cement. — Stanley Barnett, Iron Mountain, Mich.

Threading with Unused Portion of Lathe Lead Screw

Many small engine lathes are equipped with a lead screw as the only means of moving the carriage, which means that the screw is constantly used for all work and not for threading only, as would be the case with a lathe provided with a feed shaft as well as a screw. Consequently the lead screw will soon wear and become unfit for really accurate threading. Most of the wear will come upon that portion adjacent to the headstock, since the majority of the work done is on short pieces. The portion of the lead screw at the tailstock end of the bed, therefore, will usually be found to be in good condition, and when an accurately threaded piece of work, relatively short in length, is needed, it is well to make use of this part of the screw.

One method of doing this is shown in the illustration; an extension arbor is threaded on one end, and an auxiliary faceplate screwed on. This end is taper-bored for a 60° lathe center, or an accu-

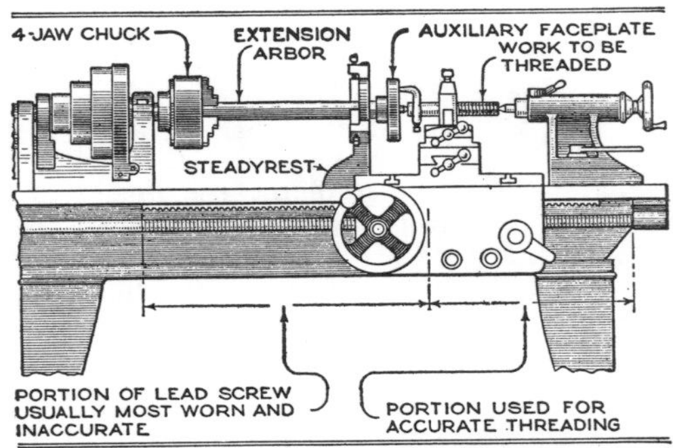

To Cut Accurate Screws on a Lathe That Has No Feed Shaft, and on Which the Headscrew is Worn, an Auxiliary Arbor and a Faceplate are Used

rate universal chuck is screwed on in place of the faceplate. Just behind the faceplate or chuck, the end of the arbor is supported in the lathe steadyrest and the other end either in a four-jaw independent chuck, or provided with a dog with means for holding it firmly against the driving plate. In this way the headstock spindle is extended and the work threaded in the usual way, but the carriage with the threading tool will be fed along near the tailstock end of the bed, and the work will be more accurate.

Poppet-Valve Turning Fixture

While there are many types of valve-facing fixtures obtainable, the device illustrated can be built from scrap parts at practically no expense. There is only one adjustment on this fixture and that is the combined feed screw and tail center, the position of which may be varied to fit valves of different sizes.

The base is made from a simple casting, or a slab of 3/8-in. iron or steel plate can be used. In the case of a casting, the base and bearing lugs are cast integral with it, but if a built-up base is decided on, they will be made from steel and riveted in place. These bearings are drilled and tapped for 1/4-in. capscrews, the vees accurately cut, and fitted with latch-type clamp plates, as shown in the detail, for the caps of the bearings, and to make them adjustable for any size of valve within the capacity of the fixture. The latch plates have one plain hole, and the other is slotted out so that it is not necessary to remove the caps each time a valve is inserted or removed. The tailstock, carrying the feed screw, is made, as shown at the lower left, so that it may be alined with the center hole in the head of the valve after the latter has been tightened in its bearings. Feed against the cutting tool is effected by turning the screw, which forces the face of the valve against the edge of the tool. The tailstock is held square by the squaring plate fastened to the front side of the bracket. A stud and wingnut are used to clamp the tailstock to the bracket.

The cutters are clamped to an alining plate as illustrated; this plate is either built up or machined from a solid piece of steel, and is fastened to the base, with small flat-head screws, at an angle of 30° to the valve stem. The cutters are made from 3/16-in. tool steel, hardened and ground to the shapes shown. A dog for turning the valve is made of steel, and provided with a setscrew; the handle proper is made from 5/16-in. drill rod, bent and provided with a loose pipe handle. —J. V. Romig, Allentown, Pa.

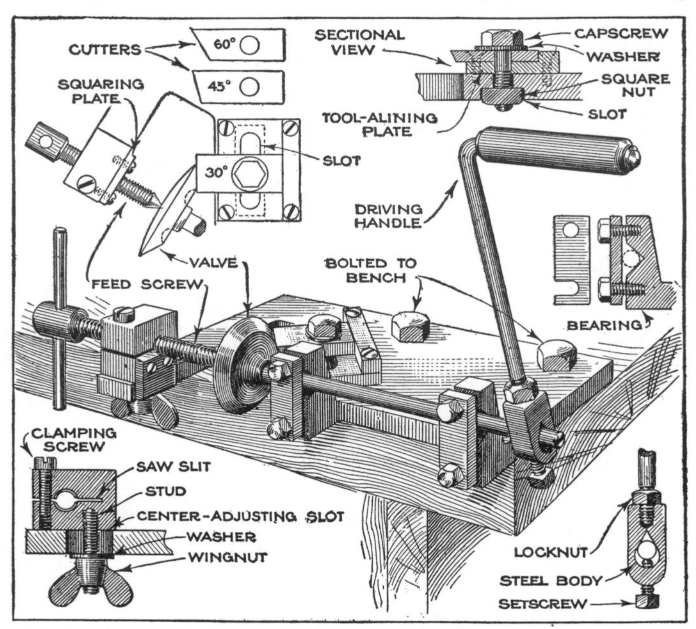

Refacing Automobile and Other Internal-Combustion Engine Poppet Valves on an Adjustable Fixture That can be Assembled from Easily Obtained Materials: It can be Bolted to the Edge of a Bench

Welding Automobile Springs

Automobile springs present special difficulties to the acetylene welder because of the unusually severe strains set up by the unequal expansion and contraction of the metal. Hairline cracks frequently appear radiating from the finished weld.

A good method of welding springs is as follows: Bevel both pieces at the joint in the usual manner, and after clamping in position, play the torch flame along the center of the spring for a distance of about 3 in. on both sides of the joint, until the metal is heated to redness. This insures even expansion throughout the width of the spring. Starting from the center of the groove, proceed partly to fill it in both directions to the edges, afterward filling completely in the same manner. If the weld is carried straight across from edge to edge, the edge first welded will cool sufficiently to warp the spring. Automobile springs should not be welded except in cases of emergency, as the repaired spring is never as strong as before, nor is it usually so well hardened and tempered.

Cover for Fire-Hose Rack

The appearance of a fire-hose rack in office buildings and schools can be made much more presentable by providing it with a heavy tin or light galvanized-iron cover of the type shown in the illustration. The cover is open at the bottom and one end, and is slipped over the hose in the manner indicated. As it fits loosely, it can be quickly removed whenever necessary.

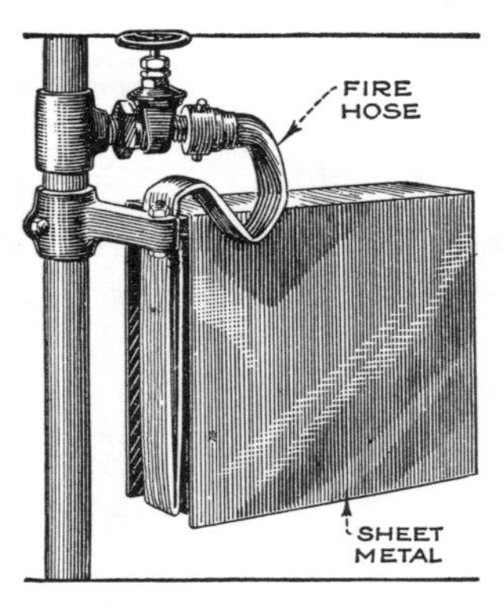

Homemade Wooden Pulleys

There are times when a wooden pulley is needed in a hurry for temporary or permanent use. Much time and labor can be spent on the making of these pulleys, or they can be easily and quickly made, depending on just how the maker goes about the job. Turning the circumference and boring the hole is a waste of time. A small pulley can be cut and shaped on the bandsaw in less time than is required to set up the job on a lathe, and a pulley cut on the bandsaw in the way described in this article will answer the purpose just as well as one turned.

In the making of a wood pulley it is common practice first to turn it and drill the hole, or to saw the pulley on the bandsaw and then to drill the holes for the clamping screws. When doing this, considerable trouble is experienced, both in holding the halves together while drilling the holes, and in drilling them.

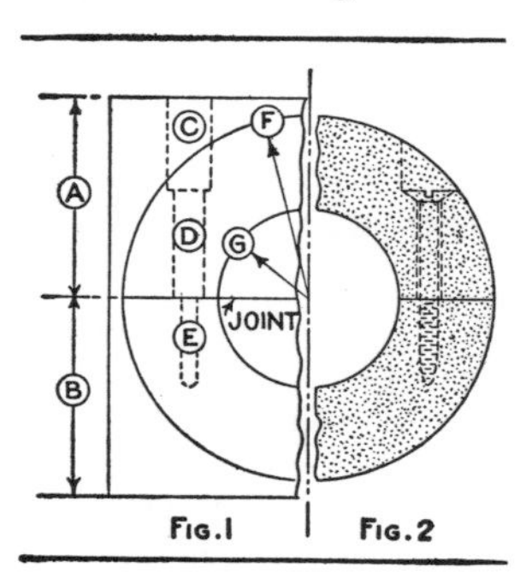

The method here described is an improvement over the old one. Two pieces of wood, A and B, of the exact width of the pulley, but about 3/8 or 1/2 in. larger than the radius of the finished pulley, are temporarily fastened together with four spots of glue and held in a clamp until dry. The two circles F and G, which represent the circumference and the bore of the pulley, are drawn on the ends of the glued blocks with a pair of compasses. The holes E, for the clamping screws, are laid out and drilled before the pulley is cut. For narrow pulleys, only one of these screw holes is drilled on each side of the center. The holes are counterbored as shown at C and D in Fig. 1. The screws are next driven in until the heads come below the circumference of the outside circle F, and the pulley sawed, on this circle, on the bandsaw. The screws are then withdrawn and the two blocks pried apart so that the inner circle can be sawed out. The halves of the pulley are then ready for final assembly on the shaft, as shown in Fig. 2. In the case of a pulley made to fit a shaft of small diameter, the bore of the pulley may be shellacked or varnished and then sprinkled with emery.

Tightening Hoops on Wooden Tanks

The photographs show two useful tools for driving up, or tightening, the hoops on wooden tanks. The one on the left-hand side is made from an old sledge hammer, the sides of which are ground concave. It is used to hammer the hoops tight.

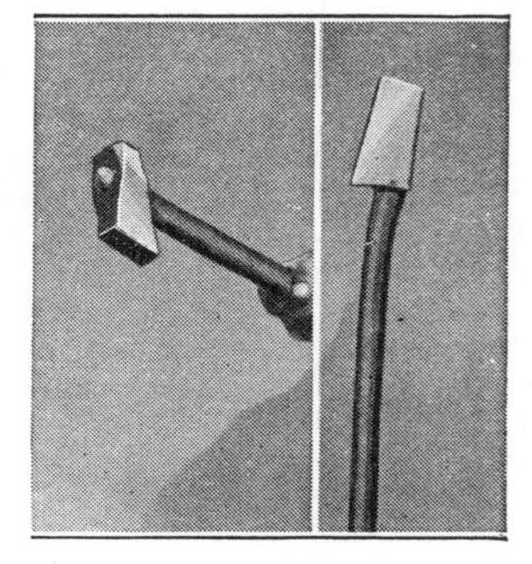

The second and larger tool is made from an old buggy axle. An iron head, of the shape shown, is welded on one end. This tool is used to pull or push the hoops down when they cannot be reached with the hammer.

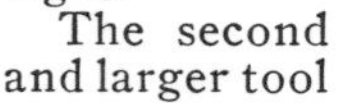

Locating Concealed Piping

After all traces of ditches where water piping has been laid have disappeared, and information concerning the exact location of the piping is not available, one faces a difficult problem when it is necessary to locate the whole length of piping in order to make a tap at a certain point.

As the beginning and ending of the piping is generally accessible, the course of the remainder can easily be determined by the simple method of passing an electric current through the piping and then traversing the area above the pipe system with a pair of telephone receivers connected to a coil of wire. The piping is located directly underneath the points where the loudest buzz is detected in the head phones.

A storage battery and an interrupter are connected in series across the ends of the piping, as shown in the diagram. A common buzzer or doorbell makes an excellent interrupter to be used with a 6-volt battery. The coil of wire that is connected to the headset is 1 or 2 ft. in diameter, and consists of 50 to 100 turns of ordinary bell wire.

The interrupted electric current flowing through the piping sets up an intermittent magnetic field around it. When the "exploring coil" intercepts the magnetic lines of force, an electric current is induced in the coil. As this induced electric current is intermittent, due to the intermittent nature of the magnetic field, the diaphragm of the receivers will vibrate, causing a buzz. This buzz will be loudest when the exploring coil is as near to the piping as possible and parallel to it. Receivers used in radio work are more

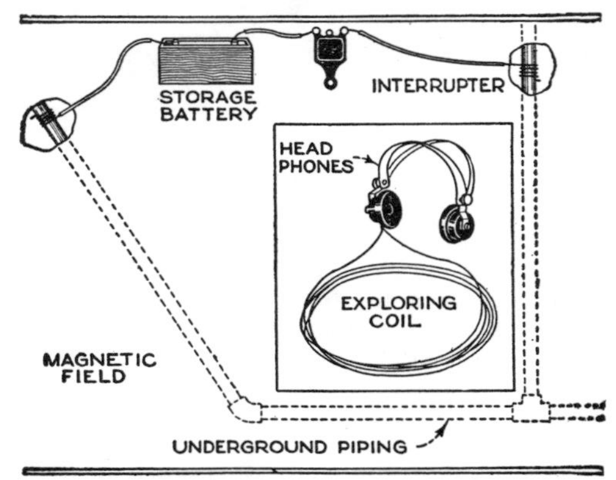

A Method of Determining the Location of Underground Water Piping, When All Traces, Except the Above-Ground Heads, have been Lost

sensitive than ordinary telephone receivers.—Philip G. Benholz, East Orange, N. J.

Ingredients for Concrete

Concrete cannot be expected to be any better than the materials used in preparing it. The cement, even in strong mixtures, is only a small part of the total bulk, and it will not make strong sand of clay and mud, nor tough rock of crumbling stone. For this reason a good grade of sand and gravel should always be used.

Corrugated Iron Used for Awning

The illustration shows a permanent awning erected above the doorway of a

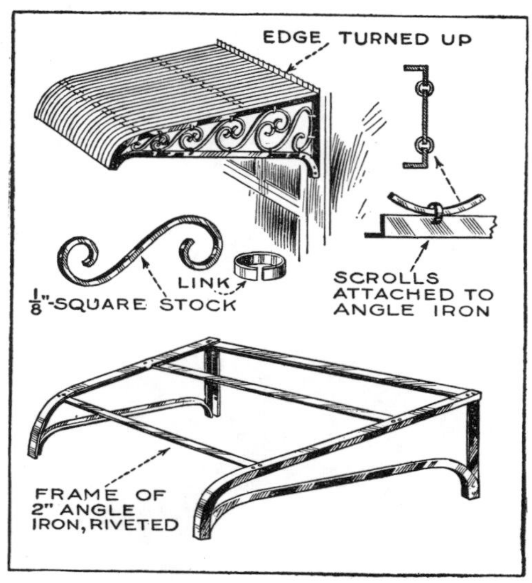

A Permanent Door and Window Awning That Requires Practically No Attention and Presents a Very Attractive Appearance

shop. It adds considerably to the attractiveness of the shop and has also the advantage of requiring practically no attention beyond an occasional coat of paint.

The framework consists of two brackets made of 2-in. angle iron, braced with flat crossbars. The corrugated-iron top is rolled at its edge to conform to the curvature of the supports and is attached to the crossbars with small bolts. Light bar stock, 1/8 in. square, is bent into scrolls as shown, and these are fastened to the angle-iron brackets, and to each other, by links made of the same material.

Mulching Young Fruit Trees

With the approach of spring many gardeners will be seeking some sort of mulching material for their berry bushes and young fruit trees. Sawdust will no doubt be used extensively, as it is easily obtainable. In applying it, however, great care must be taken not to spread it in layers more than 2 in. thick, as the sawdust heats the roots greatly when spread to a greater depth than this; it has been known to scald the roots to such an extent that the plants eventually died. Small chips, shavings, or wood pulp, when available, provide a much better mulching material than sawdust.

Drilling Holes in Glass

The photograph shows how large-diameter holes are drilled in glass windshields for the installation of spotlights that swivel in a fitting mounted in the glass of the windshield itself. The tool is merely a brass tube that has been

Method of Drilling Circular Holes in Windshields for Spotlights: It Requires Only Three Minutes to Cut a 3-Inch Hole in the Glass

notched on the cutting edge, as shown, and is used with an abrasive. The brass tube is mounted on a disk, fitted with a ½-in. shank, which is held in the chuck of a portable electric drill mounted on a drill stand. The operation of drilling the hole in the glass requires but three minutes. The abrasive used is No. 60 carborundum, made into a paste by the addition of water.

Cleaning Out Crankcase with Oil Gun

In many cars that have a force-feed oiling system, only a small quantity of oil in the crankcase is actually consumed, but the oil must, nevertheless, be renewed occasionally, as a very little gasoline in it makes it unsafe, and it becomes dirty and unfit for lubrication. During cold weather, considerable gasoline finds its way past the piston rings, owing to the fact that the choker is used freely. This means frequent crawling under the car to get at the drain plug, a job that is particularly unpleasant at that season.

In trying to find a more convenient method, a driver hit upon the scheme of pumping the oil out by means of a pump, and found this method entirely satisfactory. A short length of flexible tubing is clamped to the nozzle of an oil gun, and the other end is inserted through the oil-gauge hole. It is possible to reach the lowest part of the crankcase with the flexible spout. After the oil is all out, a couple of gunfuls of kerosene, squirted against the wire-gauze screen around the pump, will clear it of sediment.—J. G. Brown, Evanston, Ill.

A Homemade Wood Grainer

In order to do an artistic and natural job of wood graining, variety and irregularity of grain must be introduced. To do this, one must provide himself with a complete set of grainers of different sizes and designs, and this proves rather expensive where only an occasional job is done. However, excellent grainers, that I have found just as good as the purchased ones, can be made of material easily obtainable, as illustrated.

The block is a piece of quarter-round molding, of any desired size. Pieces of small, hard rope, preferably sash cord, are fastened to the curved surface of the block by means of brads, in the manner indicated. The heads of the brads are sunk into the rope so that there will be no danger of marring the surface of the work while graining. The rope will absorb some of the paint the first time the grainer is used, but after it is filled, it will be found to give better satisfaction than the rubber-faced grainers commonly used, as the rope wipes cleaner and leaves a more natural impression. A hole is drilled in the block and a handle is fitted into it. The length of the block is determined by the width of the boards to be grained.

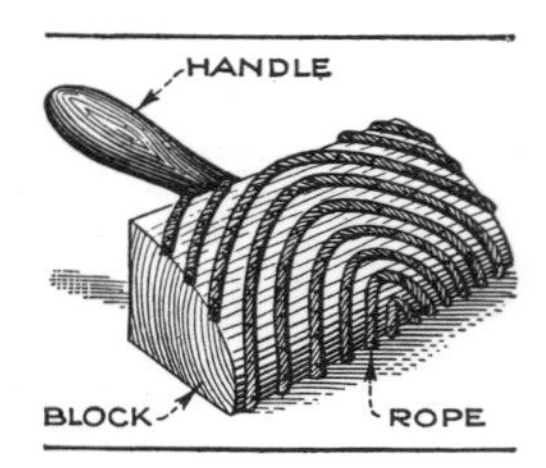

In use, after the ground color is applied, the grainer is drawn slowly along the board toward the operator, and at the same time gradually rocked over. Graining compounds, to imitate any wood, can be purchased in small quantities and at reasonable prices from any color house. —John L. Dougheny, Toledo, Ohio.

¶Setscrews can be tightened without the usual danger of twisting them off, if the heads are lightly tapped with a hammer while drawing them tight with the wrench.

A Homemade Electric Light for the Farmyard

By J. R. KOONTZ

FARM-LIGHTING plants are now universally used in the country, and, in many communities, the city lines are extended to serve the farmers for miles throughout the surrounding territory. In addition to the lights in the house and outbuildings, many farmers would like to install a few yard lights, were it not for the expense involved.

This was the case on our farm, until we determined to make the lights ourselves; one of the resulting lights is shown in the accompanying photograph, and, as each one costs only about $1.30 for material, we made three or four, where we would have been obliged to use only one, had it been purchased.

Yard Lights are Easily Made in Any Farm Workshop, and will Add Much to the Comfort and Convenience of Work around the Yard at Night

A 4-ft. piece of ½ by 1½-in. iron is bent at right angles, as shown in detail drawing, one end being 20 in. long, the other 28 in. Drill two holes in the 20-in. leg, to fit the ⅜-in. bolts used to fasten the bracket to the post. Two similar holes are also drilled in the other leg, one 2 in. from the end, for the bolt that holds the reflector, the other 18 in. from the end, for the braces.

A galvanized-iron sheet, 18 in. square, is cut in the form of a circle, and a V-shaped cut made in it, as shown, the cut being 6 in. wide at the edge, and carried to the center. The disk is then bent or rolled to a conical shape, and the edges, which should overlap about 1 in., riveted and soldered. A ⅜-in. hole is punched in the center. A block of cypress, or other wood that will not rot when exposed to weather, is shaped, as shown, to fit the reflector, and drilled for a ⅜-in. bolt, the head of which should be sunk into the wood; a nut locks the block in place, a leather washer being used between nut and reflector, to prevent water from soaking into it. The reflector is then bolted to the bracket with a nut and washer.

A 4-ft. length of ¼-in. round iron is cut in two, and two braces, with an eye formed on each end, made as indicated. These are bolted loosely to the bracket, as shown in the assembled view, and the places where the outer eyes rest on the reflector are marked. Holes to fit stove bolts are punched at the marked spots, and the porcelain knobs assembled, passing the stove bolts through the knobs, reflector, and braces, and using a leather washer between each knob and the reflector, and metal washers

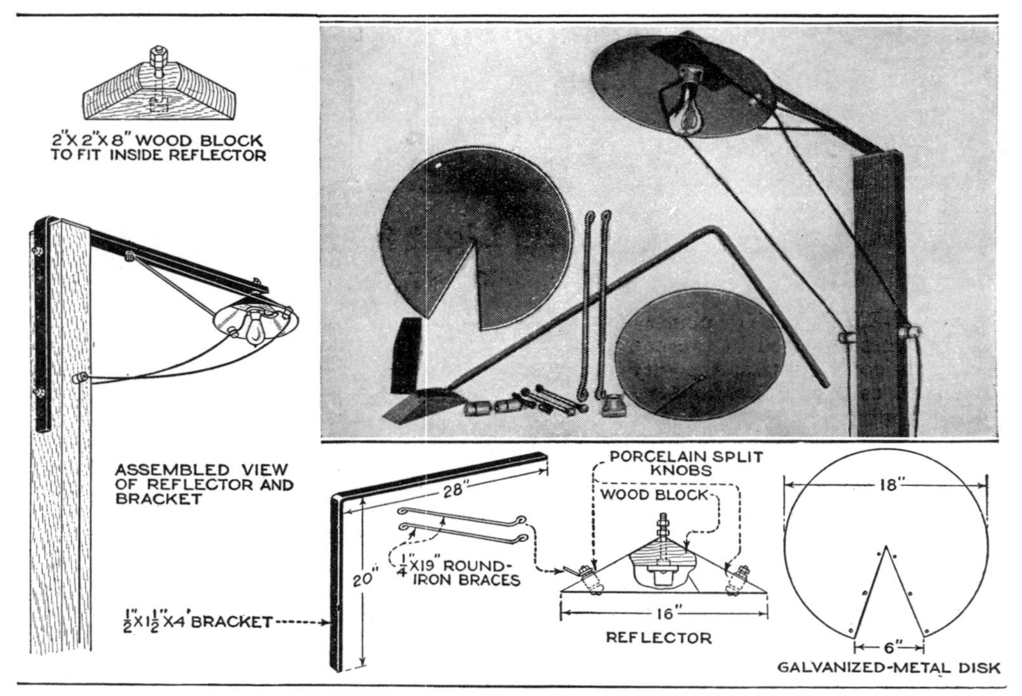

The Photos Show All the Material Necessary to Construct the Yard Light, Together with a Completed Fixture. The Drawings Show Details of the Various Parts Used, and the Method of Assembling Them. The Cost of the Purchased Material for the Fixture Shown Was Only $1.30

under the nuts. Do not draw the nuts tight until the wires are in place.

The lamp receptacle is now screwed in the center of the wooden block, the wires attached to it, and led through the slots in the knobs, and the knobs and braces are drawn up tight. A coat of good paint or enamel completes the job, except for bolting the bracket to the post, and leading the wiring, through knobs screwed to the post, to the switchboard.

The necessary materials for each light, with the prices paid for them, are:

4 ft. of ½ by 1½-in. flat iron	$ .40
1 piece of 18 by 18-in. galvanized-iron sheet	.35
4 ⅜-in. bolts	.10
4 ft. of ¼-in. round iron	.10
1 porcelain receptacle	.15
4 split-knob insulators	.10
2 stove bolts and 2 wood screws	.10
Total	$1.30

These prices will vary a little in different localities, but not much. They do not, of course, include the pole, but this may usually be picked up around the farm, or the lights may be bolted to the buildings, if found more convenient, and the poles thus eliminated.

Cleaning Greasy Clutches

One of our heavy derricks, which was of the cone-clutch type, with wooden friction blocks, caused considerable trouble by the friction blocks not taking hold when the levers were operated, due to oil that had saturated the surface of the blocks. This trouble made frequent renewals of the blocks necessary.

It happened, one day, that a lighted match was carelessly thrown into the machine, with the result that the oil quickly ignited. To extinguish the flame, the operator used the fire extinguisher, which was filled with a solution of carbon tetrachloride. In doing this, the solution was also squirted over the friction blocks. When the machine was again used, the friction blocks took hold as if new, the solution having dissolved the oil on their faces. A large can of the solution was then obtained, and used to clean the friction blocks whenever necessary.

The solution has also given good results in cleaning greasy automobile clutches and oily brake bands. It is much better than gasoline or kerosene, and is, of course, safer than these, because it is not inflammable. It will not injure wood, leather, or fabric. Although the cost of carbon tetrachloride is greater than that of gasoline and kerosene, its superior cleansing qualities make up for this difference. It evaporates rapidly, and therefore should be kept in a closed can.

Care should be taken not to get the solution on the skin, as it is very irritating, nor in the eyes, which it will cause to smart.—A. S. Jamieson, Springfield, Massachusetts.

Fixture for Relining Brake Bands

The fixture illustrated has been found to facilitate greatly the relining of brake bands. It consists of a steel riveting block to which a lever bracket is screwed or welded, as shown. In this bracket, the lever, the construction of which is clearly shown, pivots. A strong coil spring, held in place by two studs, presses the forked end of the lever tightly on the face of the riveting block, so that when the brake band is inserted between the two, it is held securely. The rivet is pushed through the hole in the band, which is then placed between the riveting block and lever, the rivet being under the opening in the jaw. The pressure of the lever forces the rivet through the lining; the ends can be bent over in the usual way by means of the ball end of a light hammer.

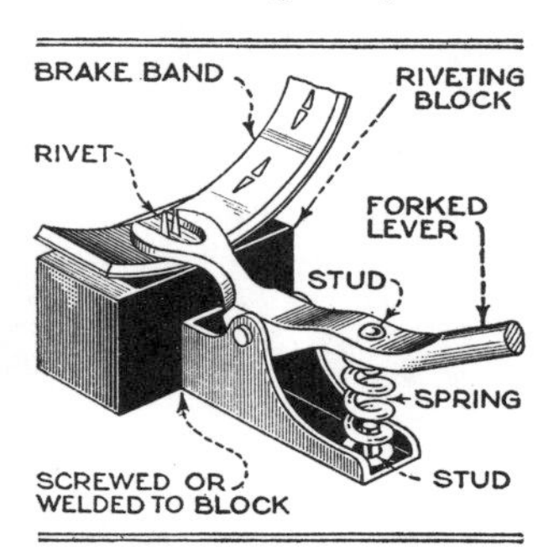

Finger Protector for Files

When squaring holes and slots with a square file, the fingers are likely to be pinched between the file and the work, on the backward stroke. This particular cause of minor shop injuries can easily be eliminated by using a finger protector on the file. Some use a piece of leather for this purpose, but this is not satisfactory on a lengthy job, as it soon works loose, and, if pushed on tightly, cannot be removed as quickly as it might be. The spring-steel clip shown has two holes in line, one fitting the file neatly and the other a little larger. On the same side as the larger hole, the spring is doubled over, and the end ground concave, so as to bear on the file corners. This concave end holds the clip in place on the file. To put on or remove it, the ends of the clip are squeezed together slightly so that the concave end clears the file corners and allows the clip to slide easily.

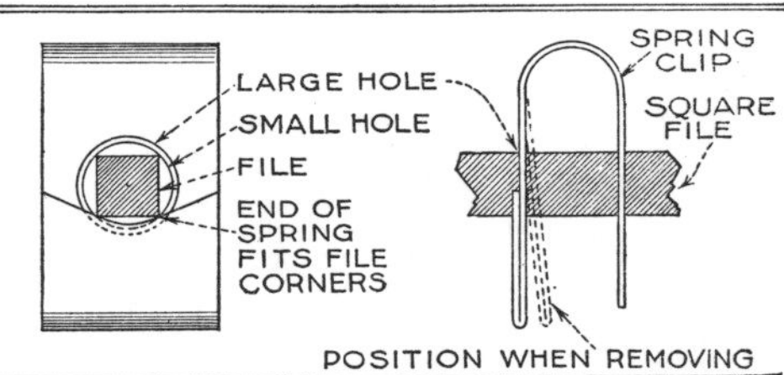

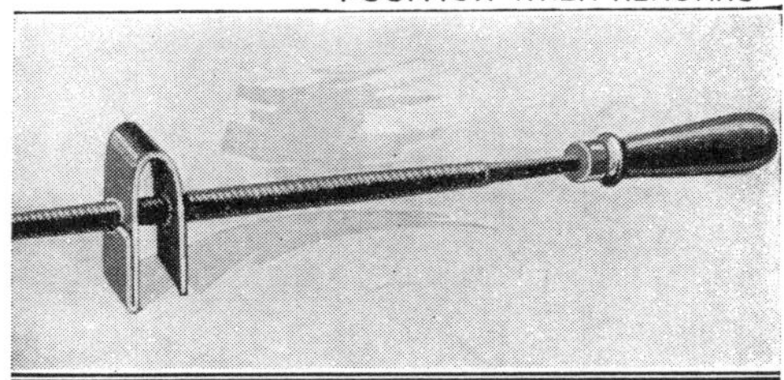

Above: Details of Spring Clip That Prevents the Workman's Fingers from being Pinched between Work and File. Below: Clip in Place on File

Holder for Reference Drawings

A draftsman can keep his reference drawing before him and work with ease if he uses the wire holders shown in the illustration, instead of keeping the reference drawing on his board, where it is in the way. The holders are made of No. 4 galvanized-iron wire, bent to the shape indicated, so that they will clamp over the edge of the drawing board. They can be set in various positions to suit any size of drawing. The edges of the drawing or print are folded around the holders and attached to them by means of spring paper clips, four usually being required.

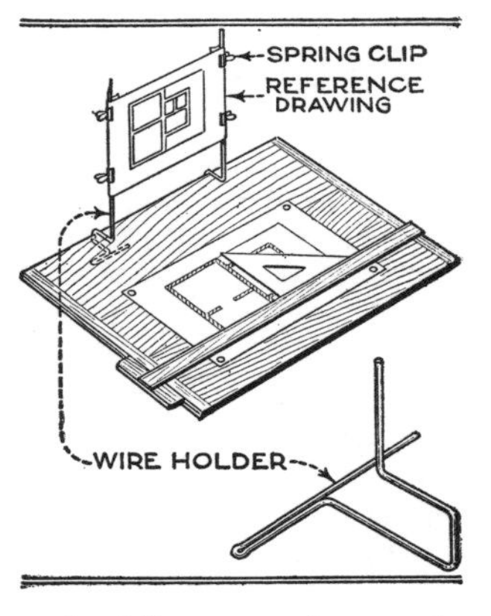

Wire-Cutting Fixture

In a machine shop where a certain job called for the production of a great number of pins of various sizes, ranging from ¼ in. to 3 in. in length, and from ⅟₁₆ in.

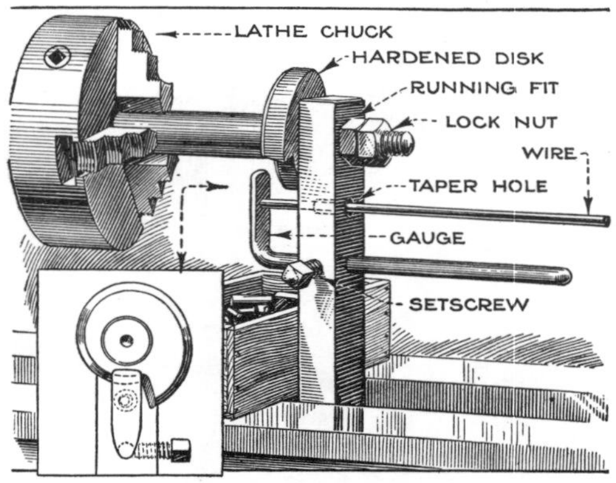

An Easily Made Wire-Cutting Fixture Arranged on a Lathe: It will Cut Various Sizes of Pins Accurately to Any Length

to 3/16 in. in thickness, an adjustable wire-cutting fixture was arranged on the lathe as indicated. With this fixture it was found possible to cut the pins accurately to any desired length, and at a rate of approximately 100 to 150 per minute.

The body or post of the fixture consists of a hardened and ground 7-in. length of 1-in. square steel, fastened to the lathe bed. Three holes are drilled through the post, as shown; the upper one, which supports the arbor, is reamed to a running fit; the tapered hole below it is for the insertion of the wire, and the lowest hole for holding the gauge. A setscrew is provided to hold the gauge tightly in any position. The arbor is made of mild steel, ¾ in. in diameter and 8 in. long, turned down near one end to 9/16 in. in diameter, wide enough for the cutter; then turned to a ½-in. diameter for a distance equal to the thickness of the fixture body and the width of two lock nuts. The 9/16-in. portion, and the outer end of the ½-in. part, are threaded. The cutter is a hardened-steel disk, shaped as shown, with a 9/16-in. tapped hole in the center. The arbor is held in the lathe chuck, and the fixture assembled as shown. The lathe is run as fast as the wire can be fed by hand, between each "stroke" of the cutter.—H. Mayer, London, Eng.

¶For all diameters the transverse pressure on a boiler is double the longitudinal pressure.

A Novel Valve-Grinding Tool

When grinding the valves of an automobile engine, the heads are given a partial revolution in their seats, grinding both valve and seat at the same operation, the usual means of imparting this motion being a screwdriver or a suitable bit held in a brace.

The drawing shows a tool that can be quite easily made, with which the valves may be ground rapidly by a continuous turning motion in one direction only, the tool itself reversing the motion. The frame is made of flat bar steel, with suitable brackets for supporting the vertical spindle and wooden disk, as illustrated. Two cork pulleys are attached to the spindle, and these bear against cork pads attached to the wooden disk. The length of the center bracket should be such that the cork pulleys and pads are compressed slightly when coming into contact with each other.

It will be seen that the number of cork pads on the handwheel is uneven, with no two of them directly opposite each other, and it is by this means that the spindle is

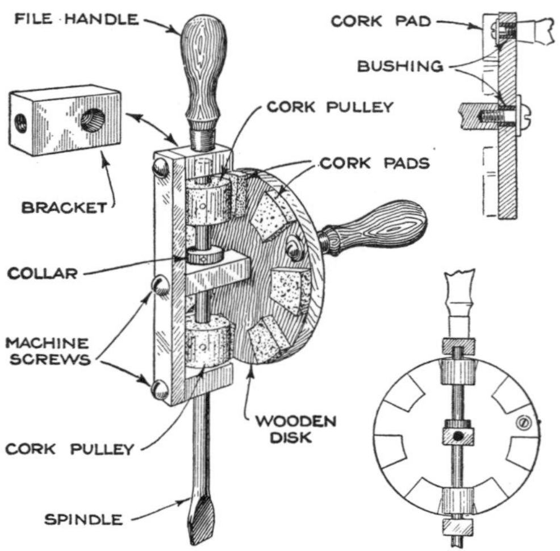

A Valve-Grinding Tool for Internal-Combustion Engines That Imparts the Proper Back-and-Forth Rotation to the Valves While Turning the Handwheel in But One Direction

rotated back and forth while turning the handle in but one direction. The number of pads is immaterial; they may be 3, 5, 7, or more, according to the distance it is desired to rotate the valves, and, of course, the larger and fewer the pads the greater the amount of rotation. Consequently, having an odd number of pads, and no two directly opposite, but one pad can come into contact with any one of the pulleys at a time, and as these contacts alternate between the upper and lower pulleys, the direction of rotation of the spindle is correspondingly reversed.—R. H. Kasper, Philadelphia, Pa.

Simple Attachment for Testing Cylinders

In a shop where large numbers of oxygen cylinders, and similar pressure vessels, were tested daily, a hydraulic test pump was used to pump up the 5,000-lb. pressure required in each cylinder. Due to leakage at the valves and connections, it was found difficult, when the pressure in a cylinder began to drop, to determine whether the cylinder was defective, or the valves and fittings leaking.

After considerable experimenting, the simple method of testing illustrated in the drawing was adopted. A special cylinder cap, made of solid steel, was fitted with an accurately fitting screw, and a pressure gauge. A stuffing box and gland packed the screw, and a packing ring closed the joint between cap and cylinder.

The cylinder is filled with water, and the cap screwed on, the water that occupied the neck filling the hole in the cap. The screw is then screwed down until the required pressure shows on the gauge, and the cylinder allowed to remain under

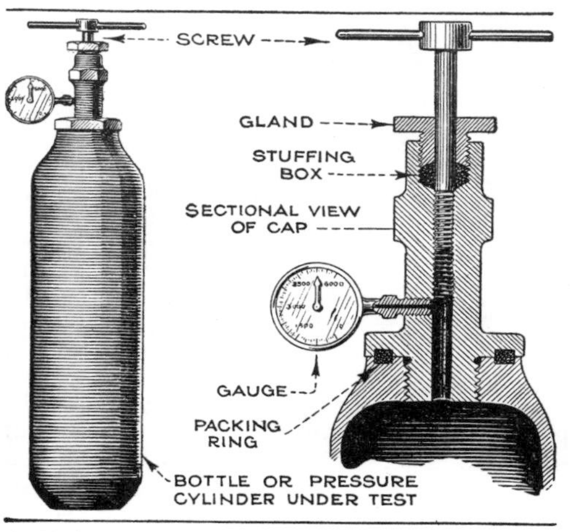

A Simple and Effective Method of Testing Pressure Vessels: Any Leakage That Takes Place While Testing can be Detected Immediately and Stopped

this pressure for five minutes. If no drop in pressure takes place in this time, the cylinder passes inspection. Any slight leakage that may take place through the stuffing box is noticeable at once, and is stopped by screwing down the gland.

Handy Glaziers' Pliers

Glaziers, and other workers in glass, will find the tool illustrated of great assistance in making clean cuts; it is par-

Attachment Welded to Pliers Enables Glazier to Break Off Narrow Strips of Glass with Little Danger of Leaving Rough Edges

ticularly useful when a narrow strip of glass is to be broken from a sheet.

The tool consists of a pair of pliers, to the jaws of which strips of flat iron, about 3 in. long, are welded or brazed. These strips must, of course, seat on each other accurately, so that when applied to the glass an even pressure is brought to bear at all points. The increased area covered by the strips eliminates the usual "nicking" of the narrow strip in small pieces, which leaves the work very ragged.

Testing Hair Springs for Magnetism

A very delicate tester for magnetized hair springs, where even the smallest compass at hand is not deflected, is made by pulling a single fiber out of a silk thread, fastening one end to a short piece of soft-iron binding wire, and the other end to the cork of a small vial or bottle, so that, when the cork is in place on the bottle, the wire will be suspended horizontally near its bottom. The thread may be fastened to the cork and wire by means of a drop of shellac. A very slight magnetic influence will be sufficient to influence the light piece of iron wire, whereas it might have absolutely no visible effect on a small compass needle.—Andrew C. Cole, Chicago, Ill.

Making a Four-Inch Bench Slotter

By J. V. ROMIG

THE bench slotter described in this article will prove a useful addition to the equipment of the small workshop or mechanical laboratory. It is designed to be made with as little labor and expense as possible, so as to bring it within the reach of those who possess only a lathe and the usual hand tools, and who do not wish to have much of the work, if any, done outside their own shop.

The two straight movements of the slotter table, together with the circular one, permit the production of shapes that cannot easily be machined on the shaper or planer, as, for example, circular arcs and parts, in combination with straight portions. Narrow grooves and keyseats in wheels and levers are also easily cut, with the work lying on the table, while, on the shaper or planer, work of this character would require angle brackets and projecting tools. In addition to these advantages, the layout lines on the work are always in plain view, and working closely to them is rendered much easier than on planer or shaper. The only castings necessary are the bed, frame, table, and cone pulley; the rocker arm, link, and connecting rod may also be made in cast iron, if desired, or built up from cold-rolled steel, or forged.

Perspective View of the Finished Slotter: This will Prove a Valuable Machine in the Small Shop, and One Well Worth the Time Spent in Its Construction

The pattern making involved is simple, and should present no difficulties to those accustomed to the use of woodworking tools. Care should be taken to allow enough stock for shrinkage and machining, and to provide plenty of draft and good fillets in all corners. If in doubt how the pattern should be made, consult the foundry where the pieces are to be cast; many valuable hints can be picked up there, and the advice given may make a big difference in the cost of the parts.

The bed is made of box section, and is shaped or planed true and smooth on its upper face; a rough cut should be taken over the bottom flange also, so that the machine will bed firmly and truly on the top of the bench.

The frame casting, a perspective view of which is shown in Fig. 6, is planed or shaped true on the bottom, and the ram slots shaped out close to size and square with the bed, on all surfaces. The frame is fastened to the bed with 3/8-in. capscrews.

The ram is made from a 13½-in. length of 1¼-in. cold-rolled steel, carefully straightened and squared, and trued to a surface plate or good straightedge, by scraping. The ram slots are scraped to a good sliding fit on the ram, and the 3/8 by 2½-in. cold-rolled steel plates, that hold the ram in place, fitted and scraped also. The ram is drilled from one end with a 5/8-in. drill to a depth of 13⅛ in., and a 15/32-in. hole is drilled to meet this hole from the other end. From the end of the latter hole, a ¾-in. slot, 2 in. long, is cut through the ram, and the clamp pin, made as shown in the detail in Fig. 4, fitted in place. The slot in the pin is made 5/8 in. long by 9/16 in. wide, so as to allow plenty of clearance for the tool-clamp rod.

This rod is turned down from a 15-in.

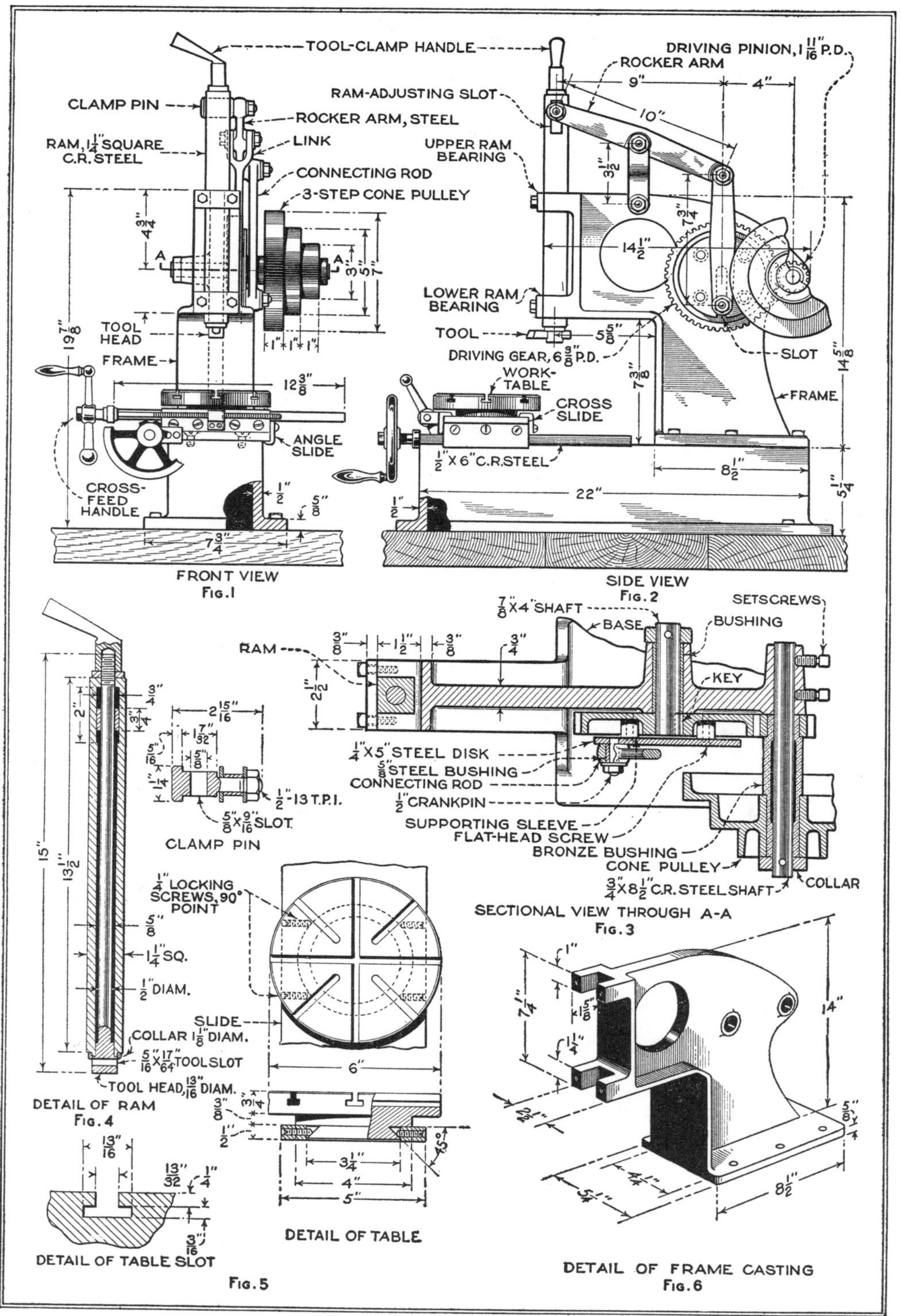

Figure 1, Front Elevation of Completed Machine; Figure 2, Side Elevation; Figure 3, Sectional View, Showing Details of Driving Mechanism; Figure 4, Section of Ram, Detail of Clamp Pin and Tool Head; Figure 5, Plan and Part Section of the Table and Dimensions of Slot; and Figure 6, Perspective View of Frame Casting

length of 7/8-in. cold-rolled steel, or may be built up by threading a 1/2-in. rod into a short length of 7/8-in. stock. One end is turned down to 13/16 in., and slotted for the 1/4-in. tool bits used; a short length is turned down to an easy fit in the 5/8-in. hole in the ram, and the remainder is 1/2 in. in diameter, threaded at the upper end for the tool-clamp handle, which can usually be picked up at a junk store, or made from cold-rolled stock. A 1/8-in. collar, serrated on its lower face, and hardened, is used on the tool head between tool and ram.

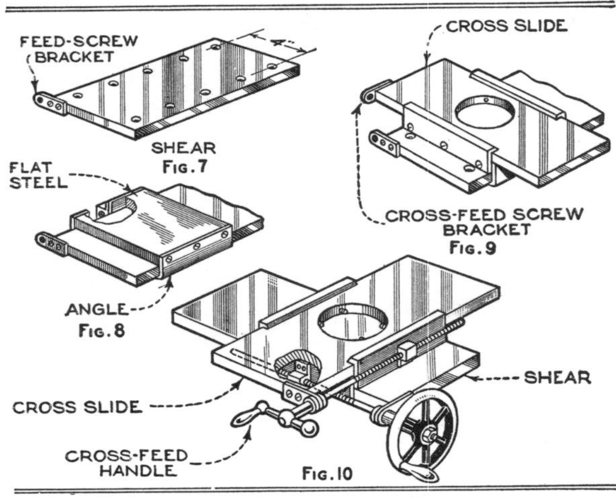

Figure 7, Shear, Which is Fastened to Bed; Figure 8, How Slide is Attached to Shear; Figure 9, Cross-Slide Fastenings; and Figure 10, Complete Slide Assembly

The driving mechanism is quite simple to construct, and consists of a pair of gears, about 1-to-3 1/4 ratio, a three-step cone pulley, connecting rod, rocker arm, and link. The cast-iron cone pulley, after being turned to size, is bored to a driving fit on a bronze bushing, which also carries the 1 11/16-in. pitch diameter driving pinion. The whole assembly runs on a 3/4-in. shaft, 8 1/2 in. long, fastened in a boss on the frame by two 3/8-in. setscrews. A pinned collar holds the assembly on the shaft. The bushing is counterbored to act as an oil reservoir, and an oil hole should be drilled in it, tapped, and fitted with a screw, to permit easy lubrication.

The large gear, which is 6 3/8 in. in pitch diameter, is keyed to a 7/8-in. shaft, 4 in. long, which runs in a bronze bushing pressed into the boss in the frame, a pinned collar being used on the other end of the shaft. A 5-in. disk, made of 1/4-in. plate, is fastened to the gear by flat-head screws, the disk being held out from the gear by four sleeves, fitting over the screws. A slot is cut into the disk, from the edge, past the center, for the 1/2-in. crankpin. The crankpin can be moved to any position in the slot, to adjust the stroke of the ram, and clamped by tightening the steel bushing on which the connecting rod runs. A careful study of Fig. 3 will make all these details clear.

The connecting rod, as explained before, may be a casting, forging, or built up from cold-rolled steel, as may also the link and rocker arm; all should be fitted with bronze bushings, and provision made for oiling. The pins, including the crankpin, should be made of hardened tool steel, and are 1/2 in. in diameter.

Plenty of clearance, to allow the rocker arm to swing, should be allowed in the yoke of the link.

The method of building up the table slides is very clearly shown in Figs. 7 to 10. The shear, shown in Fig. 7, is a piece of 1/2 by 6-in. cold-rolled steel, fastened to the bed by 1/4-in. flat-head screws, spaced about 1/2 in. apart. The shear must be scraped flat and true, and fitted with a flat steel bracket for the feed screw.

The slide is fastened to the shear, as shown in Fig. 8, by means of angles made of 3/16-in. thick sections of angle iron, carefully machined and screwed to the slide. The cross slide is fitted in a similar manner, as in Fig. 9, and is bored out in the center to fit the lower boss of the table, and drilled and tapped for four 1/4-in. headless locking screws, as shown in Fig. 5. All plates are 1/2 in. thick, and the slide is fitted with two bronze nuts, to fit the 3/8-in. feed screws, as shown in the various drawings. The screws may be fitted with built-up handles, as shown on the cross-feed screw, or with handwheels made from old valve wheels.

The table slots should be cored in the casting, to the dimensions shown, to avoid a subsequent milling operation, and the table machined as indicated in Fig. 5. The four screws that engage its tapered lower face exert a downward pressure, holding the table firmly.

When it is desired to rotate the table for circular work, the clamp screws are loosened slightly, and the table turned by means of a bar inserted in one of the slots. By using a 12-in. bar, a very sensitive feed may be obtained. For taper cuts, the work is lined up with shims of the proper thickness.

Standard ¼-in. tool-steel bits are used for most work; for small internal slotting, ¼-in. tool steel, bent and forged to the proper shape, may be used.

A cone pulley, of the same size as that on the machine, is keyed on the countershaft, and a ¾-in. belt used.

Engine Exhaust Heats Oil

To thin the oil in the cylinder oil cup of a gasoline engine during cold weather, arrange the exhaust pipe so that it directs the hot gas against the oil cup. This can be done by using a few elbows and some short lengths of pipe. The pipe used for this purpose must be of larger size than the regular exhaust pipe, in order to compensate for the increased back pressure that results from the use of the elbows.

Two Files Used for Gripping Tool

Two flat or half-round files and a short length of pipe will make an excellent substitute for pliers when these are not at hand or when they do not exactly answer the purpose. This gripping tool has been found very useful to remove dowel pins with protruding heads, when it is impossible to hammer them out, or difficult to pull them out with pliers; and also for removing the ends of bar stock that frequently stick in the collet of a screw machine or turret lathe.

The photograph shows how the tool is used. The ends of the files are stuck into

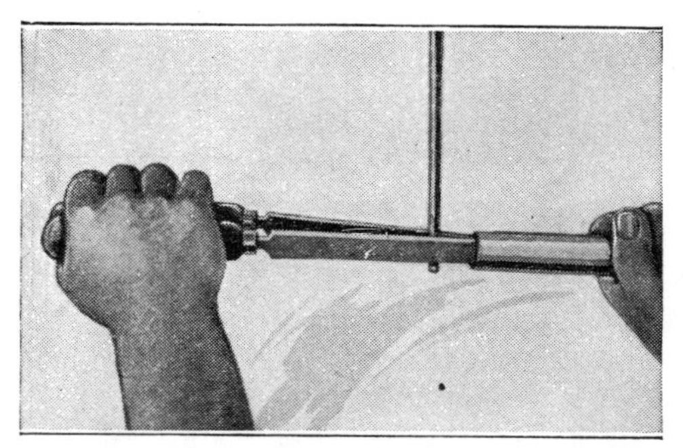

A Handy Gripping Tool, Improvised from Two Files and a Length of Pipe, Is an Excellent Substitute for a Pair of Pliers and in Some Cases Is More Suitable

the pipe and the pin is caught between them. By pressing the handles together, the files grip the work tightly. The crosscut surface of the files prevents them from slipping, no matter how hard they are pulled or turned around. Considerable leverage can be obtained by using long files and a long pipe.

Lathe Improvised from Hand Grinder

I was confronted with the task of making a number of turned wooden handles at a time when I could not get to a

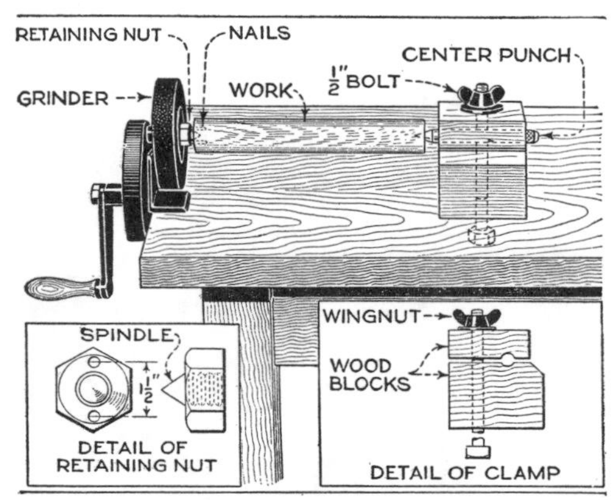

A Hastily Improvised Lathe That Accomplishes the Work of Turning Wood with Surprising Speed and Ease, Considering Its Crude Construction

lathe; the job, however, was satisfactorily accomplished on a lathe hastily improvised from a hand-power bench grinder. Two small holes were drilled to a depth of ¼ in. in the face of the nut holding the emery wheel on the shaft. The holes were 5/32 in. in diameter, and spaced 1½ in. apart, as shown in the detail. The grinder was clamped firmly to the left end of the bench, and served as the headstock of the lathe. The tailstock and center were made from a center punch and a simple wooden clamp, as shown. A ½-in. bolt was used to fasten the tailstock in place on the bench; this bolt passed through a hole in the bench and was provided with a wingnut to permit adjustment of the center. The work to be turned was prepared by centering at each end, and driving two pins, made from nails, into one end, so that they fitted into the holes drilled in the nut of the grinder. The work was placed in position with the pins seated in the holes, and was held securely by bringing the center into place and tightening the wingnut. A block of wood served as a rest.

The arrangement may be improved upon considerably by filing down the end of the grinder shaft to a 60° point, like a lathe center. If it is not desirable to have a hole drilled in the bench, the tailstock may be nailed to a strip of wood and the latter clamped to the table with small C-clamps.—D. H. Palmeter, Detroit, Mich.

Laying Out Square Corners

The farmer who builds his own outbuildings will appreciate the method of laying out square corners for foundation walls shown in the illustrations. This method, while not new, is not nearly as well known as it should be, as it is about the simplest method practicable with rough equipment.

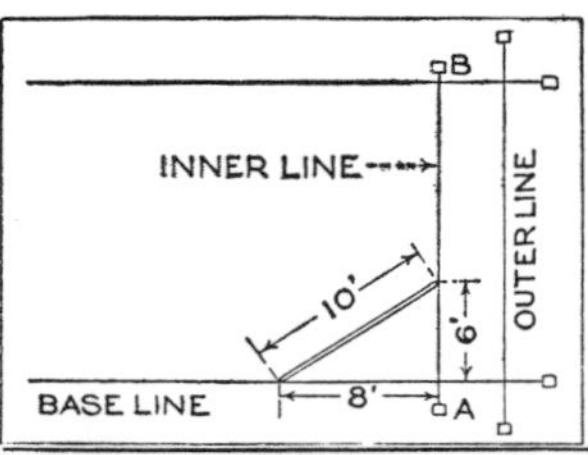

Laying Out Square Corners for Foundation Walls by Means of the 6, 8, and 10 Rule: This Is a Simple Method, and Quite Accurate

Referring to the line drawing, a base line, of hard cord, marking the outer side of one wall, is stretched between two stakes, about 2 ft. above the ground. The other lines are squared from this one. As all the lines are squared in the same manner, the description of the squaring of the inner side of the adjacent wall, as shown, will suffice.

A stake, A, is driven into the ground outside the base line, and a line stretched, at approximately right angles to the base line, to another stake, B, lightly driven outside the outer-wall line on the opposite side. From the point where this line crosses the base line, a distance of 6 ft. is measured, and a mark made at this point on the line, by tying a small piece of colored twine on it. Then, from the same point, a distance of 8 ft. is measured along the base line, and a similar mark made. A light pole is cut exactly 10 ft. long, and a short stick nailed to it at one end, the stick being cut to such a length that, when the end is rested on the ground, the pole will be just at the height of the line. This end of the pole is then set exactly at the 8-ft. mark, the stake B lifted by a helper, as shown in the photograph, and moved until the pole touches the 6-ft. mark while still touching the 8-ft. one. The stake is then driven in firmly, and the line is square with the base line.

The trench may be laid out on the ground by holding a plumb bob so that the bob line just touches the lines stretched between the stakes, and making a spade mark at the point where the plumb bob touches the earth, or by simply using a straightedge, set on the ground and held against the line.

Removing Chatter Marks in a Countersink

In spite of all care a countersink will sometimes chatter or tear, and this spoils the appearance of a job. To remove the chatter marks, place a small piece of emery cloth, with the abrasive side downward, over the hole, and bring the countersink down. In a few minutes, all the chatter marks will be polished off.

Handling Heavy Truck Wheels

When it is necessary to reline the brakes of a heavy truck, or to remove the wheels for any reason, considerable trouble is usually experienced in handling the latter because of their weight. This objection, however, can be easily overcome by jacking up the truck so that a strong plank, on two rollers, can be slipped under the wheel to be removed. The jack is then lowered until part of the weight of the wheel rests on the board. With one man at either side of the wheel, it is now an easy matter to pull off the wheel without lifting it. The wheel is replaced by reversing the procedure.—Lowell R. Butcher, Des Moines, Ia.

A Simple and Quick Method of Removing Heavy Truck Wheels: A Strong Board and Two Rollers Bear the Weight

Heater Used as Lamp

Needing some additional light in one corner of the office and not having any extra fixtures, I struck upon the idea of using the electric reflecting heater which was in the room. After removing the heating element from the socket and substituting a lamp for it, I found that the result was all that could be desired. The heater reflected the light just as well as it did the heat.—W. F. Schaphorst, Newark, N. J.

Testing Fuses with a Flashlight

Maintenance electricians and mechanics will find the simple scheme of using a flashlight to test fuses, a good one. A small hole is punched or drilled through the metal lens case, so that the end of a length of stranded wire, such as lamp cord, can be pushed through. The end of the wire is bared, twisted around the screw shell of the lamp, and soldered. The other end of the wire is soldered to a brass tip. When testing fuses, one end of the fuse is held in contact with the metal cap on the bottom of the flashlight, and the brass tip is touched to the other end. If the fuse is in good condition, the lamp will light. A small hard-rubber thimble, to fit over the tip, should be provided to keep the tip clean.

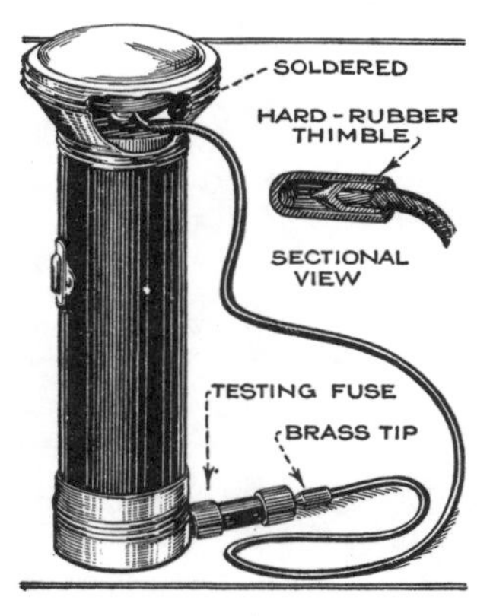

Backing Tool for Riveting

The tool shown in the drawing, while primarily designed for use in tightening loose rivets in automobile frames, will be found useful in any shop where heavy work must be riveted, as it enables one man to do the riveting without a helper.

A piece of heavy round steel is used for the rivet snap, or anvil, and it is turned and cupped on the end to fit the rivet head, in the same manner as any other snap. It is drilled, a little above its center, to fit a heavy bar handle, and a cotter-pin hole is drilled at right angles to the handle hole. The handle is drilled, at intervals of about 1 in., with a series of cotter-pin holes, and slotted at one end to fit the flat-steel hook shown, a hole for a heavy pin being drilled through the slot jaws. The hook is also drilled at 1-in. intervals to fit the cotter, and the tool is assembled as shown.

An Adjustable Backing Tool or Snap That Enables One Man to Do Heavy Riveting Single-Handed: It will Prove a Useful Tool in Any Shop

The manner of using the tool is obvious; the hook can be reversed when it cannot be caught on any portion of the work while in the position shown.

Dog for Adjusting Steel Cable

A steel cable is not considered so convenient as a chain for use as a towline, or for similar purposes, because its length cannot be adjusted so easily. However, this objection may be overcome by attaching an easily made dog to one end of the cable. The dog is made of 3/8-in. flat-steel, shaped as shown in the drawing. A cam, with a handle, is riveted loosely to the body, off center, so that when the cam is set in the position shown in the upper view, the cable is gripped tightly, and when turned as in the lower view, the cable is released. With this device, the cable can be adjusted to any length desired.—Geo. G. McVicker, North Bend, Neb.

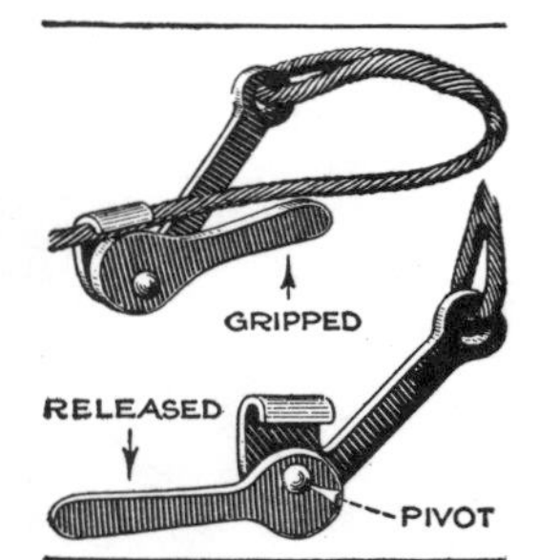

Tool for Spreading and Extracting Cotter Pins

In garages, where it is necessary to extract and spread cotter pins frequently, the special tool for this purpose shown in the drawing will be found of considerable utility. An old pair of pliers is forged and filed to the shape shown in the illustration, then hardened and tempered. A lip on one jaw opens the cotter pin and spreads it, while the notch in the other jaw prevents the head of the pin from slipping. The ends of the jaws are ground down to fit under the head of the cotter pin to extract it, as shown in the lower drawing. The jaw ends should be rounded, to prevent cutting the pin.

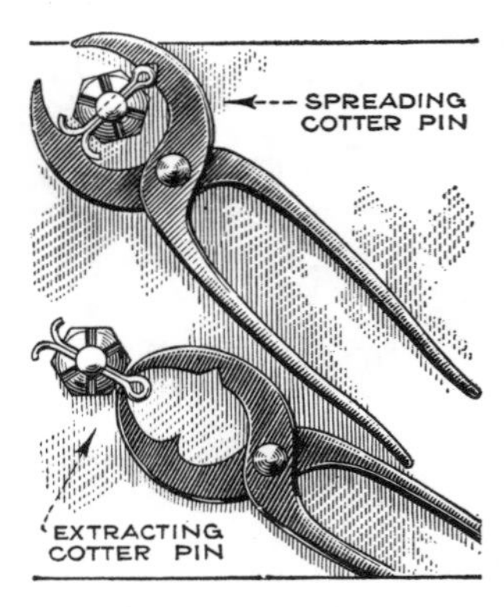

Polisher for Tempering

It is desirable to have a steel surface polished brightly before the metal is tempered, in order that the worker may be able to watch the color while tempering. An excellent emery-cloth holder, that has a soft backing, so that the abrasive surface will touch all parts when used on slightly uneven surfaces, is illustrated.

The holder is made from a disk of 1/16-in. sheet metal, bent at right angles near the center, leaving about 3/4 in. space between the two sides. A semicircular wooden block, 3/4 in. thick and 1/2 in. less in depth than the height of the sides of the holder, fits in this space. A notch is cut across the center of the block, as indicated by the dotted line in the drawing. A 1/4-in. hole is then drilled through the center of the sheet-metal sides, near the bottom. A hole is drilled through the wooden block, at right angles to the notch, for an eyebolt, the eye of which fits over a pin driven through the holes in the sides. The ends of the pin are riveted. Sheets of emery cloth are then torn into 3/4-in. strips; about 12 of these are used, the ends being caught between block and holder, and clamped securely by tightening the eyebolt. By using about a dozen strips of emery cloth, it is possible to polish the surface much better than if only one strip were used.

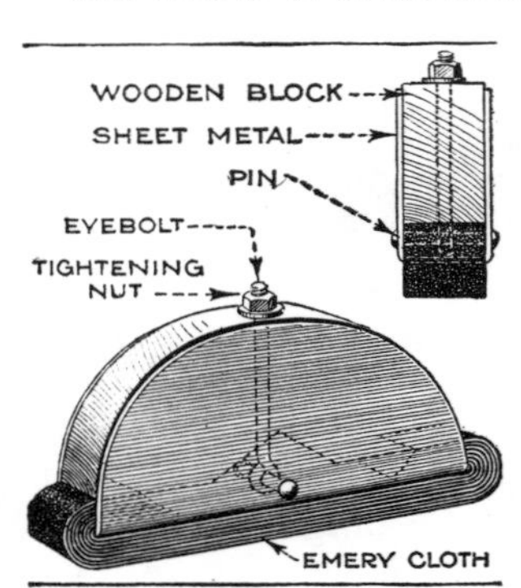

Elongating Holes in Plates

The tool shown in the illustration was used in a boiler shop when it was necessary to cut some holes of an oval shape, making the length 1½ times the width. Several attempts were first made to do this by drilling, but the drill had a tendency to run into the hole already drilled. A special chisel, made as shown in the drawing, enabled the work to be done quickly. Chisel steel, of the same diameter as the holes, was used, one end being ground down, as indicated, to form a cutting lip about 1/8 in. deep. The chisel locates itself in the hole and cuts a good chip each time it is driven through.

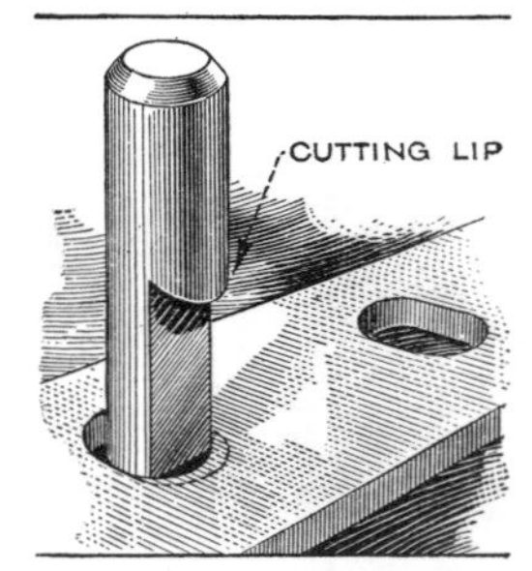

Setting Contact Points on Automobiles

An automobile equipped with battery ignition must usually have the contact points adjusted, or at least checked up, once about every 2,000 miles; this is a rather difficult operation for the mechanic, unless the breaker box is unusually accessible, because it is hard to observe the cam while cranking by hand, and if the electric starter is used, it is hard to get the shaft to stop at just the right point. If the car is a light one, it can be put in high gear on a level road, and

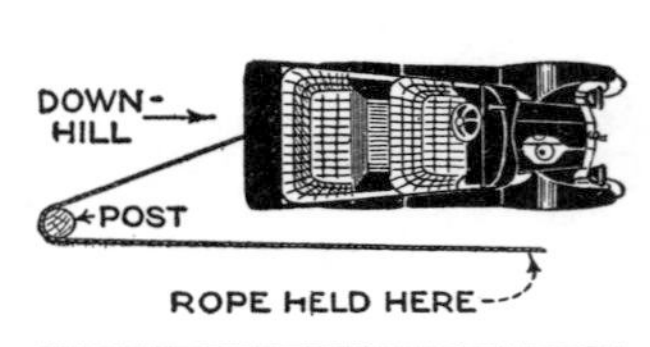

can be pushed along until the points are separated the maximum distance, when the hand brake is set to hold the car while adjusting the points.

With a heavier car, one man can still do the work, if there is a grade near by so that gravity can be utilized to help move the car. A strong rope is attached to the rear axle and brought around a tree or strong post, the rope being doubled if the car is heavy or the grade steep. While the rope is held taut from a position near the breaker box, the brake is released and the car allowed to move down slowly, by paying out the rope, until the contact points are wide open. At this position the brake is applied to hold the car, while the adjustments are being made.

Simple Planing Stop and Vise

One of the most important tools for the woodworker is his vise. Sometimes a vise is not at hand, and the woodworker is at a loss how to support his work. The illustration shows a very simple vise and planing stop that can be made at small expense; it will grip the work securely, and, if properly made, is practically unbreakable.

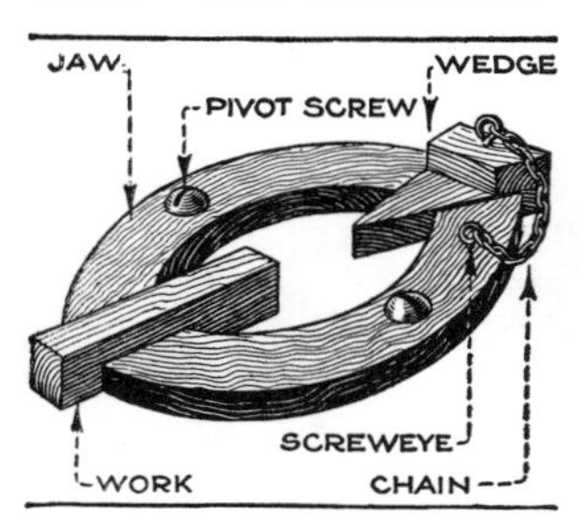

The vise consists of two curved pieces of hardwood, of a size suitable for the work for which it is to be used. A generally satisfactory thickness is about 1 inch. The pieces are pivoted at their central points on long screws that extend into the bench, or other support on which the vise is fastened. At one end each of the jaws is beveled so that a wedge can be driven between them to clamp the opposite ends on the work. To enable the wedge to be readily driven out again, a cleat is nailed on it, as shown. It is a good idea to connect the wedge to one of the jaws with a short length of chain and two screweyes, one driven into the cleat, the other into the jaw.—H. G. Schultz, Teaneck, N. J.

¶For every 10° F. added to the temperature of feed water by exhaust steam, nearly one per cent of fuel is saved.

Brush Attachment for Drawing Borders

The brush attachment illustrated is used for drawing clean, straight borders on showcards and similar work. The attachment can be made by anyone in a few moments with the help of a pair of pliers. A piece of soft-iron wire, about 8 in. long, is formed to the shape shown; two coils are made about 2 in. from one end by winding the wire around the cap of a fountain pen, or other round article of about the same diameter. The other end of the wire is then bent up to form an oval loop, as shown, so that when the arrangement is slipped onto the brush, the coils and loop will grip the handle securely. The spacing of the border from the edge of the card can readily be varied by bending the end that is drawn along the edge of the T-square or triangle.—E. E. Knight, San Diego, Calif.

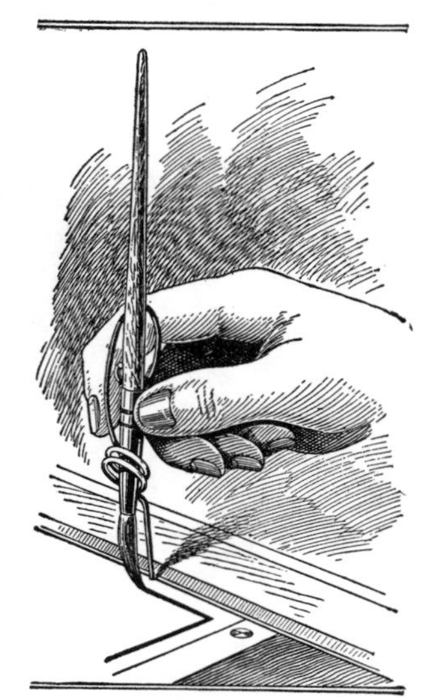

Gilding Small Articles

Small articles can be gilded in the following way: Dissolve, in 8 oz. distilled water, 1 oz. of cyanide of potassium (poison), and 32 gr. of chloride of gold, and shake well to insure thorough mixing. Cut a strip of sheet zinc, and bend it to form a hook to fit the article.

Put some of the solution in a glass or earthenware dish, then scour the article with baking soda and water to remove all dirt and grease, rinse it off, and suspend it by means of the zinc hook in the solution, until it appears very dark in color. It is then removed, and again scoured with brush and soda, which will bring out a beautiful gilded finish.

If a Roman finish is desired, the articles must be satin-finished with a wire brush before dipping, but if an English finish is desired, they are polished before dipping.

Emergency Climbing Irons

On a possum-hunting party in southern Maryland, the hunters were assembled and everything in readiness, when it was discovered that climbing irons, which were very necessary items on this trip, had been forgotten. A trip back for these was out of the question, as the time involved would mean too long a delay. The hunters were decidedly at a loss, until some one suggested applying for help to a blacksmith who lived near by.

Climbing Irons Made of Four-Foot Lengths of 1/4-Inch Steel Rod, That will be Found Very Serviceable by Linemen

The ingenious blacksmith turned out several pairs of the irons shown in a short time; each one was made of a 4-ft. length of 1/4-in. steel rod, bent to the shape shown in the drawing. One end was sharpened to a point and tempered, while the other end was formed into a 4-in. stirrup and bent around the first to strengthen it. The climbers thus made served the purpose just as well as purchased ones, and were found heavy enough to stand hard usage. Leather straps from the tire holders on the automobiles were used to hold the climbers in place. Such climbing irons can be easily made in any blacksmith shop, and many uses can be found for them around industrial establishments, and by power, telephone, or telegraph linemen.

Do not heat the work above a bare red heat when casehardening for colors, using cyanide.

Measuring Disks in Micrometer

Some kinds of work are rather difficult to measure with a micrometer. Thin round pieces, for instance, may easily be measured incorrectly if care is not taken to see that the work is held in the center of the measuring faces, and at right angles to them. Recently, among a batch of 3/4 by 1/16-in. disks, a number were found to exceed the tolerance allowed on the diameter, and it became necessary to measure the whole lot. The man to whom this inspection job was given made the simple attachment shown in the illustration, to save the time and trouble required in adjusting the pieces squarely between the micrometer anvil and spindle. The attachment is a short piece of cold-rolled steel the same diameter as the disks, drilled in the center a running fit for the micrometer spindle, and slotted with a saw a little wider than the thickness of the disks. With this little device, the job was done in a short time, as it was simply a matter of inserting the disks in the slot until the edges were flush with the attachment, when the measuring could proceed with safety, as the work was thus located square and central. After the disk was measured, the micrometer was tipped over as the spindle was turned back, releasing the disk and allowing it to fall out into a box.

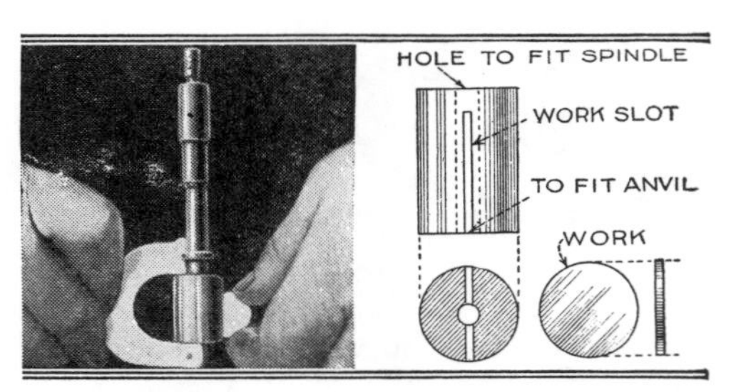

Simple Attachment for Measuring Disks with a Micrometer Caliper That Insures Each Disk being Held Square and Central between Spindle and Anvil

---

A Color Code for Fuses

In a large industrial building where renewable fuses of various capacities, but of the same cartridge size, are used, a color-code system to distinguish between the fuses has been found very useful.

The fuse cartridges are painted in different colors to indicate the capacities of the links contained in them. For instance, with the small cartridge fuse having a maximum rating of 30 amp., there are in use five kinds of links, of 5, 10, 15, 20, and 30-amp. capacity. For these links, the colors white, green, blue, yellow, and red are used, respectively. For the next size of cartridge, having a maximum rating of 60 amp., a similar code is used.

With this system, the size of fuse necessary to make renewals can be determined at a glance, insuring proper renewals without the danger of under or overfusing.

Protecting Ladle When Melting Babbitt

When starting to melt a ladleful of babbitt, put some machine oil, or grease, or even some resin, in the bottom of the ladle. This will quickly melt and catch fire, and while burning out, will melt some of the babbitt, causing it to flow down into the bottom of the ladle. This thin layer of melted babbitt will quickly conduct away the intense heat of the fire to which the bottom is exposed, and prevent it from burning out. The oil or grease will not spoil the quality of the metal.—H. Bethuel Kingsley, Fort Miller, New York.

Simple Woodworker's Clamp

A piece of wood, cut out and fastened to the workbench with wire, as shown in the drawing, makes a very handy clamp for holding several boards together at one end while working on them. This clamp is much more convenient for this purpose than an ordinary pair of wood clamps, and requires less time to adjust.

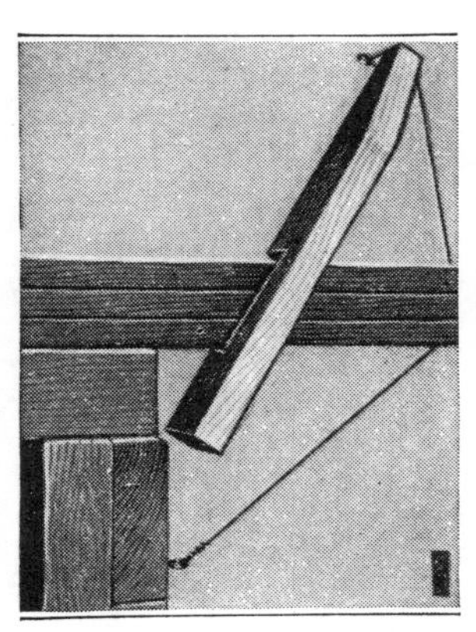

It is preferable to make this clamp of hardwood. The slot, cut out near one end, as shown in the drawing, should have rounded corners and beveled edges to prevent marking the boards on which it is used. Two screweyes and a piece of heavy flexible wire are used to attach the clamp to the side of the workbench. The wire is brought around the ends of the boards, the clamp placed on them, and the boards then shoved against the wire; this pulls the upper end of the clamp down and squeezes the boards together.

Tool for Etching Steel

The etching tool shown in the photo can be made very cheaply, and forms a

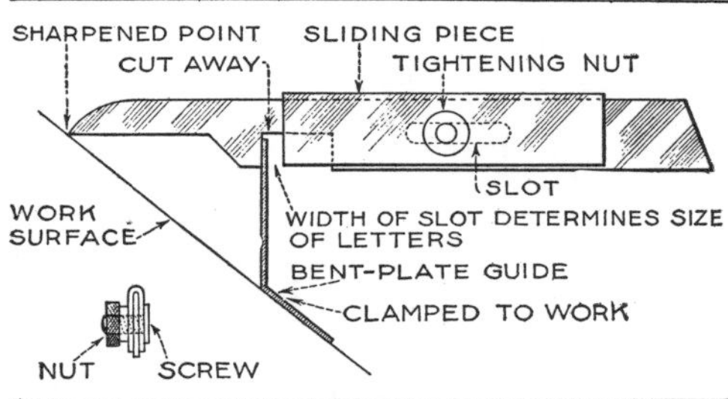

A Useful Lettering Tool for Etching Steel: The Height of the Letters is Kept Uniform and the Lettering Thus Presents a Neat Appearance

very useful device for etching lettering on steel. Beeswax and acid are used in the ordinary way, the purpose of the tool being to keep the letters in a straight line and of the same height, thus giving the inscription a neat appearance, in keeping with well-finished work.

The tool consists of three parts: the lettering tool, a sliding distance piece, and a guide, made of flat plate, bent to the shape shown. The lettering tool has a slot cut in the bottom, and is also slotted in the center, for a small clamp screw. The sliding piece is a piece of stock of the same thickness as that used for the tool, doubled to fit over the latter, and drilled for the clamp screw. By moving this piece, the width of the slot can be varied to suit the size of the letters required.

The guide plate is clamped to the work as shown in the photo, and the tool is used with the edge of the guide in the slot. It may easily be seen that the height of the letters must be uniform, as the tool can only move a distance equal to the width of the slot, when making the vertical strokes of the letters.

Making Clean-Cut Metal Stencils

By JAMES TATE

STENCIL cutting, as usually undertaken by those not "in the know," consists in attempting to cut the thin sheet brass or zinc with a chisel, or similar tool. The results are invariably unsatisfactory, as the edges of the cuts are ragged, and, when filed smooth, the proportions of the letters are changed; a burr is also thrown up on the underside of very thin stock that no subsequent hammering or filing will remove.

A simple method, and one that produces excellent work, is to etch the designs with acid. Using this process, the metal is left perfectly flat on both sides, and the outlines of the characters are smooth and regular. The stencils, particularly if made of zinc, can be produced very quickly, no great skill is required, and there is no need of finishing after the etching has been completed.

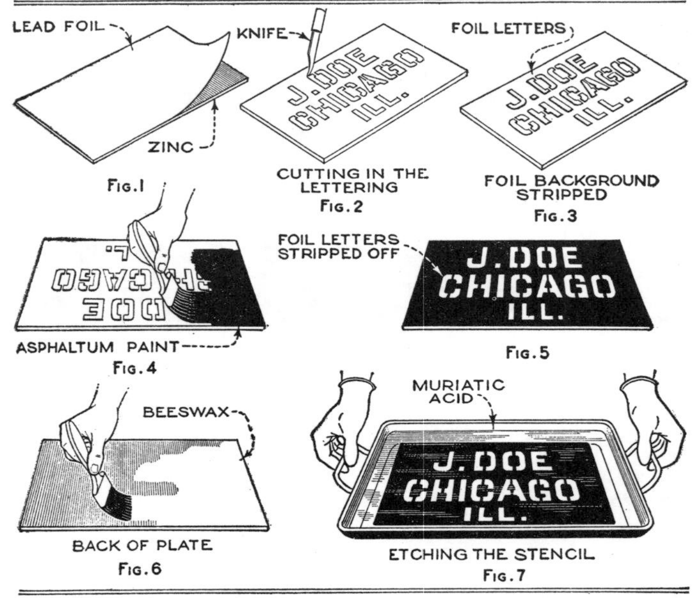

Figure 1, Applying the Lead Foil; Figure 2, Cutting In the Lettering; Figure 3, Plate Ready for Painting; Figure 4, Painting the Plate; Figure 5, Plate with Lettering Stripped; Figure 6, Preparing the Plate for Etching; and Figure 7, Etching the Work

To make a stencil in zinc, which is about the easiest metal to etch, cut the plate to size, lay it on a smooth, flat surface, and coat one side lightly with melted beeswax. The plate is then warmed slightly, to melt the wax again, and, while the latter is still soft, a sheet of lead foil, cut to the same size as the plate, is laid over it, as shown in Fig. 1, and rubbed into close contact, with a piece of hard felt or similar material. The lead foil can be obtained from any florist, or electrical-supply house, and is very cheap.

The foil is now given a light coat of beeswax, and this leaves the surface ready for the lettering to be drawn or traced upon it, with a pencil or stylus. When drawing in the lettering or design, provision must be made for the ties that hold the center portions of such letters as O, D, and C to the rest of the plate. The outlines of the lettering are then cut through with a fine, sharp-pointed knife—a photographer's etching knife makes a good tool for this—as shown in Fig. 2. The foil background is now stripped from the plate, leaving it as in Fig. 3, with only the foil lettering remaining on it. The next step is to paint the whole surface, including the foil letters, with asphaltum paint, or electrotypers' varnish; then the letters are stripped from the plate. This is best done with a needle or pin, stuck into a wooden handle, the point of the tool being inserted under an edge of each letter, the foil raised, and the letter stripped off. The foil will bring practically all the beeswax on the zinc with it, leaving a clean surface for the action of the acid, as in Fig. 5.

After the asphaltum has thoroughly dried, the plate is turned over and the back and edges coated with melted beeswax, using a brush, and taking care that every part of the surface is coated. The plate is now ready for etching.

The acid used is muriatic acid, and is poured into a shallow enameled tray. The plate is placed in the tray, face up, and the tray kept in motion until the acid has eaten through all the lettering. Care must be taken not to allow the acid to splash on the face or hands, or to inhale the fumes given off. When the etching is finished, the work is removed and washed in running water, when the asphaltum may be removed with gasoline, and the beeswax with hot water.

If asphaltum, or electrotypers' varnish, is not easily obtainable, melted beeswax can be applied to the face of the work instead, although it will make the work of removing the foil lettering a little more difficult.

Simple Chip Shield

The practice of turning brass, bronze, and similar metals at high cutting speeds often results in injuries to the operator's eyes by flying chips. This is, in most cases, easily avoided by the use of a guard or shield, the use of which should be made compulsory. A very simple chip guard is that shown in the drawing; it consists of a leather disk, screwed to a steel collar, the latter being a loose fit over the toolpost. The leather itself should be a "wringing" fit on the toolpost, and the hole should be off center, so that the disk can be swung to one side or the other to suit the work, or when necessary to change tools.

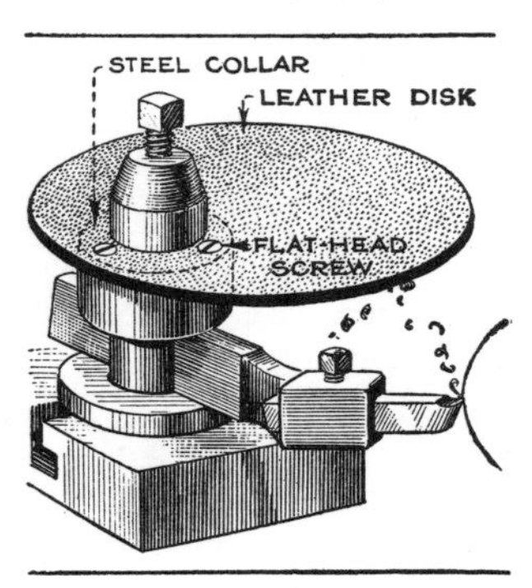

Removing Stripped Wood Screws

It often happens that wood screws cannot be unscrewed, because there are no threads in the wood; they may have been stripped by giving the screw a few extra turns when driving it in, or the threads may have disappeared due to dry or wet rot.

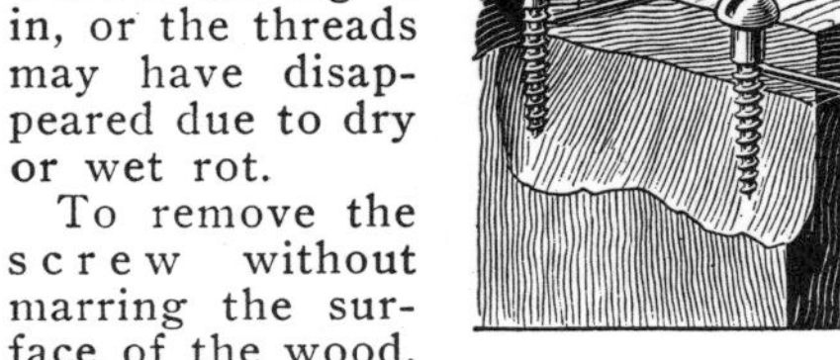

To remove the screw without marring the surface of the wood, the method illustrated may be used. Drive a finishing nail into the wood, as indicated, so that its end will come in contact with the screw thread. The screw can then be removed easily. The small nail hole is easily puttied or otherwise filled, so as to be scarcely noticeable.—H. H. Siegele, Emporia, Kan.

Reaming Axle Bushings

When inserting new front-wheel spindle bushings, it is poor practice to drive out both old bushings, and press both of the new ones in place at once, then ream them from the outside of each bushing. The result of this is that the reamer is often canted, and the hole reamed at a slight angle. To ream the holes correctly, one old bushing should be left in place to serve as a guide, as shown in the lower view. When the bushing has been reamed to size, the old one is pressed out, and the second bushing pressed in and reamed, using the first one as a guide. By employing this method the bearing of the spindle bolt can be made practically perfect.

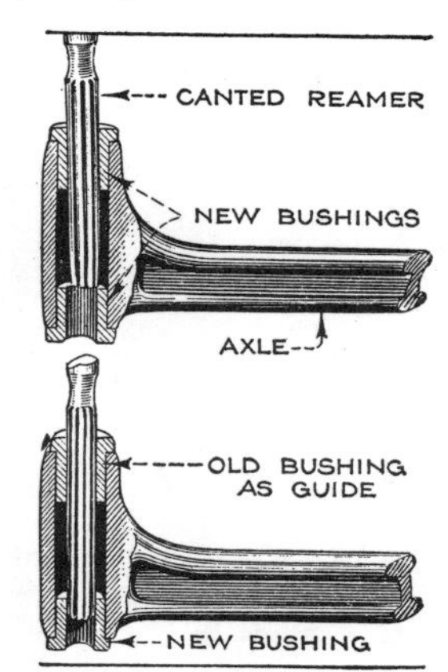

Felt Pad for Wiping Solder

A handy tool for wiping the surplus solder, when tinning the ends of pipes, or similar work, can be made very easily from two pieces of hardwood, one — the holder proper — being left plain, the other shaped to fit the hand comfortably. This handle has a step cut out at one end, and is slotted, at the same end, as shown. A piece of thin felt is fastened to the holder by screws, brought around the end, and screwed to the handle while the latter is in the position shown in the upper view. In order to stretch the felt tightly, the handle is then pulled down in line with the holder and secured with a screw and nut. Thus the whole working surface of the pad is free from obstructions, nails, screws, etc., and the material cannot "bunch" or crumple up after a short time in use.

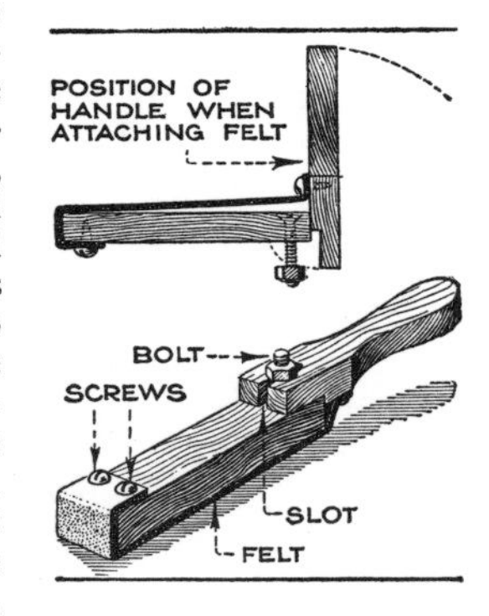

Auto Engine as Power Plant

There are many possibilities for farm use in a discarded automobile. One of the most practical is to remove and overhaul the engine and adapt it for driving the machinery in the farm workshop. Such a power plant will give good service for several years. The illustrations show an engine taken from a light car and mounted on a wooden bedplate. The only change made in the arrangement of the parts was to mount the gas tank on a high wooden frame, and to extend the transmission shaft; this extension carried the driving pulley, and was journaled in pillow blocks, fitted on each side of the pulley.

A Discarded Automobile Engine, Used to Drive the Machinery in a Farm Workshop: It Has Proved Very Satisfactory

The engine is operated exactly as when in the auto, high, low, and reverse speeds being available. After the cylinders had been reground, and new rings fitted, and when the plant had been in operation for some time, a test was made to determine the power delivered at the pulley. This proved to exceed 12 brake horsepower.—Dale R. Van Horn, College View, Neb.

Extinguishing Burning Oils and Greases

An experiment recently made to ascertain the most efficient fire extinguisher for burning oils, fats, greases, and similar substances developed a number of interesting facts.

In the majority of liquid fire extinguishers, the active agent is carbon tetrachloride, which is a noninflammable liquid at ordinary temperatures, vaporizing rapidly at a comparatively low temperature. The vapor is also noninflammable, and is heavier than air. When carbon tetrachloride is thrown upon burning wood, paper, oily waste, and similar material, the vapor formed excludes the air and the fire is smothered. However, oils or oily substances are soluble, or partly so, in carbon tetrachloride, and should this liquid come into contact with oil which is later used in the manufacture of food products, it is probable that under certain conditions the odor of the chemical would be very easily noticed. Another drawback in using the majority of liquid fire extinguishers on burning oil is that it produces an effect very similar to that of throwing water in a tank of burning oil, increasing the fire hazard because of the danger of setting fire to the building.

Most dry extinguishers contain a considerable amount of ammonium carbonate. This substance, when thrown upon burning grease, causes the latter to foam and swell, and if a kettle filled, or even partly filled, with oil or fat should take fire, and ammonium carbonate is thrown into it, causing it to foam, the vessel will in all probability overflow and in this way endanger the safety of the building.

Experiments made with flour indicated that good results would be obtained if the fire were quickly covered with a large quantity. Flour works very well with a small volume of oil, but the quantity required to put out a fire in a good-sized vessel would cause the oil to flow over the sides, and for this reason flour, unless very quickly and carefully applied, does not always give good results.

Dry sawdust takes fire readily, and unless a quantity sufficient to smother the fire is at once thrown upon the burning oil, the sawdust will feed the flames instead of quenching them. Wet sawdust thrown on burning oil produces an effect somewhat the same as water, so it is apparent that neither wet nor dry sawdust is good material to use in extinguishing a fire of this nature.

Of all the substances tested, baking soda proved to be the most efficient for putting out a fire in which fats, oils, or greases were involved. The baking soda should be dusted to a depth of about 1/4 in. over one half the surface of the blazing oil. The gas formed by the decomposing soda spreads over the uncovered portion of the blaze; this blanket of heavier-than-air gas prevents the oxygen of the air from coming into contact with the oil, and in this manner the fire is smothered.

It is essential that the baking soda be in the form of a very fine powder, for if it lumps or cakes, the lumps sink and gas is liberated below the surface of the oil; this causes the oil to foam and swell, and consequently there is danger of the oil overflowing the sides of the vessel. To prevent the baking soda from lumping in the container, mix it thoroughly with 30 per cent of very fine sand, and it will be found that the mixture is but little less effective than the pure soda.—E. O'Connor, Davenport, Ia.

Tool for Cutting Corrugated Roofing

Cutting corrugated roofing with a pair of ordinary tin snips is a tiresome job, and one that is usually rather rough on the hands. The simple tool shown in the illustration, which is made from an old pitchfork and works somewhat like a can opener, will be found much easier on the hands. The tines of the fork are cut to a length of about 4 in., and bent until the points are about 2 in. apart. The middle tine is then bent downward, as shown, and sharpened to form a cutting knife. When cutting, the outer tines will run in the corrugations on either side of the line of cut, keeping the cut straight. —H. J. Engel, New Braunfels, Tex.

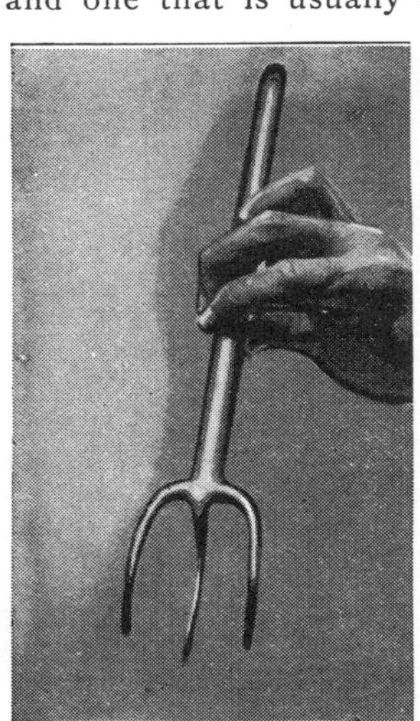

Hanging a Double-Swing Door

The photograph shows a factory door that swings in either direction and closes itself through the action of a strong coil spring. It is not necessary for the workman to stop to open the door, but simply to push the truck against it. This door is not of the common hinged type, but swings on two pivots located above and below the door, about 1 ft. from the side jamb. The only equipment required to make it self-closing, is a heavy coil spring, a wall bracket from which to extend the spring, and two lengths of chain for attaching the spring to the door in the manner indicated. The spring is brought into tension when the door is opened in either direction, owing to the fact that one chain extends to each side of the pivot on which the door swings. The woodwork of the door is protected from damage by sheet metal, fastened on each side at the height of the truck bodies.—Orin Crooker, Wheaton, Ill.

Double-Swing Door in a Factory, Opened by Simply Pushing the Trucks against It: A Spring Attachment Makes It Self-Closing

Drilling Horizontal Holes Straight

Anyone who has ever used a brace and bit knows that in the drilling of horizontal holes there is a great tendency to raise or lower the brace a trifle while drilling, which, of course, results in the hole being drilled at an angle. To overcome this tendency, slip a large washer over the bit so that it rests on the smooth shank. As soon as the bit is held at an angle the washer will travel one way or the other, and the workman can correct the fault instantly. The washer should be free from burrs.

Filing Bearing-Cap Faces

When filing down the flat faces of caps of connecting rods, bearings, and steering-gear connections to compensate for wear, the caps cannot always be held in a vise conveniently, because of their shape. An excellent method of holding them on the workbench is shown in the illustration.

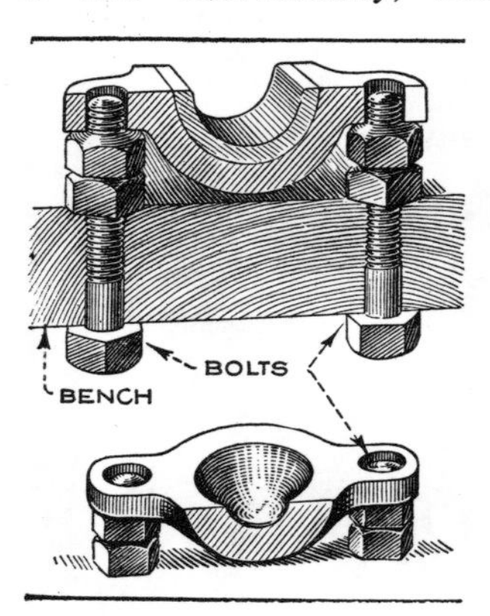

Two holes are drilled in the workbench; these are spaced apart the same distance as the bolt holes in the cap. Bolts are pushed through the holes from underneath, and nuts screwed on, to hold the bolts in place and to serve as seats for the caps. Although this method may not appear to provide a substantial support, it has been found that the cap can be filed down without any tendency to rock, providing the lowest part of the curved surface rests on the bench.

Recovering Pump Cylinder from Well

Workmen repairing a casing well had the misfortune to drop the pump cylinder to the bottom of the pipe, about 120 ft. below the ground. To raise the casing was, of course, out of the question. The only method of recovering the cylinder was to use some device, which, when lowered from the top by a rope, would engage the cylinder and draw it up. The device used is shown in the illustration.

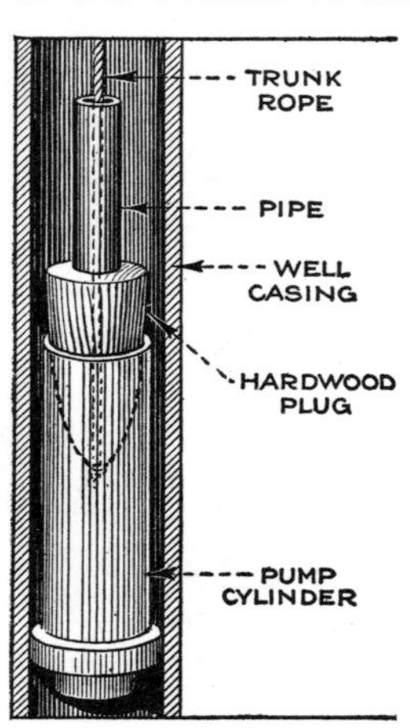

A piece of hardwood, 10 in. long, was rounded to form a tapering plug, the outside diameter of which just exceeded the inside diameter of the cylinder. A hole was drilled through the plug lengthwise, and a trunk rope passed through it and tied. After the plug was lowered in the casing, and when it was felt that the small end had entered the cylinder, a length of 1-in. pipe was slipped over the rope and allowed to drop on the plug. The impact of the pipe drove the plug into the cylinder. It was then an easy matter to lift the cylinder to the surface.

A Tire-Setting Gauge

In the shrinking of steel tires on railroad-car wheels, the side of the flange must be kept parallel to the flange of the hub liner. Measuring with a small gauge or scale is by no means easy or comfortable, as it must be done while the tire is hot. A gauge that has been especially devised to overcome this objection, and that enables the worker to accomplish the work with speed and accuracy, is shown in the illustration.

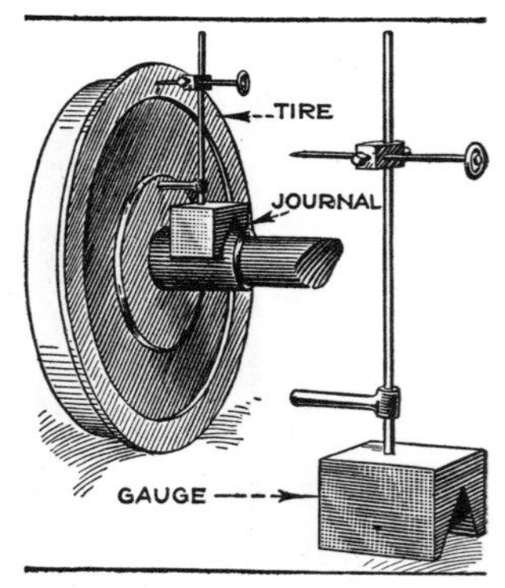

The gauge has a cast-iron base, the underside of which has a V-notch milled in it to fit on the journal. A long steel rod is driven into a hole drilled in the base, and is fitted with two fingers. The lower one is attached permanently to the rod, and, in use, is set against the liner. The upper finger is fitted in a sliding block. When the lower finger is set against the liner, the block is moved up until it is opposite the tire, then locked by a setscrew. The finger is then moved in until it touches the tire and is locked, and the gauge is swung around the journal. It is thus an easy matter to set the tire perfectly parallel with the liner.—W. S. Pickerell, Spokane, Wash.

¶An emergency valve-grinding tool can be made from a piece of broom handle, a thin piece of sheet metal, driven into the end, and two pins to hold the sheet metal in place. To operate the tool thus improvised, hold it between the palms and twirl around by moving the palms back and forth.

Concrete Runways Aid Car Repairs

BY GEORGE A. LUERS

THE runways shown in the illustration will prove of great convenience in any garage or repair shop, public or private; they are far easier to make than pits, and can be built in a few hours.

A simple wooden form is made as shown in the lower right-hand corner; only one form is necessary, although two will speed the work. When the location of the runways has been decided upon, excavations are made, about 2 ft. deep and a little shorter in length and width than the form, to allow it to rest on the edges of the hole. If there is a cement floor in the garage, it will be sufficient to chip it out to the dimensions of the inside of the form and about 1½ or 2 in. deep, and to wet the rough chipped surface thoroughly, to allow the new concrete to bond with the old.

The main form being set in place, the V-shaped form for the grooved runway is set on top of it, and clamped in place by using C-clamps on the battens on the side of the main form; a mixture composed of 1 part portland cement to 2

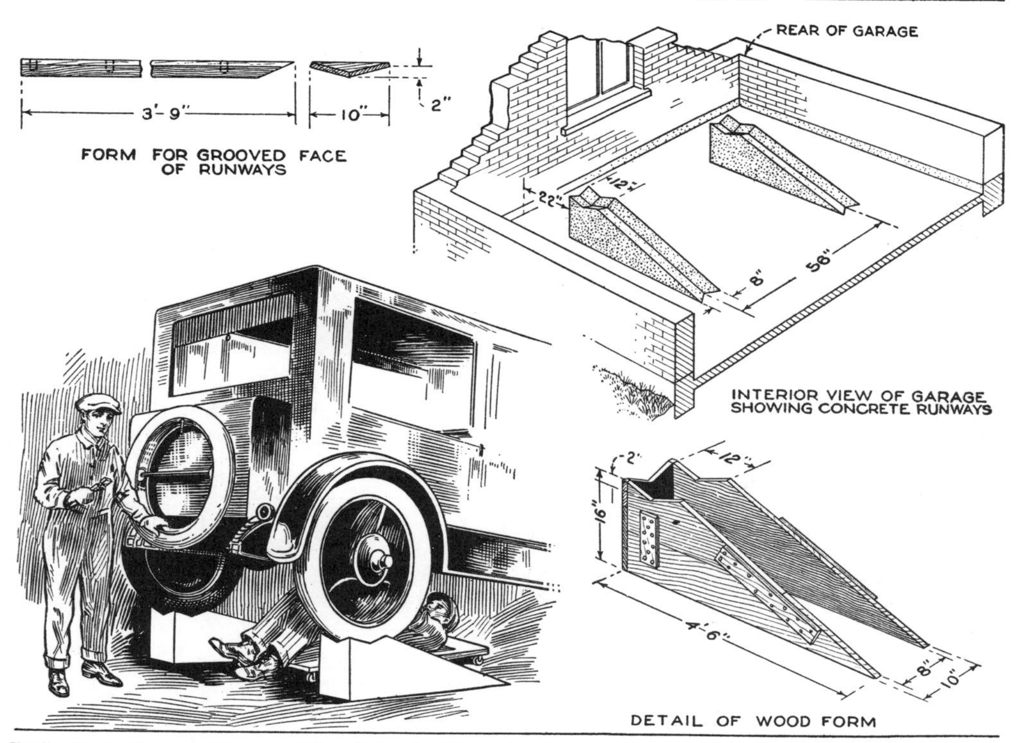

Easily Made Concrete Runways That Take the Place of a Pit in the Public Garage or Repair Shop, and Are Also Suitable for the Private Garage: The Dimensions Given Are Suitable for All Standard Cars. The Runways may be Placed Anywhere Convenient, Although Preferably Opposite a Window, to Provide Plenty of Natural Light

parts sand is poured in, and thoroughly tamped with a long iron rod, poking all corners well, to insure that there will be no pockets or unfilled places.

The depression in the top of the runway that holds the car wheel is formed with a trowel or similar tool, while the concrete is still soft, and the form is allowed to remain for at least 24 hours, when it may be removed and used for the other runway. The runways should be kept thoroughly wet for about 10 days, when they may be put in service. The car is simply driven up the runways slowly, under its own power, the depressions in the tops preventing it from being driven over the back.

The dimensions shown will be suitable for most cars, and the runways should be 56 in. center to center. They should be set near a window, to provide sufficient natural light, and far enough from the wall so that the work on the car can be performed with comfort.

New Method of Lowering Quarry Floor

The lowering of a quarry floor is usually a most laborious operation. The original quarry is generally cut to about the ground-water level, and, in making a new cut below this level, the common method is to blast out a small hole, remove the stone with a clamshell, or by some other method that is just as tedious, and then pump the water out. After that a shovel is let down into the hole, and the hole is enlarged to a proper working face.

A Time and Labor-Saving Method of Lowering a Quarry Floor to a Depth of 25 Feet below the Original Floor, by Blasting a Large Area

A new method, recently employed in an Ohio quarry, is to drill a large area with blast-hole drills, as in opening a new quarry. The entire area is shot at once with heavy charges, to break up the rock as much as possible. In this case an area, 300 by 72 ft. in size, was drilled and broken to a depth of about 25 ft. Holes, 15 in. in diameter, were then drilled close to the edge of the broken-up area, to a depth of about 30 ft. These holes, of course, were driven through broken and shattered rock, and were lined with old screen plates. Suction intakes were let down into the drill holes, and the entire area was pumped out. A steam shovel was then set to work at the edge of the blasted area, and worked right down to the new level.

Internal Limit Gauge

While internal limit gauges, for determining the minimum and maximum allowable sizes of holes, are usually marked to distinguish the "go" and the "not-go" ends, the figures or letters are quite small, and they must be read each time so that the proper end may be used.

To eliminate this trouble, we knurled all our gauges on the "not-go" end, so that the inspector would know, by feel, which end he was using.—J. H. Moore, Toronto, Can.

Slide for Tool-Chest Drawers

There are several types of slides used for tool-chest drawers, but the one illustrated is novel and will be appreciated by woodworkers. The slide is metal, and is used on a tool box having an open front, similar to a machinist's tool chest. A brass channel is screwed to each side of the drawers, and brass strips, an easy fit in the channels, are fastened to the sides of the box, as indicated. The metal slides have a long life, do not warp nor permit the drawers to rub against each other, and support the drawers firmly when the latter are drawn almost all the way out.

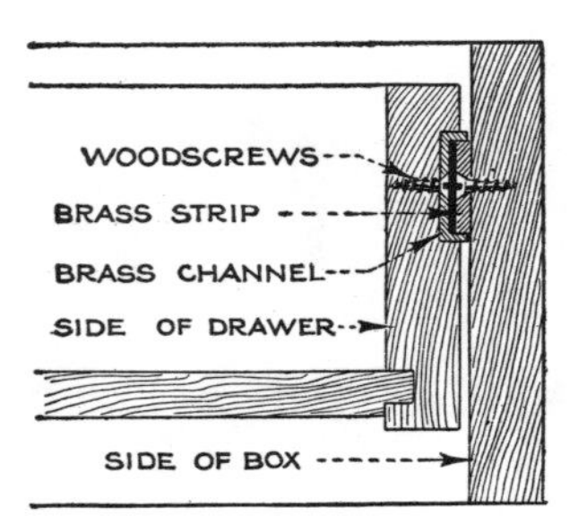

Fence-Post Attachment Made of Pipe

When it is desired to run a slanting wire fence on the top of the poultry fence, wooden slats, nailed to the fence posts, are generally used to support the wire; these, however, are not as a rule satisfactory, as they are neither as strong as they should be, nor do they last as long as desired.

A better and more substantial type of support can be made from 2-ft. lengths of pipe, flattened on one end for a distance of 8 in. and bent to a 45° angle as shown. The upper portion is slotted with a heavy hacksaw blade, for the reception of the barbed wire, and the flattened portion is nailed to the outside of the fence post with long spikes. Paint, applied both internally and externally by dipping, will keep the pipe from rusting.

After the wire has been pushed into the slot, and has been pulled up tightly, a blow with a light hammer on the edge of the slot will clinch the wire. This arrangement is the simplest and most effective way of fastening the wire to the pipe.—J. V. Romig, Allentown, Pa.

A Slanting Fence Top That Keeps the Poultry in the Yard: The Supports for the Barbed Wire are Made of Pipe

Truck Attachment for Handling Armatures

It is usually a difficult and time-consuming task to move heavy armatures, as they must be handled with great care in order to avoid damaging the winding, commutator, or the shaft. A couple of iron arms, attached to an ordinary two-wheel hand truck, have been found to facilitate this work greatly. The arms are bent as shown, faced with sheet lead, and bolted to the truck in place of the regular bracket. Armatures up to 15 and 20 in. in diameter, or other machine parts mounted on shafts, can readily be handled by one man on a truck of this type, providing, of course, the length does not exceed the distance between the arms.—Chas. J. Le Compte, St. Louis, Mo.

Attachment for Hand Truck That Facilitates the Handling of Armatures: With It One Man can Handle an Armature That Ordinarily would Require Two Men

Rack for Drying Blueprints

Drying blueprints on a rack, as shown in the drawing, is a considerable improvement on the usual method of drying them over a line. A triangular frame of wood is built, as shown, the wooden crosspieces having a number of small spikes driven through them so as to project about ½ in. in front. The crosspieces are set far enough away from each other to allow a good circulation of air around the wet prints, when they are hung on the points to dry. A pan underneath catches the water dripping from the prints.

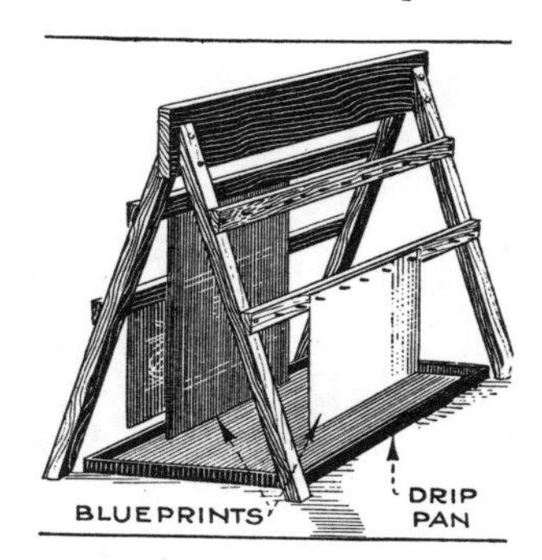

Height Gauge Made from Planer Gauge

The addition of a blade to the common planer gauge provides the mechanic with a very satisfactory height gauge. The blade is made of tool steel, ground to a knife edge, as shown, slotted, hardened, and tempered, and the bottom surface ground true. The knurled screw that fastens it to the gauge has a thread of the same size as the regular extension blocks for the gauge. The gauge is set, in the usual manner, with an outside micrometer, and the blade then clamped in place. With the use of the extension blocks, the gauge has quite a wide range of adjustment.—G. W. Nusbaum, Takoma Park, D. C.

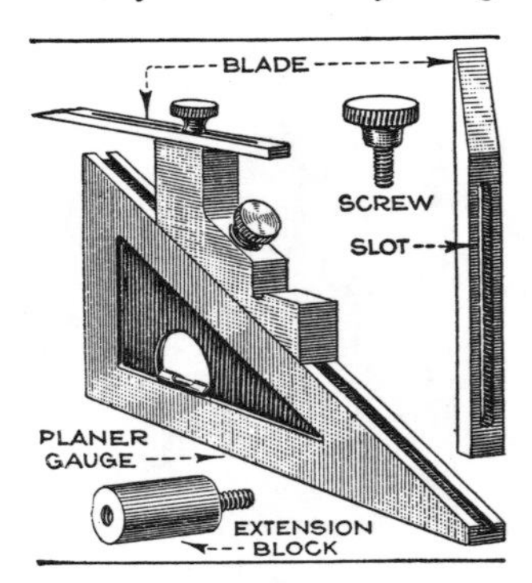

Extractor for Locomotive Brasses

Many railroads are compelled to maintain small repair shops at outlying points to take care of engines running on branches, or shifting at junction points, and, as these shops are not usually fully equipped, many ingenious labor-saving devices are devised in the shops themselves.

One place, not equipped with a drop pit, was experiencing considerable trouble in removing journal bearings from engine-truck and trailer-truck boxes, as these were slid into the box from the center of the engine, and it was extremely difficult to obtain any hold on the bearing when in place in the box, even after the "sponging cellar" was removed. The extractor illustrated was found to lessen the trouble considerably. After removing the sponging cellar, the engine is jacked up, and a chisel inserted between the crown of the brass and the box. An opening is thus made into which the extractor is thrust, far enough for the lip on the end to catch the inner side of the brass. Then, by using a wrench on the square head of the long screw, the bearing can easily be withdrawn from the box. With a bearing that has run hot enough to melt the babbitt, and where the latter has run down over the axle and cooled, this has proved to be about the only method of replacing the bearings without dropping the wheels, a practice that is not always applicable in small repair shops.—C. A. Sprout, Lancaster, Pa.

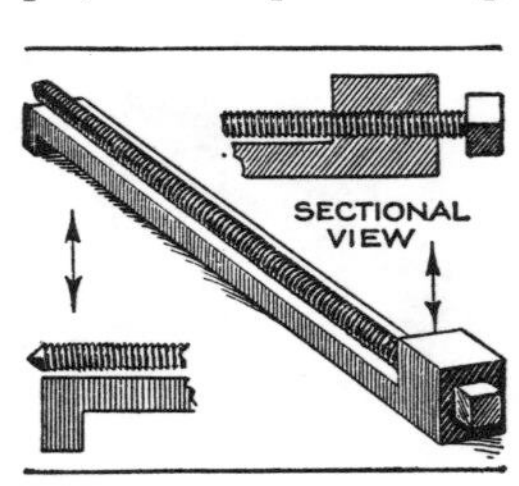

Trick Lock for Workbench Drawer

A trick lock for the workbench drawer is shown in the drawing. An ordinary butt hinge, with one leaf fastened to the underside of the drawer, as indicated, so that the loose leaf will drop down of itself, is all that is necessary. A false bottom is nailed under the drawer to conceal the hinge. A small hole is drilled in this bottom, directly under the hinge, so that the movable leaf can be pushed up with a pencil, or with the finger, to permit it to be passed over the lower edge of the drawer opening in the bench. When the drawer is closed, the leaf drops down, and prevents the drawer from being opened by anyone not acquainted with the secret.

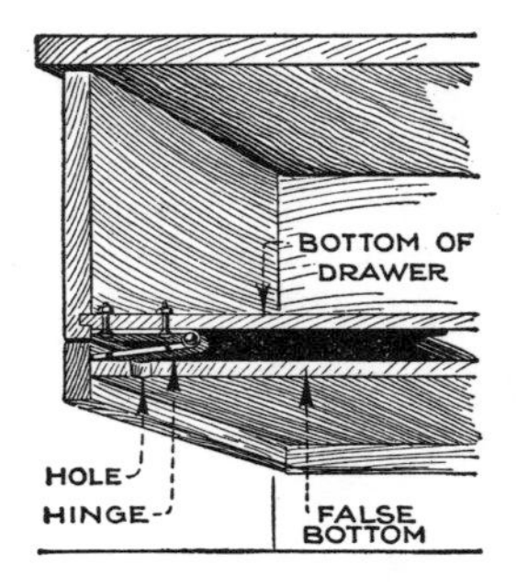

Flushing Sewer by Water Pressure

When a sewer becomes clogged with lint, as is often the case in laundries, it is quite a problem to clean it out thoroughly and quickly.

It has been found that water under pressure is about as good a means of flushing the sewer as any. The water main is connected to the sewer above the trap, as shown. The connection is, of course, made as tight as possible, so that it will be waterproof and stand considerable pressure without blowing out. A good method of connecting is to use a coupling that will fit inside the sewer pipe, at one end, and reduced at the other to

2 in., and to stuff the space between coupling and pipe with rags. Then, by wedging and bracing the coupling in place with a few heavy pieces of lumber, the connection is made secure. A 2-in. pipe is then connected from the coupling to the water main.

Water, under pressure of about 60 lb., is then turned on, and the obstruction will be forced away. By employing this means, the expense and time of digging up the sewer are eliminated.

Radius-Finding Tool

The tool shown in the illustration will be found very useful to machinists, patternmakers, and others. With it the diameters of broken gear wheels, pulleys, and other parts, of which only a portion of the rim remains, can be found, or the radius of any arc determined. It consists of two arms, cut from sheet metal to the shape shown, and slotted along their centers, to fit a small clamping screw with a flat head. Two points are filed on the end of each arm, as indicated in the drawing, on a line square with the centers of the arms. When in use, the four points are brought into contact with the curve or arc, and the nut tightened. The flat head of the screw has a fine mark in the center, and measurements may be made with a pair of dividers from this mark to one of the points. A wide range of radii is covered with this tool.

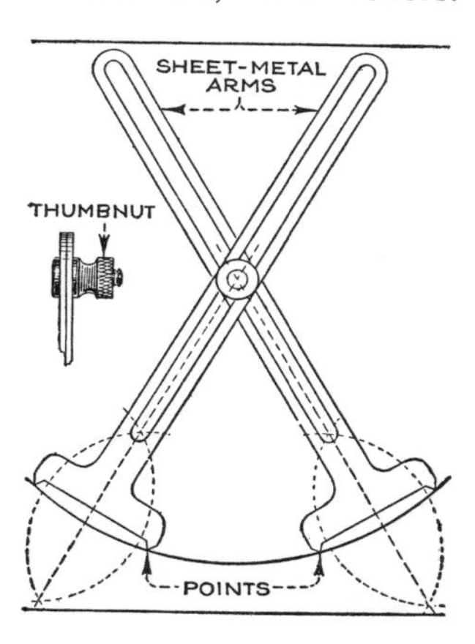

Cementing Gasoline-Line Couplings

While working on gasoline equipment, such as stove burners, one will often find a union or coupling that leaks, no matter how much white lead or other compound is applied. It has been found that if the ends to be connected are given a liberal application of ordinary liquid glue, tightened, and allowed to dry, the joint will be permanently leak-proof.

Novel Spanner Wrench

The illustration shows a spanner wrench that can be used on a large variety of work. It is made of bar stock, bent to the shape indicated, with the ends overlapping for the length of one side. A number of grooves are filed between these ends, as shown, to allow the insertion of small pins. A bolt or screw passing through the center of both ends enables the pins to be clamped in position. By having the grooves cut uneven distances apart, almost any desired spacing can be obtained. If necessary, a handle can be passed through the wrench to obtain greater leverage.

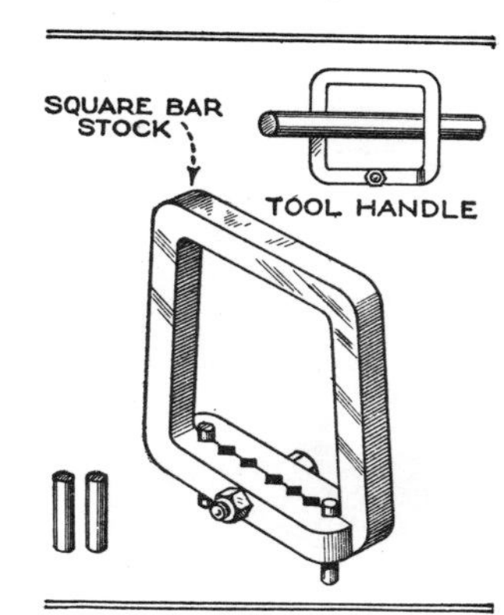

Pulling Pump Cylinders

The tool illustrated was improvised to pull up a pump cylinder that had fallen to the bottom of a well, and was found very satisfactory. It consists of an iron bar, to one end of which two iron dogs are loosely pivoted, as shown, on a rivet extending through both dogs and the bar. Small pins are driven into holes drilled in the bar, below the dogs, to keep them from falling below a horizontal position. Both dogs are pointed at the end, as indicated, and, when horizontal, measure a little more across than the inside diameter of the cylinder. The bar is threaded at the upper end, a length of ¾-in. pipe screwed onto it, and the device lowered into the well, additional lengths of pipe being screwed on, until the bar strikes the bottom of the cylinder. Upon pulling up on the pipe, the dogs dig into the wall of the cylinder and allow it to be lifted with ease.—Ed. Henderson, Lake Mills, Ia.

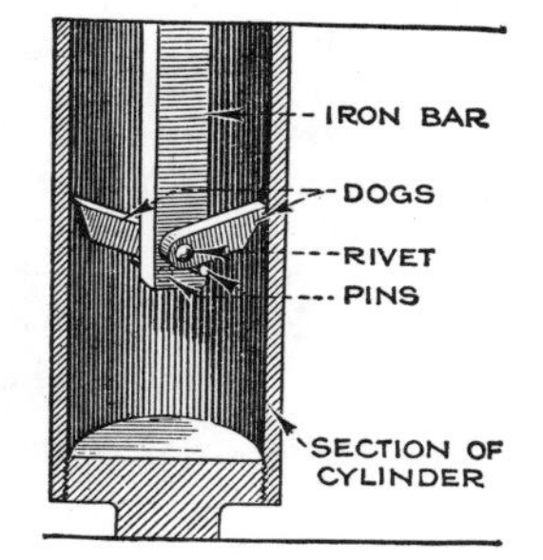

Shield for Post Holes

When setting up large posts or poles, a considerable quantity of dirt is usually pushed into the hole by the end of the

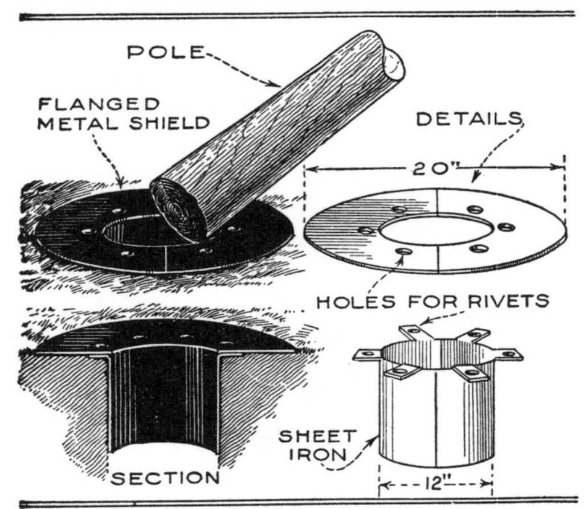

A Metal Shield That Prevents Dirt from being Pushed into the Hole When Setting Up Large Posts or Poles

pole, and this very often must be removed in order to sink the pole to the proper depth. To eliminate this difficulty a sheet-iron shield for the hole has been found very useful.

The shield consists of two semicircular lengths of sheet iron, to which a split flange is riveted, as shown at the right. The exact dimensions of these parts, of course, depend on the diameter of the poles, although the dimensions given in the drawing will serve in most cases. The guard is inserted in the hole as indicated, and can easily be removed after the pole has been set in place.

Tool Holds Auto-Cylinder Blocks for Preheating

An Indianapolis welder uses the simple but ingenious tool shown for handling automobile-cylinder blocks in a preheating furnace. It is usually necessary, when preheating the blocks, to turn them over often, and this tool reduces the labor required to the minimum.

The apparatus consists of a short piece of 3-in. pipe, welded to a long piece of 2½-in. pipe, which is drilled for a cross handle. A tee, which is a sliding fit on the 2½-in. pipe, is fitted with a smaller pipe, and this, in turn, with an elbow and horizontal pipe which has a hoist hook on it, to allow the assembly to be suspended from a crane.

The 3-in. pipe is fitted with a casting, as shown, which is fastened solidly to the pipe by setscrews, and which carries two arms, made of 1-in. square steel, bent at right angles, and held in a slot in the casting by means of a setscrew and plate, as shown in the sectional detail. These arms straddle the cylinder block, and support it, when the 3-in. pipe is thrust into the cylinder, and permit the cylinder to be manipulated in any manner that may be desired.

The crane used has a track running over the furnace, and the hoist can be swiveled so as to bring the block to any desired position.

The furnace used is of firebrick, built on an iron table, and is provided with doors, about 6 in. deep, swinging on a vertical rod which is welded to a clamp and fastened to the table. There are six doors, so that a six-cylinder block can be handled if necessary.

If a four-cylinder block is in the furnace, and it is necessary to turn it, the procedure is as follows: Four of the doors are opened, the remainder being kept shut, to conserve heat as much as possible; the 3-in. pipe is then thrust into a cylinder, with the arms straddling the block. The block is hoisted enough to enable it to be withdrawn, the setscrew on the tee is loosened, the block turned by means of the handle, the screw tight-

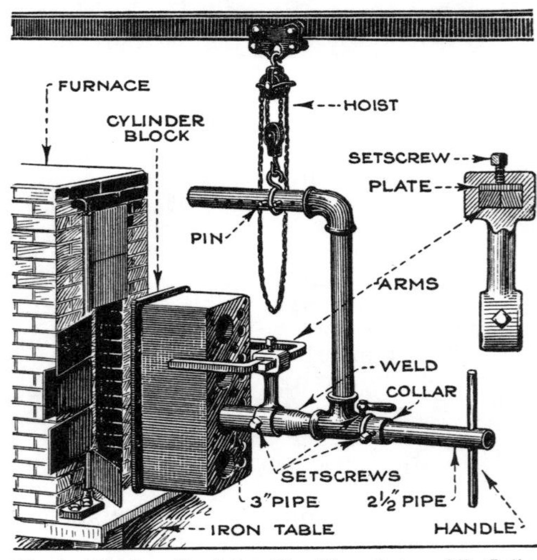

Simple Rigging Used for Handling Automobile-Cylinder Blocks When Placing Them in a Preheating Furnace, or Removing Them for Welding

ened, and the block replaced. There is no heavy lifting, no loss of time, and no waste of heat.—L. C. Land, Greenfield, Indiana.

Building a Small Horizontal Steam Engine

By HAROLD E. BENSON

THE small engine described in this article was built by the writer in his spare time—about an hour a day for four months—and drives the machinery in a small shop. At 40-lb. gauge pressure, the engine runs at 150 r.p.m., under full load, and delivers a little over .4 brake horsepower. A cast steam chest, with larger and more direct steam ports, to reduce condensation losses; less clearance in the cylinder ends, and larger bearing surfaces in several places, would bring the efficiency of the engine up to a much higher point than this. In the writer's case, however, the engine is delivering ample power for the purpose to which it is applied, and consequently these changes were not made, but, if the engine is to be used for continuous rather than intermittent service, it would be foolish to waste power costing more than the changes needed to conserve it.

It might be remarked, at this point, that no method of construction described here is to be taken as the best; many better methods of making each part will doubtless occur to the reader. Some improvements that were thought of too late to be incorporated in the engine will be mentioned in the proper place.

The cylinder, shown in Fig. 1, is made from a piece of steel pipe, selected with special regard to the condition of the inner surface. This may be bored to size, and lapped, or ground. A standard inside diameter will make the fitting of a standard auto-engine piston ring easy. The ends are threaded on the lathe, standard pipe-thread size, while supported on two conical hardwood blocks, held on a threaded mandrel, and drawn firmly into the cylinder ends with nuts and washers. The standard mandrels for this purpose, if available, are more convenient. The rectangular plate A, that supports the rear end of the cylinder, is also bored and threaded on the lathe, using a four-jaw independent chuck to hold it. This plate, the rear cylinder head, and a copper gasket are clamped together, and the similar holes in each all drilled at one time.

The front cylinder head is a pipe cap, the exterior of which is turned to present a more pleasing appearance, and drilled and threaded to receive the stuffing box, Fig. 2. The distance between the edge of the front-end steam port and the inner side of the cap, when screwed home, should be much less than that shown, not over 1/4 in., for efficiency, and the same at the rear end. When the cap has been permanently screwed on the cylinder, one side is flattened, as shown, on the shaper or grinder, and the steam ports laid out and drilled. It would be a decided advantage to make these ports as much larger than given as is possible, as the efficiency with 1/2-in. ports is far below what it might be.

View of the Engine Complete, Ready to be Mounted on the Bed and to be Connected to the Steam Line: The Total Cost of Building Was $15.40; This may be Considerably Reduced by Following Closely the Directions Given

To make the stuffing box, a length of 2-in. cast-iron rod is drilled to fit the piston rod, then turned out at the front, recessed to a width of 5/8 in. for the packing, and threaded to fit the gland nut. The piece is then reversed in the lathe, and the outside threaded to fit the cylinder. After cutting off, the wrench flats are ground on the shoulder. The gland nut is made of brass-bar stock, threaded to fit the stuffing box, and the hexagon ground on it. When the parts are assembled, with the packing in place, the piston and rod should work smoothly, but stiffly, in stuffing box and cylinder, and be almost immovable when the ports are closed.

The piston is made of cast iron, and undercut to reduce the weight, as in Fig.

3. The groove is turned to suit a standard 3/16 by 3-in. piston ring. The piston rod, which is of steel, must be fitted to the piston with great care, to insure their being exactly square with each other. If the face of the piston is square with the edge, the inner nut on the rod faced off square in the lathe, while on the rod, and the piston and locknuts then put on and tightened, no difficulty should be experienced.

The steam chest, shown in Figs. 4 to 7, is the hardest part of the engine to make. In this case, it is built up, using a square bar for the port block, an angle piece for the bottom and side, two endpieces, and a cover.

The port block, Fig. 5, is made of soft steel, the ports being drilled in as indicated by the dotted lines, from the ends and front, so as to provide a continuous passage for the steam. The exhaust port is drilled in from the front and bottom faces. The endpieces of the steam chest are held in place by short 1/2-in. capscrews, tapped into, and closing, the holes in the ends of the port block, and by long 5/16-in. bolts connecting the outer edges. The stuffing box on the front endpiece, Fig. 7, is made by brazing a blank nut to it, and making a snug-fitting gland for it, as shown in Fig. 8. The gland is drilled a neat fit for the valve rod, and for the 1/4-in. bolts that draw it into the stuffing box against the packing.

All parts of the steam chest are ground flat and smooth before assembling, and, when chest and cylinder are completed, are brazed together, all joints, the exhaust pipe, and the supports being brazed at the same time. When brazing, the steam ports should be plugged from inside the cylinder, to prevent any spelter from flowing into and closing them. The steam-chest cover is not brazed on, but is held by 1/4 by 3/4-in. screws, entering the port block, and by long bolts at the outer edge, passing through a heavy strip of iron below the chest. Packing is used on the steam-chest cover joint.

The slide valve, Fig. 9, is cut from a block of soft steel, or cast iron, the opening in the face being cut as deeply as possible, drilling the center hole first, and plugging it to obtain centers for the drilling of the outer holes. If the steam ports are enlarged, the dimensions of the valve must be changed; the new dimensions can be found by making a full-size layout of the ports and valve, or by making cardboard models of steam chest, valve, and ports, and adjusting these until the correct dimensions are obtained.

There is room for considerable experiment on the valve; any textbook on steam engines will provide suggestions for adding lap to the valve, to cut off the steam before the end of the stroke, and since it is comparatively easy to make this part, it is well to fit the valve to the engine after the latter is complete.

The crosshead and guides, shown in Figs. 12 and 13, are simple in construction. If a shaper or planer is available, a better construction may be made by following any of the designs seen on large engines. Oil cups on each bearing will furnish sufficient lubrication.

The connecting rod, Fig. 14, is made of 1-in. square stock, turned to a diameter of 1/2 in. in the center. The "big end" is drilled larger than the crankpin, and then sawed as indicated, so that the upper piece may be removed. Bolt holes are drilled through both pieces. When the engine is assembled, shims are placed between the halves of the big end, and babbitt poured through the oil-cup hole, around the crankpin, using putty dams on each side of the bearing. Small holes are drilled in the walls of the crankpin-bearing seat, before babbitting, to anchor the babbitt in place. The other end of the rod is fitted with a yoke and wristpin, as indicated, the diameter of the pin being made as large as possible, and run in babbitt bearings. Large-engine practice may be followed here, if desired; in fact, it will pay to study the details of large units, and to follow them as closely as possible everywhere, remembering that this description does not pretend to show the best practice, but only how the job may be done with material at hand.

The eccentric is turned from round stock, 2 in. in diameter, cutting the sheave first, then changing centers to turn the boss. The latter should be left long enough to enable it to be held in a chuck for drilling, after which it may be cut to length; the boss may be fitted so as to bear against the outboard crankshaft bearing, to prevent side motion of the crankshaft, instead of using collars.

The eccentric rod and strap are made of a length of 1/8 by 1/2-in. flat iron, as shown in Fig. 15. The valve-rod end should be fitted with a wristpin and yoke as on the connecting rod, instead of the construction indicated, which is only shown to give the dimensions. The strap that fits the groove in the eccentric is lapped to a smooth bearing surface by clamping it round a mandrel covered with fine emery and oil, and grinding until the strap fits the eccentric sheave perfectly.

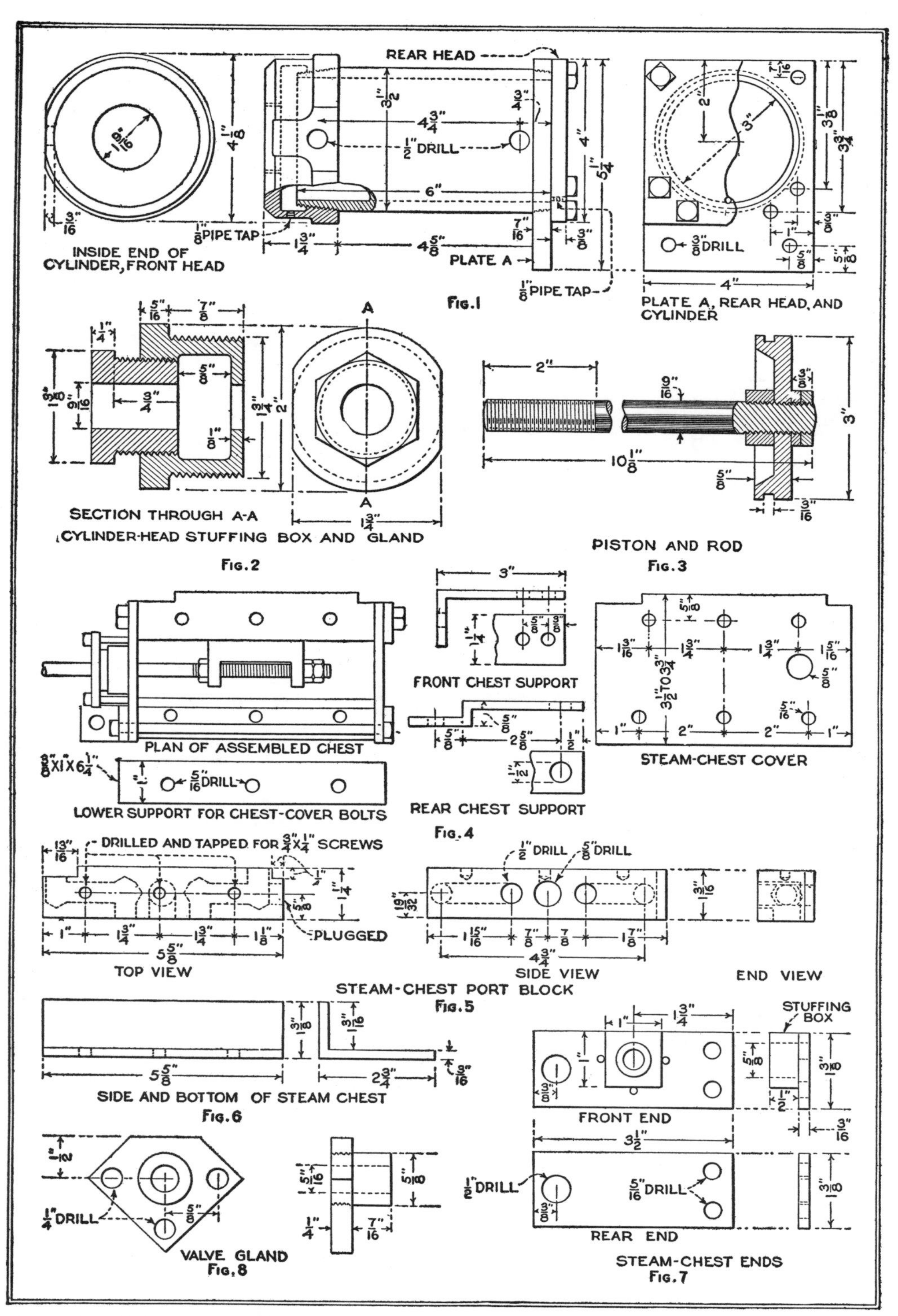

Figures 1 to 3, Complete Details of the Cylinder, Stuffing Box and Gland, Piston and Piston Rod; Figures 4 to 7 Show the Component Parts of the Steam Chest, as Built Up, and an Assembly View of the Finished Steam Chest, without the Cover; Note Carefully the Method of Drilling the Steam Ports in the Block Shown in Figure 5, and the Position of the Various Parts in the Assembly View

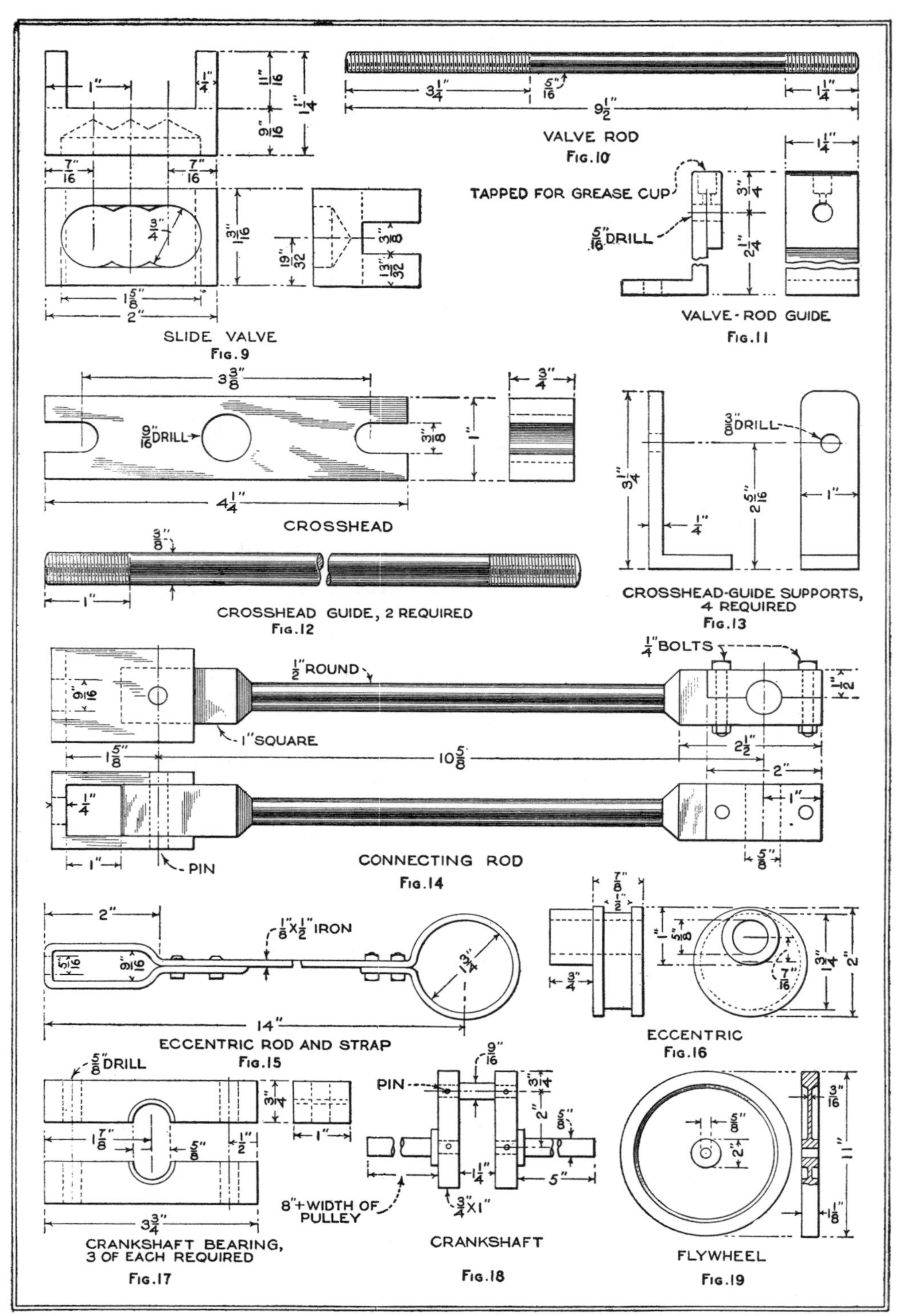

Figures **9** to **11**, Details of the Slide Valve, Valve Rod, and Guide, Showing How Opening is Drilled in Valve; Figures **12** and **13**, Crosshead, Crosshead Guides, and Crosshead-Guide Supports; Figure **14**, Detail of Connecting Rod; Figures **15** and **16**, Eccentric Rod and Strap, and Eccentric Sheave; Figures **17** and **18**, Crankshaft Bearings and Crankshaft; Figure **19**, Side View and Part Section of Flywheel

The crankshaft may be made in two ways. It may be built up as shown in Fig. 18, the ends of the shaft and the crankpin being threaded, or shouldered and pressed into the webs, and pinned. This method requires great care and accuracy, to keep the shaft ends and pin square. The shaft may also be turned from a solid bar of steel, turning the crankpin first, then moving the centers and turning the main shaft. This method makes a fine crankshaft. After turning the crankpin, the space between the webs must be blocked firmly with a piece of metal or hardwood, to prevent the webs from being sprung in when turning the main shaft.

To set the valve, the crank is put on the forward dead center, and the eccentric set 90° ahead of it, then locked. The eccentric may be led or advanced a few degrees after the engine has been running, if necessary.

The flywheels are cast slightly larger than the size shown, then turned down on the lathe until of the proper weight. This will depend upon the speed of the engine, the load, and other factors; the flywheels on the writer's engine weigh 10 lb. each, and it will be noticed that as much of the weight as possible is concentrated in the rim, the web being made as thin as practicable. The wheels are keyed to the shaft, the keyseats being cut by holding the shaft stationary in the lathe, while running the cutting tool horizontally by means of the carriage feed, and feeding the tool with the cross feed.

The construction of the three crankshaft bearings, Fig. 17, is obvious; they are drilled out, while clamped together, to allow babbitting, the metal being poured through the oil-cup holes, which are easily redrilled and tapped afterward.

The engine base, shown in the assembly views, is made of oak, 2 by 8¾ by 25 in. in dimensions. A heavy iron base bracket, or reinforcing bar, Fig. 20, is fastened to the rear of the base with lagscrews. The holes in the front of the bracket are tapped to take the cylinder and steam-chest support screws, or they may be drilled plain and pockets cut directly behind them, in the base, to receive nuts for the screws. After the cylinder assembly has been bolted down, the crosshead guides may be bolted in place, so that the crosshead will come to within an equal distance of each support at the ends of the stroke.

When constructing an engine in this manner, it is best to build the cylinder and steam chest first, and make the subsequent parts conform to the dimensions of these parts. This is essential, in any event, in the case of the crosshead-guide supports and valve-rod guide; these should not be drilled until the crosshead is attached to the piston rod and the valve rod to the valve, and the correct height for the holes determined. The same thing applies to the other supporting brackets. The center of the crankshaft must, of course, be the same as that of the piston rod. The base is cut out to clear the crank and connecting-rod end, and the bearing-bolt heads countersunk in the underside of the base. The base may be attached to a concrete or brickwork bed, if desired, by means of bolts set in place in the bed.

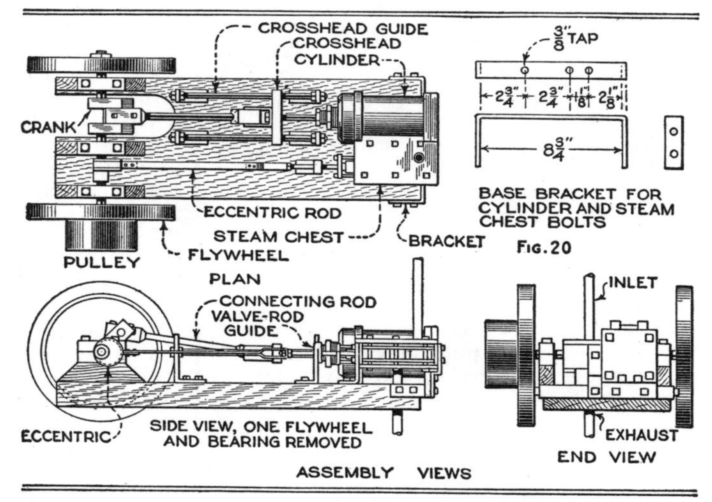

Plan, and Side and End Elevations of Horizontal Steam Engine Assembled: Figure 20 Shows the Bracket Used to Fasten the Rear-End Cylinder and Steam-Chest Supports to the Base

For lubrication of the piston, a standard cylinder lubricator, costing about $5, should be purchased, as it is not advisable to attempt to make this fitting.

The cost of this engine was $15.40 complete, most of the material being new; part of the material was wasted in experimenting, and the cost of the engine could be cut in half, were the work to be done over again.

Guard for the Planer

The illustration shows a very good knife guard for the wood planer. It is made of ¾-in. pine, cut to the shape

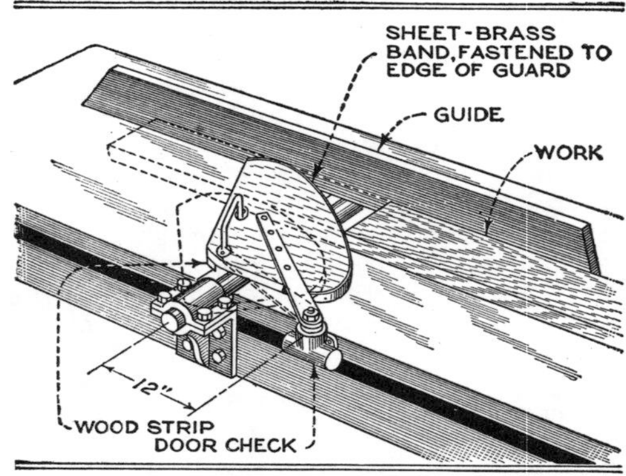

An Automatic Safety Guard for the Planer, Mounted on a Door Check: The Knives are Covered at All Times

shown, and is attached to a flat-iron lever fastened to the spindle of a common door check, which, in turn, is screwed to the edge of the planer table. The door check holds the guard tightly against the work guide, or against the edge of the work. The revolving knives are covered at all times. The edge of the guard is faced with a band of sheet brass to prevent wear. A drawer pull may be attached to the upper side of the guard to facilitate handling it on wide work.

Protecting Edges of Concrete Steps

To prevent the edges of concrete steps from being broken by the impact of heavy barrels, boxes, etc., it has been found very practical to reinforce them in the manner illustrated. Strips of galvanized iron, or other metal, as long as the steps, or at least as long as the part subjected to most wear, are bent and imbedded in the concrete, as indicated. The part of the strip imbedded is first perforated with 1-in. holes along both sides, leaving a space, about 1 in. wide, that is exposed on the edge of the tread.

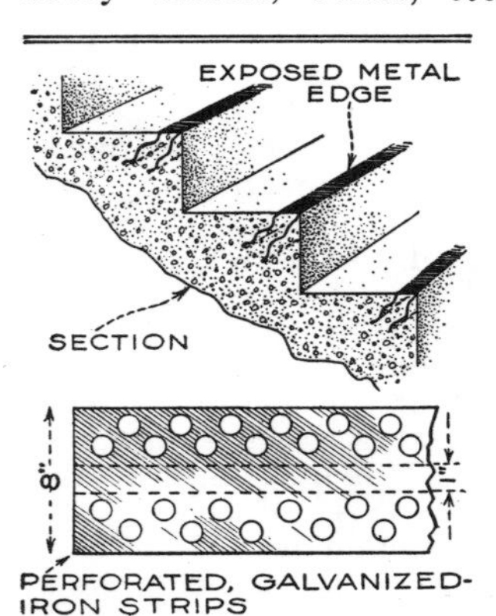

The concrete steps to the basement of a warehouse that were reinforced in this way have withstood the jars of heavy boxes for two years, and the edges do not yet show any evidence of the hard usage to which they have been subjected.

Setting Milling Cutters to Depth

The drawing shows a neat little device to aid the milling-machine operator in feeding cutters to accurate depths. It is hard to tell just when the cutter actually touches the face of the work, although, if this can be determined accurately, the rest is merely a matter of feeding the cutter to the depth indicated by the graduations on the handle.

The tool is made of thin spring steel, bent as shown, and with the ends doubled over. A short piece of 3/16-in. wire is passed through holes drilled in the body, and bent over at both sides.

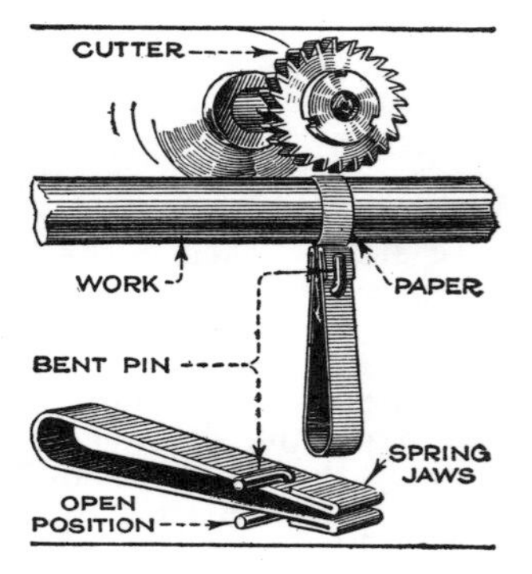

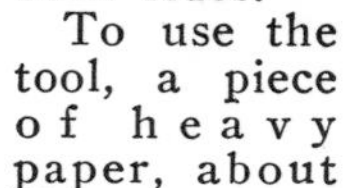

To use the tool, a piece of heavy paper, about ½ in. wide, is wrapped tightly once around the work, and the ends are caught in the jaws of the tool, which are closed on the paper by swinging the bent pin to the position shown. The table of the machine is then brought up, and at the same time run back and forth, until the revolving cutter cuts through the paper. The tool, of course, drops as soon as this occurs, warning the operator that the cutter is in contact with the work.

Scriber Set in Fountain Pen

The mechanic frequently finds it necessary to carry a scriber around, so that it is available whenever needed, but to carry it in one's pocket is rather dangerous. To overcome this difficulty, a scriber point can be set securely in the barrel of a fountain pen in the same position that the pen point and feeder otherwise occupy. The cap is screwed on the barrel as usual.

Flux for Brazing

The usual method of applying borax to metal before brazing is to apply it to the metal dry, after the metal has been thoroughly scraped or cleaned. It has been found, in a large coppersmith's shop, that a better way is to coat the metal with a solution of boracic acid. The advantage of this is that the solution penetrates every crevice, and covers the surface completely, thereby protecting it from oxidation and also from impurities while brazing. The boracic-acid solution is made by adding quantities of the acid to hot water, allowing it to remain for several hours, with an occasional shaking, and then bottling the liquid for future use.

Wall Troughs for Poultry Feed

Cleanliness and economy are effected in the chicken pen by the use of wall troughs for feed, such as shown in the illustration. They keep the feed clean, and prevent the hens from getting into the feed and scratching it out.

The upper detail shows a grain, dry-mash, or grit trough. It is made of wood, to the dimensions given, and is hung on the wall so that the bottom is about 2 in. above the ground. The lower detail shows a vegetable trough, made in a somewhat similar manner, with the exception that the front of the trough is made of coarse wire netting. Beets, potatoes, and green feed are deposited in the trough, and the hens pick them away, through the mesh, until the very last scrap disappears.

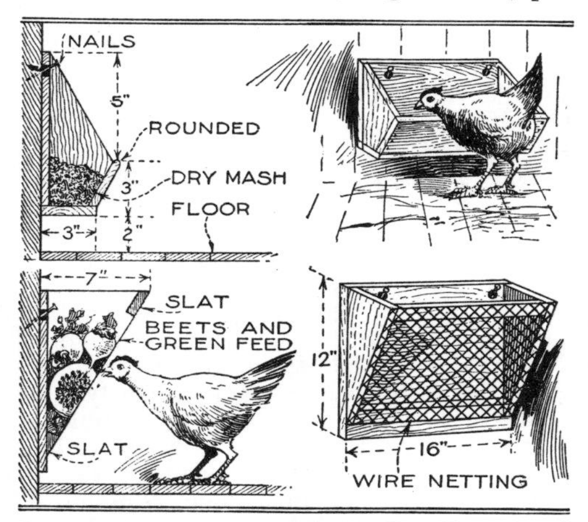

Wall Troughs for Poultry Feed: The Upper Detail Shows a Grain Trough and the Lower Detail a Vegetable Trough

Holding Containers on Bench

The drawing illustrates an excellent method of holding small bottles and containers in place on the workbench, to prevent them from being upset, pushed off, or broken accidentally.

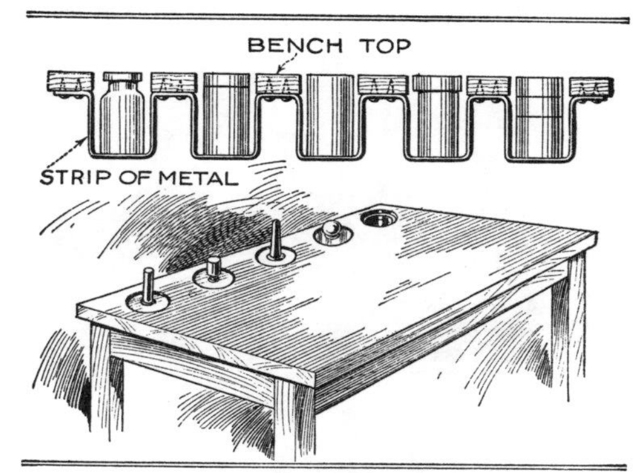

Neat and Convenient Method of Holding Containers on a Bench to Prevent Them from being Overturned Accidentally, or Damaged

A number of holes are bored through the bench top, near the rear edge, so that the bottles will be well out of the way. A strip of metal, bent as indicated, and fastened to the underside of the bench top, holds the containers in place. The holes are bored of various sizes, corresponding to the diameters of the bottles, and the metal strip is bent so that the top of each container is flush with the surface of the bench top.

An Improvised Trammel

Frequently the machinist or carpenter needs to describe a circle or arc beyond the range of the ordinary dividers. This is easily done by clamping the dividers and a scriber to a stout wooden strip, in the manner illustrated. The pointed ends of both scriber and dividers are spaced a distance apart approximately equal to the radius of the arc to be described, and exact adjustment can then be made by means of the screw on the dividers. This trammel serves just as well as the regular instrument.

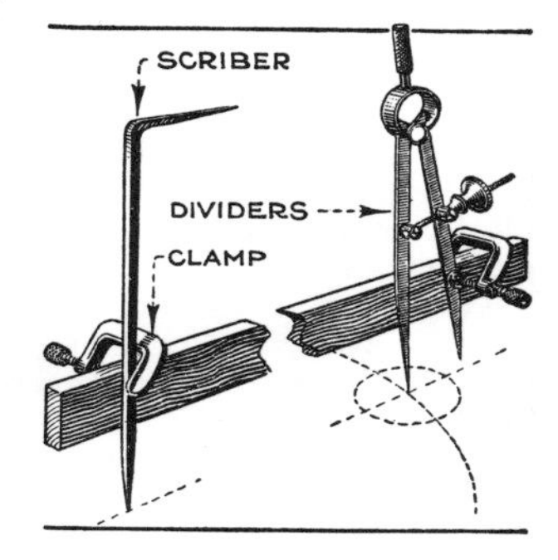

Removing Willows from Open Drain

It is usually a difficult matter to remove willows from the banks of a small stream of water, except in the dry sea-

An Effective Method of Removing Willows from an Open Drain with the Beam of a Breaking Plow Hooked behind the Roots

son, and, at that time, other farm duties, such as cultivating and harvesting, are pressing and require all of the time. Hence the work of removing the willows is often neglected until the channel is almost choked.

By employing the method shown in the photographs, I was able to remove the willows easily and completely during the wet season. I obtained the beam of an old breaking plow, and after heating it, gave it a quarter twist a few inches from the back end, so that the share was turned at right angles to the beam. This blade I sharpened, and then replaced the clumsy plow clevis on the end with a smaller one.

With a few feet of log chain attached to the beam, and a team of good horses to pull the plow, the sharpened end was hooked behind the roots, and the team started. The result was that the blade drew still deeper under the roots and removed not only the roots and bushes, but, at the same time, a considerable portion of the earth that had accumulated in the ditch.

I have found this method quite the speediest I ever tried.—Elmer Hufferd, Rushville, Ind.

Tamping Explosives

Metal tools of any kind should never, under any circumstances, be used for tamping explosives in bore holes, or to press the charge into place, even in soft ground, as there is always the danger of striking a pebble, which might produce a spark sufficient to ignite the charge.

For loading and tamping, only a wooden tamping stick should be used. For shallow work, an old broom handle is ideal; for deep holes, when a long stick is needed, a straight sapling can be used to advantage.

For tamping horizontal holes, where a heavy tamping stick, such as one made of oak or hickory, would be difficult to manipulate, a stick made of a light wood, such as pine or bamboo, is very desirable. Bamboo fishing poles, which are light, straight, and strong, make ideal tamping sticks under these conditions. It is positively dangerous for a powerful man to ram a charge of high explosives into a bore hole with a heavy tamping stick, even if it is made of wood.

In deep holes, a very long, cumbersome tamping stick would be necessary, so a tamping block is used in holes that are vertical, or nearly so. This consists of a round piece of wood, from 3 to 6 ft. long, and a little smaller in diameter than the hole, so that it will slide easily in it. A small rope is attached to the center of one end, by boring a hole diagonally from the center out through the side, countersinking the hole on the side, then threading the rope through the hole from the end, knotting it, and pulling it back, so that the knot is drawn into the countersink and does not interfere with the sliding of the block in the hole.

The block should be made of hardwood, to resist wear, no metal parts should be used, and it should not be too heavy. It is operated by raising it a foot or two and allowing it to drop on the "stemming," as the tamping material is called. The block, of course, is withdrawn when fresh stemming is dropped into the hole. The tool recently described by one of our contributors, which was made from a long bolt, has been condemned by the leading explosives experts and insurance companies, for the reasons stated above, and our readers are warned against its use.

¶Are you in doubt as to the best type of radio instrument to construct or purchase? Write to our Bureau of Information.

Sleeping Porches for Hospital

The illustration shows how an old western hospital was converted into a modern open-air sanitarium by reconstructing the windows so as to permit the beds to be pushed out onto small porches.

The window openings, which were of the ordinary size, were cut down to the level of the floor. A small porch, supported by iron brackets, was built on the outside of each window. A light metal railing was built around the porch and fastened to the wall, and the porch was screened in to keep out flies and other insects. Two doors were substituted for the part of the wall that was cut out below the window, as may be seen in the lower photograph.

With this arrangement the bed can be drawn into the room during stormy weather, and the doors and window closed. No drafts are encountered when the doors and windows of the rooms are kept closed. Shades can very readily be attached to the porch screens to keep off the rays of the sun, if desired; however, no shades are used on the building shown in the photograph, although it is located in a country where the sun shines with little interruption for long periods.—Edward H. Flaharty, Denver, Colorado.

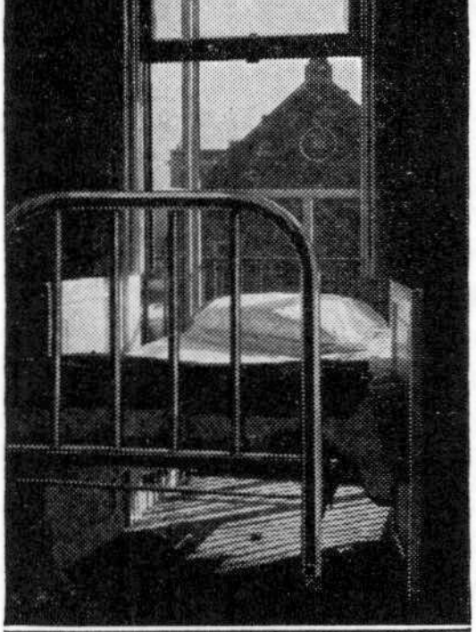

Above: Exterior of an Old Hospital That was Converted into a Modern Open-Air Sanitarium. Below: Interior of One of the Improvised Sleeping Porches

Reseating Globe Valves

After the seat of a globe valve had been ground several times, it became necessary to renew it. Instead of employing the usual method of tapping out and using a threaded seat, I made a plain tapered seat and forced it in place. The job was accomplished quickly because no tapping was necessary. Hard metal was used for both seat and valve.—Robert D. W. Berry, Philadelphia. Pa.

Handling Cable Ends

Anyone who has used a wire cable for hoisting purposes, or elevator work, knows the difficulty of passing the end through a hole or eye only slightly larger than the cable itself; the end will twist and turn or flare out regardless of how well it has been wired, and perhaps the tie wire must be driven back to permit the cable to pass through.

To overcome this difficulty, wire the cable as usual on the end, and also 6 in. from the end. Heat the end of the cable with an acetylene torch, or dip it first in molten lead for a few minutes, to draw the temper, and then in soldering flux, and solder. When cool, file off the surplus solder, and with a pair of heavy pliers twist the cable tightly. It will be found that it will remain twisted and can be bent any way desired. By heating the cable the hemp core is burned out, making the cable smaller. When using this method, always cut the cable long enough to allow the end to be cut off after the cable clamps are in place.

Making Tight Hose Connections

To make a tight rubber-hose connection to an air or acetylene tank, or to connect two pieces of rubber hose on a short nipple, heat the tapered end of a punch and insert this into the end of the hose for a few moments, just long enough to melt the surface of the rubber slightly. Then slip the hose over the nipple as quickly as possible. It will be found that the hose will slip over the nipple very easily, providing, of course, that the nipple is not too large. After the rubber has cooled, it will be on so tight that it cannot be removed except by cutting. No wires or clamps are necessary on a connection made in this way.—W. E. Rausch, Milan, Mich.

A "Sun Porch" for the Beehive

The newest "wrinkle" in beehive construction is the "sun porch." It is made of wood, with a glass front, and fits snugly into the opening of the hive case, as indicated in the photograph. It is claimed that the attachment adds to the warmth of the hive, and prevents much of the bee mortality that is usual during winter and early spring.

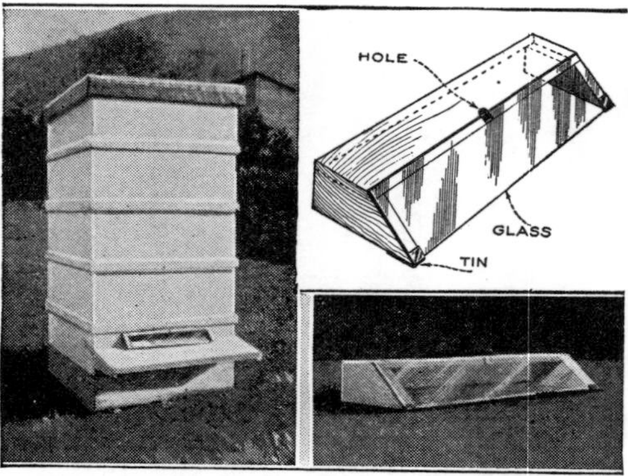

A Detachable Glass "Sun Porch" for the Beehive That Prevents Much of the Usual Bee Mortality during Winter and Early Spring

The porch provides a protected and well-lighted air space, about 5 in. wide, between the inner and outer entrances, into which snow and rain cannot penetrate, and enables the bees to bring out the dead ones all through the winter, so that the floorboards are kept sweet and clean. The framework of the sun porch is made just large enough to fit in the outer entrance of the hive case, and to butt against the block of the inner entrance. The glass front, which is cut to fit the framework, projects about 2 in. over the alighting board. A small piece of tin is nailed on the bottom of each of the sloping ends of the frame, and is bent up in front to form a holder for the glass. When the glass is in position, the bottom edge is about ½ in. above the alighting board, so that the bees have a clear entrance all along. A ½ by ¾-in. slot is cut in the center of the framework, at the top of the glass, to allow any bees that may run up the glass to fly out.

The sun porch makes it possible for the bees to be left with little or no attention throughout the winter, as there is little danger of suffocation through the blocking of entrances by snow or ice. In the early spring, the space inside the glass is heated by the sun, and the bees revel in this and become warm before flying out. The porch also acts as a protection against robbing. It is easily removed or placed in position.—R. Franklin Mundorff, Kansas City, Mo.

Window Display for Coal Dealer

A retail coal dealer has arranged a display that is considerably more attractive than the usual assortment of lumps placed on exhibition in the office window. Wooden boxes, about 3 in. wide and as deep, were made in the form of letters spelling the word "coal." These boxes were painted white for the sake of contrast, filled with small lumps of coal, and placed in the window.

Oil Distributor for Milling Machines

The illustration shows an oil distributor that will supply a large surface, and that is especially valuable on form-milling cutters, to wash chips away. It is made of a piece of fine wire, twisted into a decreasing-pitch spiral, and mounted on a forked support, as shown. The weight of the oil running down the spiral causes the latter to revolve, at a speed dependent upon the amount of oil supplied. When the oil reaches the sharp twist where the pitch of the spiral is smallest, centrifugal force causes the oil to fly off. The area covered by the spray of oil depends upon the distance of the spiral above the work, the size and shape of the spiral, and the amount of oil supplied. The ends of the spiral are pointed to reduce friction and are set in punch marks made in the ends of the forked support.

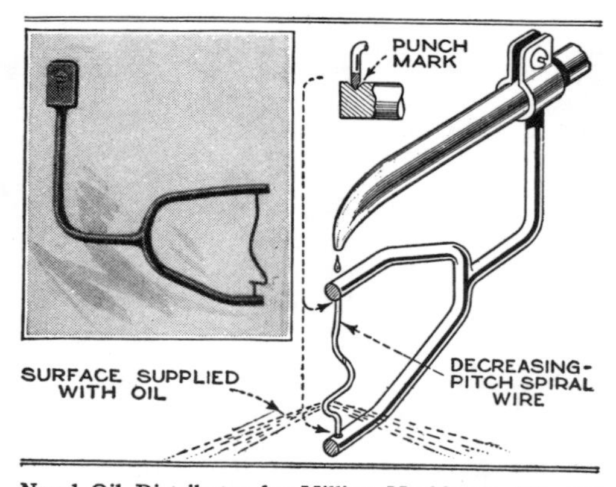

Novel Oil Distributor for Milling Machines: The Oil Running down the Spiral Causes It to Revolve, and the Final Twist Throws the Oil Off

Green-Gold Plating Solution

A green-gold plating solution for jewelers' use can be made by using regular yellow-gold solution, and adding to it, while plating, ordinary silverplating solution, watching the article closely until the desired color is obtained. Use a green-gold anode, and attach to the same wire a lead anode, the same size as the gold one. After plating, the high lights are brought out by rubbing with a wet finger, dipped in bicarbonate of soda.

Homemade Gas Torch

Sometime ago I saw a homemade gas torch used for heating a collar on a large shaft. The torch was made of pipe and fittings, and was so arranged that either a yellow or a hot blue flame could be obtained by the use of a sliding-valve arrangement to regulate the air supply.

The nozzle is made from a piece of 1½-in. pipe, 18 in. long, slotted as shown, threaded at one end, and provided with a cap. A hole, drilled in the exact center of the cap, is threaded to receive the jet.

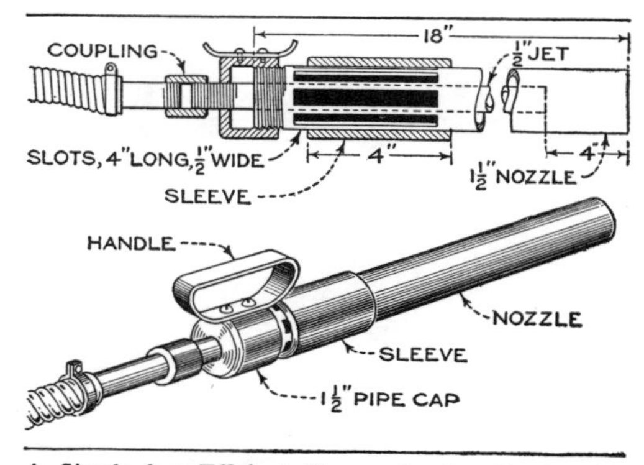

A Simple but Efficient Homemade Gas Torch with Which Either a Yellow or a Hot Blue Flame can be Obtained

This consists of a piece of ½-in. pipe, 15 in. long, having one end threaded for about 3 in., and screwed into the cap, as shown, so that the end of the jet comes about 4 in. from the end of the nozzle. A sleeve, made from a 4-in. length of pipe, is slipped over the nozzle to cover the slots; the sleeve should be a good sliding fit on the nozzle. The handle can be made from a length of strap iron, riveted or screwed to the cap as shown. The amount of gas fed to the torch is controlled by a valve in the line, and the air supply by means of the sleeve over the air slots.—L. B. Robbins, Harwich, Mass.

Improving the "Steamboat"

The drawing shows an improvement on the "steamboat" used for tracing designs and drawings. The improvement consists in fitting two wooden clamps on opposite sides of the box to hold the work securely on the glass, and to prevent it from being moved accidentally while tracing.

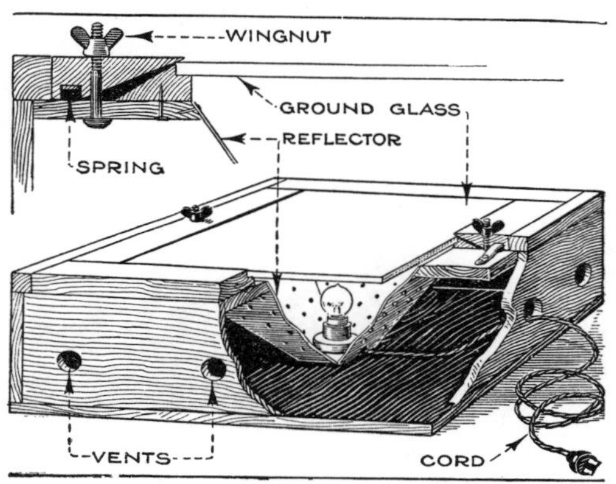

A "Steamboat" can be Greatly Improved by Providing It with Two Wooden Clamps on Opposite Sides to Hold the Work on the Glass Securely

The clamps are maple strips, held in place with bolts provided with wingnuts, as indicated. A flat steel spring is fitted under each clamp, to raise it when the wingnut is loosened in order to make it easy to insert the work.

Removing Tight Bolts or Screws

A convenient and effective method of removing tight bolts or screws is to place an ordinary detachable socket from a wrench set over the nut, so that two wrenches can be applied at the same time, as shown; the larger wrench on the side end of the socket keeps the socket from splitting open under the force applied to it with the smaller wrench. In almost every case this method will be found to loosen the bolt, without springing a good wrench, which is often done on jobs of this kind.

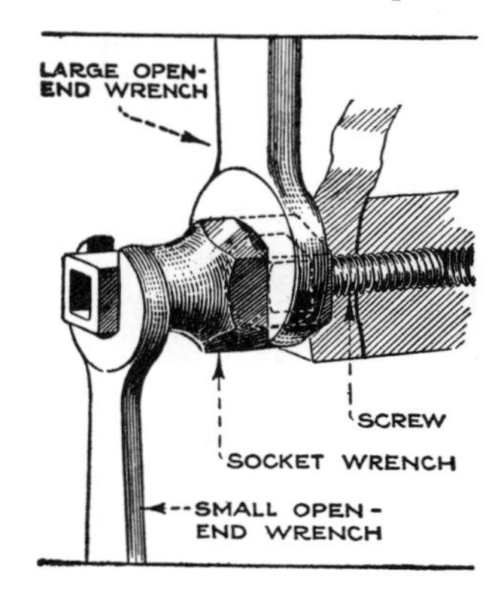

Serviceable Homemade Hoist

The portable hoist shown in the illustration has been found of great utility by a contractor whose work involves the placing of concrete burial vaults weighing about 1,800 pounds.

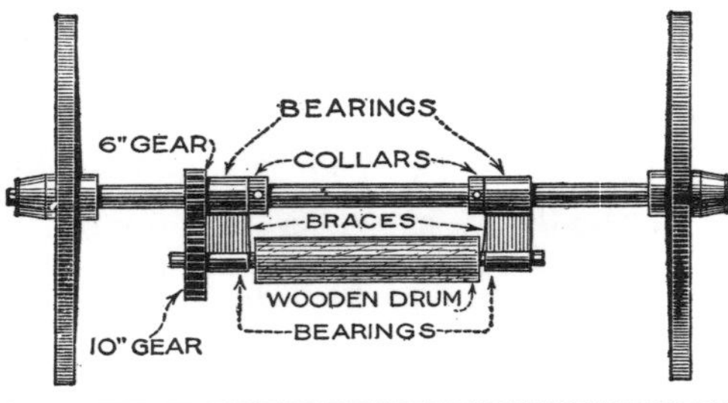

Above: The Homemade Hoist Set Up Ready for Use. Below: Details of the Hoist Mechanism

The legs of the hoist are 12-ft. lengths of 4 by 4-in. stock, two of the legs being braced in the form of a triangle by a crosspiece and uprights of the same stock. The other leg swings, on a 1-in. bolt, between the first two, at the apex of the triangle. This leg is swung out when the hoist is to be used, and folded in against the other two when the hoist is to be hauled away.

A 6-in. wooden drum is fastened to an axle that runs in bearings bolted to the vertical 4 by 4-in. pieces, and a 10-in. gear is keyed on one end of the axle. This gear meshes with a 6-in. gear, keyed on a shaft that runs in bearings mounted on the other side of the uprights, and two buggy wheels are fastened to the outer ends of the shaft. By loosening the collars shown in the detail, the shaft can be slid endwise, to put the gears out of mesh, when moving the hoist.

A heavy piece of wood, 2½ ft. long and fastened to one of the legs by a bolt, so as to permit its being pressed against the rim of the wheel, is used as a brake when lowering the load, and a long iron bar, sliding in a flat-iron bracket bolted to one of the legs, can be used to hold the load at any desired height, by thrusting it between the wheel spokes.

A heavy block and tackle is slung from the center leg by a clevis, the end of the cable being attached to the drum. Two long bolts, fastened through the triangular-frame legs, about 3 ft. from the bottom, provide handholds for moving the frame about, and spikes are driven into the lower ends of each leg to prevent slipping.

A large hook, fastened to the upper end of the center leg, allows the hoist to be attached to the rear end of a truck or car.—J. C. Coyle, Colorado Springs, Colo.

Guide and Die for Punching

When punching holes in sheet metal, it is sometimes difficult to locate the die exactly under the punch, especially when the holes to be punched are at some distance from the edge. To facilitate punching such holes, I made the tool shown in the illustration. It consists of the two opposite outer leaves of an elliptic rear spring. These I heated, straightened out, and cut to a convenient length, and then fitted the sockets so that, when hinged together, there was no sideplay. I drilled holes of various sizes through both pieces, after hinging, and then retempered the pieces. The tool thus made is placed over the sheet, so that a hole of the proper size is over the place where the hole is to be punched. It is then an easy matter to punch the sheet; the bottom piece serves the purpose of a die and is always in the exact position to receive the punch as it is driven through.—G. G. McVicker, North Bend, Neb.

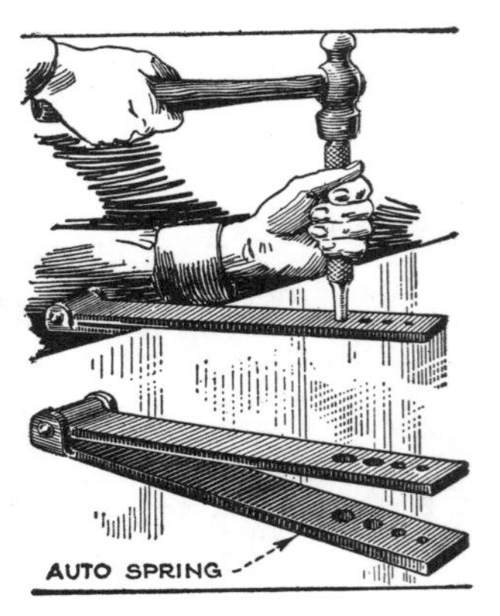

A Convenient Welding and Cutting Table

BY A. S. JAMIESON

A GREAT many pieces sent to the welding shop for repair are very awkward to set up or clamp while being welded. The illustration shows a table, in use in a shop doing much repairing, that will clamp and hold almost any piece in any desired position, and that has saved a great deal of time and money.

There is very little machining to be done on the table, beyond drilling and tapping. The top, which is 4 ft. square, and the legs, 24 in. high, are made of 2-in. angle iron. The top is cut and assembled on the floor, and all joints "tacked"; the legs are clamped on and tacked also, whereupon all joints are securely welded. A 3-in. length of the same angle iron is welded to the inside of each leg, to support the table top as shown in the detail, Fig. 1; no other bracing is necessary.

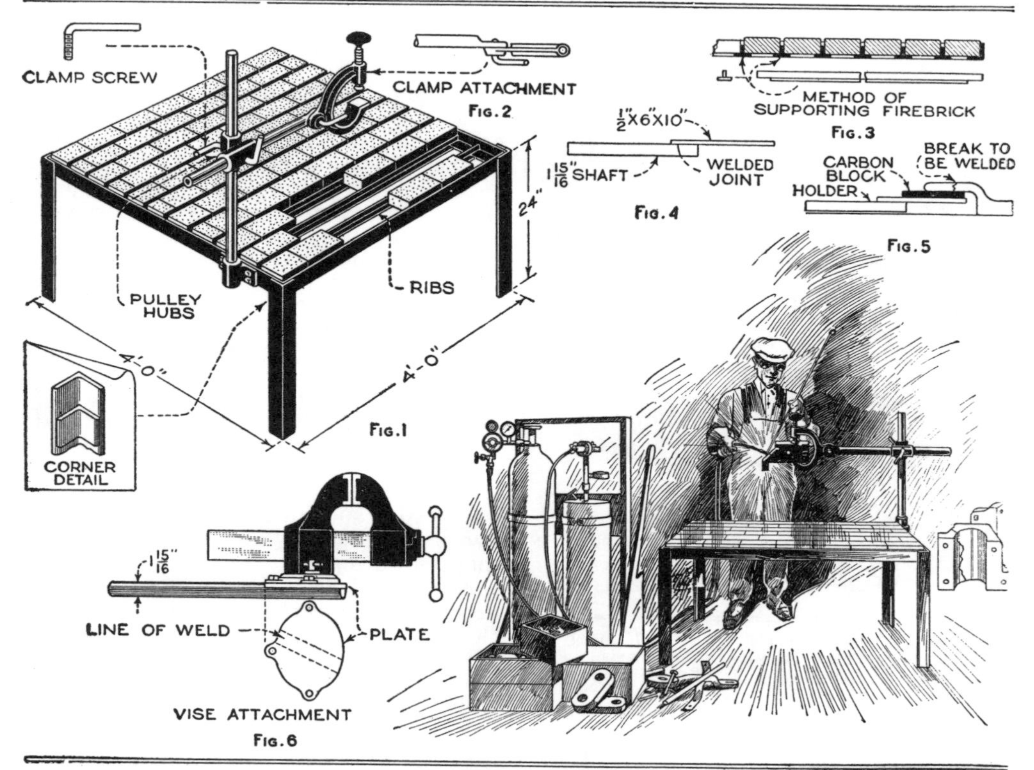

Convenient Worktable for the Welding Shop: By Means of the Attachments Shown, Work of Any Shape can be Held. The Firebrick Top Permits Cutting to be Done without Injury to the Table

The work support is made by welding a disk, of ½-in. plate, on one end of an old pillow block, and bolting the block to one side of the table; a 3-ft. length of 1 15/16-in. shafting fits in the block. Two old pulley hubs, 1 15/16-in. shaft size, are ground smooth and welded together, at right angles, drilled and tapped for clamp screws, and slipped on the upright, as shown. A second 3-ft. length of 1 15/16-in. shafting, forged or cut flat on one end, and fitted with a heavy C-clamp, as shown in Fig. 2, is then slipped into the horizontal hub, and the clamp fixture is complete. To attach the clamp to the shaft, an ear is welded onto it and drilled, the shaft being drilled and tapped for a clamp screw. The ends of the clamp screws are casehardened.

The top of the table is provided with a number of ribs, made of T-iron, as shown in Figs. 1 and 3, to support standard firebrick. Considerable cutting is done in this shop, and, when this is done, several of the bricks are removed, and the work is placed over the hole in the table. The slag goes through the top and does not affect the table, nor does it fly all over the operator.

The attachment shown in Fig. 4 is simply a 1/2 by 6 by 10-in. plate, welded to a length of the 1 15/16-in. shafting. This is used, as shown in Fig. 5, for offset pieces, or for lining up work of uneven thickness, and is exceedingly useful.

The vise attachment, shown in Fig. 6, also adds considerably to the effectiveness of the table. The piece of 1/2-in. boiler plate used to support the vise is welded to the shaft at an angle, so that there will be no interference with the vise bolts.

Small Ammonia-Carrying Drum

The small ammonia-carrying drum described in this article was designed and built for the purpose of eliminating the necessity for handling large and heavy drums, when only small quantities of ammonia were needed, as in repair work or for charging, in small household plants, which need only from 2 to 5 lb. of refrigerant.

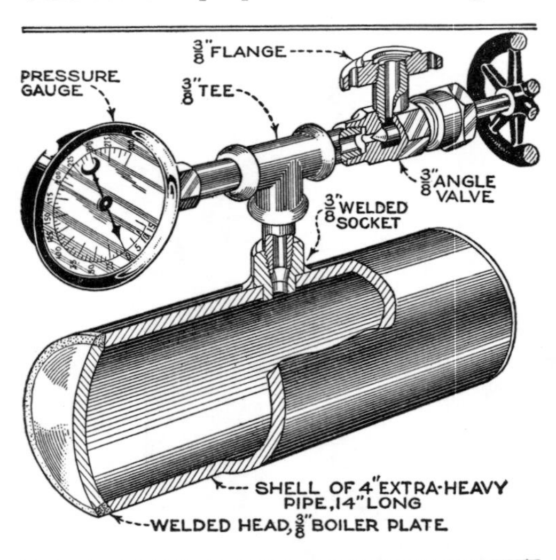

A Small Ammonia-Carrying Drum That Is Ideal for Carrying Small Quantities of Ammonia for Repair Work

The drum is made of extra-heavy pipe, to the ends of which heavy boiler-plate disks are welded. The ends are dished after cutting, as shown, for strength. The angle between the edges of pipe and disks is just right for the reception of the welding metal. A steel socket, tapped for 3/8-in. pipe, is welded in the side of the drum, and into it a 3/8-in. nipple is fitted; on the nipple, in turn, is screwed a tee, and 3/8-in. nipples connect the tee to a gauge and to an angle valve. The combination gauge is an essential part of the device; it should read to at least 15 in. vacuum, and up to 300 lb. pressure. The angle valve is of standard construction, and should seat tightly, in order to hold the high pressure of the ammonia. On the outlet side of the angle valve is mounted a 3/8-in. companion flange that is used to connect the valve to a large drum, when charging. All fittings must be extra-heavy.

To fill the drum with ammonia, it is first exhausted by means of a vacuum pump, until the gauge shows a vacuum of 15 in. Connection is then made to a large ammonia drum, through a short nipple and a companion flange, and the two valves opened, until the pressure in the two drums is equalized, when the valves are closed, and the drum disconnected. To ascertain the weight of the charge, the drum should be weighed before and after filling. The nipple between the two valves should be short, as the amount of liquid between the two valves is lost when the flanges are separated.

Before using the drum it should be tested under high pressure for leaks. An all-steel or iron drum is necessary, as ammonia corrodes other metals suitable for valves.—J. V. Romig, Allentown, Pa.

¶Beeswax makes a better lubricant for tail centers than the usual white lead, oil, or grease.

An Advertising Novelty

One of the leading clothing houses in Denver has, in addition to a well-arranged window display, a small electric push-button switch on the outside of the building, so wired that any passer-by can illuminate the interior of the store at night, in order to obtain a good view of the elaborate clothing display inside, on models and in glass showcases. A small brass plate, reading "Press Button to See Interior of Store Lighted," calls attention to the arrangement. The lights remain on only as long as the button is pressed down, so that no current is consumed needlessly.—Edward H. Flaharty, Denver, Colo.

Interchangeable Chuck for Woodturning

In pattern shops equipped with only a few lathes, but employing many patternmakers, it frequently happens that one has to wait his turn to use the lathe. As the setting up of a job in the lathe often consumes just as much time as the turning operation itself, it has been found, in one shop, that the provision of interchangeable chucks and plates enables the workmen to set up many of the jobs at their benches, and thus eliminates much of the lost time.

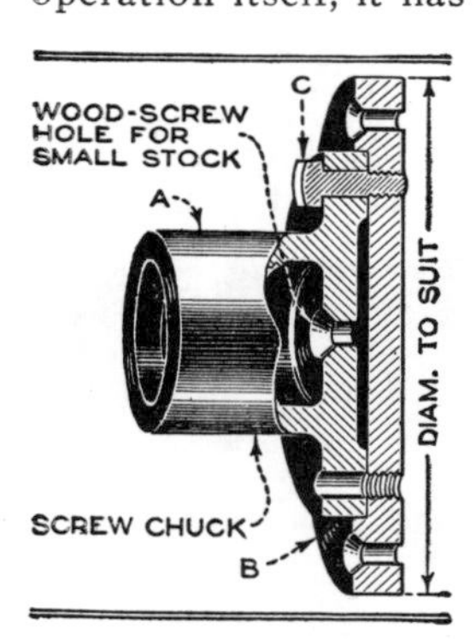

The chucks are made in two parts, of cast aluminum, and finished all over. The illustration clearly shows the construction. The chuck A is drilled and countersunk in the center to receive a No. 14 or 16 chucking screw, for use on small jobs. For large jobs, a flat faceplate, B, is used. This is drilled and tapped to receive the clamp bolts C, and is recessed at the back to make a snug fit on the chuck. All chucks are made of the same diameter, and the bolt holes are all spaced alike, so that one plate will fit a chuck on any lathe. When another job is to be turned in a hurry, and work is already on the chuck, all that is necessary is to remove the faceplate from the chuck and substitute another plate. Also, when it is desired to change from one lathe to another, to facilitate the work, the plate is simply changed from one chuck to another.

Detachable Letter Shelf for Desk

The desk worker will find the detachable shelf shown in the illustration serviceable for carrying reference books, correspondence, or the telephone, when the desk top is so covered with material that additional space is necessary. The shelf consists of a piece of 1-in. wood, hung from the side of the desk as indicated, the long hook bolts attached to one end of the board engaging with screweyes driven into the side of the desk. More than one shelf of this kind can be used, and, of course, the size of each may be varied to suit the user.

A Detachable Shelf on the Side of the Desk Provides Additional Space for Reference Books, or the Telephone

Fixture Holds Horn for Adjustment

Anyone who has occasion to test and adjust automobile horns will find the fixture illustrated a great convenience and timesaver. It consists of two uprights mounted on a wooden base, one having a V-shaped cut, as shown, and the other a series of small holes, drilled in a vertical line to accommodate a pin. The horn is laid in the "V," and the end hooked under the pin, the weight of the mechanism at one end holding the horn securely in the fixture. Such a horn support not only leaves both hands free, but also eliminates the time-consuming adjustments that are necessary when clamps are used.—Emil J. Bachmann, Keene, New Hampshire.

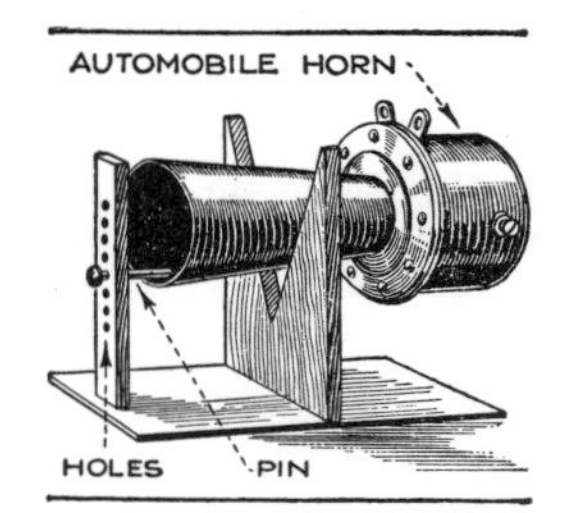

A Homemade Drill Press

A small vertical drill press is at times a necessary tool in the home workshop, though there may not be sufficient use

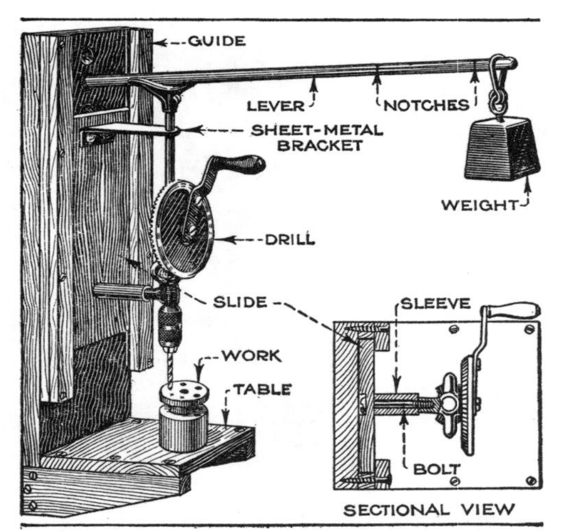

A Vertical Drill Press, for the Home Workshop, That Proves Quite a Time and Labor Saver

for it to justify the purchase of one. However, a drill press that will give satisfactory service can readily be made of material that is available in almost any shop.

An ordinary breast drill, mounted in the manner illustrated, is used. A machine bolt, pushed through a hole in a wooden slide, and also through a metal sleeve made of pipe, as shown, is substituted for the stationary handle. The head of the bolt is counterbored flush with the back of the slide. The upper end of the drill is held in place by a sheet-metal bracket, screwed to the slide and drilled to fit the breast-drill shank.

The slide fits neatly behind wooden guide strips, that hold it to a heavy wooden back so that it can be moved up or down. The table is securely attached to the lower end of the back with wooden braces and wood screws, and must be made strong enough to withstand considerable pressure.

A number of holes are drilled in the center of the back, as shown, about 1 in. apart and large enough to accommodate a wooden lever; a broomstick will serve for this. The lever is notched on one end at several points, as indicated, placed over the breastplate of the drill, and the end inserted into one of the holes in the back. By suspending a weight from the lever, as indicated, pressure is applied to the drill. The pressure can be varied by moving the weight, the notches serving to keep the latter from slipping out of position.

If it is desired to run such an improvised drill press with an electric motor or from a shaft, the hand crank is removed and a suitable pulley is bolted to the large gear. Care must be taken, of course, to use a pulley of such size that the drill will be run at a suitable speed.—J. H. Garety, Charleston, S. C.

Making Up Shipping Cartons

The homemade bench shown in the photo, which is used to make up corrugated-cardboard shipping cartons, is well adapted to the purpose, and the method employed for obtaining the greatest possible adhesion between the flaps, to which adhesive is applied, is rather novel. The boxes are mounted on wooden forms, fitting the inside closely, as shown, and hollow, hinged wooden lids, filled with bricks to make them weigh about 50 lb. each, are let down on the flaps after these have been given a liberal application of adhesive. The adhesive used is silicate of soda, which sets very quickly.

By using a double bench, having six sealing forms on each side, it is possible

A Bench Used for Sealing Paper Cartons: One Hundred Boxes per Hour can be Sealed by One Man

for one man to keep busy working around the forms without pause; by the time he has sealed the twelfth box, the first may be removed. The boxes can be sealed at a rate of approximately 100 per hour.

Keep the spark plugs adjusted to the gap specified for the car. Do not guess at the distance, but use a gauge to test the gap.

EQUIPMENT FOR AUTOMOBILE-TOURIST CAMPS

By A.J.R.Curtis and J.Tate

Part I—Gateposts, Pump Base, Ranges, Seats, and Tables

AMERICA is rapidly getting acquainted with itself. The motorist who does any touring at all meets numerous transcontinental and interstate tourists on the roads around his city, and auto campers almost without number. Many people of means choose an extended tour, camping along the way, as the most interesting and restful vacation possible, while, to many a family of modest circumstances, "camping out," via auto, offers the only opportunity of enjoying an inexpensive rest period.

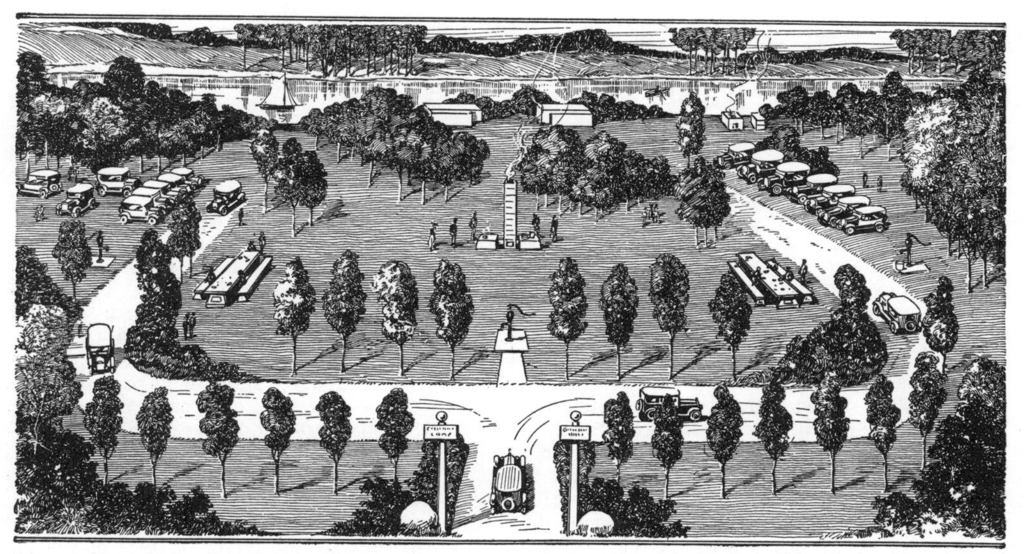

Layout of Small Automobile-Tourist Camp, Showing Minimum Amount of Equipment That should be Provided: Toilets, Incinerator, and Garbage Can are Shown in the Background

Until quite recently, public-camp sites have been scarce, and, where they did exist, cooking and toilet facilities were primitive, and, in many cases, the camps were dirty, badly drained, and altogether uninviting.

Now, however, many communities are studying the question of how to make the automobile tourist comfortable, and are making provision for clean, attractive camp sites. The advantages of a public camp are numerous. In the first place, it keeps the camper from "squatting" where he is not wanted, and in the second, just as good roads have often trebled traffic in any section, so good camp facilities quickly increase the number of the better class of campers visiting a community, to the increased prosperity of local business.

The equipment described and illustrated in this article is very simple to construct. Any man who can handle hammer and saw can quickly make the forms necessary. If a number of men in each community will give a few hours' time to the project, the only expense involved will be that of the lumber for the forms, and the materials for the concrete. This would even be a fine project for the local troop of boy scouts, and, under competent supervision, would not be at all beyond its powers.

These are merely suggestions; in many communities it may be preferable to turn the work over to the local contractor, who, with the accompanying illustrations to guide him, can, in a very short time, transform the bare site into a splendid camp.

The layout shown in the first illustration is suggestive only, since the actual layout will depend entirely upon the size and shape of the plot of ground available, and upon the number of tourists expected. All the equipment shown, however, should be included at the start, and additional units erected if those shown are not sufficient to care for the campers.

When selecting a site, one that is level, well wooded, and well drained should be chosen, if possible. The last-named feature is one that is too often neglected, and while it may not always be possible to obtain a naturally drained site, it is a very easy matter to drain one, using concrete tile. Where drainage is necessary, the accompanying table will be found very useful, as it will insure that the proper size of tile, installed to suit conditions, will be used.

The table shows the area that may be drained with various-size tile mains, and indicates the effect of the slope at which the tile is laid. The table is based on a run-off of ¼ in. in 24 hours; in sections where rainfall is extremely heavy, or is of the nature of downpours, a run-off of ⅜ in. or even ½ in. is used as a basis for calculation. For a ⅜-in. run-off, just two-thirds as many acres will be drained by a certain size of tile as the figure shown in the table, while, if ½ in. of water must be carried off in 24 hours, the tile will serve only half the acreage shown. For example, a 4-in. tile, laid with a 1¼-in. slope per 100 ft., will drain 3 acres, carrying off ¼ in. of water every 24 hours. If it must carry off ⅜ in., it will drain only 2 acres, and if ½ in., only 1½ acres. The amount of tile used, therefore, and the spacing of the mains, depend on local conditions of rainfall.

The entrance to the camp should be designated by one or two large and attractive signposts; the design shown in Fig. 1 is an excellent one, as it carries a light so that it may easily be read at night, and is sufficiently heavy and rigid to resist chance knocks and sideswipes, such as tourists often heedlessly inflict.

The post is made long enough to allow at least 6½-ft. clearance under the sign, and should be imbedded in the ground for at least 3, and preferably, 4 ft. The post tapers from 8 in. square at the bottom to 6 in. square at the top, and carries a 12-in. globe. The signboard is 3 in. thick and is cast integral with the post; it is made from 24 to 40 in. high in order to accommodate the desired lettering. The form for making this post is shown in Fig. 2, and is decidedly simple. It is so made that the flat side of the signboard is uppermost, and the 3-in. rib forming the continuation of the post, on the bottom. The beveled edges on post and signboard are formed by triangular molding, as shown. The 1-in. conduit for the electric-light wires is laid in place after the concrete has been filled in to half the thickness of the post, and the reinforcing bars for post and signboard placed in like manner. The conduit and bars may be made up and held in position in the form by means of wire ties, if desired, and laid in place in the form before any concrete is placed, but, in this case, special care must be taken to work the concrete completely into the corners and between the bars and conduit, by means of small iron rods.

The lettering may easily be cast integral with the signboard by means of a form top, a part of which is shown in Fig. 3. The outlines of the letters are laid out on the top, the letters sawed out, as indicated, and the interior portions of letters such as O and A fastened in place by means of short sheet-metal straps. As soon as the form is filled, this top is nailed or screwed over the signboard portion, and the letter spaces filled in. The letter openings should be beveled slightly, so that the top may be removed easily when the concrete has set.

The concrete used should be a 1:2:3 mix, that is, mixed in the proportion of 1 part Portland cement to 2 parts sand, and 3 parts clean pebbles. The lettering form may be filled in with a mixture of 1 part cement to 2 parts marble dust; this

AREA DRAINED BY TILE MAINS								
SIZE OF TILE	FALL PER 100 FEET							
	1¼ IN. OR 0.1 FT.	2⅜ IN. OR 0.2 FT.	3⅝ IN. OR 0.3 FT.	4¾ IN. OR 0.4 FT.	6 IN. OR 0.5 FT.	9 IN. OR 0.75 FT.	12 IN. OR 1.0 FT.	24 IN. OR 2.0 FT.
INCHES	ACRES	ACRES	ACRES	ACRES	ACRES	ACRES	ACRES	ACRES
4	3	6	7	8	9	10	13	18
5	7	10	12	14	15	19	23	32
6	12	17	21	24	27	33	38	55
8	26	37	45	60	74	85	106	125
10	50	70	85	100	110	140	195	225
12	86	118	45	165	175	230	265	380
15	152	215	270	310	355	430	500	720
18	250	360	440	515	575	720	820	1150

Table Showing Correct Sizes of Tile to Use for Draining Camp Sites: It is Based on a Run-Off of ¼ Inch in 24 Hours

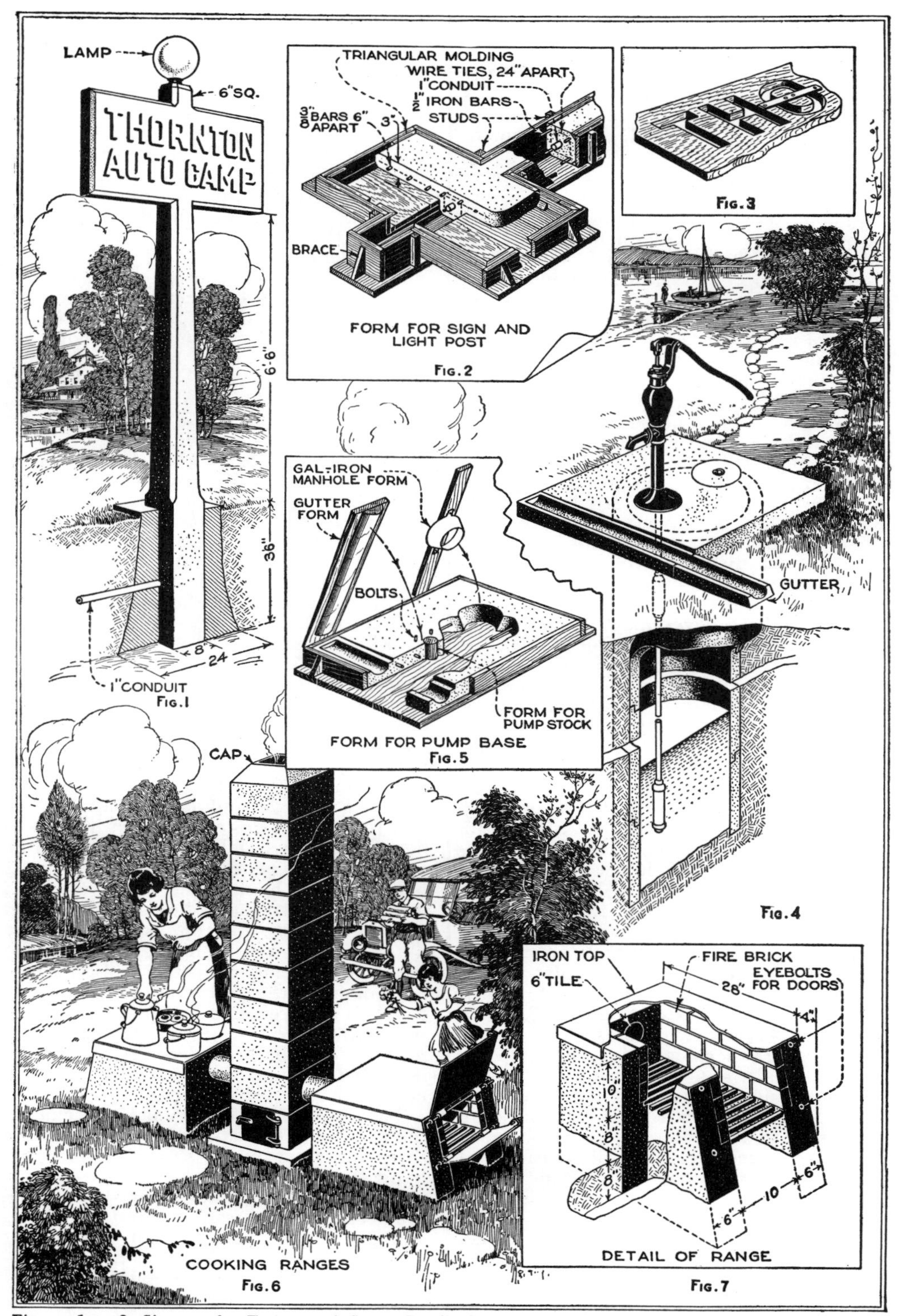

Figures 1 to 3, Signpost for Entrance of Camp, Detail of Main Form, and Form for Casting Letters; Figure 4, Well Curbing, Pump Base, and Gutter; Figure 5, Form for Pump Base, Showing Method of Making Manhole; Figure 6, Cooking Ranges and Chimney in Use, and Figure 7, Full Details of Individual Range

will make the letters stand out sharply against the background. The materials required for this post are 1½ sacks of cement, 3 cu. ft. of sand, and 4½ cu. ft. of pebbles.

A good water supply is essential within the camp, and unless city water mains are available, one or more good wells must be provided. The well curbing is generally built as shown in Fig. 4, and a 5 or 6-in. slab top, cast in the simple form shown in Fig. 5, placed over it, as indicated. The manhole form is simply made of galvanized iron, conical in shape, and provided with two ears, nailed to a cleat, which, in turn, is nailed in position on top of the form. The form for the pump stock is a tapered block of wood, oiled, and placed in position in the center of the bolts that are to hold the pump; these are wired in position. The gutter may be formed as indicated, or made by means of a trowel while the concrete is still green, and should be carried out a short distance from the well, by means of separate gutter units, to prevent puddles around the well.

The manhole cover may be cast, using the inside of the galvanized-iron form, at the same time as the rest of the slab. It should be reinforced with short lengths of iron rod, laid crisscross, and be provided with a lifting ring, made from half of an old bridle bit, or from a hitching-post ring, the end of which is provided with a large washer and nut. The iron form must be well oiled before pouring.

The slab top is reinforced with ⅜-in. rods, spaced 6 in. apart, and placed as indicated. A 1:2:3 mix is used for this job also, and approximately 4½ sacks cement, 9 cu. ft. sand, and 13½ cu. ft. pebbles will be required for the cover; for each 10-ft. length of gutter, 1¾ sacks cement, 3½ cu. ft. sand, and 5¼ cu. ft. pebbles will be required, and for the curbing, for each foot of depth, 1½ sacks cement, 3 cu. ft. sand, and 4½ cu. ft. pebbles.

Stoves are necessary for the preparation of meals, and those shown in Fig. 6 will be found very satisfactory. They may be used singly, located back to back on each side of the chimney, or on all four sides, as necessary. The dimensions of the ranges are shown clearly in Fig. 7, and the form in Fig. 8. The top is made of No. 12 sheet iron, flanged as shown, and the grate of ¾-in. square bars, cemented onto the ledge that supports the fire-brick lining. The doors are made of sheet iron, with ears formed on the top for hinges, and swing on iron rods held in eyebolts cast in the concrete.

It is best to use commercial 16-in. concrete blocks for the chimney, but where these are not easily obtained, the blocks may be cast in the form shown in Fig. 8. Concrete tile, 6 in. in diameter, may be used to connect the ranges to the chimney, or where several stoves connect with one stack, common stovepipe may be used instead; the stovepipe allows considerable independent movement of stoves and chimney, without causing cracks. For each range, 3¾ sacks cement, 7½ cu. ft. sand, and 11¼ cu. ft. pebbles will be needed, together with one 6-in. concrete tile, thirteen 16 by 16 by 8-in. chimney blocks, one 16 by 16 by 4-in. cap, 1 sheet-iron top, 2 iron stove doors, 4 eyebolts, about 3 ft. of ⅜-in. rod for hinges, and 1 cast-iron clean-out door.

The lunch tables and benches shown in Figs. 9 and 10 will prove very popular. They resist upsetting, do not rot or warp, and can be scrubbed easily.

Two forms are necessary for the bench, one for the pedestals and the other for the top slab. The pedestals are cast vertically, as indicated in the detail. The top slab is cast horizontally, and is reinforced with ⅜-in. bars, placed 4 in. apart lengthwise, and 24 in. apart crosswise. The pedestals are set up on bases cast into the ground, the proper distance apart, as indicated by the dotted lines, Fig. 9, and may be joined to the bases by a cement-mortar joint as indicated in one of the details showing the pedestal-and-slab joint. Pedestals and bases may also be cast together, if desired, and set into holes dug in the ground. The top may be joined to the pedestal in two ways: by bolts, in which case the latter are cast into the pedestal, and holes for their reception cast into the top, as shown in the illustration of the table-top form; or by means of a cement-mortar joint, the upper edges of the pedestals being slightly beveled, and recesses formed in the slab to receive them. The tops and pedestals may be cast in one piece, reinforced as indicated in one of the details, but this method is not recommended.

The table, Fig. 10, is made in exactly the same manner as the benches, and the three units set up as shown in the plan lying on the table.

For each bench, the materials required are: cement, 1½ sacks; sand, 3 cu. ft., and pebbles, 4½ cu. ft.; for the tables: cement, 3 sacks; sand, 6 cu. ft., and pebbles, 9 cu. ft. For the complete assembly of two benches and table, 6 sacks cement, 12 cu. ft. sand, and 18 cu. ft. pebbles will be required.

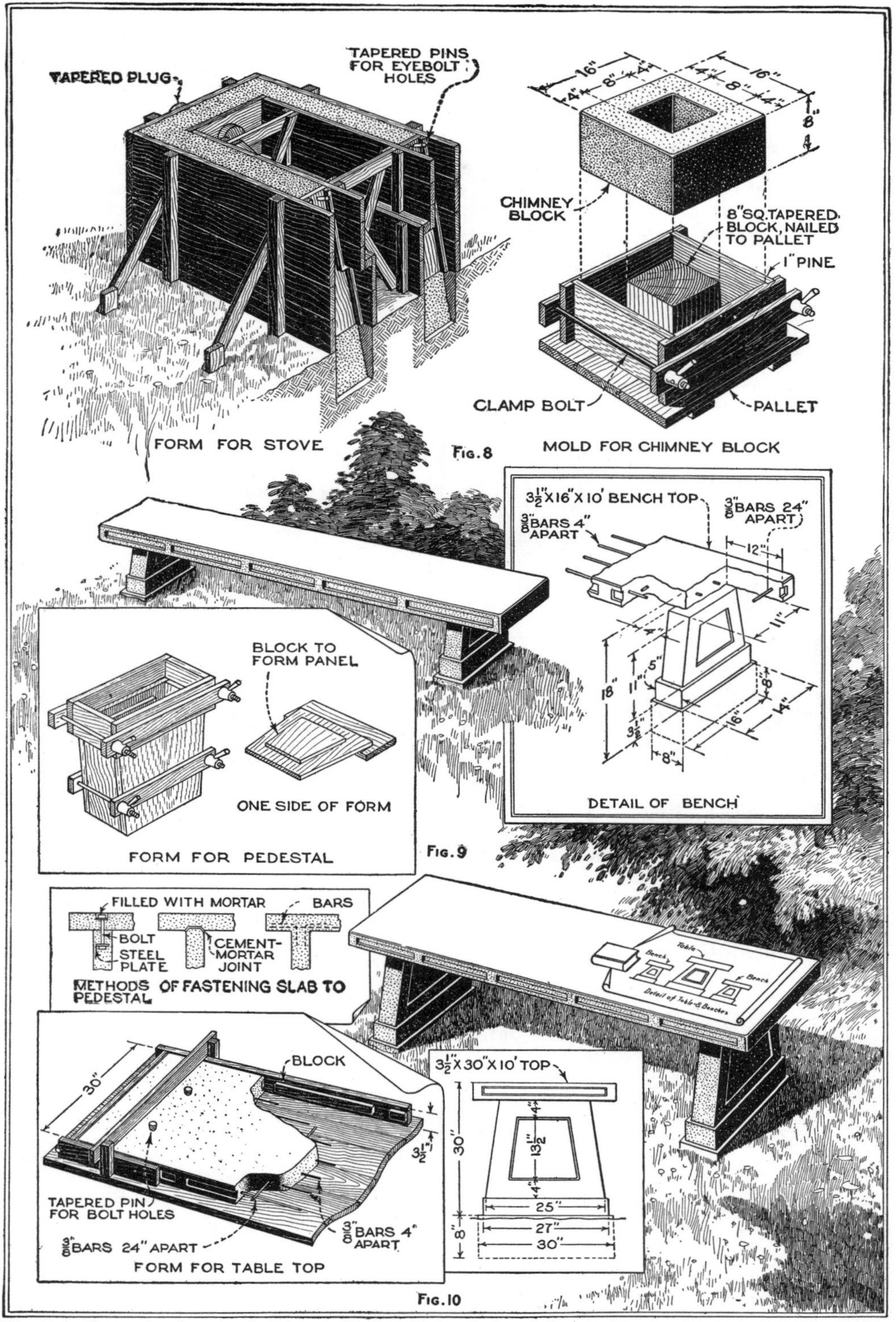

Figure 8, Forms for Stove and Chimney Blocks; Figure 9, Lunch Bench, Showing Method of Making Pedestals; Figure 10, Table, Showing Part of Form for Top, Methods of Joining Top to Pedestal, and End Elevation of Assembly of Benches and Table. Forms for Tables and Benches Are Alike, Except in Size

The forms for all these pieces are very simple; all there is to remember is that the interior of the form must be an exact duplicate of the piece to be made, and that the forms must be well enough braced to resist sagging or spreading under the weight of the concrete. Forms must always be oiled or greased before placing the concrete, and all blocks forming holes, recesses, or panels given plenty of taper, to permit easy withdrawal. The lumber used should preferably be green; if seasoned lumber is used, it should be thoroughly wetted. Forms that are to be used for only one piece need not be elaborate, and may be nailed together, but those used for duplicate pieces, such as the bench and table pedestals, must be made to be taken apart without damage, and must be fastened by means of clamp bolts, as shown, or by similar fastenings.

Additional equipment, suitable for larger and more pretentious camps, will be described in the August issue.

Tripod Drill Used as Hand Drill

The engineer supervising the development of the Skagit River for power purposes, finding that the excavation for the power house would necessitate an unusual number of drill holes, improvised a drill that proved very speedy and serviceable.

Adaptation of a Tripod Drill for Use as a Portable Hand Drill for Vertical Holes of 6 Feet and Over

A drill of the Leyner type was removed from its regular mounting, and, after suitable handles, made of round steel, had been attached to it as shown in the photo, was used as an ordinary hand drill. It had almost twice the drilling speed of the latter, but, of course, it was a little more difficult to move, owing to its weight. For vertical holes of 6 ft. and over, it was found highly satisfactory.—Aaron Evans, Rockport, Wash.

¶If the auto fan belt slips, turn it over. The fresh surface will usually cling to the face of the pulley when the oily inner surface will not.

Scribing Lines on Round Work

I have often tried to mark a true line around the circumference of a cylindrical body, such as a shaft, pipe, or piston, but have always experienced trouble in scribing it exactly, until I hit upon the following scheme: Take a piece of paper having a straight edge and wrap it around the cylinder so that the edges line up where they overlap. Then scribe a line along the edge and it will be found perfectly true.—John A. Blaker, West Auburn, Massachusetts.

Metal Index Tabs

Brass letters and figures, embossed on the pattern-shop embossing machine, make good index tabs for the shop catalogs, books, or card files. The tabs are cut to shape as shown, a couple of indentations punched in them with a center punch, and the backs then coated with shellac. When this is nearly dry, the tabs are pressed into place on the book pages or cards.

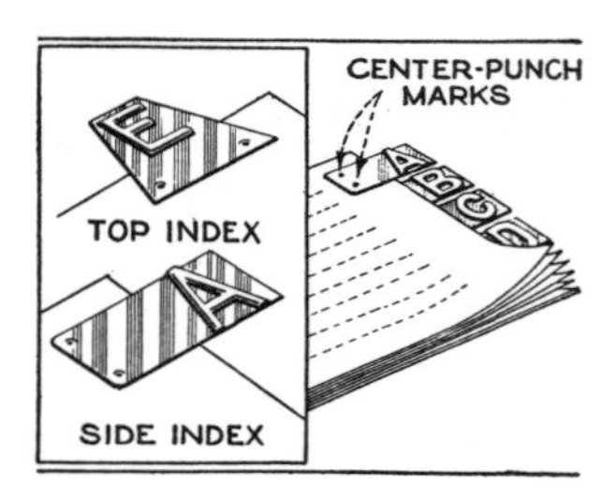

Sawing and Filling Holes in Slate

When rebuilding a large power-house switchboard, one of the old panels was found to be 6 in. too wide for the new board. It was sawed down, on the job, in the manner shown in the illustration. The panel was placed on two wooden horses, 2 ft. high. A wooden handle was fitted on one end of a 3/4 by 14-in. power-hacksaw blade, and a coil spring fastened to the other end. A length of cord was attached to the coil spring, passed through a staple driven into the floor, in line with the cut as indicated, and the end fastened to the horse so as to permit adjustment. Considerable pressure was thus placed on the saw, so that it was possible to saw the slate at a rate of 14 in. per hour, which is much faster than usual when sawing slate by hand.

The location of some of the instruments was changed on the panels; this left a number of holes, which were plugged in the following way: Just enough water was added to some Portland cement to enable it to set, making a very dry mixture. A block of wood was clamped over the hole to be plugged, and the cement tamped in until the hole had been filled to within 1/32 in. of the surface of the panel. The block of wood was then removed, and the other end of the hole tamped until the cement at this end was also 1/32 in. below the face of the panel. The cement was allowed to set for

Sawing Slate Panels: The Pressure Applied by Means of the Spring Lessens the Time and Labor Required

24 hours. A thick paste, made of slate dust and boiled linseed oil, was then forced into each end of the hole, and allowed to project about 1/64 in. above the surface of the panels. When the mixture was dry, the material was dressed down flush with the face of the panel by means of very fine emery cloth, which had been almost worn out in polishing copper busbars. The panels were then polished with oil, and the places where the holes were plugged could not be detected.—Ben Buck, San Francisco, Calif.

Convenient Tool Tray

The illustration shows a simple portable tool tray that has been found to be of considerable utility to automobile mechanics. It consists of a 1-in. board, about 12 in. wide and long enough to bridge the distance between the radiator and cowl of an average-size car. A hole, about 3 in. in diameter, is cut at one

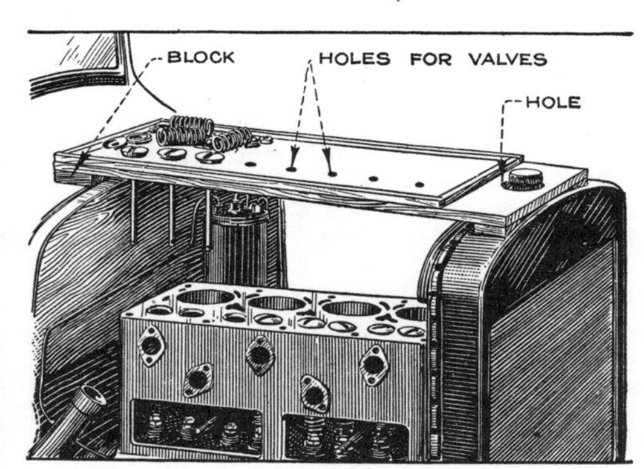

A Tool Tray for the Auto Repairman That Saves Many Trips to the Bench

end to fit over the radiator cap, and small blocks are tacked to the corners, to keep the board from rocking, or slipping over on either side. Strips of wood are nailed on top, at the edges, to prevent screws, small springs, etc., from rolling off, and a number of holes are drilled through the board, as shown, to accommodate engine valves.

The use of this tool tray does away with the habit of laying tools on fenders, which is highly objectionable, as it mars the varnished surface. The tray also saves the mechanic numerous steps, as all the tools needed for a job may be kept on the tray within easy reach.

Secure Latch for Paddocks

It is desirable to have the gates of stables and paddocks provided with a latch that cannot be opened by the horses. A good latch, that is absolutely secure, and has been found to be very useful on the stallion paddock at the University of Illinois, is shown in the photo. The gate is made so that it touches the gatepost at the bottom first, and the top must be sprung in in order to hook the latch. There is not a chance for the gate to open when the latch is in position; the harder the stallion rubs or pushes against the gate, the tighter the latch becomes.

EQUIPMENT FOR AUTOMOBILE-TOURIST CAMPS

By A. J. R. Curtis and J. Tate

Part II—Vaults, Bath, Garbage Boxes, Incinerators, Washing Platform, and Fountain

THE equipment shown in the camp layout given in Part I, while quite suitable for a small village or town camp, cannot be expected to serve where a very large volume of tourist traffic is certain or expected.

The equipment shown in the layout below, however, should enable a city to cater to a large number of tourists without overcrowding. The arrangement of the units, as in the smaller layout, is entirely suggestive, and will depend almost entirely upon the shape of the lot. In any event, garbage cans and incinerators should be placed a good distance from the tables, yet not so far that their use will be a burden, and therefore likely to be slighted.

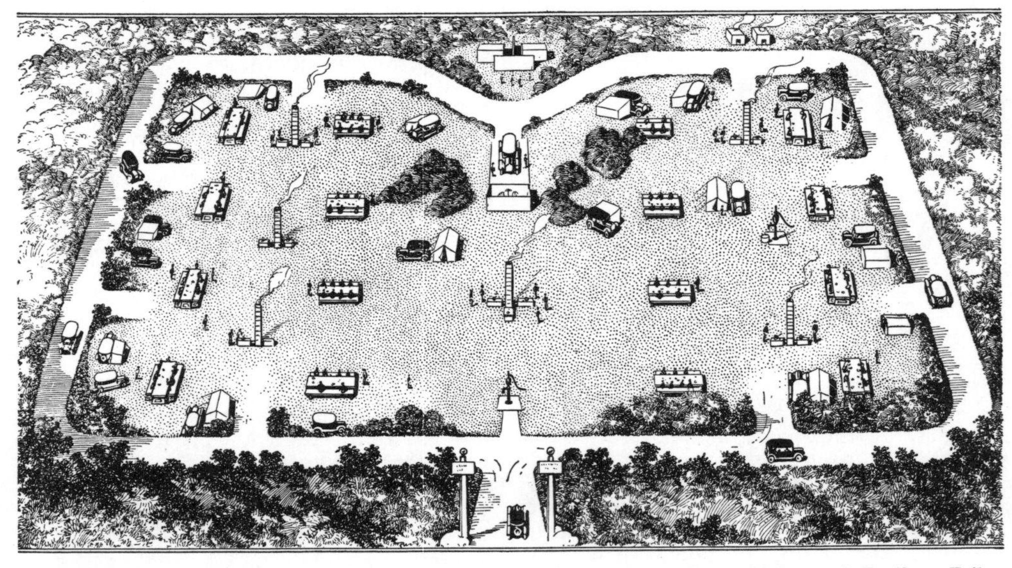

Suggested Layout for Automobile-Tourist Camp with Equipment for a Large Volume of Traffic: Toilets, Incinerators, Washing Platform, and Shower Bath may be Seen in the Background

Toilet facilities in most camps are so poor as to constitute the principal objection, by many people, to the use of such camps. This not only keeps many tourists away, but is a positive menace to health, turning an outing for recreation into a period of exposure to dangerous germs. Where sewage systems are not available, a septic-tank system, or vaults such as shown in Figs. 11 to 19, should be installed.

The concrete vault proper is shown in Fig. 11, a section in Fig. 13, and a view of suitable forms in Figs. 15 and 19. The lower part of the vault is cast in place, as shown in Fig. 15. The form shown can be made of light lumber by anyone who can use hammer and saw, and need not be at all elaborate, so long as it is strongly enough braced to support the concrete; the layer of concrete forming the bottom is placed first, then the form is set in, braced in position, and the side walls poured.

While the bottom part is curing, the upper part may be made. A form that molds the slab floor and seat supports is shown in Fig. 19. This also need not

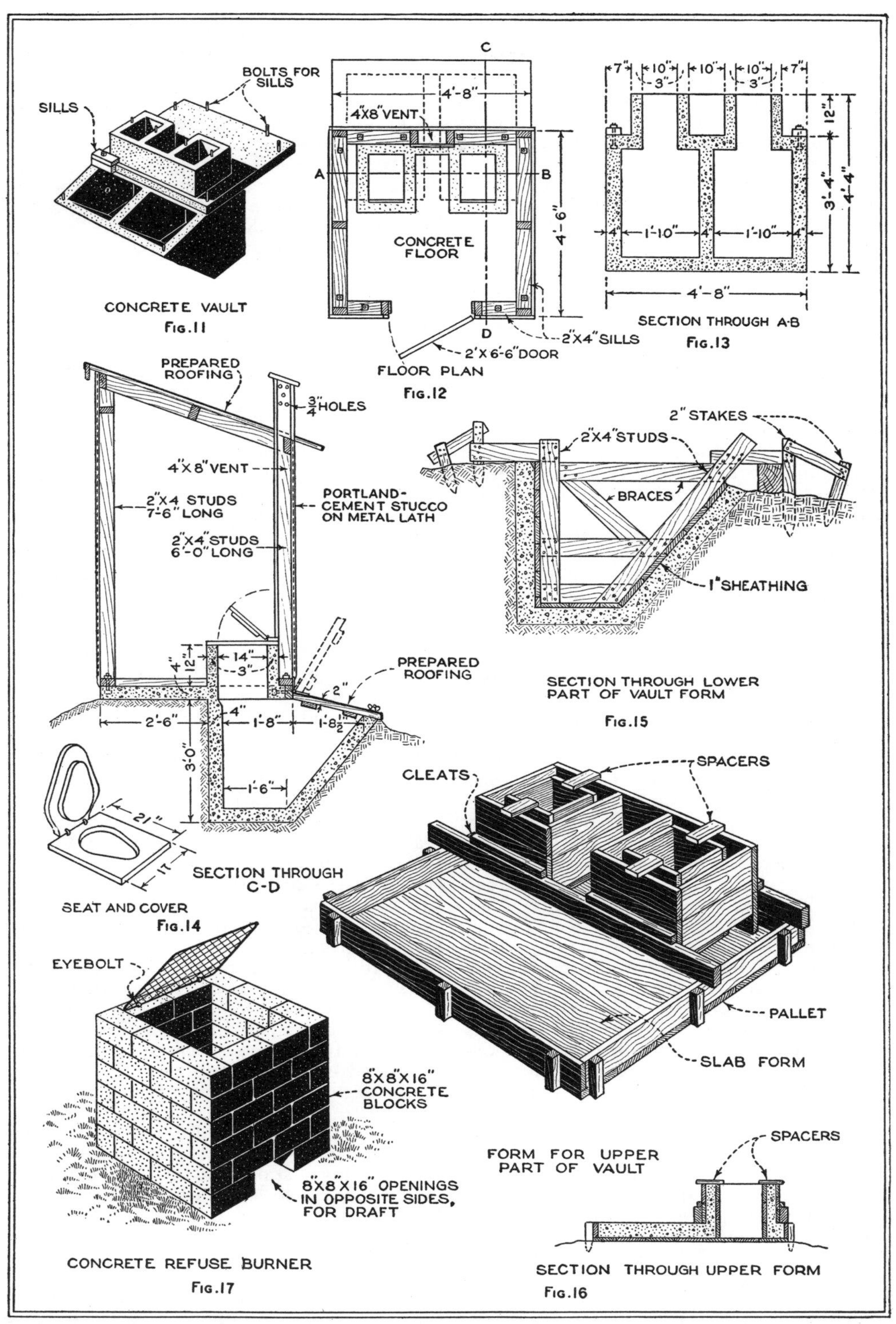

Figures 11 to 16 Show a Very Easily Constructed Vault for Toilet Purposes, Where a Sewage System is Not Installed, or Where No Disposal Field for a Septic-Tank System Is Available. Figure 17 Shows a Simple Concrete-Block Refuse Burner or Incinerator

be elaborate, as it will only be needed for one or two pieces. When cured, the slab can be moved into position, and the joint between upper and lower parts made with neat-cement mortar.

The housing may be made of concrete, cement plaster on metal lath, brick, or wood, as convenient. The wood sills for the structure, if the latter is made of metal lath and stucco or wood, are attached to the vault by means of bolts imbedded in the concrete, as shown. The construction shown in the drawing is Portland-cement stucco on metal lath, with wood studs, vent, and roof, and serves well. It would perhaps be well to have this part of the work, or at least the plastering, done by a competent contractor. The concrete used is a 1:2:3 mix, and approximately 7 sacks cement, 13½ cu. ft. sand, and 20 cu. ft. pebbles will be required.

In order to keep the camp neat and orderly, refuse burners and garbage cans should be provided. The burners, or incinerators are best made of concrete blocks, 8 by 8 by 16 in. in size, as shown in Fig. 17. The draft openings are made simply by leaving one block out of the lower courses, on opposite sides. A cover, made of heavy wire netting, bound with ½-in. round-iron bar, should be provided, to keep charred paper, etc., from flying around the camp. The eyebolts for attaching the cover, are set into holes chipped in the blocks and filled with neat cement. Sixty blocks will be necessary for each burner.

The garbage cans, Figs. 18 and 19, are made in one piece of concrete reinforced with wire mesh, the walls being 2 in. thick. The forms for these need no description, as the method of making them is obvious. The bolts for the top covers and the clean-out door hinges are imbedded in the concrete when it is placed. A 1:2:3 mix is used here also; 2 sacks cement, 4 cu. ft. sand, and 6 cu. ft. pebbles being used for each container.

Where running water is available, an automobile-washing platform, shower bath, and drinking fountain will be highly appreciated.

The washing platform, Fig. 20, is merely a 10 by 18-ft. concrete slab, with a low curb on three sides, and a gutter, running to a sewer, on the fourth. Most cross-country tourists wash and lubricate their own cars, so a floor of this type will be well patronized. The floor should slope ¼ in. to the foot toward the gutter, but the curb is level all around; this, in a floor of the size specified, will make the curb 1½ in. high at one end, and 6 in. high at the other. The slab itself is 6 in. thick. With what has been shown of form construction previously, no difficulty will be experienced in making this platform. The concrete used for the floor should be a 1:2:3 mix, while that for the curb should be 1:2½:4, the amount of material necessary being 31 sacks cement, 66 cu. ft. sand, and 10 cu. ft. pebbles.

The simple shower bath shown in Fig. 21 is another highly desirable feature. The walls are simply made of Portland-cement mortar, plastered on both sides of metal lath, and the frame is 2-in. angle iron, imbedded in the footings and braced by ½ by 1½-in. flat-iron bars, where necessary. The floor and footings are cast in one piece, and the floor beveled from the sides toward the center drain pipe, in the shower compartment, while the cement is still soft. The dressing compartment is fitted with a seat and clothes hooks. No top is necessary on the structure. The floor is made of 1:2:3 concrete, the footings of 1:2½:4, and the walls of 1:3 mortar; the material required is 35 sacks cement, 100 cu. ft. sand, and 38 cu. ft. pebbles.

The fountain shown in Fig. 22, while not essential, will prove of convenience. The water-supply and drain pipes are first placed and connected, and the slab and pedestal cast around them. Slab and pedestal can be cast all in one piece; note that a step, 8½ in. high, is provided on each side of the pedestal, for the convenience of children. The paneling on the sides of the pedestal is formed by means of blocks, tacked to the form sides, as shown in Fig. 9, Part I. For the fountain, 3¼ sacks cement, 6¼ cu. ft. sand, and 10 cu. ft. pebbles is necessary, a 1:2:3 mix being used throughout.

A camp provided with equipment of the type described in this article will be a credit to any community, and, as emphasized in Part I, will attract the better class of tourists, thereby benefiting local business.

When the volume of tourists has become large enough, it will pay to have an employe stationed at the camp to sell supplies, to keep the grounds clean, and to render service of one kind or another to the tourists.

¶Sand or pebbles for concrete work must be clean. If coated with clay, for example, the cement cannot adhere to the surface, and thus cannot perform its binding function.

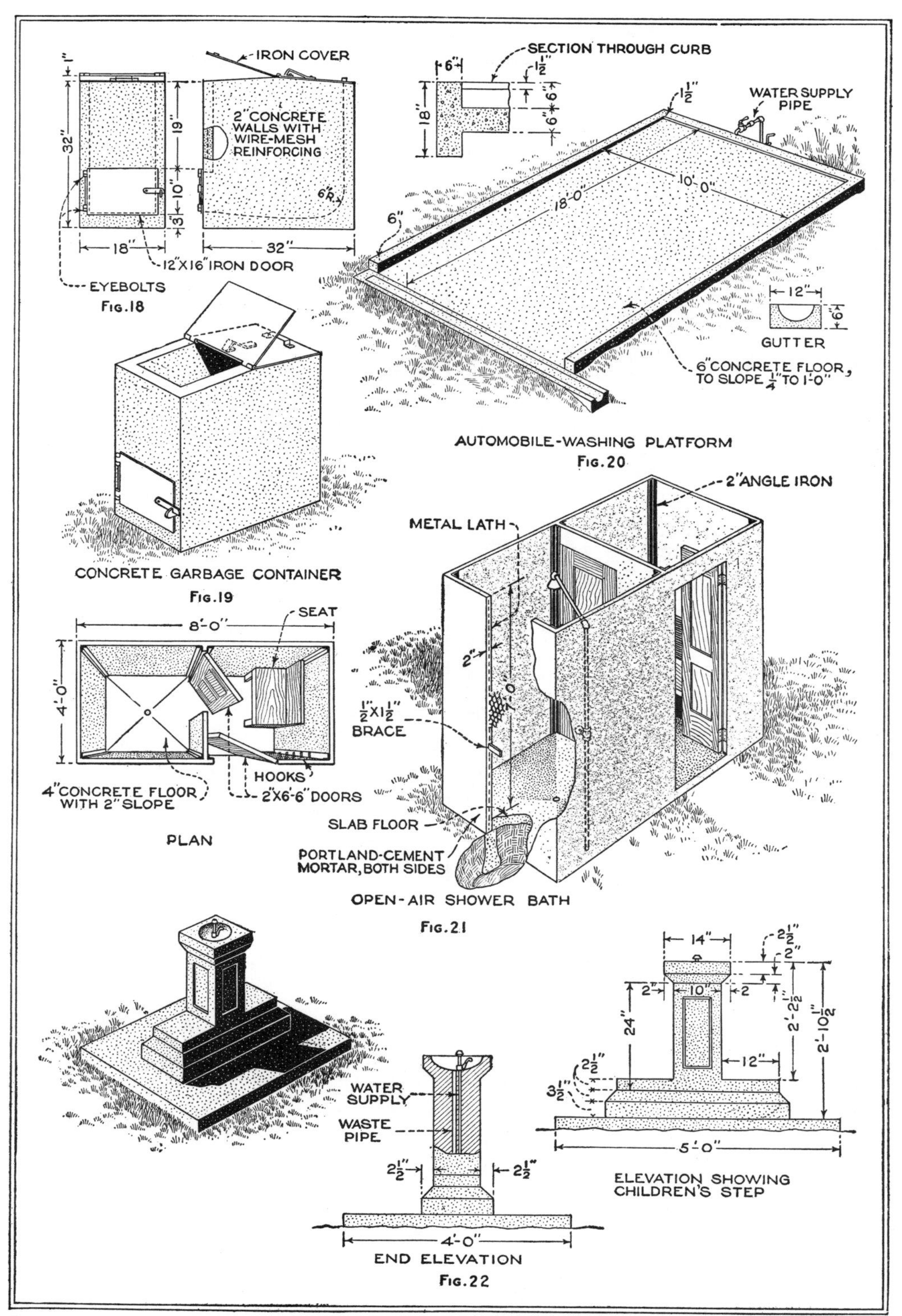

Figures 18 and 19: Concrete Garbage Container, of Good Design, and Easily Constructed. Where Running Water Is Available, the Automobile-Washing Platform, Shower Bath, and Drinking Fountain, Shown in Figures 20 to 22, can be Provided, and will be Greatly Appreciated

Planer Converted into a Shaper

No matter how well planned and equipped a machine shop may be, there usually comes a time when the largest available machine is just too small for a big job. These big jobs must be done, and, rather than farming them out to another shop, the management orders the job to be done in some manner that calls for ingenuity. The arrangement illustrated for converting a planer into a shaper is an example. The work machined with this tool consisted mainly of large engine frames and roll housings, which were too long and heavy to pass through the planer housings.

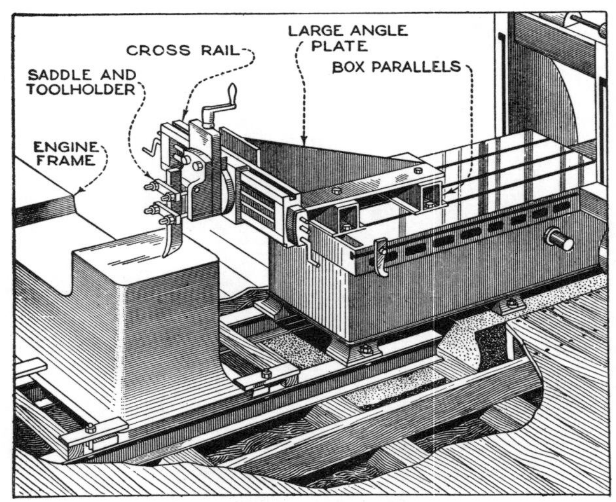

An Attachment That Adapts the Planer to Operations on Work beyond the Capacity of the Housings

The method used in converting the planer to its new use was quite simple. The planer cross rail was removed from its housings and mounted on a large cast angle plate as illustrated. This angle plate, with the cross rail attached, was then set up on box parallels and clamped to the table. The work was supported on heavy I-beams which were bolted to the lower flange or feet of the planer bed. Bolting the I-beams to the base of the machine in this manner made it necessary to remove about 3 ft. of the foundation. After the beams had been attached, they were leveled with the planer table and supported on timber sills. This arrangement for supporting the large work was made flush with the shop floor and formed a permanent addition to the planer equipment.

After the work had been leveled on the supporting steel beams, it was clamped in position. The saddle and toolholder were fed by hand, and were able to work over as wide a range as though mounted on the housings. The overhang of the cross rail was made as short as possible, the work being positioned close to the end of the planer shears. Considerable power is saved by this method of machining heavy work, as the weight of the cross rail and angle plate is negligible when compared with the weight of the job.

When the cross rail is mounted high, it is advisable to ballast the table with a few heavy castings in order to hold it firm.

Tightening Pipe-Line Hangers

A common hanger for supporting light pipe lines that are used in connection with exhaust fans, and for similar purposes, consists of a bracket made from two pieces of thin, flat iron, fastened at one end to the wall or roof, bent at the other end to inclose the pipe, as shown in the illustration, and fastened with a screw and nut. Anyone who has done the job knows how difficult it is to bring the ends of the bracket close enough to allow the screw to be inserted and the nut to be started, especially as the operator is nearly always perched on a ladder. On a lengthy job of piping, using these hangers, it was found that the tool shown in the drawing greatly facilitated the work.

To make the tool, a long ½-in. screw was ground at one end to the shape of a screwdriver point, and a pin driven through the other end to serve as a handle. An old collar of suitable diameter was obtained, and the screw run into the ½-in. setscrew hole already in it. In use, the screw is turned back far enough to allow the collar to be slipped over the ends of the bands, and the small clamp screw is dropped into place. The ½-in. screw is

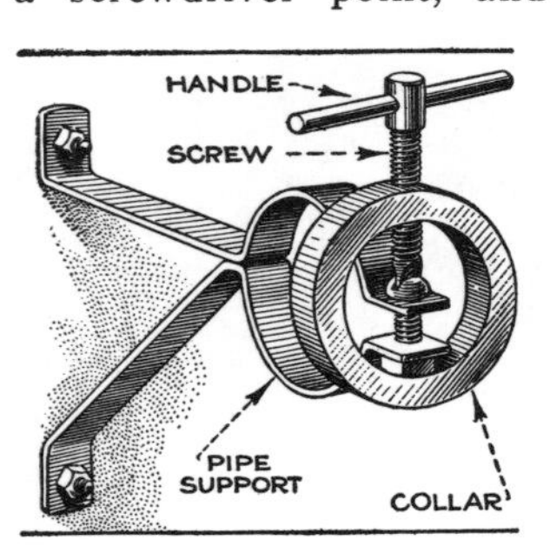

then run down until the screwdriver point engages the slot and drives the screw home. In this manner the ends are readily forced together, and when the screw projects through the bottom lug, the nut is slipped in place, the final tightening being done with a wrench after the tool has been removed.

A Good Wire Straightener

The making of an odd coil spring or two, in the small shop, is always more or less of an experiment, and often several springs must be wound before one suitable for the purpose intended is made. The tool shown in the illustration has been successfully used for straightening these scrap springs, to reclaim the wire for future use.

A rectangular piece of ½-in. steel is used for the body. A ¾-in. hole is drilled in the center; a ⅛-in. hole in each side, for the wire; a 5/16-in. plain hole in one end, and a 5/16-in. tapping hole in the other, as shown. The plain hole is fitted with a sliding handle, with a ⅛-in. hole drilled through it near one end, and a threaded 5/16-in. rod is screwed into the tapped hole.

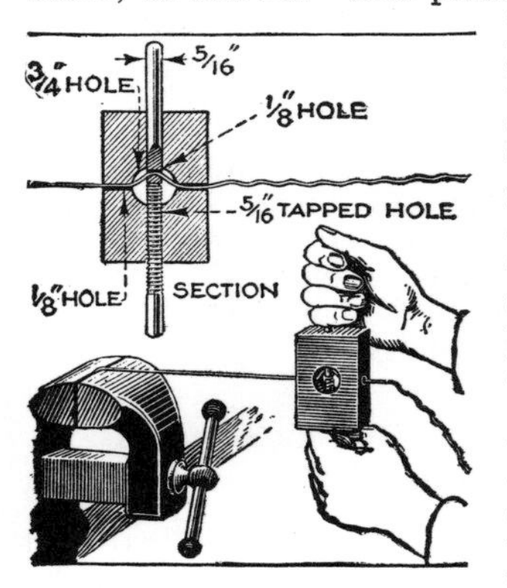

To straighten out a spring, one end is held tightly in a vise; the other end is gripped in a pair of pliers, and the spring pulled out until the wire is as straight as possible. The handles of the tool are then adjusted until the hole in the end of the plain handle is in line with the ⅛-in. holes in the body, and the tool is pushed onto the wire and up to the vise.

The threaded handle is then screwed in, until sufficient tension is put on the wire to straighten it, when the tool is drawn along as shown. To prevent the plain handle from falling out when the tool is not in use, a few punch marks may be made around the inner end, or a piece of wire put through the hole and the threaded handle screwed tight.

The edges of the holes are rounded to allow the tool to slide on the wire without cutting or scraping it.

Quick-Acting Miter-Box Clamps

The carpenter's usual method of attaching his miter box to a sawhorse has several disadvantages. It is generally necessary to nail cleats across the top of the sawhorse to provide a base wide enough for the legs of the miter box, which, in turn, must be screwed or nailed to the cleats.

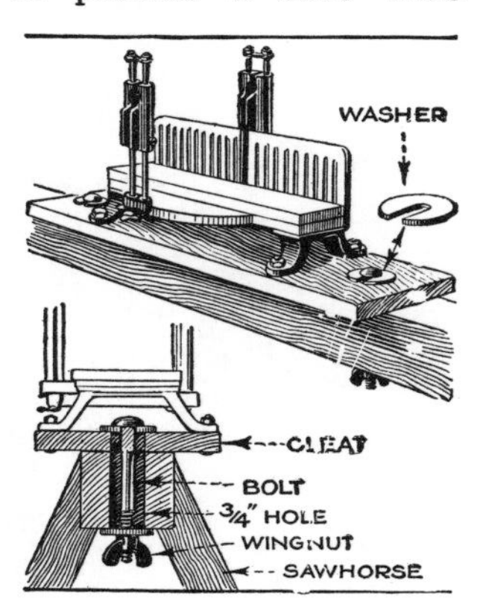

A better method was devised by a California carpenter, and is shown in the drawing. The miter box is screwed or bolted permanently on a board or cleat, and the cleat is clamped to the sawhorse by means of two carriage bolts, slipped through ¾-in. holes drilled in both cleat and sawhorse. A slotted washer is slipped under the bolt head when the bolt is pushed in position from below, and the wingnut on each bolt tightened, clamping the miter box securely on the horse. To remove the miter box, it is only necessary to loosen the wingnuts so that the washers can be slipped out, and the bolts will drop out.

Clamp Protects Portable-Lamp Connections

Trouble is usually experienced with electric extension cords fitted with portable lamps of the type illustrated, as the cord is easily pulled out of the socket. This trouble can be overcome by fitting the lamp handle with a small sheet-metal clamp, the upper detail showing the pattern of the clamp and the lower detail how it is bent. A small bolt is fitted on the clamp proper, so that it can be tightened on the lamp cord. The other part is screwed to the end of the handle as indicated. With this in place, the part of the cord inside of the lamp holder will not be subjected to any strain.

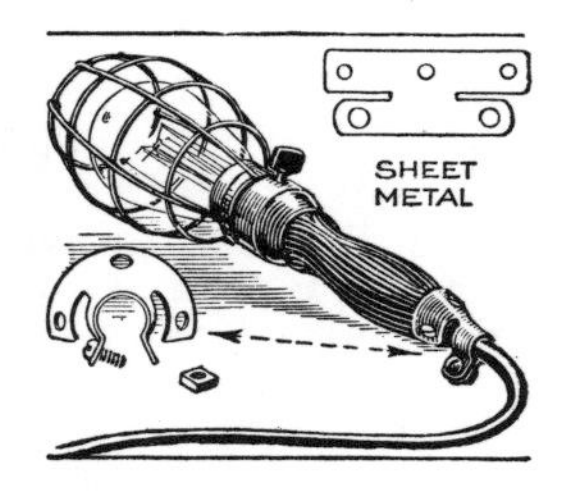

Attaching Wire to Concrete Posts

A good method of attaching wire to concrete fence posts is shown in the drawing. One side of the post, as far as it extends above the ground, has small grooves formed in it, about 2 in. apart. These grooves are made by wooden strips nailed to the face of the form in which the posts are made. The fence wire is laid in the grooves as shown, and bound in place by a short length of wire, passed around the post and twisted around the fence wire.—Warner H. Ellis, Keenes, Ill.

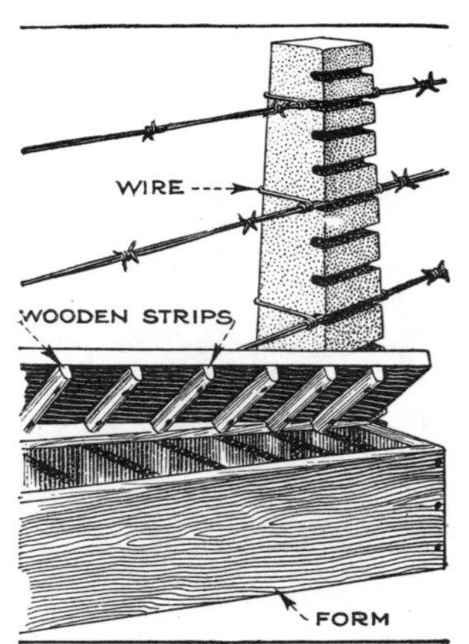

A Milling-Machine Drill Chuck

In order to line up the point of a drill to a punch mark on the work held on the table of a machine, it is, of course, necessary that the drill should run true. To obtain this accuracy, something more than the ordinary drill chuck is needed, for drills have a habit of running true in the shank but out at the point. This may be the fault of the drill, but is more often the fault of the chuck, which, unless it is a new one, has a tendency to throw the drill point slightly out. To overcome this, the drill chuck shown was designed.

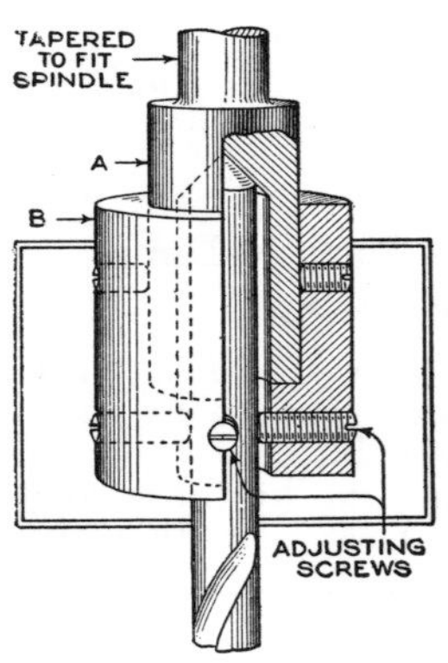

It is made in two pieces, the part A being turned to fit the spindle and bored out with a conical seat at the bottom. The sleeve B is bored at one end to slip over the inner piece, the opposite end being bored to the same size as the opening in A. The outer piece is bored and tapped to take four screws for truing purposes, and two setscrews to hold it to the shank. As shown in the drawing, several different drill sizes can be held in the holder. In operation, the drill is pushed into the chuck until it rests in the conical seat provided for it, and the four adjusting screws are tightened to line up the drill approximately, after which the drill can be trued up as accurately as desired by loosening or tightening the screws after the manner of a four-jawed chuck.

Removing a Broken Screw

The removal of a broken stud or setscrew, that has rusted in place, usually requires considerable time and patience. Before resorting to annealing and drilling, the method shown in the drawing should be tried, if possible.

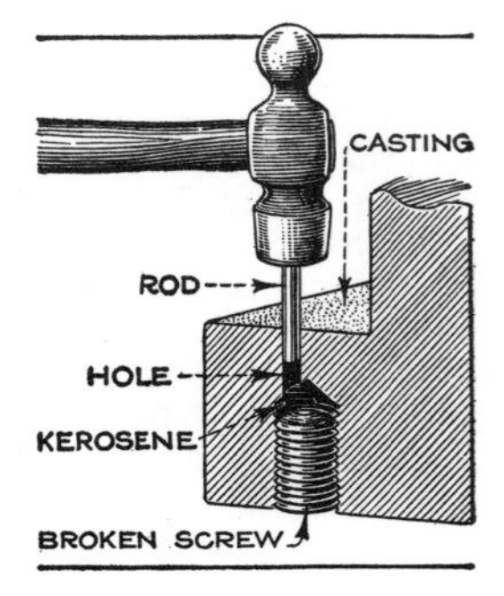

Invert the piece in which the screw is situated, and drill a small hole into the screw hole, as shown in the illustration. Fill this hole with kerosene and insert a short rod of the same size as the hole. By hitting the rod a hard blow, the kerosene will be forced around the threads, after which it is easy to remove the screw with a hammer and chisel.

Making Push-Button Switches Water-Tight

Push-button switches in exposed places can be protected from water by covering them with rubber, attached as shown in the illustration. For a single-gang switch, a rubber sheet, about 4 or 5 in. in dimensions, should be used. Such a piece can be cut from an old inner tube. The rubber is attached to the wall around the switch by means of a narrow frame, cut from a piece of sheet brass, and drilled to receive small brass screws. A snap switch can be protected in the same way, except that a larger sheet of rubber is required, to allow the knob to be grasped and turned.

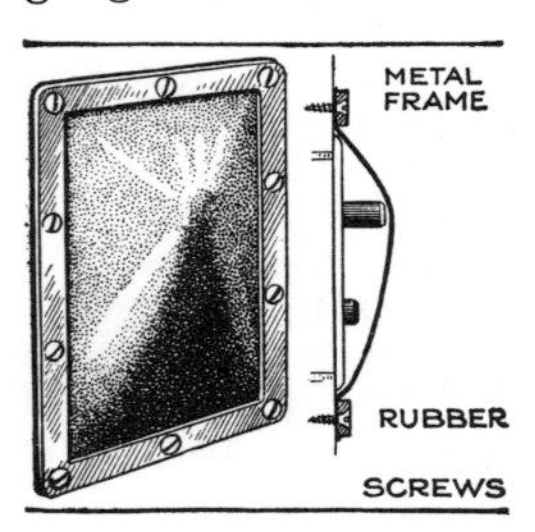

Making Small Commutators

Drum commutators for small experimental motors and dynamos are usually made by driving a length of brass tubing over a fiber rod, fastening the ends with machine screws, and then cutting the tubing lengthwise into segments. A better method is to make up a fiber body, considerably larger in diameter than the finished commutator, by pressing together a number of thick fiber disks on a mandrel, the same size as the motor or dynamo shaft. Copper or brass rods are then driven into holes drilled lengthwise through the fiber cylinder, as shown in Fig. 1. The whole cylinder is turned down until the rods have been cut away to about half their diameter, as in Fig. 2, leaving a series of segments, separated by the fiber insulation, with a flange at each end. The diameter of the rods used for the segments is determined to a great extent by the number of segments necessary; the larger the number of segments the smaller the rods. Before turning down, each rod is drilled and tapped, through the fiber, at one end, and small brass machine screws are screwed in, to hold the rods in place, and to serve as terminal fasteners for the armature winding, as shown in Fig. 3.

A disk-type commutator can be made in a similar manner and with less work. In this case the segments are round copper or brass plugs, turned down for a portion of their length, and driven into holes drilled in a fiber disk as shown in Fig. 4; brass screws are used in this type also, to hold the plugs in place.

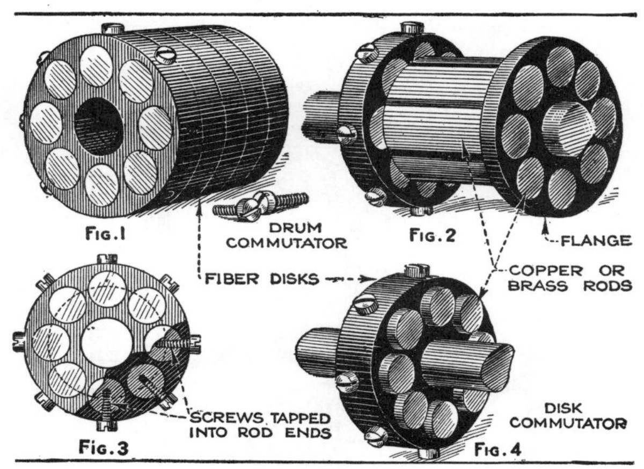

Figures 1, 2, and 3, Drum Commutator, and Figure 4, Disk Commutator, Made of Fiber Disks and Copper Rods

Holding Thin Tubes in Hacksaw Vise

Sawing thin tubing in the power hacksaw is always an awkward and time-consuming job, as the material must be gripped tightly enough to prevent moving, yet without distorting it. The device shown in the drawing will simplify the work considerably, and will more than pay for the time spent in making it, whether this job be a "stock" one, or only done from time to time. A piece of angle iron, rather shorter than the width of the vise jaws, is used for the body, and is drilled and tapped, at its center, for a knurled-head screw. Next a length of small, round, cold-rolled steel is bent to form a rectangle, the length of which is sufficient to allow it to slip over the angle iron, while the width is a little more than the length of the knurled screw.

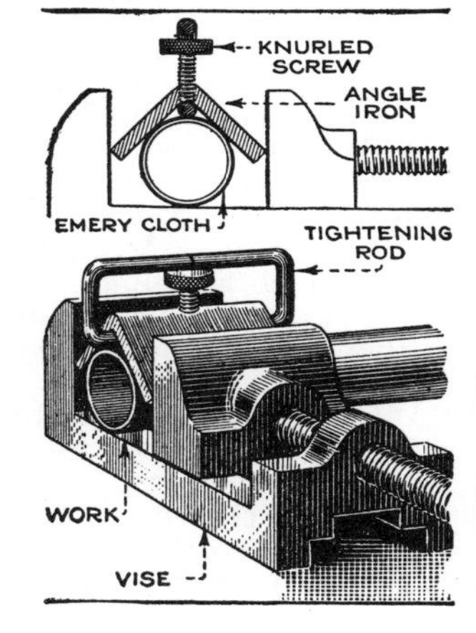

The method of using the device is as follows: The tube is first wrapped, the length of the angle iron, with emery cloth, folded back to back, so that the emery is on both surfaces. Then, with the screw backed out, so that the rod lies snugly against the iron, the angle iron is pressed down tightly on the tube, and the vise is closed on the iron. The tube is now held snugly without the pressure of the vise acting directly on it. To keep it from moving under the saw, the screw is tightened.

It is not necessary to loosen the vise each time the tube is moved forward, releasing the pressure on the rod sufficing to enable the tube to be moved. When the holder is not in use, the screw is backed up against the rod.—Harry Moore, Montreal, Can.

Foot-Power Grinder for Small Shop

BY C. RABER

A FOOT-POWER polisher and grinder that can be used for sawing, and for driving a small lathe, as well as for grinding, in a small workshop, is shown in the illustration. The easy running of the machine, and the convenience of the pedal arrangement, enable the operator to use both hands for the work.

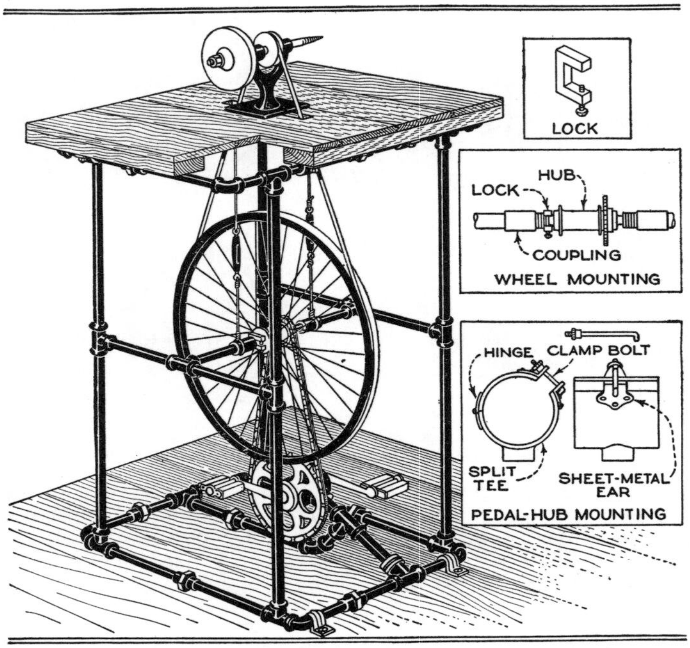

A Foot-Power Grinder Used in a Small Workshop: It is Also Used as a Buffing Wheel, a Circular Saw, or to Drive a Lathe

The frame is constructed entirely of pipe and fittings, and the driving mechanism of bicycle parts. The pedal-hub mounting consists of a regular bicycle-pedal hub, held securely in a large tee, which is split and fitted with a hinge and clamp as shown in the lower detail. Crosspieces in the center of the framework hold the wheel in position so that the small sprocket on the wheel hub is in line with the large pedal sprocket. The method of mounting the hub is shown in the center detail. The ends of the spindle are carried in nipples on each side, and the lock shown in the upper detail is used to prevent the cone from being tightened by the wheel when the latter is turning. As the greatest strain to which this part is subjected is downward, supporting wires, fitted with turnbuckles, are connected to the pipe couplings and to the underside of the table, as shown.

The table consists of a frame, made of 2 by 4-in. stuff, to which a ½-in. top is nailed. The grinder head is bolted or screwed to the top so that a small V-pulley, mounted on its shaft, is exactly in line with the bicycle wheel. A belt is then passed over these two wheels, and the grinder is complete. The top should be securely attached to the frame, and the frame to the floor, by means of pipe straps.

Copying Newspaper Halftones

Many good photographers fail to get successful results when trying to copy pictures in newspapers or magazines. Success is assured if the directions given below are closely followed.

Place a piece of ground glass in a printing frame, ground side up. On this, lay a thin piece of clear celluloid and place the picture face down upon it. Fasten the back of the frame, and stand it on a table squarely in front of the camera. Illuminate the picture from the front, to avoid reflections, but do not let the light shine into the lens.

Use a "process" plate, not the ordinary kind; this is slower in action, hence an exposure of about double the usual time must be made. Focus carefully and do not shake the camera during exposure.

The ground glass will eliminate the grain of the halftone and paper entirely. If the halftone screen is a very coarse one, it will be found better to reverse the glass, thus placing the ground side farther away from the face of the picture.

¶When examining the storage battery of a car to see if any water is needed, do not simply test one cell; examine them all. One of the cells may be cracked, and will require water oftener than the others. It is a good idea to examine a storage battery once every two weeks. In adding distilled water to the battery, always bring the level of the electrolyte ½ in. above the top of the plates.

Homemade Metal Lath

By using homemade metal lath on an outside stucco job, a considerable saving was effected. The price asked for regular metal lath by dealers was about 38 cents per square yard, while the homemade kind cost about 10 cents. Lengths of No. 8 galvanized wire were first tightly stretched over the wall vertically, spaced about 10 in. apart, and nailed at both ends; 2-in. mesh poultry netting was tacked over this, then lengths of No. 18 wire were laid horizontally, spaced about 4 in. apart, and nailed at the ends. The whole was stapled down well and the cement was applied in the usual way. —A. L. Neuenschwander, Miami, Fla.

Bracing Chimney Extension

A tinsmith who was confronted with the problem of erecting an extension on a low chimney, without attaching guy wires to the roof, braced the extension in the manner shown in the drawing.

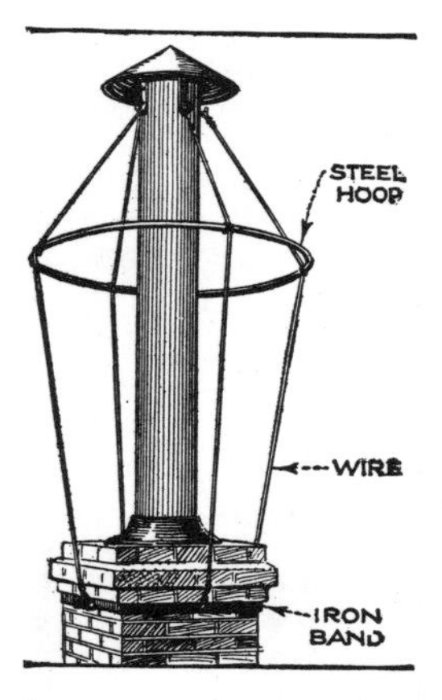

An iron band was bolted around the chimney as indicated, and stovebolts were fitted in holes drilled on each side, for the guy wires. The latter were fastened to the top of the chimney extension and to the stovebolts, and were spread apart by means of a steel hoop, which was held in position by wrapping each guy wire around it once. This bracing made the extension so strong that it has withstood the heaviest gales

Making the Farm Engine More Convenient

The problem of holding down a gasoline engine, without resorting to the usual method of bolting it to the floor, was solved by the portable and adjustable base shown in the drawing. Two heavy wooden beams are bolted to the underside of the engine, their ends projecting far enough to be used as handles. Two similar beams, somewhat shorter, are permanently attached to the floor so that those on the engine will fit between them. A removable rod is then pushed through holes drilled in all four beams, to lock them together and hold the engine down securely. One hole is drilled through each outside beam and a series of holes through the inner ones so that the two

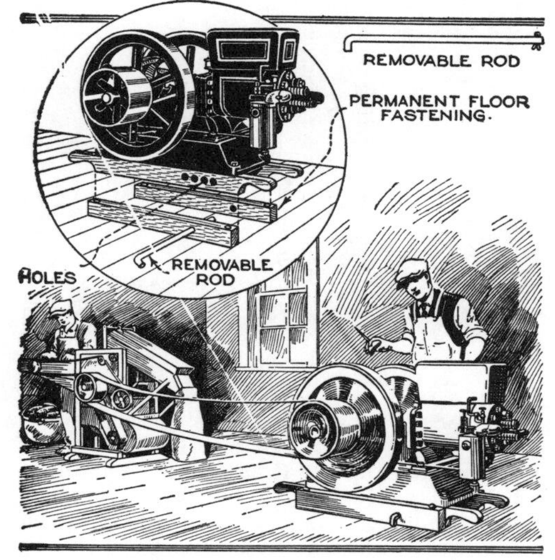

A Base That Makes the Farm Engine Readily Portable, Yet Secure When in Use

base members can be locked together at different points, to obtain proper belt tension. Floor beams of the same type are attached near every engine-driven machine, so that, to attach the engine, it is only necessary to slide it into place and slip in the rod.

Flatiron Coil Used in Ignition System

A Wisconsin flour miller eliminated the use of dry cells for low-tension ignition on his stationary gas engine by substituting a flatiron heating element. By so doing he also avoided the expense of renewing the cells, which is incident to dry-cell ignition systems. The flatiron coil was connected in series with the 110-volt lighting circuit and the ignition circuit of the engine, on the positive side. The coil was suspended in the air, where it could not come in contact with any inflammable substance, as it became very hot when used for any length of time. Although a good, hot spark was provided with this arrangement, there was only a small current consumption, and there was nothing to get out of order easily.—Paul L. Fetherston, Jackson, Michigan.

Mixing Feed for Hogs

The novel method of slopping hogs shown in the photo is in use on an Iowa farm, and has been found a great time and labor saver.

The iron tank shown in the foreground

A Novel Method of Slopping Hogs: Both Troughs can be Refilled While the Hogs are Feeding

is placed at one end of the concrete watering trough, and can be filled with water from the pipe that supplies the trough. The tankage, shorts, or other ground feeds are mixed in the tank and enough water run in to make a thin slop. Then the valve indicated by the arrow is opened, and one of the troughs filled, whereupon the valve is closed again, the pipe swung over to the other trough, and this one filled. The valve and tank, and the inner ends of the troughs, are fenced in as shown, so that the hogs will not interfere with the filling operation, and the hogs are not turned into the yard until both troughs are filled, so that each one has an equal chance to get its portion of the feed.

Lubricating Derrick Sheaves

It is almost impossible to get the average derrick operator to oil the sheaves at the top of the derrick, as it is necessary to climb the mast. On an 80-ft. derrick we overcame this difficulty by running a 1/4-in. pipe along the mast to within a few feet of the top, and fitting a length of flexible metallic hose on the end to reach the center pin of the sheave. Metallic hose comes in sizes appropriate for this purpose, together with the necessary fittings, which are a solder nipple on one end and a 1/4-in. pipe-thread nipple at the other. At the bottom of the length of pipe, an elbow, taken from one of the popular high-pressure auto-greasing systems, was fitted. A good grade of grease, that does not harden in cold weather, was used, the entire pipe being filled with grease by means of the high-pressure grease gun, so that at any time afterward, a push on the grease gun below forced the grease into the sheave pin. This method of lubricating has also been found practicable on all our clamshell buckets, and on the derrick engine. In places where the nipple was likely to be broken off, the old oil cup on the bearing was removed, and a solid plug was substituted for it. Another plug of the same size was drilled and tapped to take one of the grease nipples. When it was necessary to oil the bearing, the solid plug was removed, the one with the nipple screwed on, and the grease gun applied.—A. S. Jamieson, Springfield, Mass.

Enameled Ware Repaired by Brazing

Enameled ware can be repaired easily and permanently by brazing, the small tip of an ordinary welding or acetylene brazing torch being the most suitable to do the work. Remove all rust and dirt around the hole with hydrochloric acid, or with a piece of emery cloth. Apply heat, and melt the flux and spelter around the hole, spreading the spelter over the hole with an iron wire, flattened on one end. The spelter will unite with the enamel, making a permanent repair.—M. Van Slyke, Jacksonville, Fla.

A Handy Spike-Pulling Tool

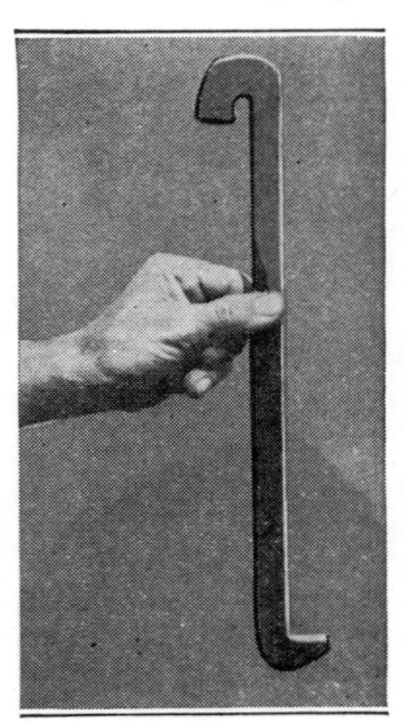

It is frequently necessary to tap or remove spikes and other parts so close to the ground that there is not enough room below for the head of the hammer, to say nothing of the space required for swinging it. The tool illustrated will prove of considerable assistance in cases of this kind. The lower hook is inserted beneath the head of the spike to be drawn, and the hammering is done on the underside of the upper hook.—H. J. Engel, New Braunfels, Tex.

Attaching Wagon to Harvester-Thresher

BY GEO. G. MCVICKER

WITH the speeding up of crop production, great improvements have been made in machinery for planting, tending, and harvesting, but many manufacturers, when building an implement, plan only for the operation of one particular machine at a time. This leaves it to the farmer to devise hitches that will enable him to use several machines together.

Harvester-threshers seem to be built with the idea in mind that horse-drawn wagons will be used to take care of the threshed grain, and hence the horses that the farmer had hoped to dispose of when buying his tractor, must be kept and used.

One western farmer has disposed of this problem in the following manner: The wagon that receives the grain is attached to the tractor by means of a hinged arm fastened to the tractor drawbar, as shown in the illustration. The hinge shown, which is made from short pieces of flat iron and iron rods, allows the arm to support the wagon tongue without the use of a tiebar. Into the outer end of the hinged portion, a large staple is driven, just

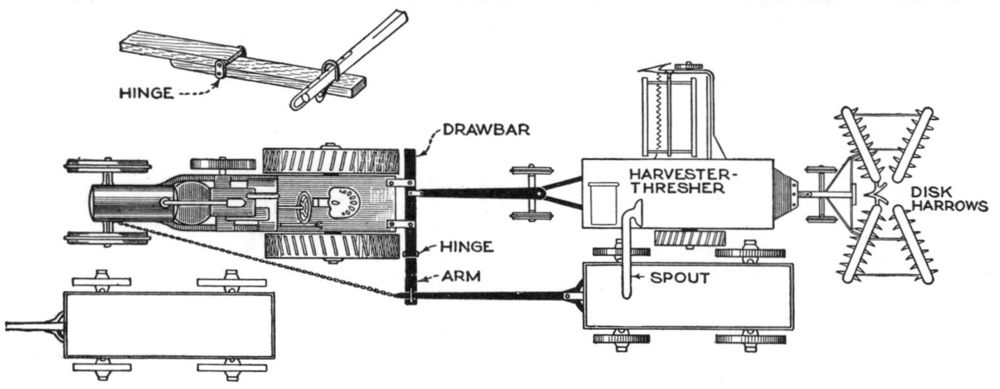

Method of Hitching Wagon to Harvester-Thresher to Receive the Threshed Grain: Above, Photo Showing Outfit in Operation; Below, Layout of Tractor, Thresher, Wagons, and Harrow, with Detail of Drawbar Hitch

far enough to allow room for the wagon tongue to enter freely.

The wagon, when first hitched on, is connected close to the arm by means of the chain shown, the front end of the chain being attached to the tractor. This allows the rear end of the wagon to be filled; the chain is then let out a little more, allowing the wagon to fall back as the harvester moves forward. This is continued until the wagon is evenly filled.

The empty wagons are left in the position shown at the lower left, and, when one is ready to be hitched on, the chain is unhooked, the arm thrown up so as to pass the empty wagon, then dropped, and the wagon coupled on as before.

In the harvesting season in the central and western plains, the crop is not only harvested and threshed in one operation, but the seed bed is prepared, at the same time, by a disk harrow, attached to the rear of the combined machine.

There is always a side draft in these large harvester-threshers, due to the cutter bar extending so far to one side. In attaching the harrow to the rear of the machine, the drawbar or hitch should be made adjustable, so that the harrow can be set sufficiently to one side or the other to counteract this side draft. This is particularly convenient when harvesting on sidehill fields, where the machine has a tendency to creep down.

Cleaning Drill Holes in Rock or Concrete

When drilling holes in rock or concrete by means of a star drill, the dust that collects in the hole can be cleaned out with a blower of the kind shown in the illustration. The blower is merely a length of $\frac{3}{8}$-in. light brass tube, flared slightly at one end by inserting a hexagon-headed bolt or screw into it, and tapping the pipe with a hammer, as shown in the upper detail. After dropping the flared end down near the bottom of the hole, the dust is blown out quickly and thoroughly. It is necessary, of course, to keep the eyes closed while blowing, to keep out the dust.

Blowpipe for Removing Accumulated Dust from Holes Drilled in Rock and Concrete

In hard rock, when it is necessary to use water on the drill to keep it cool, the resulting "mud" in the hole can be picked out by gently tamping the blowpipe down, which will pack the mud in the end of the pipe. The pipe is cleaned by blowing, tapping, or by pushing a wire through it.—Dr. G. E. Abbott, San Diego, California.

Novel Skinning Knife

When skinning a beef carcass there are two dangers for the novice: one is cutting a hole in the hide, which decreases its value, and the other is leaving too much flesh on the hide, which causes a heavy dockage. A useful skinning tool, which eliminates much of this trouble, is shown in the illustration. It consists of a pair of ordinary 6-in. pliers with a hole drilled through each of the jaws, and in each handle, as indicated, the pliers being annealed for the purpose. A piece of spring steel, about 1 in. wide, is drilled and attached to the jaws by means of pins riveted loosely through the holes. Two safety-razor blades are attached to the spring by means of small bolts, fitted with thumbnuts; the cutting edges of the blades project about $\frac{1}{16}$ in. beyond

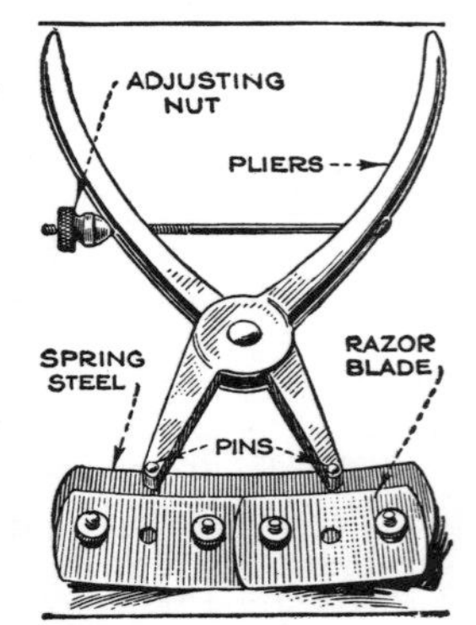

the edge of the spring, and the inner ends overlap, as shown. A small, long bolt, fitted with a thumbnut, is passed through the holes drilled in the handle, to complete the device. By slightly pressing the steel spring between the jaws and screwing up the thumbnut on the handle bolt, the blades will be bent in a curve to suit many parts of the carcass. The tool is manipulated with one hand, being pushed along with the protector next to the hide, and the separated part of the hide is held with the other hand.

Funnel for Filling Crankcase

The funnel illustrated has several advantages over many other types used for pouring oil into the filler spout on an automobile crankcase, as it has no restricted opening, and is independent of the measure. A number of funnels of this type, varying in size, are used in a gasoline-service station in Washington, D. C. They are made of sheet metal, such as galvanized iron, which is available almost everywhere and can readily be bent to the shape shown. The oil may be poured as rapidly as it can be taken by the filler spout on the engine. A considerable saving of time is effected by the use of these funnels, and they are cheap to make; for this reason particularly they are recommended for service stations.

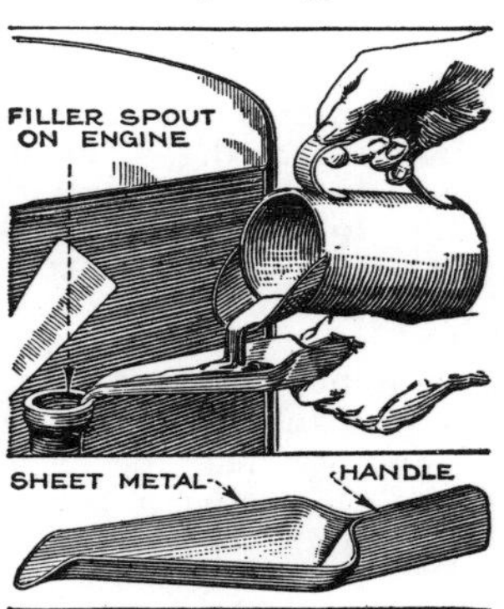

Collapsible Baskets Simplify Fruit Display

The proprietor of a fruit store, who made a practice of changing the display in his show window every day, found that the fruit could be removed quickly, and without any danger of injury, by using collapsible baskets of the type illustrated. In addition to their usefulness in removing the fruit, these baskets also served to keep the piles of fruit intact, as the rims of the baskets supported the bottom layer of each pile.

Each basket consists of a cloth bag, tacked to a barrel hoop, to which half of another hoop is riveted to serve as a handle. These hoops are covered with

Collapsible Cloth Baskets Support Piles of Fruit in Show Windows and Facilitate Their Removal

colored crêpe paper to give them a neat appearance. When the fruit is displayed in the window, the basket is folded down neatly, as indicated, the fruit being piled inside of the rim. To remove the fruit, the basket is lifted and the pile is carried away. This method of removing fruit from show windows is especially valuable during winter, when the fruit must be removed every evening to prevent it from being injured by frost.

Curing Misfiring of Truck Engine

The erratic firing of a light-truck engine when running at low speeds, caused by the leakage of air around the intake-valve stems, was cured in the manner illustrated. The valves and cages were removed, and the upper end of the guide in each cage counterbored, to a depth of 1/4 in., with a drill bit 1/4 in. larger than the valve stem. In the stuffing box thus formed, a couple of felt washers were placed, and a light coil spring put over them, and held in position by the mainspring washer and pin, forcing the felt tightly against the stem and shutting off all leakage. A few drops of oil were applied to the washers occasionally, to prevent wear of the guides and stems.—Maling C. Metzer, Silver Creek, Neb.

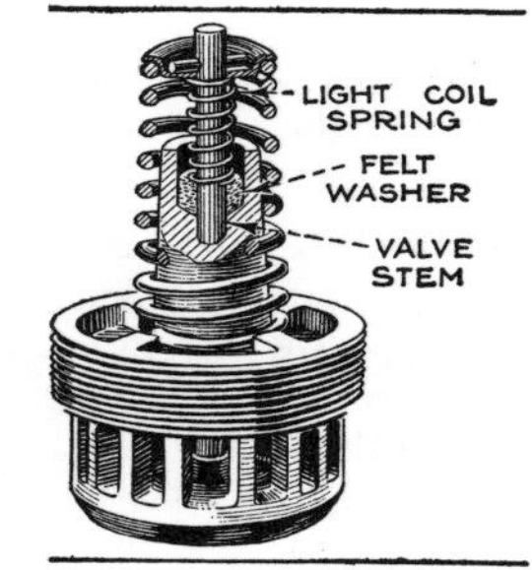

Vise Grinder of Simple Design

The simple grinder shown in the drawing will prove of convenience in a small workshop, where there is not enough

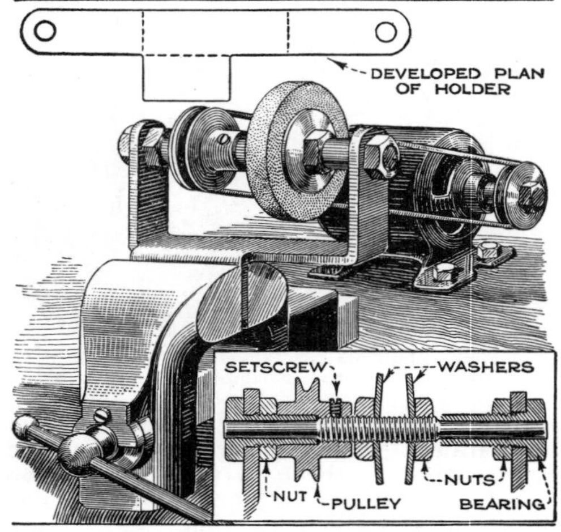

A Simple Grinder Held in the Vise Is of Considerable Advantage in the Small Workshop

space for a stationary grinder, or where a stationary grinder would not be used often enough to justify its installation. The holder that supports the spindle is made in one piece; it is cut from boiler plate and bent to the shape shown, leaving two lugs to carry the bearings for the spindle, and one for holding the fixture in the vise. A V-pulley and an emery wheel are mounted on the threaded spindle, and bronze bearings are threaded into the lugs and fastened by locknuts, as shown in the lower detail. An electric motor is fastened to the workbench behind the vise, the slots in the base of the motor permitting proper adjustment of the belt.

Removing Rock Coatings from Fossils

The delicate task of removing the final rock coatings from newly unearthed fossils has been much simplified by the research scientists of the California Academy of Science, who have successfully used for this purpose the unusual combination of the hottest flame known to industry, and a drop of cold water.

The new method not only facilitates what otherwise is a most difficult task, but it also reduces the danger of breaking or otherwise injuring the fossil during the final step of cleaning the rock coating from it. A fine jet of oxyacetylene flame, the temperature of which is about 6,300° F., is directed upon the last of the rock coating remaining on the fossil. Immediately afterward, a drop of cold water is put on the heated spot. The heating and cooling takes place too quickly to cause expansion and contraction of the fossil underneath, so that only the outside rock cracks and breaks away, leaving the fossil itself uncovered and uninjured.

This method is especially useful if the fossil is irregular in shape. If it is large, the rock coating must be broken off in small pieces. The method bids fair to become the standard practice with fossil experts, because it reduces to a minimum the risk of damaging the fossils while they are being cleaned.—Roswell S. Britton, New York City.

Novel Sampler for Deep Wells

The device shown in the illustration was improvised to obtain samples of water from the bottom of a 160-ft. well. It consists of a frame carrying a burnt-out electric lamp, which is filled with water by having the tip broken off automatically when the device strikes bottom.

The lamp, and the mechanism for breaking the tip, are held by a strap-iron frame, bent to the shape indicated. A spring mousetrap is attached to the frame in an inverted position, so that its lever,

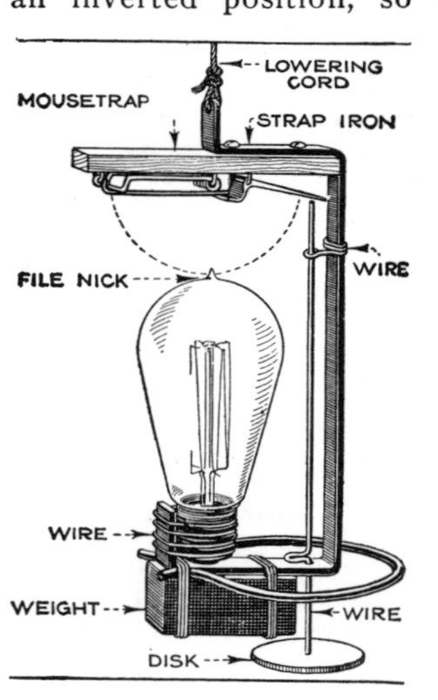

upon swinging around, hits the tip of the lamp, and breaks it off. The trap is tripped by means of a plunger, which consists of a length of wire with a disk soldered to the lower end, as shown; the plunger is pushed up and springs the trap when the disk strikes the bottom of the well. A sharp bend in the wire prevents the plunger from falling out of the frame, and a circular wire guard, about twice the diameter of the plunger disk, prevents the trap from being sprung should the device accidentally come in contact with the wall of the well. A weight is attached to the lower part of the frame to insure its sinking in a vertical position. A coil of heavy wire, attached to the lower end of the frame is used like a screw socket, the lamp being screwed into it. After the lamp is in position, a file nick is made in the tip to localize the break as much as possible. The water is quickly drawn through the small opening thus made, and the device is then raised to the surface where the water can be examined.

Drill-Press Bolt Holder

The holder shown in the illustration is handy when using bolts in the plain slots of a drill-press table. It not only keeps the bolts from turning when the nut is tightened, but also prevents the bolts from falling to the floor when the nut is removed. Some wire and a length of tubing are the only materials necessary to make it. The tube is bent to the U-shape shown, but before doing so, a length of wire is placed in it; after the tube is bent this wire is looped over at both ends. A latch is next made of the same size wire and attached, care being taken to leave the eye large enough to allow the latch to swing in and out of the opposite loop. When using the holder, the U-shaped wire is pushed through the slot in the table with the latch thrown back. To lock the holder, and to keep the bolt in position, the latch is swung around and pushed through the wire loop. Where it is necessary to use a bolt continually in a plain slot, considerable trouble can be avoided by using this holder, as with it a bolt can be held just as easily in a plain slot as in a T-slot.

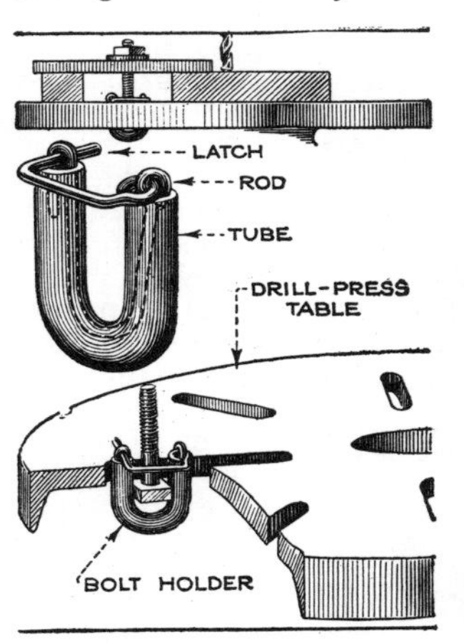

When milling operations are finished, the cutter should be removed from the arbor, cleaned and placed in a wall cabinet or drawer, where it is kept from contact with other tools.

Detachable Top for Open Truck

The drawing shows a simple detachable top for an open express-truck body. It consists of a heavy-canvas covering, held

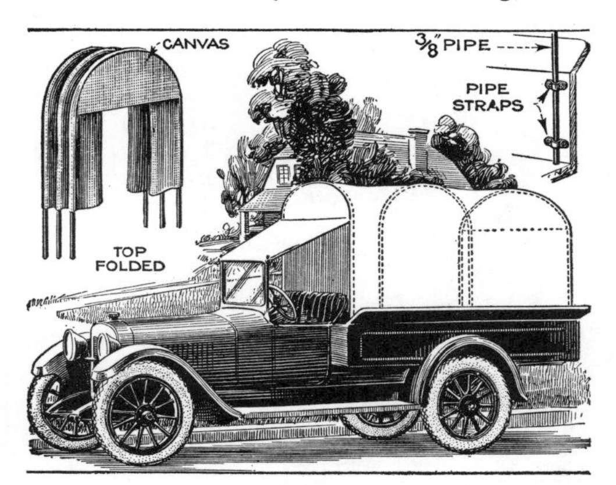

A Canvas Covering for the Open Express Truck: It can be Attached or Detached in a Moment

by three ribs made of 3/8-in. pipe, bent to the shape indicated. Semicircular pieces of canvas are used at the ends of the top, and an additional flap covers the driver. The top canvas is attached to the ribs by strips of canvas, sewed across them, and, when the top is erected, the flap is attached to the edge of the windshield as shown. The ribs are held by means of pipe straps screwed to the sides of the truck body, two straps being sufficient for each leg. A canvas top of this kind can be conveniently carried in the truck body.

C-Clamps Support Ladder While Hanging Eaves Trough

When hanging an eaves trough, it is necessary to fit the upper end of the ladder with some attachment that will enable it to clear the trough. A simple and satisfactory attachment consists of two ordinary 4-in. C-clamps. These are fastened on the end of the ladder, as shown in the illustration, so that the thumbscrews rest against the first row of shingles.—W. B. Nicholson, Detroit, Mich.

Valve-Cage Puller

On engines having overhead valves, a common method of removing a valve cage is to pry it out. The disadvantage of this practice is that the valve is frequently bent, making necessary a tedious repair job, or the renewal of the valve. To do the work without danger of injuring the valve, a simple cage puller of the type shown in the illustration has been found serviceable. It consists of a short length of pipe, with an internal diameter larger than the diameter of the cage, and a U-shaped steel rod, bent to form a hook for gripping the spring-retaining cap on the valve stem and fitted with a setscrew as shown. The hook is engaged with the cap and the setscrew tightened on a heavy steel bar placed across the pipe, releasing the valve cage from its seat without any danger of bending the stem.

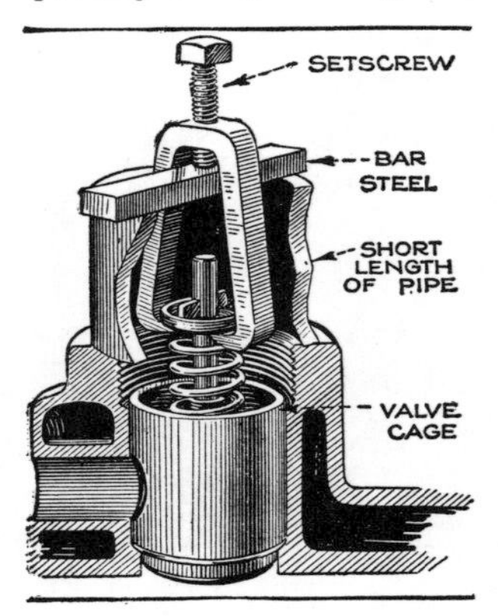

Holding Small Screws in Lathe

Any lathe hand who has attempted to hold small, short screws in a small chuck or in a drill chuck, while machining them, will appreciate the advantages of the screw holder shown in the drawing, which will hold them firmly even where only two threads can be used to chuck them. A short piece of cold-rolled steel, of suitable diameter, is either turned taper on one end, to fit the lathe spindle, or straight, to be held in a universal chuck; the other end is threaded, and a short length turned down to a small diameter, as shown. A knurled sleeve is then made to fit the threaded end, and is drilled and tapped, at its center, to fit a standard hexagon-head capscrew. Several of these capscrews are drilled and tapped, along their axes, to fit the various sizes of screws.

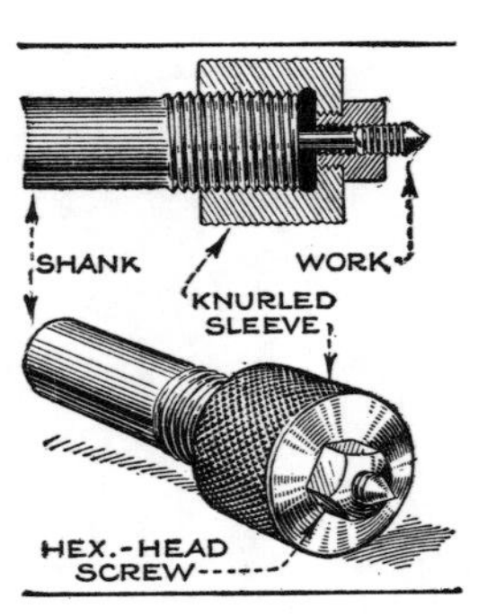

To machine a screw, the sleeve is screwed outward a few turns, the screw is placed in position, and the sleeve screwed inward, when the small-diameter nose of the shank butts against the screw, and locks it firmly. After machining, half a turn of the sleeve will release the screw, so that it can be unscrewed with the fingers.

Changing Base Connections of Bayonet-Socket Lamps

To adapt a double-contact automobile lamp for a single-contact socket, first see if one of the contacts makes connection with the lamp base. If so, well and good; if not, a connection must be made, which can be done with a drop of solder, or by means of a very thin-brass strip. A small strip of brass is soldered to the other contact, and doubled, as shown, so as to cover the center of the base; then a mica disk is placed in the fold, and cemented in place with shellac.

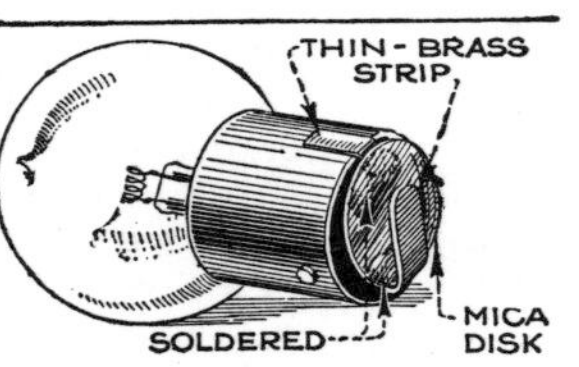

DOUBLE CONTACT TO SINGLE

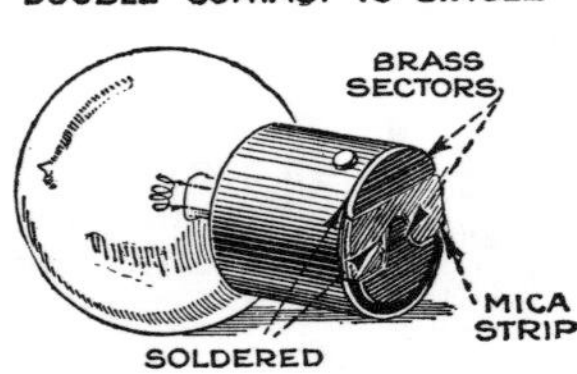

SINGLE CONTACT TO DOUBLE

A single-contact base is adapted to a double-contact socket by filing the center contact down until it is nearly flush with the bottom, and soldering on a T-shaped brass strip or sector, as shown in the lower detail, care being taken that the strip does not touch the base. Another brass strip, making contact with the base, is soldered opposite this, as indicated. A strip of mica, covering the arm soldered to the center contact, is then cemented in place. The sectors must, of course, be arranged in such a position with respect to the pins that proper contact will be made in the socket.
—H. H. Parker, Oakland, Calif.

¶Manganese steel is not susceptible to magnetism and cannot be magnetized; therefore, parts made from this material cannot be held on magnetic chucks.

Protecting Pipe Covering

The magnesia covering used on steam pipes has not much mechanical strength, as it is covered only by a thin layer of cloth, and hence does not offer much protection to pipes passing through floors, or along walls where they are likely to be struck by trucks or material. A good, substantial protection for the covering was provided, in one such case, by inclosing the covering, to a height of 6 ft. above the floor, with a stovepipe-iron shell. The edges of the shell are crimped outward, so that a "key," made from a narrow strip of the same metal and having the edges crimped as shown, can be pushed over the edges of the shell, to draw it tightly around the covering and lock it. Keys of the same size can be used with various sizes of shells, the latter being cut to suit the diameter of the pipes and their covering. After the key has been pushed into place, the seams are carefully pounded down with a wooden mallet.

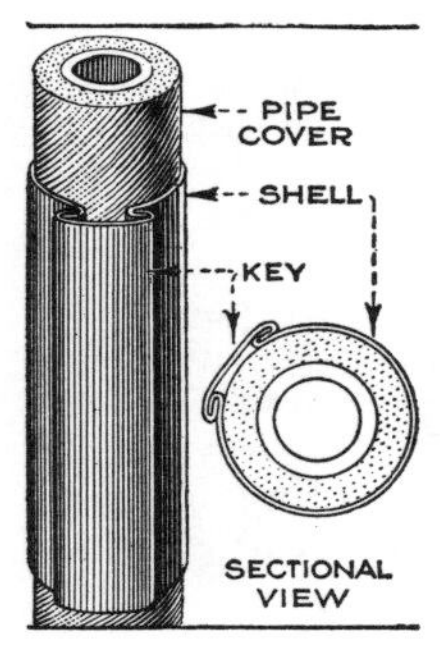

Placing Concrete in Water

If concrete is emptied loose and allowed to sink through water, so much of the cement is washed away that the mixture is spoiled. In the absence of other means of depositing the concrete, the device shown, which is called a "tremie," can be used to advantage. This device consists of an 8-in. galvanized sheet-iron pipe, reaching from the surface of the water to the point where the concrete is to be laid, a funnel with a bail being provided on the top of the pipe, so that it can be hoisted and lowered easily. In use, the pipe is completely filled with concrete, the bottom end being held down to prevent the concrete from running out. When the pipe is full, it is slightly raised to allow the concrete to run out gradually.

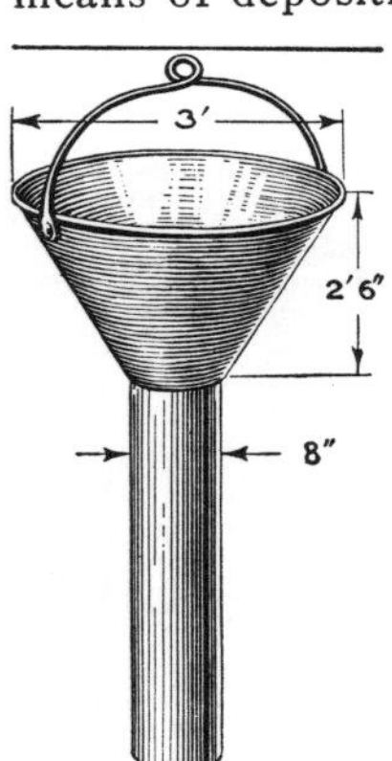

Tool for Peeling Logs

Peeling the bark from logs is heavy work, and any tool that will simplify it is worth making. Such a tool is shown in the drawing. It is simply an old hoe, with the neck straightened as indicated, and the blade formed slightly convex to fit the side of an average-size log; this is done by heating the neck and blade to a cherry red and then forging. The blade is sharpened, on the log side, with a file. In using this tool, the worker stands erect and can peel the log with surprising speed.—Jos. C. Coyle, Colorado Springs, Colo.

Wire Clamp for Garden-Hose Connections

The illustration shows a simple device for clamping rubber-hose connections with wire. The device consists of a ½-in. bolt, about 6 in. long, threaded its entire length and rounded at its end, to prevent injury to the hose. The bolt is screwed through a steel bar, drilled and tapped to fit and having notches filed around each end.

When using the device, a suitable length of galvanized-iron wire is bent to a U-shape, and wrapped around the hose in the manner indicated, the ends being drawn up tightly and wrapped around the notches in the steel bar. The bolt is then screwed down against the "bottom" of the U, until the wire is tightly drawn around the hose, after which it is only necessary to swing the tool over, thus bending the wire, and to cut off the ends about ½ in. from the bend. A pair of pliers is used to clamp the ends down.—John H. Yeakel, Everett, Wash.

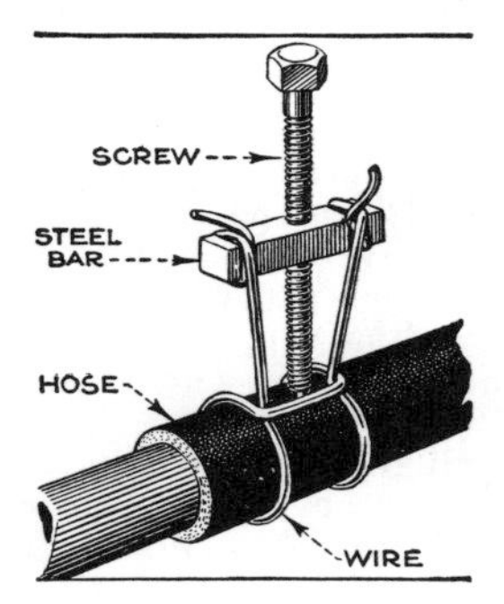

Increasing Usefulness of Small Grinders

An ordinary small emery-grinder head can be converted into a most useful and versatile machine tool at slight cost, and with the expenditure of a little time. The tool can be used for disk grinding, sawing and ripping of boards, turning pattern work, and various other purposes.

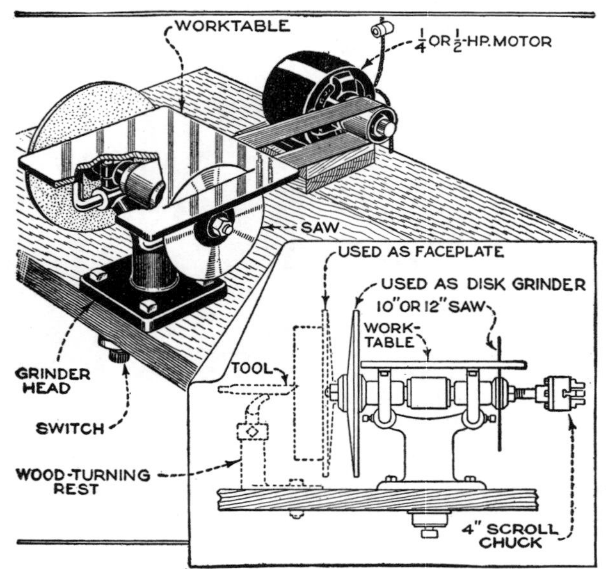

The Usefulness of the Ordinary Motor-Driven Grinder is Greatly Increased by Providing It with a Few Simple Attachments

A worktable, made of sheet steel or hardwood, is mounted on the grinder head. It is held by two round-steel brackets that slide into the usual work-rest holes and are locked by setscrews. In case a metal top is used, it is drilled and countersunk for flat-head screws, and the ends of the two brackets are tapped to receive them. For a wooden top, wood screws are used, the brackets being split and spread, and the ears drilled and countersunk on the underside. A slot is cut near one end of the table for a small circular saw that is attached to one end of the emery-grinder shaft. The other edge of the table should come within 1/8 in. of the disk grinder that is attached to the other end of the shaft. This is a simple faceplate, similar to that used on patternmakers' lathes, with screw holes drilled in it for fastening the work. It is faced with abrasive disks for use as a disk grinder, or may be reversed, as shown by the dotted lines, and used as a faceplate for wood turning, a tool rest being bolted to the bench for this, as indicated.

If the length of the grinder shaft permits, a 4-in. scroll chuck, fitted with a screw flange, is attached as shown in the lower view. This chuck will be found useful for filing, polishing, and drilling, the latter being accomplished by pressing the work against the drill, which is held in the chuck.

An electric motor of 1/2 or 1/4 hp. is used, a snap switch being located on the underside of the workbench, near the edge, as indicated. As it is necessary to have a wide range of speeds, interchangeable pulleys of different sizes must be provided for the motor shaft. The motor should be mounted on a sliding base, so that one size of belt can be used for all pulleys.

Removing Broken Screws

The acetylene torch, which is part of the necessary equipment of most shops and garages, is of considerable assistance in the removal of broken screws in metal. Weld onto the screw a piece of metal that will project above the surrounding surface. When the screw contracts upon cooling, it becomes loose in the threads, and can then readily be removed by gripping the projecting piece with a pair of pliers.

Thumbtacks Used as Battery Markers

The owner of a battery-service station uses numbered thumbtacks on storage batteries to identify them while being repaired or recharged. Sets of thumbtacks, numbered from 0 to 9, are provided, the numbers being stenciled on with paint. The use of thumbtacks for marking is much better than using tags, as the latter are likely to be torn off. A record, corresponding with the number shown by the tacks, is made in the books, and the tacks remain in place until the job is complete and the battery called for, when they are removed and used again.

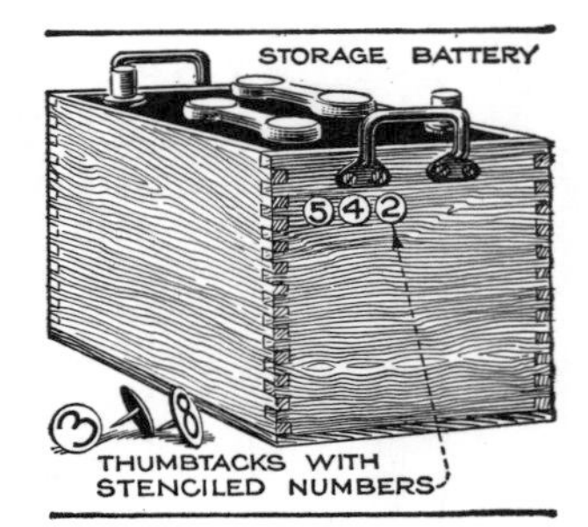

Bathtubs for Cooking Vessels

A canning plant that is remarkable for its many cost-saving features, employs ordinary enameled bathtubs as cooking vessels, in which certain foods are given their preliminary heating. In this way the purchase of several expensive pieces of equipment has been avoided.

The tubs are mounted on trucks so that they can easily be moved from place to place about the factory. In use, a tub is filled with the food to be processed, and is then placed where a steam pipe carrying live steam, can be dropped into it. After the preliminary cooking is finished the truck is wheeled to the point where the cans are filled. An advantage of this method is that the tubs are easily cleaned and sterilized, and, besides, no discoloration is imparted to products heated in them. Furthermore, as they can be moved, they are more convenient than the ordinary stationary kettles. The tubs are also used for mixing sirups, and even brine.—Orin Crooker, Wheaton, Ill.

Carbon-Removing Tool

Many uses can be found for discarded hacksaw blades fitted in a holder similar to the one shown in the illustration. The method of construction makes this tool particularly handy for breaking up the carbon that accumulates in automobile piston - ring grooves, as any number of blades necessary to fit in the grooves can be used while the others are folded back into the holder. The latter is made of 1/16-in. sheet steel, bent over as shown, and drilled near the end—the same size as the holes in the blades—to take the screw and nut that hold the blades in place. Blades broken in the center are long enough for the purpose. The set of blades should be ground down on the end to make them all of the same length, which gives a better appearance to the tool and makes it more handy to use.

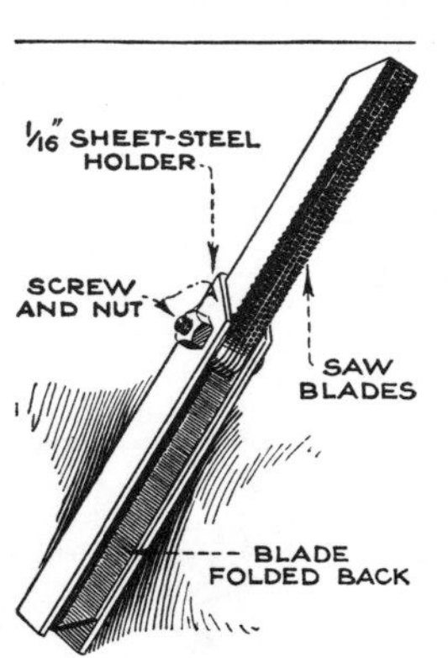

Draining Oil Trucks

Large factories using oil for fuel usually have an underground concrete storage tank to conform to the requirements of fire-insurance companies. These storage tanks are filled from large oil trucks that drive over the top of the tank and discharge the oil by gravity. Difficulty has been found in completely draining the oil trucks, owing to the fact that the tank on the truck has a slight pitch forward.

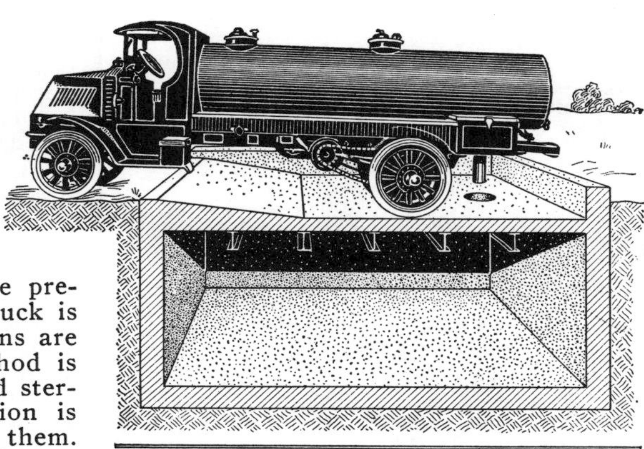

Trucks Unloading Oil or Gasoline by Gravity can be Drained Entirely If the Tank Top is Formed So That the Truck Inclines toward the Rear

The illustration shows a very practical method of draining the trucks. The top of the tank is formed, as shown, with an 8-in. drop, and a ramp to enable the trucks to be driven on and off easily. When the truck is in position over the tank, the rear wheels are thus 8 in. below the front wheels, which allows all the oil to drain out of the tank. The truck will stand in position without the use of the brakes.—G. L. Munroe, Fall River, Mass.

Making Tight Joints with Undersize Threads

When laying some 6-in. water pipe in a small town, all the pipes having been cut at the shop, it was found that the threads on two of the pipes had been cut so small that the pipe could be screwed into the fitting up to the last thread, with the result that the joints were not water-tight. To make them fit properly, the threads were first thoroughly cleaned, then tinned with solder, using a paste flux and wiping the surplus solder off with a cloth. The joints were then screwed up, and found to be perfectly water-tight.

Cheap and Serviceable Water Cooler

The water cooler shown in the illustration will be found serviceable in shops and factories where a large supply of cool drinking water is required. It consists of two sections of vitrified-clay pipe; one section is 24 by 36 in., and the other 12 by 36 in. in dimensions. A cement base is made by setting the larger pipe on a flat surface, and pouring cement into it, then pressing the smaller pipe into the concrete as shown. The surface of the base between the pipes is slanted to the drain pipe, and the surface inside the smaller pipe is sloped to an outlet pipe, which, together with the drain pipe, is placed in position before the concrete is poured. The outlet pipe is provided with a faucet on the outside. As it is rather difficult to drill the hole through the outside clay pipe, this should be done at the yard where it is purchased.

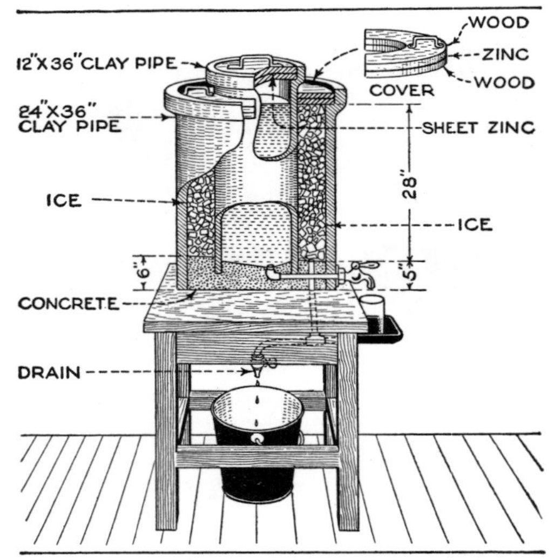

A Cheap and Serviceable Water Cooler for Use Where a Large Quantity of Drinking Water is Required

The whole can be conveniently mounted on a sturdy wooden table or bench, and a drip pail provided underneath. Double-thickness wooden covers, with a piece of sheet zinc between the layers, are provided on both pipes as shown, that for the outer pipe being made in two sections. The space in the smaller pipe is used for the water, its capacity being about 13 gallons, and the space between the two pipes is packed with crushed ice. The entire cost of the water cooler is approximately $9.—Louis Davis, Nashville, Tennessee.

A Self-Closing Oil Container

In a shop that builds small meters, all shafts, before assembling, are inspected by being revolved by hand on bench centers, the centers being touched, before the shaft is mounted between them, by a fine wire carrying a drop of light oil. It is essential that the oil be kept perfectly clean, as a speck of dirt on either center might result in a false test, so the automatically closing oil container shown in the drawing is used.

The container is made of wood and brass tubing; the wood is used for the base and the two uprights, and the tubing for the oil container and cover. Before fastening the uprights to the base, a slot, about 3/8 in. wide and 2 in. long, is cut in the tube that is to hold the oil, and the ends of the tube are serrated, or "nicked" with a file, so that the tube will not turn in the upright. Leather washers are fitted tightly into the ends of the tube, and the ends pressed into the uprights. The cover is also made of brass tubing, and slips over the first piece. It is cut a little shorter than the first piece, for clearance, sawed lengthwise, and one edge of the cut bent outward. To one end of this edge is fastened a wire spring, as indicated; the curved edge also serves as a handle.

The photograph shows the container closed, and the other illustrations show the details of construction. When the operator desires to dip the wire in the oil, he turns the cover around until the opening is uncovered. As soon as the cover is released, it is snapped back to the closed position by the wire spring.—Harry Moore, Montreal, Can.

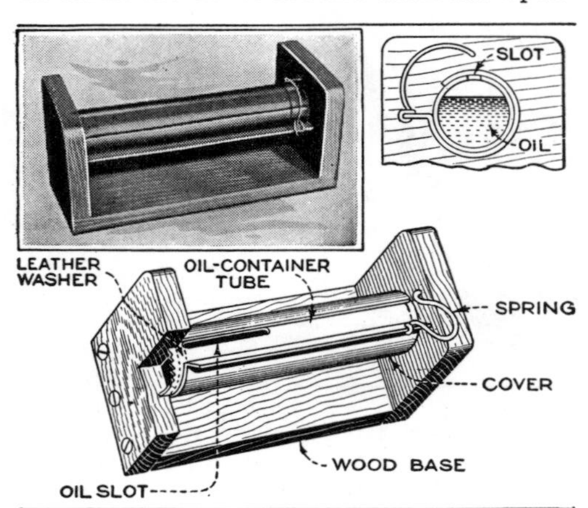

A Self-Closing Oil Container: Upper Left, the Container Closed; Right and Center, Details of Construction

An Upright Tool Cabinet

The tool cabinet shown in the illustration is made almost entirely of 1 by 12-in. finished lumber. It is divided into two parts: the cabinet proper and a drawer section. The cabinet section provides space for the larger tools, and the drawers contain nails, screws, small tools, and miscellaneous material.

Tools such as chisels, screwdrivers, pliers, etc., are conveniently supported on the wall of the upper section by means of strips of leather, attached to the wall with small round-head screws. Hammers and similar tools are held in place by long screws partly driven into the wood, while saws are slipped into the slotted shelf shown in the compartment at the left. Tools are also hung on the inside of the doors. A few shelves, arranged near the bottom of the larger compartment, provide space for small boxes of tools, such as taps and dies, or for books and catalogs relating to tools.

The drawers in the lower section may be subdivided in any suitable manner, and one or both of the drawers provided with sliding trays for holding screws or nails of various sizes. All the major dimensions of the cabinet are given in the drawing, and the construction is quite obvious. The details may, however, vary to suit the builder of the cabinet.—C. N. Schuette, San Francisco, Calif.

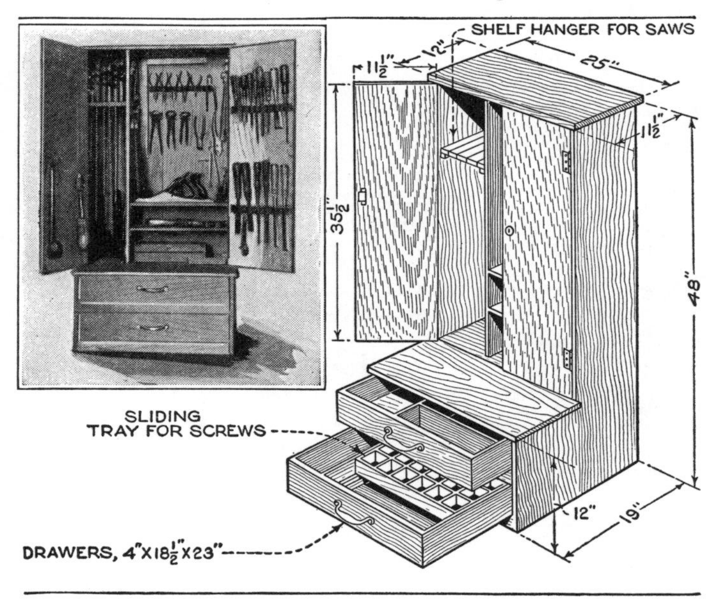

An Upright Tool Cabinet of Excellent Design: Left, Photo of Cabinet, Showing Arrangement of Tools; Right, Perspective Drawing, Showing All Important Dimensions

Reboring a Turret-Lathe Bed

The drawing shows a simple method of reboring a turret-lathe bed, when it is not convenient to move the part to a machine shop for reboring. An angle plate, with a hole drilled through one side, is used as one bearing for the boring bar, and is clamped to the lathe bed as indicated. A bushing in the hole in the opposite side of the lathe bed serves as the other bearing. The bar itself has a fine thread on one end, and a nut is used to feed it.

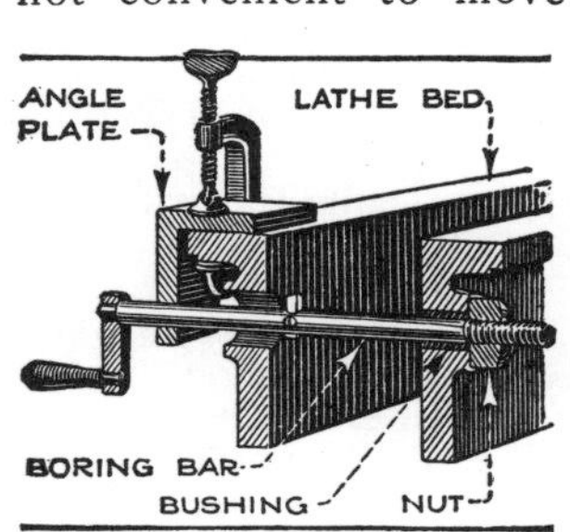

Cutting a Belt for Cone Pulleys

When cutting a belt to length for cone pulleys, the "cut-and-try" method occasionally gives good results, but more often does not. The following method, however, always gives correct results: Place the belt on the pulleys as shown in the drawing at the left; stretch the belt; mark and cut it, and make the joint in the customary way. When the joint has been made, place the belt on the proper steps, as shown on the right. This method also saves time.

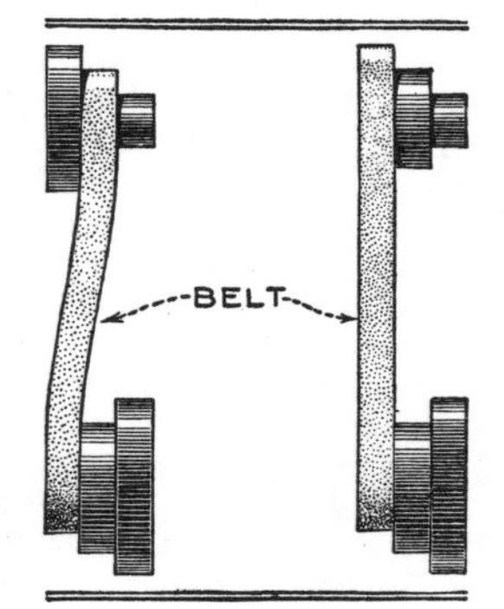

Marking Wooden Boxes

The methods described in this article were used, with satisfactory results, for marking a large number of fruit boxes and trays with the owner's name and address, and will prove equally useful wherever quantities of wood surfaces are to be marked or lettered permanently. At first, a bronze burning die was used, and while the results were fairly satisfactory, depressed blackened lettering, formed with the same die under pressure, was found to be neater and could be made more quickly. For rough work, the burned lettering answers very well, and this method has the advantage of requiring no vise or press, and of ease of application, as the hot die can be applied while the surface is in any position.

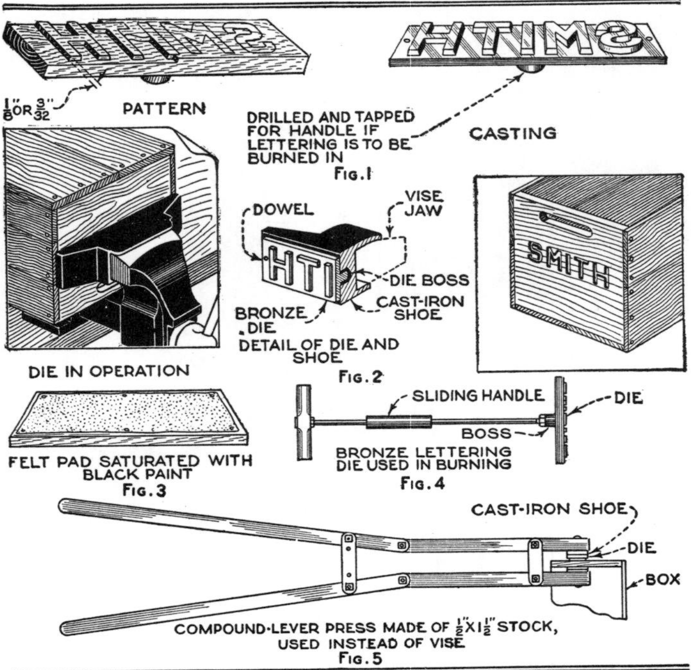

Figure 1, Method of Making Pattern for Die; Figure 2, Shoe for Holding Die in Vise, and Die in Use; Figure 3, Pad for Applying Paint; Figure 4, Die for Burning In Lettering; Figure 5, Press for Heavy Work

For either method, the first operation is the making of the pattern for the die; this requires nothing more than skill with a pocketknife, although a set of small chisels or regular woodcarving tools will expedite matters. The letters should be made at least ¾ in. high, and be as plain as possible, as this will help in producing a good casting. The wood used is cherry or mahogany, about ½ in. thick, and the letters should stand up from the surface from 3/32 to ⅛ in., the outlines should be as sharp and clean as possible, and, of course, the letters must be cut reversed, as shown in the drawing. If more than one line of lettering is required, it is best to make separate dies for each line, as it may be desirable, at times, to use but one line—the owner's name, for instance.

The die should have a boss cast on the back, to be drilled and tapped for a handle, if the die is to be used for burning. A casting can be obtained at any brass foundry; if the pattern is supplied to the foundry, the dies should cost about $1 each. Bronze is better than brass, as a rule, especially for a burning die; either of the two is preferable to cast iron, as a smoother casting is obtained, and one that is easily touched up with file and chisel. If a good casting is obtained, all that is necessary is to smooth up the faces and edges with a file, taking care to keep the surfaces true.

To use as a burning die, a long ⅜-in. steel-rod handle is screwed into the boss, and fastened by a locknut. A sliding handle, made from a piece of pipe, is then slipped on, and a wooden cross handle fastened on the end by means of nuts and washers, as shown in Fig. 4. The die is heated nearly red-hot, in any convenient manner, pressed firmly on the surface to be marked, and removed as soon as the lettering is burned deeply enough.

If a large vise is at hand, a better job can be done by coating the faces of the letters with paint, and pressing the die into the wood, between the vise jaws. A large vise will take a single line of letters, but a double line, or a single line used in a smaller vise, demands the use of shoes or pads to take the pressure.

Two heavy iron or steel plates may be used, with the dies pinned to one of them, but a better method is to make a pattern and have two shoes, as shown in Fig. 2, made of cast iron. No machine work will be required on the shoes; if the die extends beyond the vise jaws, the shoes should extend the full length, as shown, and have lugs at top and bottom, to fit over the vise jaws. Holes drilled in the face of one shoe will accommodate the bosses on the dies, and dies and shoe should be drilled, and dowels fitted, to hold the dies in position. One shoe can be drilled for two dies, and the other for one, in case it is desirable, at some time, to use but one die.

A felt pad, tacked to a board, as shown in Fig. 3, is saturated with black paint, and applied to the die, being careful to get just enough paint on the die to cover the letter surfaces. The box is then placed in position, and the vise closed; considerable pressure must be applied, and the die should be sunk into the wood about 1/16 in.; of course, this applies to soft wood, as so deep an impression cannot be made in hardwood.

Sometimes the use of a compound-lever press is preferable to using the vise, and Fig. 5 shows clearly how such a press may be made from 1/2 by 1 1/2-in. cold-rolled steel. The dies and shoes are used as before; by pressing the handles together, the die will be forced into the wood.

Stand for Welding Hose

In most shops the welding hose is allowed to drag on the floor when the torch is in use. This not only wears the hose rapidly, but, where much cutting is done, the hose is constantly being burnt. To eliminate this trouble, one shop uses the hose stand shown in the illustration.

It consists of a 3/4-in. pipe, 4 ft. long, threaded on both ends, one end being fitted with a reducing coupling, and the other with a tee. A 3/4 to 1/2-in. coupling is used, a hole being drilled through the 1/2-in. end and tapped for a thumbscrew. Short nipples are screwed into the run of the tee, and this end of the fixture is anchored in a circular concrete base, a barrel hoop being used as a form. A length of 3/8-in. iron rod is bent to the shape shown, and the straight end inserted into the coupling, where it can be locked at any desired height by means of the thumbscrew. The hose hanger consists of part of an old motorcycle rim, fitted with a hook, and a spring clip to keep the hose in place. In use, the standard is moved close to the work, and the part of the hose not in use is coiled on the hanger and clipped. This fixture not only saves the hose, but, if the hose is adjusted on the hanger properly, helps to balance the heavier torches.

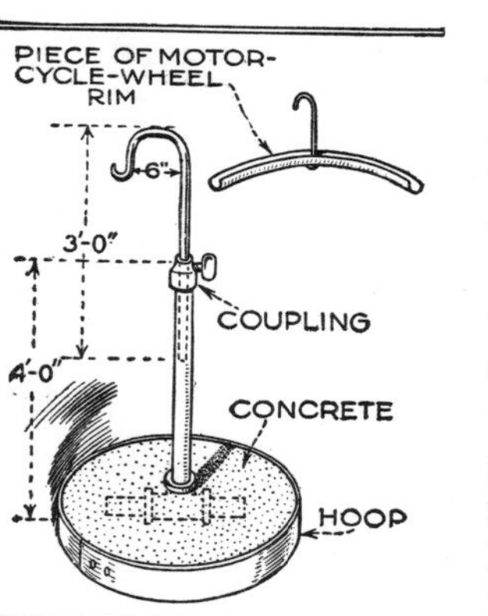

Novel Transom Control

The writer recently saw, in an old mill, an odd homemade control arrangement with which window transoms could be adjusted quickly and held securely.

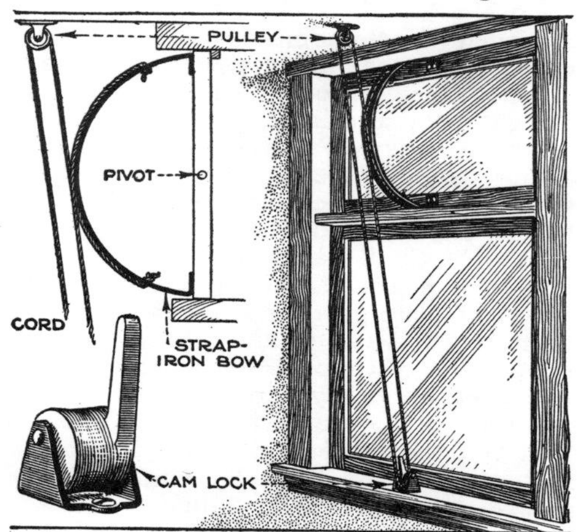

A Homemade Transom Control That Is of Considerable Usefulness, Where a Quick and Secure Adjustment Is Desirable

The transom is pivoted at its center, and a length of strap iron, bent to the shape of a bow, is attached to the frame as indicated. Holes are drilled near the ends of the bow to permit a length of sash cord to be attached to it by passing the ends through the holes, and knotting them. The sash cord passes from one end of the bow over a V-pulley screwed into the ceiling, then through a cam lock attached to the lower window sill, and back again to the other end of the bow. The purpose of the cam is to hold the transom securely in any desired position. The operation of the device is apparent from the drawing.—W. Burr Bennett, Scranton, Pa.

Wire-Gate Tightener

The device illustrated, which is used to tighten wire-fence gates, is of considerable utility, as it can be tightened or

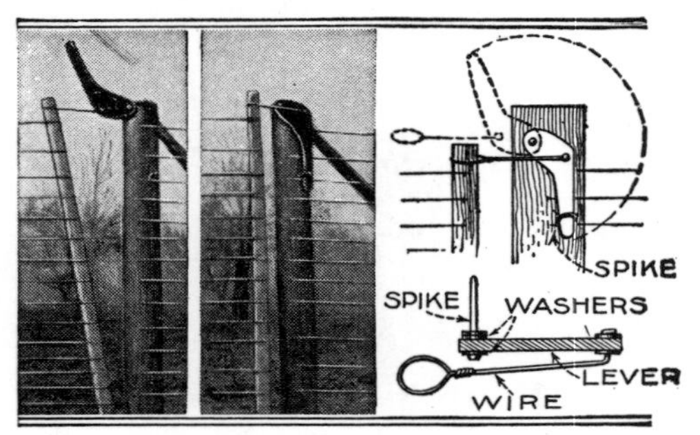

A Convenient Wire-Gate Tightener: Left, Photos Showing Device in Use; Right, Details of Construction and Assembly

loosened in a moment, and eliminates entirely the unsightly sagging of the gate.

A loop of wire or iron rod, fastened to the gatepost, and into which the end pole of the gate is set, is used at the bottom, as no trouble is experienced in keeping the gate tight here. The tightener is attached to the top of the gatepost; it consists of a thick hardwood cam or lever, cut to the shape shown, and fastened loosely to the post with a large spike so that it can swing freely, a washer being slipped on the spike on either side of the lever. A heavy-wire or iron-rod loop is attached to the lever, as shown, so that the wire will be drawn back a few inches when the lever is swung around and locked. A spike should be driven into the post at the point indicated, and bent so as to hold the lever in the closed position. On long gates, it is sometimes advisable to use a tightener at both top and bottom, but on smaller gates the one at the top is usually sufficient. To tighten the gate, put the gate pole in the lower loop, then, with the lever in the position shown by the dotted lines, slip the upper loop over the top of the pole, and draw the lever back.—Jonas Byberg, Silverton, Oregon.

A Lathe Kink

It is usually found convenient to keep the compound rest of a lathe set at an angle of 30° to the cross slide. In reducing the length of a piece being turned, advantage may be taken of this practice, as it affords a simple means of accurately gauging the cut. At the 30° setting, feeding in the compound rest a certain distance gives the tool a lengthwise movement of exactly half that amount. For instance, if the work is found to be .007 in. too long, lock the carriage, bring the tool up against the end of the work with the compound rest, withdraw the cross slide, set the compound rest in .014 in., and the tool is in position to face the work to exact length.—J. Rouse, San Francisco, Calif.

Hinge Stops for Casement Windows

Casement windows sometimes fold back against lighting fixtures, with the result that the window panes or fixture globes may accidentally be broken. To avoid this, a simple and inconspicuous hinge stop can be provided, consisting merely of a small machine screw, tapped into the hinge as shown.

Open the sash as far as possible, and make a scratch on each hinge, at the point where the half of the hinge on the sash comes over that on the jamb. Close the sash, and make a prick-punch mark in the center of the middle portion of the hinge, 3/32 in. outside of the scratch.

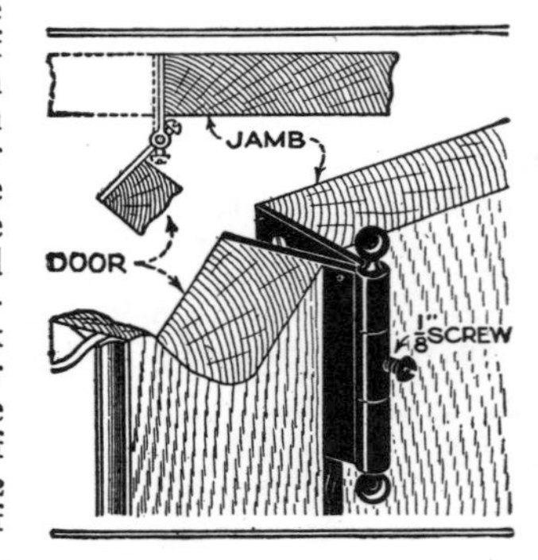

Drill and tap for a 1/8-in. machine screw, and cut the screw to such a length that the head will project about 1/4 in. If something more ornamental is desired, special screws with fancy heads may be used.

Emergency Thumbtacks

Emergency thumbtacks can readily be made from small pieces of thin sheet brass, slit on the edge and bent at right angles, as indicated. An old pair of ordinary paper shears can be used for cutting the slit. The cut is made at a slight angle from the edge to make a sharp and thin point that can easily be pushed into the wood.—Ben Frantzreb, Indianapolis, Ind.

A Portable Electric Forge

BY EDWIN M. LOVE

A PORTABLE forge, large enough to take care of any ordinary automobile or wagon work, is a great convenience in and around the small workshop, and will also be appreciated on the farm. The one shown in the illustrations has proved its usefulness in the shop where it was built, as it can be moved about easily. The blower is operated by electricity, which is available in cities and towns, and also on most farms.

The frame of the forge consists of the rear end of an automobile frame, cut to a length of 4½ ft. and covered with a

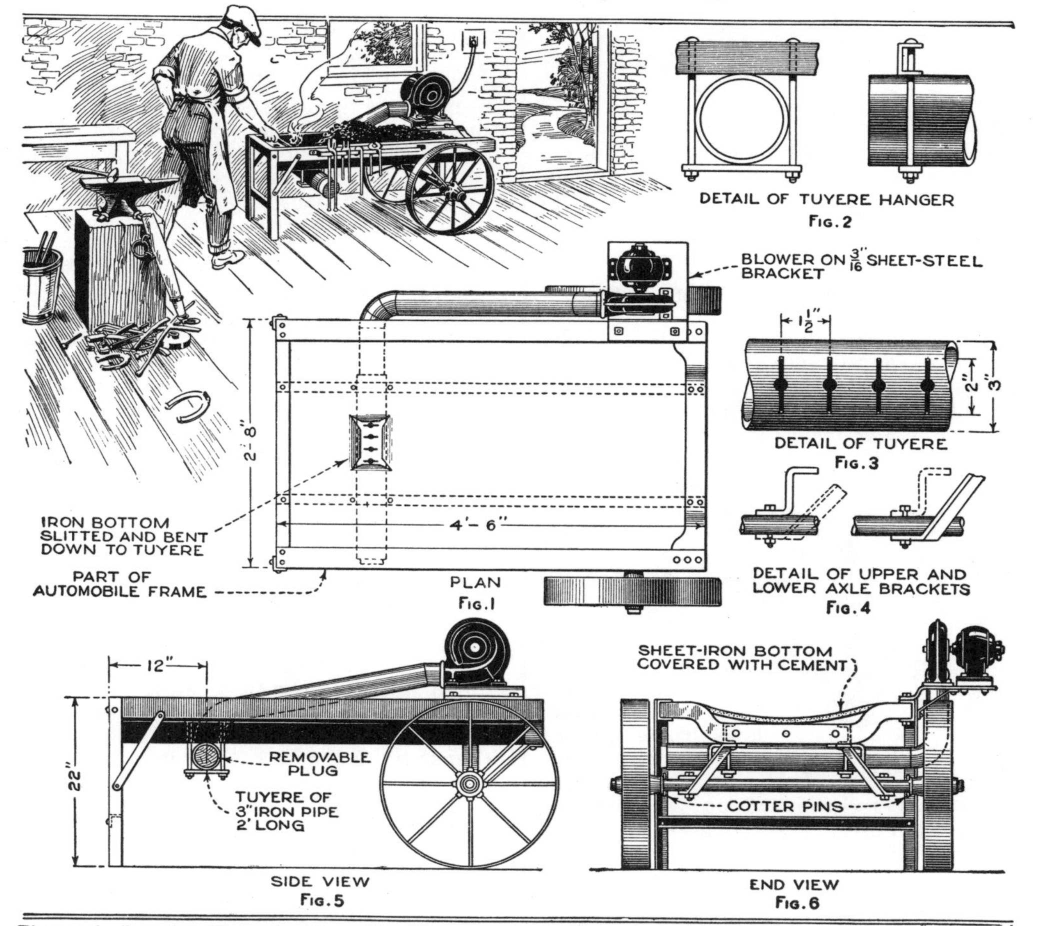

Figures 1, 5, and 6 Show the Plan, Side View, and End View of the Forge. Figures 2, 3, and 4 Give Details of the Tuyère Hangers, the Tuyère Draft Outlets, and the Axle Brackets

heavy dished sheet of iron; over this a 3-in. layer of cement is laid, to protect the iron from the intense heat of the fire. To this frame is attached an axle with two steel wheels and two legs, as indicated in the illustration. The axle is a 1½-in. iron pipe, bolted rigidly to the frame by means of four flat-iron brackets, as shown in Figs. 4 and 6. The wheels

Rear View of a Portable Electric Forge That Is Very Convenient for Use in the Shop

themselves are the kind used on farm implements, and can be found in most junk heaps. The legs at the front of the forge are lengths of angle iron bolted to the corners of the frame, and supported by flat braces, attached as shown. An electric motor and a small blower are securely bolted to a 3/16-in. sheet-steel bracket, which extends over the left wheel and is bolted and braced to the frame. A 3-in. sheet-steel blower pipe extends from the blower to the tuyère, which is made of the same-size iron pipe, and is located underneath the front end of the forge. The tuyère is suspended by hangers from two lengths of channel iron running lengthwise underneath the frame, and is bolted to it at each end, as indicated by the dotted lines in Fig 1. Each hanger, as shown in Fig. 2, consists of two long bolts and a cross plate, drilled to slip over the ends of the bolt and held by nuts. The open end of the tuyère is closed with a removable wooden plug, so that the ashes that sift through the draft outlets can easily be removed. The draft outlets of the tuyère, as shown in Fig. 3, are simply holes and cuts in the pipe; they are made by drilling four 3/8-in. holes and slitting the pipe crosswise, 1 in. on each side of the holes, with a cutting torch. At the point where these draft outlets are located, the iron bottom of the forge is slitted; the slits are 4 in. long, and the flaps thus formed are bent down to the tuyère and cement-lined.

Supporting Long, Thin Bars

The support shown in the drawing will be found very useful by anyone having a variety of bar work to do on the lathe, especially when the bars are long and small in diameter. Centering does not work very well in these cases, the diameter not being large enough. A piece of 5/8-in. cold-rolled steel rod is bent over as shown, one end fitting into a holder that is turned on the shank to fit the tailstock sleeve. When these two parts are finished so far, they are fitted together, and a hole is drilled through both. Three other holes in line with this one are similarly drilled, then all are reamed for a taper pin. The pin is driven tightly into the holder and the first hole in the rod, and a hole for one size of bar is then drilled and reamed through the opposite end of the support, using a drill held in the lathe chuck. The taper pin is then driven into the next hole in the support, and another size of hole is drilled and reamed, and so on. When in use, the support is held in an upright position on the tailstock, the taper pin being inserted in the hole in line with the hole required for the work, which is held on the other end by a collet or a three-jaw chuck.

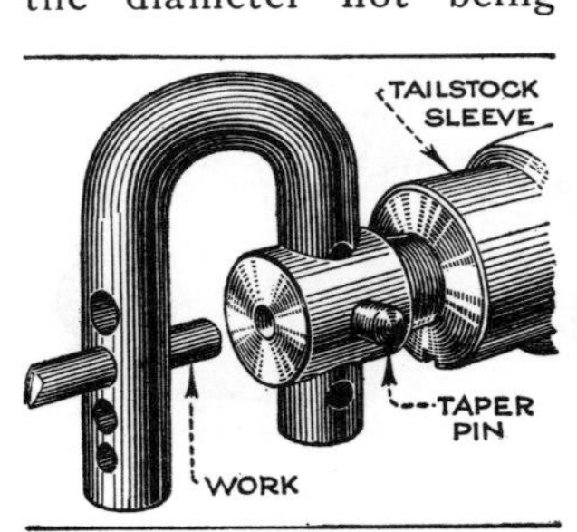

Etching Glass

Most of the processes for etching on glass call for hydrofluoric acid, which is difficult to obtain and to store, and is so violently poisonous that it is even dangerous to health if inhaled; it also causes intense irritation to the hands. However, a dilute solution, for immediate use, is easily made by dissolving 20 gr. of sodium fluoride in 10 oz. of water, and adding 15 minims of hydrochloric acid (poison). This solution should be used with care, the hands being protected with rubber gloves and the solution handled in rubber or wax-covered trays.

Combination Dowel and Bolt

Bolts, studs, or capscrews cannot be depended on to prevent lateral shifting of assembled machine parts, their main function being to hold the parts closely together. To prevent lateral shifting, taper pins or dowels are usually used, if there are no machined male and female interlocking sections provided. In cases where there is little room for dowels, hollow dowels can be used, the bolts then passing through the dowels, as indicated. The holes are taper-bored, or taper-reamed, and a taper bushing is driven in, then the bolt, stud, or capscrew is passed through and tightened. If a taper dowel is impracticable, a parallel hole is drilled, and a cylindrical bushing driven in. The bolts should fit freely in the bushings.

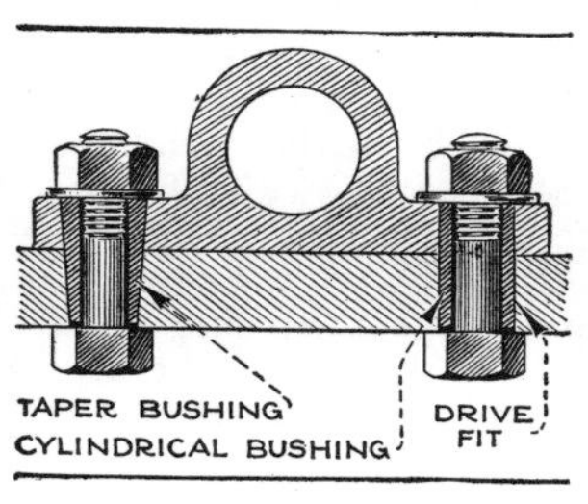

Homemade Horizontal Tool Grinder

A horizontal tool grinder is often more convenient than the common vertical kind. A novel tool grinder of this kind for the home workshop is shown in the accompanying photograph.

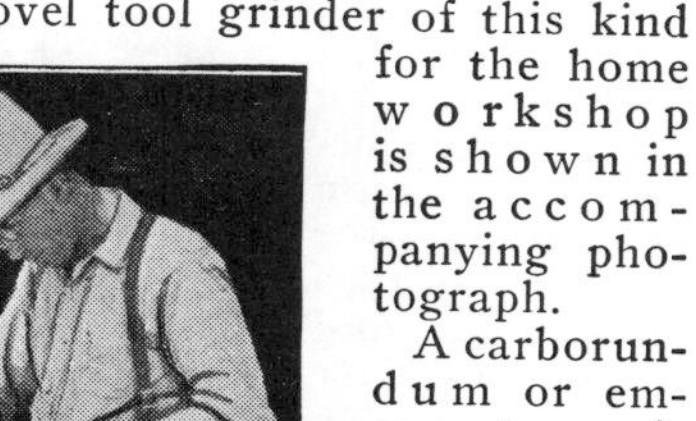

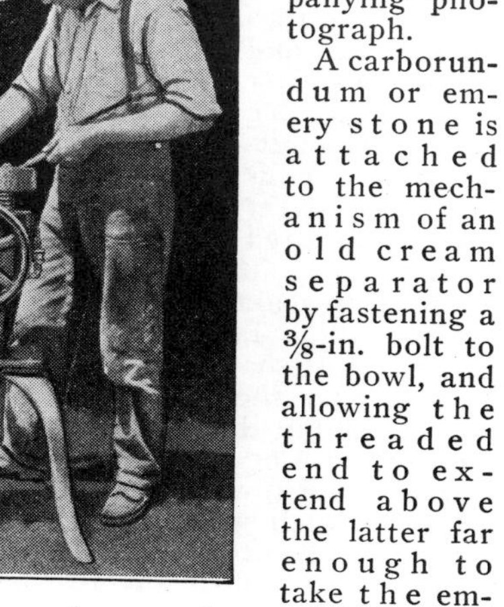

A carborundum or emery stone is attached to the mechanism of an old cream separator by fastening a ⅜-in. bolt to the bowl, and allowing the threaded end to extend above the latter far enough to take the emery wheel, washers, and nut. The advantages of this grinder are its substantial base, high gear, and convenient working height.

Live-Stock Frame for Farm Scales

The photograph shows a frame for farm scales, mounted on rollers and a track, so that it can easily be pushed over the scales when needed for weighing live stock. It is substantially built and well braced at the top, a feature that is not possible with a frame that must be taken apart in order to move it off and onto the scales. This kind of frame saves considerable time and much lifting, as it only takes a few moments to push it into place over the scale platform and to open the end gate.—J. C. Allen, LaFayette, Ind.

Convenient Live-Stock Frame for Farm Scales: It is Mounted on Rollers Running on Tracks

T-Slot Cleaner

When equipped with a tool like that shown in the drawing, it is an easy matter to clean out machine T-slots thoroughly from end to end. A piece of round steel is used for the handle, and a flat piece, shaped to fit the slots, is fastened to it loosely by a washer and screw. In assembling the tool, the handle is attached to the scraper so that the former rests on the surface of the table when the T-piece is in the slot. By making it this way, the tool can be drawn along forcibly without jamming in the slot. When using the tool, the straight part is run through the slot first to break up the cuttings, and then the other end is turned down and run through it to finish the operation.

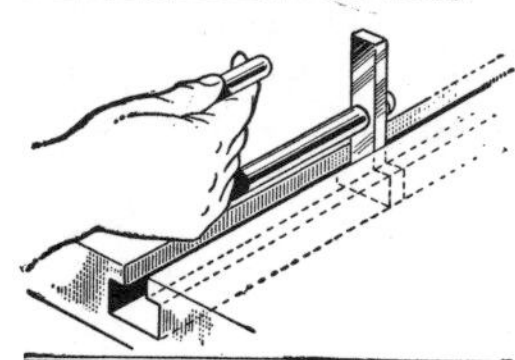

Rafter Design for Semimonitor Laying House

In the simple rafter design illustrated, cross braces are dispensed with, thus eliminating undesirable roosting places for the

A Semimonitor Laying House with a Simple Rafter Construction Having No Cross Braces

fowl, and permitting a much lower roof construction than usual, which makes for a warmer house. The rafters are joined in pairs, a bolt being used to fasten them at the point of junction, as shown; washers are used on both ends of the bolt so that it will not tear through the rafters. One rafter is extended a few feet beyond the bolt, and a vertical brace is attached to it near the end, and to the other rafter below. Windows are fitted between the vertical braces as shown in the drawing. Rafters for spans not greater than 12 ft. may be made of 2 by 4-in. material, but for spans between 12 and 18 ft., 2 by 6-in. stuff must be used.—Edward R. Smith, Walla Walla, Wash.

Floating Nut and Washer for Arbors

An ordinary nut and washer, used to tighten work on a threaded arbor, serves very well when the face of the work is square with the axis, but there are occasions when the work is not square or the face is left rough. Some method of "floating" the washer must then be tried, or else the arbor will be bent when the nut is tightened. The nut and washer shown were designed to be used on work having one face milled off at an angle, the pieces being afterward finished off in the lathe on a threaded arbor. The shouldered nut is turned to a radius on one end and the washer turned to fit it. The bore of the washer should be larger than the diameter of the arbor shank, in order to allow for the necessary "float." To keep the nut and washer together to facilitate handling, and also to exert a slight tension to keep them both in line when off the arbor, a rubber gasket is fastened to the back of the washer by four screws, as indicated. A thin sheet-metal washer underneath the heads of the screws will prevent them from cutting into the rubber. With the floating movement shown, the nut always tightens up in line with the shank of the arbor, and thus there is no danger of straining and bending the latter.

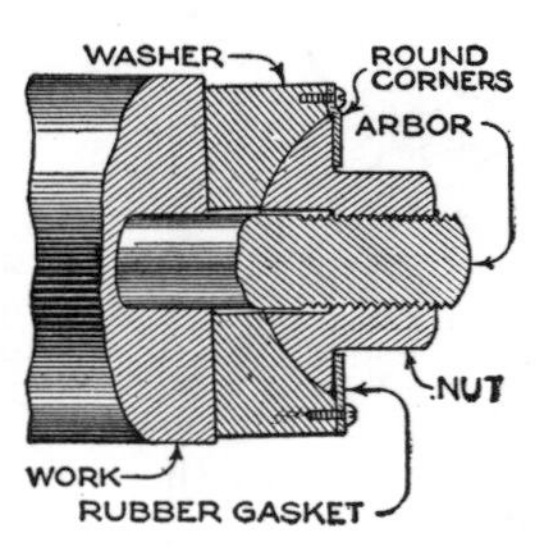

Blowing Soapstone through Conduit

Soapstone is generally used by electricians to facilitate pulling rubber-covered wires through conduit, but it is not an easy matter to force the soapstone through long lengths of conduit. On large jobs where compressed air is available, the soapstone can be blown through with the device shown in the illustration.

It consists of a tin compression-top can, with an inlet for the compressed air and an outlet for the soapstone. The inlet, which can be located conveniently on the cover, is fitted with a union on the end for connecting to the air hose, and a stopcock for controlling the supply. The outlet, which consists of a street elbow, is fitted on the side as indicated. Rubber gaskets are used to make the connections on the can air-tight. To use the device, a handful or two of soapstone is put in the compression can, the street elbow is inserted into the end of the conduit through which the wire is to be run, and the air pressure is then applied, which will blow the soapstone through with considerable force, and will prevent it from accumulating in the pipe. Very little air pressure is necessary; and as any high degree of pressure will blow the top from the can, the stopcock should be opened gently.—W. W Parker, Lead, S. D.

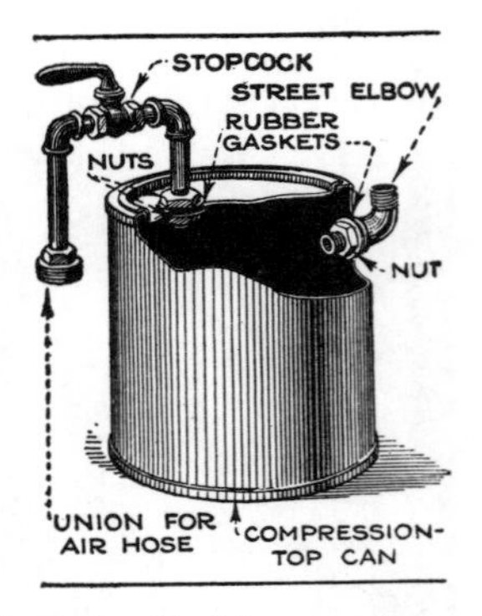

Increasing Capacity of Acetylene Generator

A welder who uses a popular make of acetylene generator found that it did not generate rapidly enough to supply a heavy welding tip for a considerable length of time. To remedy this, he cut a section from an old hot-water tank, welded the two remaining pieces together, and connected the resulting tank with the generator, as illustrated in the drawing. The regulator was put on the auxiliary tank The generator was thus enabled to store a larger quantity of acetylene, and the feeding mechanism operated with greater efficiency, with the result that a large tip could be used without difficulty.

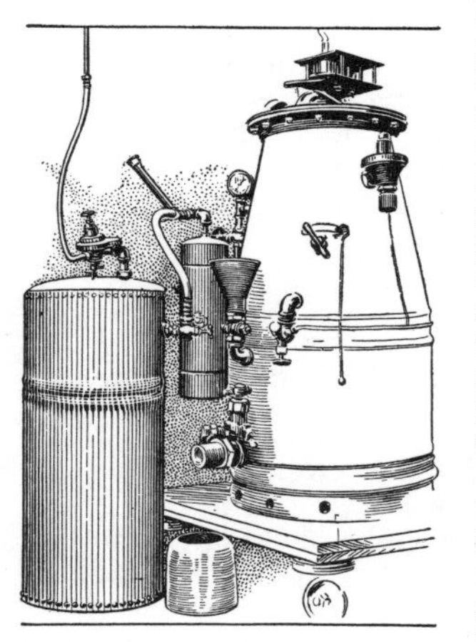

An Emergency Elbow

When installing a large overhead-irrigation system, we found that an additional 3-in. elbow was needed, and as it was necessary to finish the job at once, we resorted to making an elbow from a piece of pipe. A 4-in. length was threaded at both ends and a V-notch cut out of the center as shown, the cuts being made with an acetylene torch. The back of the pipe, which was left untouched, was heated to a cherry red and bent as indicated, so that the ends of the pipe were at right angles to each other, a carpenter's T-square being used to test the accuracy of the angle. The seam was then welded, with a heavy fillet; this completed the elbow, which served the purpose just as well as an ordinary one.—A. S. Jamieson, Springfield, Mass.

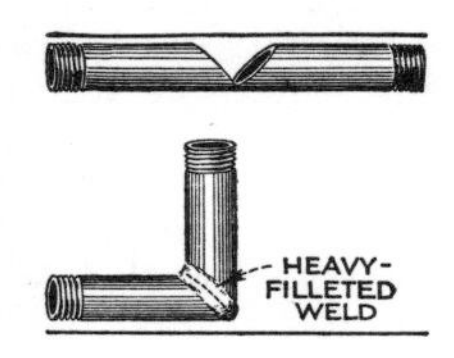

¶When making finishing cuts on a milling machine, use a fine-toothed mill.

Car Inspector's Tack Hammer and Journal Hook

The combined tack hammer and journal hook shown in the illustration is simple to make and has proved to be of considerable usefulness for railroad-car

A Combined Tack Hammer and Journal Hook That Greatly Facilitates Railroad-Car Inspection

inspection, as it eliminates the necessity of carrying separate tools. This tool allows the inspector to do his work without getting oil on his hands, and as a result the record books and "bad-order" cards will be clean. The tool can be made from a scrap coke fork. One end is bent over to form a hook for "feeling" the journals to detect cuts, etc., and a hammer head and claw are formed at the other end. The tool is strong enough to be used for prying doors open. The measurements of the tool are given in the detail, but can, of course, be varied as desired.—T. B. Aldridge, Jr., Denver, Colo.

Novel Method of Lowering Tank into Pit

An ingenious method of lowering a large steel fuel-oil tank into its pit, in the absence of suitable derricks or tackle, was adopted in a small British Columbia generating plant. All the tank outlets were plugged, the pit was filled with water, and the tank simply rolled into it. It naturally floated on the surface of the water, which, when pumped out, allowed the tank to sink into position gradually.—G. R. Dyment, Hamilton, Can.

Supporting a Long Discharge Pipe

When installing a 5-in. centrifugal pump to furnish water for the screens at a gravel-washing plant, it was decided to run the discharge pipe so that no bend

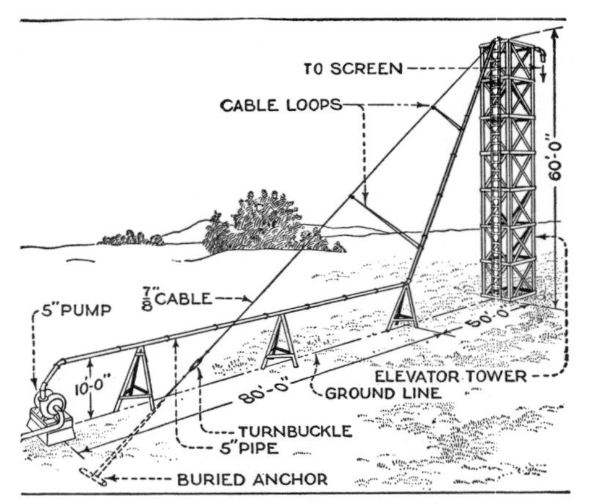

Efficient Method of Supporting a Long Discharge Pipe at a Gravel-Washing Plant

would be greater than 45°, in order to eliminate friction as much as possible. The pipe was run from the pump to an elevation about 10 ft. above the ground, and was carried for a distance of about 80 ft. at this elevation, three tripods being used to support it. A 45° bend was then made, and the pipe run up to the top of a 60-ft. elevator tower. The pipe was strong enough to support itself while being erected, but sagged about 2 ft. in the middle, necessitating additional support. A 7/8-in. cable was run from the top of the elevator tower to an anchor in the ground near the pump. A turnbuckle was fitted in the cable near the ground, so that it could be reached easily. Two loops were clamped around the main cable and the pipe as shown, and, by screwing the turnbuckle, the middle of the pipe was lifted until it was straight. This arrangement, which eliminated clumsy timber supports, has been in use for two years and has held the pipe quite securely.

The ease of erection of this support is one of its commendable features. The anchor was fixed first, and the cable was then run from the top of the tower to the turnbuckle, and then attached to the anchor, being drawn tight by means of rope blocks before clamping it to the turnbuckle. To get the loops of cable around the main cable and the pipe, a snatch block with a hand line was attached to the main cable at the top. A seat was attached to the hook of the snatch block so that a man could ride down the cable. A set of rope blocks were also hung on the main cable with a sliding sling around the pipe. As the man was lowered to the position of the lower loop, he slid the set of rope blocks along with him, these being used to draw the main cable and pipe together before attaching the cable loops. After the lower loop was made and clamped to the main cable, the process was repeated at the upper loop, and the man then pulled back to the top of the tower The turnbuckle was then screwed up a few turns to straighten out the pipe.—A. W. Burg, Lake View, Ia.

Holding Belts for Cutting and Punching

The drawing shows how a belt repairman utilizes his tool box as a holder for the ends of the belts while measuring them for cutting and punching. One end of a leather strap is nailed to one side of the box; the other end of the strap is left loose and has a number of holes punched in it. A slide catch, made of stout wire, is used to hold the strap. This wire is bent to a hook shape at one end, so that it will enter the strap holes and a hole in the box, and is held to the box by means of a couple of staples, as indicated. The ends of the belt are clamped by placing them between the box top and the strap, the latter being pulled tight and the hook passed through the strap into the hole in the box. The belt is held securely, as the weight of the contents holds it down while it is unrolled.

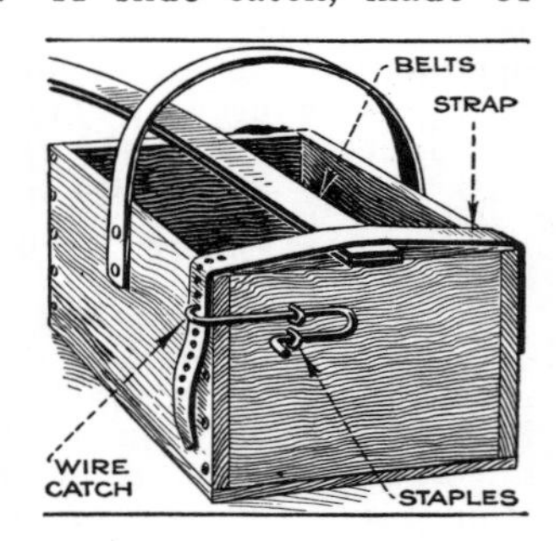

Filing Crosscut Saws

The work of sharpening crosscut saws is greatly facilitated by marking off the correct tooth angle, which is 30°, on the top of the saw clamp at 1-in. intervals. If the file is kept parallel to the marks while filing the saw, the angle of the teeth is sure to be correct.—Fred W Page, Winfield, Kan.

A Reboring Fixture for the Garage

BY J. V. ROMIG

WHEN the automobile engine is being thoroughly overhauled, all connecting rods and pistons are refitted. Oversize wristpins are usually fitted where the original ones are worn enough to warrant it, the wristpin holes being reamed to fit.

The reaming process is not a very accurate one, and many pistons so fitted either stand "cocked" in the cylinders, causing excessive wear and unsatisfactory operation, or, if the connecting rod is twisted and set so that the piston will check with an alinement gauge, the wristpin itself is not properly fitted, and wears rapidly. A better way to fit new wristpins, and one that insures alinement, is to rebore the holes, and to use the reamer merely to size them.

The fixture described in this article will do this job perfectly and quickly, and can be used for a multitude of small boring jobs where accuracy is required; for instance, connecting rods can be rebored, after babbitting, by the addition of two V-blocks to the fixture. Anyone with ordinary mechanical skill can build the tool easily, and will be more than repaid by the improved quality of the work done with it.

Reboring a Connecting-Rod Big End with a Portable Hand Fixture: Note How the Rod is Clamped

The worktable, full dimensions of which are given, is made of gray cast iron, from an easily made pattern. The top and edges must be planed perfectly flat and at right angles, and particular care should be taken with the planing or shaping of the 2-in. side groove, and the 2¼-in. top groove, to insure that they are square with all surfaces.

The table is mounted on a 3-in. pipe column, which screws into a threaded hole in a boss on the underside of the table casting. The base of the column is a pipe flange, by means of which the machine is bolted to the bench. All parts should be screwed up tightly.

Two slots are cut through the front of the table, as shown, for the passage of the boring-head clamp bolt, and holes for ½-in. studs drilled and tapped in the surface of the table. Holes for ⅜-in. screws are drilled and tapped in the back edge of the casting, to hold the braces.

The boring-bar head is a bronze casting, 9½ in. long over all, and is machined as shown in Figs. 1, 2, and 5. The arms are bored and threaded for the 1¼-in. boring bar; this job is best done by clamping the head to the faceplate of a lathe, after shaping. The arms are then drilled and tapped for the adjusting screws and slitted, as shown in Fig. 2. The boring bar, which is made of steel, is now turned, bored, and threaded, as shown in Fig. 3. The thread pitch is 32 per inch, and the screw should be fitted accurately in the arms of the head. As will be noted, there are two boring bars, a main bar and an auxiliary one. The main bar is 9½ in. long, and is turned down to 1⅛ in. diameter for about ¾ in. at each end. At the nose end, a ⅜-in. square hole is machined for the tool bits, and at the other, a ⅝-in. round hole for the crank handle. The latter is made of ⅝-in. cold-rolled steel, turned down to ½ in., except for the ball end and the center portion, which latter is left ⅝ in. in diameter to fit the hole in the bar. A setscrew hole is drilled and tapped in this ⅝-in. section for the clamp screw.

The tools are clamped by means of a ⅝-in. tool pin, sliding in the hollow bar, and pushed against the bits by means of the tool-clamp screw just mentioned. One end of the pin is spotted to receive the pointed end of the screw.

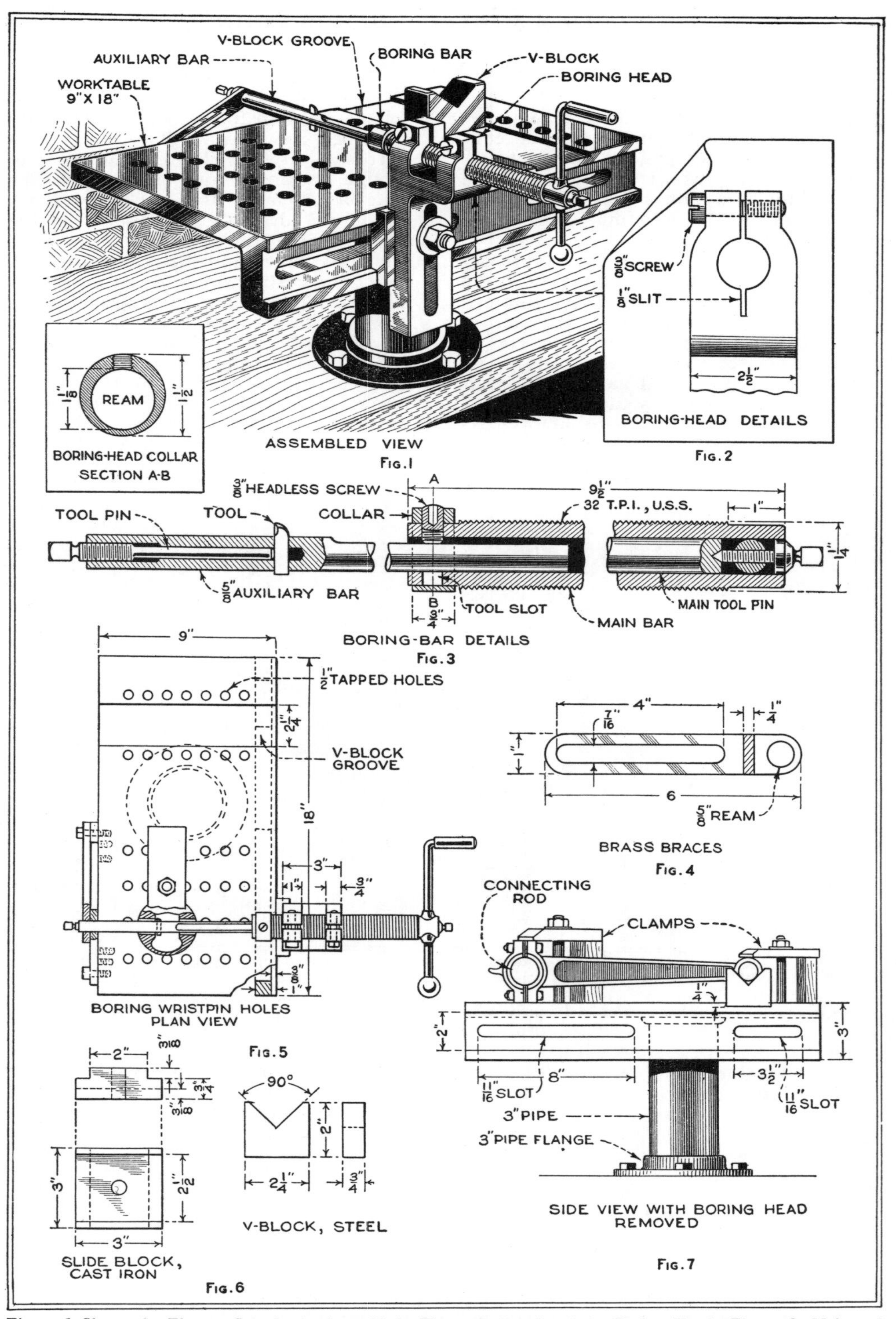

Figure 1 Shows the Fixture Completely Assembled; Figure 2, Details of the Boring Head; Figure 3, Main and Auxiliary Boring Bars; Figure 4, Braces for Auxiliary Bar; Figure 5, Set-Up for Boring Wristpin Holes; Figure 6, Dimensions of Blocks, and Fig. 7, Method of Reboring Connecting Rods

When boring wristpin holes, it is necessary to use an auxiliary bar, which is shown in position in Fig. 1, and in detail in Fig. 3. This bar telescopes into the larger one, the main tool pin first being removed, and is locked in position by the special collar shown in the detail. The headless setscrew in the collar is run through the tool-bit hole in the main bar and tightened on a flat milled on the auxiliary bar. The tool in this bar is also clamped by a tool pin, which, in this case, is a part of the clamp screw.

When boring a piston of large diameter, it is necessary to adjust the bar for each hole. The use of the auxiliary bar also necessitates the making of the brass or bronze braces shown in Fig. 4. These are fitted as indicated in Figs. 1 and 5, and keep the bar true and steady.

The feed is secured by the action of the threaded bar, turning the crank to the right feeding the bar forward, and to the left, backward. If it is desired to cut on the backward movement, the tool, of course, must be reversed. When the work is clamped close to the head, quite heavy cuts can be taken in the softer metals.

The method of boring wristpin holes is indicated in Fig. 5. To insure accuracy when sizing, after the holes are rebored, a shell reamer should be used, held on the boring bar. For connecting rods, two V-blocks should be made, hardened and finished by grinding so as to be as accurate as possible; these must fit snugly, without any side play, in the groove in the table top. When reboring a connecting-rod "big end," a wristpin is slipped through its bearing and laid on the V-blocks, one being placed on each side of the bearing. The rod is then clamped down, as indicated in Fig. 7, and bored, using only the main bar, with the assurance that all bearings will be square.

When boring the wristpin bearing for an oversize pin, the same method is followed, using a mandrel in the big-end bearing. As the feed is 1/32 in., the tools used should be ground with a flat top, slightly over 1/32 in. wide, so that the tool marks will overlap.

Bushings that are too small in the bore can be rebored by clamping them in one of the V-blocks; the machine can also be used for most work that cannot be handled in the drill press because of the lack of large drills, and, as no power is necessary, it may be carried close to the work, and clamped or bolted to any convenient bench.

Suction Cleaner for Machinery

A handy suction cleaner for use around machines, such as knitting and paper-perforating machines, weaving looms, etc., is a great convenience. A cleaner of this kind can readily be made to operate on compressed air, if constructed as shown in the illustration. It is made from a discarded benzine can and a few standard 1/2-in. pipe fittings. The bottom of the can is cut out, leaving a margin of about 1/4 in., to which is soldered a piece of fine brass screen. The cap of the can is removed and a short nipple soldered in its place. A tee is screwed on the nipple, and a length of pipe, about 1 ft. long, into the tee, this pipe being flattened at one end so that the opening will be about 1/8 or 1/16 in. wide. It is not essential to have the pipe straight; it may be bent to any convenient shape, and its length may also vary to suit the user. Another short nipple is screwed into the tee, as shown, to permit the attachment of the air hose. The rapid passage of air from the hose through the can creates a strong suction in the pipe, and the dirt and scraps of light material are easily picked up and deposited in the can. Where fine dirt or dust is to be cleaned up, a cloth bag, such as a mailing bag, is tied over the bottom of the can to retain the fine particles. Unscrewing the connection at the tee permits the contents of the can to be shaken out.—H. I. Wheeler, Westwood, Mass.

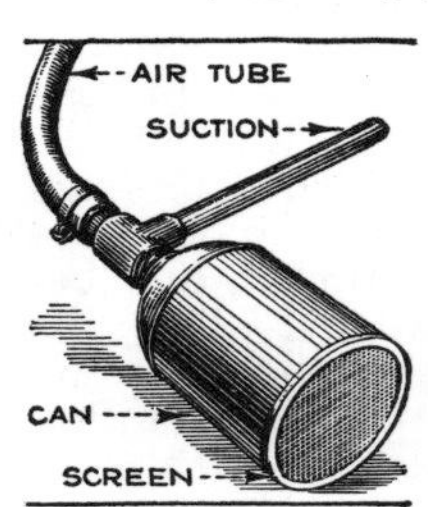

Comfortable Handles for Buckets

I have found that a short length of flexible metallic tubing, such as is used by electricians, provides a comfortable handle for a bucket. It is slipped over the wire handle with which the bucket is equipped. On a job where we had several heavy paint buckets to carry, all of them were fitted with these handles, which made the job very easy on the hands. Pieces of waste tubing can be picked up around almost any new building where the wiring is being installed. —Reuben Stafford, Jr., Washington, District of Columbia.

Making Window of Dark Room Light-Proof

The method of making the window of the dark room light-proof shown in the drawing should prove of interest to professional photographers, or even to the amateur, as it is a very simple one. This is the method used in Popular Mechanics' dark room, and has proved entirely satisfactory.

Strips of wood, ½ in. thick by 5 in. wide, and as long as the window frame, are fastened to the wall on either side of the window, as shown. On the outside of these strips, ¾ by 1¾-in. strips are nailed, and ½ by 3¼-in. strips attached to them by hinges. The 5-in. and hinged 3¼-in. strips are faced with felt, as shown in the sectional view, the window shade, when down, being gripped tightly by the felt. Wooden turn buttons are used to clamp the hinged strips when closed, and two other buttons, mounted on strips of wood fastened to the wall below the window, are used to hold the lower end of the shade tightly against the wall. The shade roller is inclosed in a light-tight box, as shown in the perspective and front views.

When the shade is up, the hinged strips are open; when it is desired to darken the room, the shade is drawn down, fastened by means of the lower buttons, and the hinged strips closed and clamped tightly by means of the side buttons. The free working of the shade is thus not interfered with in the least, while it is perfectly light-proof in use.

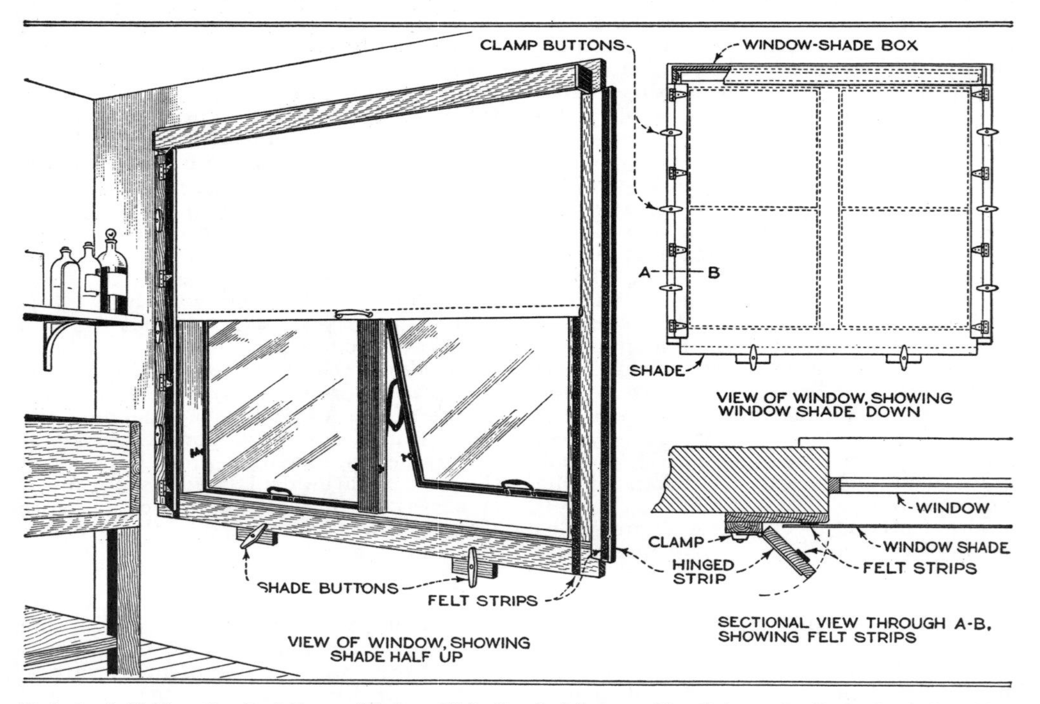

Method of Making the Dark-Room Window Light-Proof of Interest Not Only to the Professional, but Also, Because of Its Simplicity, to the Amateur Photographer

Soldering Tinfoil

When making fixed condensers for use in radio work, it is often desirable to solder leads to the tinfoil sheets. This is difficult to do because the solder does not readily adhere to the tinfoil, and because the foil melts so easily. This difficulty can be avoided by placing the foil on a sheet of copper, and using a flux made of vaseline, paraffin, and sal ammoniac. The vaseline and paraffin, in equal parts, are heated and mixed together. While the liquid mixture is still hot, half the total bulk of sal ammoniac is added. The whole is then thoroughly mixed and allowed to cool. The flux thus made is effective, providing, of course, the work is thoroughly clean.—Leroy Western, Plainfield, N. J.

Tail Center for Wooden Arbors

The use of a wooden arbor is at times necessary in woodworking and pattern making, for special work; emery and sandpaper wheels are also usually mounted on wooden arbors. However, workmen sometimes hesitate to use one because the wood around the tail center has a tendency to split open while revolving at a high rate of speed, which loosens the arbor and is, of course, dangerous. This danger can be eliminated by screwing a combined brass nut and center on the end of the arbor. The nut is made of hexagon brass stock, threaded to screw on the wooden end, and is center-drilled to fit the lathe center, as indicated in the illustration.

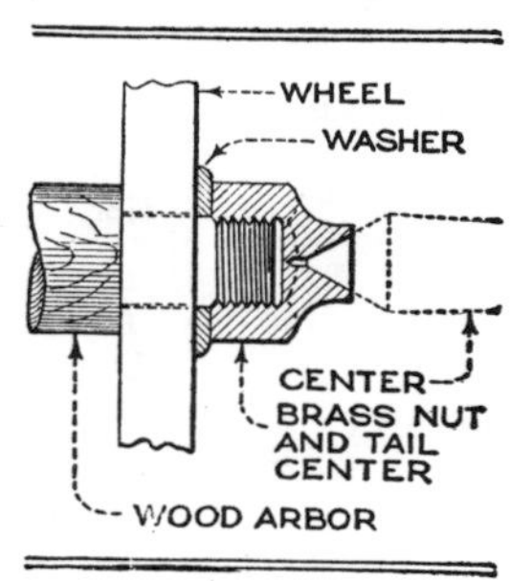

Pipe Fitter's Vise Support

Pipe fitters usually do their work before the inside of the building is finished, and, consequently, it is often a problem to find a suitable place for the pipe vise, particularly in the basement. The arrangement illustrated makes it possible, however, to use a pipe vise wherever the floor joists are exposed, anchorage being obtained by a pin driven into the wire-wound foot of the upright. A 2 by 4-in. stick is used for the upright, with two pieces of 1½-in. boards bolted to opposite sides, for clamping the device to an overhead floor joist. The pin in the bottom end is made from ¾-in. rod, and is allowed to project about 3 in., fitting into a small hole drilled in the joist. In the basement, a hole may be chipped in the floor, and a wood block fitted to take the pin, as shown, or a small hole drilled right in the floor. In either case, it is a simple matter to fill up the hole.

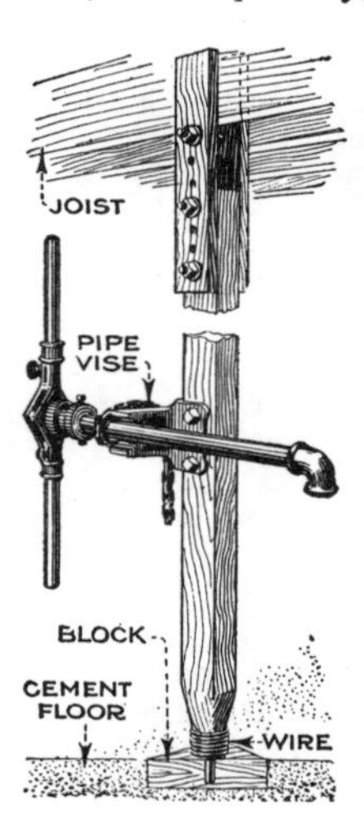

Clamp for Cylinder Grinder

A mechanic, finding that the regular clamps furnished on his cylinder-grinding machine did not hold the cylinder block solidly enough to prevent a slight vibration—which tended to produce imperfect cylinder walls—constructed the clamp shown in the photograph to overcome the difficulty.

An Additional Clamp on a Cylinder-Grinding Machine to Prevent Vibration

It consists of a U-shaped frame, made by welding together 1-in. iron bars, and hinged to lugs bolted to the grinder carriage. A hole is drilled and tapped in the horizontal bar to receive a setscrew fitted with a crank handle. When the cylinder block has been placed in readiness for grinding, the clamp is swung to a suitable position over the block and the setscrew is screwed down against it. Since the clamp has been used, vibration marks and spoiled cylinders have been eliminated.

A Sprinkler Guard

The moving stairway in a large department store ran close to a line of sprinkler piping, and the sprinkler-head links were often accidentally broken or brushed by parcels carried by persons using it, or tampered with by meddlers. To prevent this, a simple guard was made and placed over each head within reach of the stairway. The guards consisted of a clamp made of sheet metal, fitting around the base of the head, and provided with a number of U-shaped wires, soldered into holes drilled in the upper edge of the clamp, as shown. Since installing these, no further trouble has been experienced.

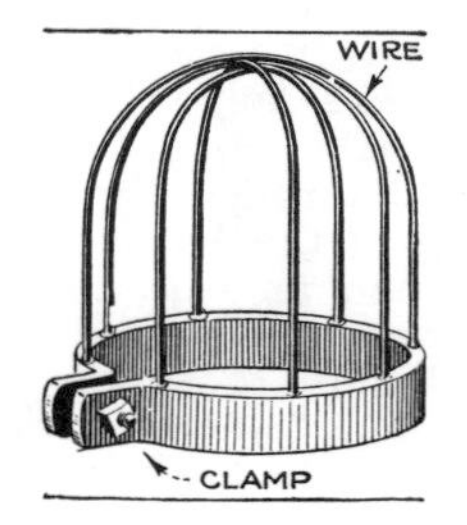

Lifter for High Drawers

In stores where an increase of stock of small parts makes it necessary to put in drawers above the original ones, if lack of floor space does not permit addi-

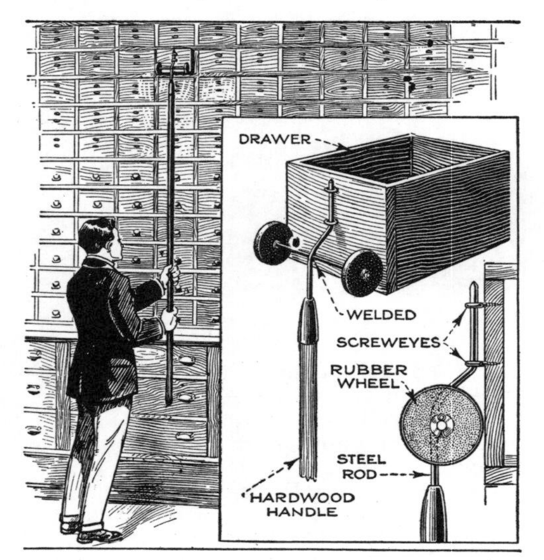

Handy Drawer Lifter for Reaching High Drawers in Stores Where a Rolling Ladder is Not Fitted

tional cabinets, or it is not desired to install these, a rolling ladder is commonly used. However, a good substitute for a rolling ladder is a drawer lifter of the kind shown in the drawing. This even has advantages over a rolling ladder in that it does not take so much space, and as several may be provided if necessary, no time is wasted in waiting for the ladder until some one else has finished using it farther along the shelves.

It consists of a strong hardwood handle on which is fitted a short length of steel rod, bent to the shape shown. A crosspiece of the same size steel rod is welded across the first piece, and small rubber wheels are fitted at each end, these being kept in place by means of cotter pins and washers. In use, the bent rod is slipped into screweyes driven into the front of each drawer, and it is then an easy matter to pull the drawer out and lower it. The length of the handle depends on the height of the upper line of drawers.—L. H. Georger, Buffalo, N. Y.

Steam, rising from water at its boiling point of 212° F., has a pressure equal to that of the atmosphere, or 14.7 lb. per square inch.

An Offset Screwdriver

For working in very close quarters, an offset screwdriver of the type shown in the drawing will be found very useful. It consists of a handle carrying a head that has four narrow blades formed on it. Each blade is set at an angle of 45° with the two on each side of it, so that in using the tool, it is only necessary to move the handle slightly before one blade can be engaged in the groove of the screw. Where headroom is limited, and a screwdriver can-

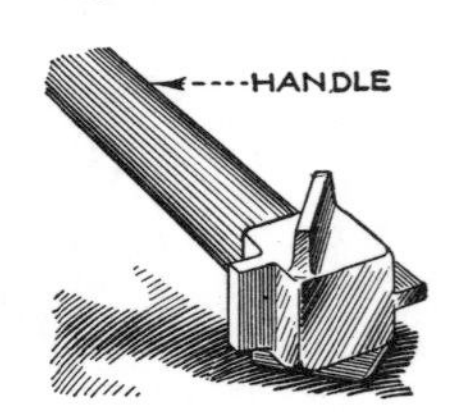

not be used, this tool will be found to remove the screw much more quickly than the common close-quarters screwdriver, which has but two blades, set at right angles to each other at opposite ends of the handle.

A Good Cabinet Scraper

The illustration shows an easily made wood scraper that has been found very practical for cabinetmakers and other woodworkers. It consists of a wooden handle, shaped square, with slightly rounded corners and edges. The head is square and has a tongue formed on it as indicated. The scraper blade consists of the end of an old plane bit, and is attached to the handle by means of a lag screw or

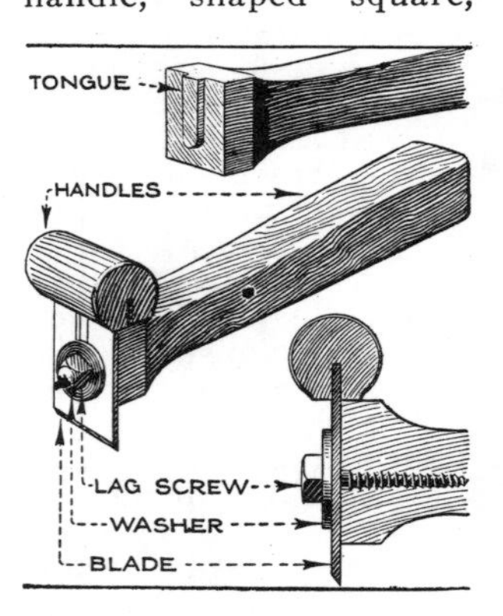

round-head screw driven into the end, a hole being first drilled in the handle, to prevent splitting. If a lag screw or round-head screw is not at hand, a nut can be countersunk to take the head of a flat-head screw, and the two soldered together. To protect the cutting edge of the blade, a short piece of round hardwood, about 1 in. in diameter, and slotted to fit the blade snugly, is provided. This piece is used as a hand rest when using the scraper, being then attached to the top of the blade, as shown.—M. E. Duggan, Kenosha, Wis.

Rotary Blower Made from a Tin Can

BY HOWARD GREEN

A ROTARY blower that will suffice for the small shop or laboratory can be made with nothing but ordinary tools, except for the wooden end disks, which should be turned in a lathe for best results. However, if the disks are carefully sawed out, even the lathe will not be needed.

The rotor is made from a sheet-metal cylinder, for which purpose a strong tin can may be used; if an extra good job is desired the cylinder may be built up of heavy sheet metal, using wooden ends. A ½-in. hole is made in each end of the can, ⅞ in. from the center, and the holes are reinforced by riveting or soldering on washers with a ½-in. opening; both holes should line up exactly. A piece of ½-in. shaft is fitted through the holes, leaving about 1¼ in. projecting at one end and 2 in. at the other. Triangular notches are filed in each washer and corresponding grooves are cut into the shaft, so that a piece of brass wire can be forced into each of the small keyways thus formed; the shaft is then soldered or brazed to the can, and the outside ends of the keys cut off flush with the washers.

The casing requires two disks, about 6¼ in. in diameter and ½ in. thick; holes are drilled at their centers for the short lengths of brass tubing that form the rotor-shaft bearings. The bearings are forced tightly into the holes, and oil holes drilled in them. The housing is then made from sheet metal, as shown in the drawing, and screwed to the disks, leaving a large opening for the air intake and forming a discharge passage at the top. The wooden ends must be spaced, so that the rotor can turn freely, with about 1/32 in. of end play. The rotor is put in place before the casing is finally assembled. The discharge opening should be curved, as shown in the section, to provide an easy passage for the outgoing air.

The leather flap valve is an exceedingly important part of the blower; leather that is fairly thick, but very soft and pliable, usually gives the best results. It is attached to the lip of the discharge opening with small rivets, as indicated. It will be observed that there is a little clearance between the rotor and casing so that the former can pass the flap at each revolution without sticking.

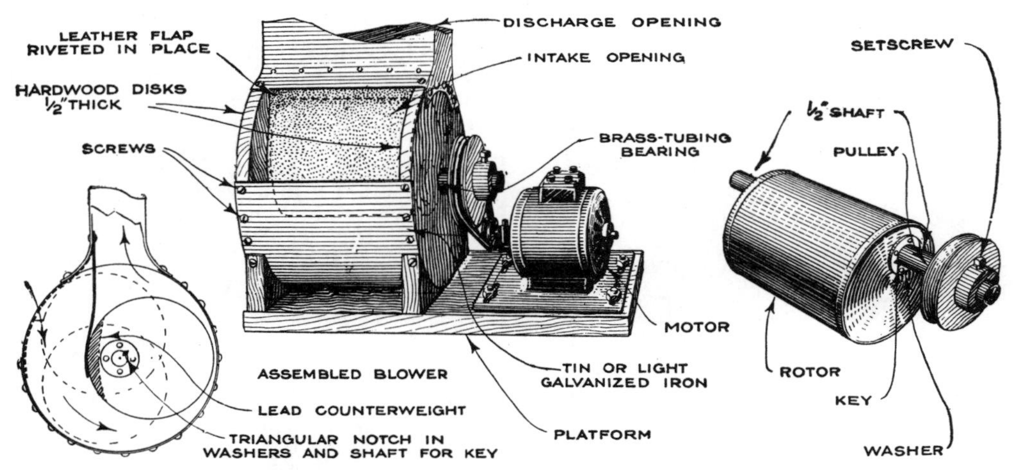

Where a Fairly Large Volume of Air at Low Pressure is Required in the Small Shop, a Blower Made from a Tin Can and Some Scrap Materials will do Satisfactory Work

The rotor should be counterbalanced so that it will run smoothly. When it has been finished, rig up the end disks of the casing temporarily so that the shaft can be put in place and rotated. Attach strips of lead temporarily to the outside of the rotor, at the point nearest the shaft, and run the rotor at a speed of about 250 or 300 revolutions per minute to see how it balances. Try pieces of different weights until one is found that allows the least vibration and seems to balance the rotor properly. When the right weight has been found, melt the lead and pour it through a hole in the end of the can so that it will settle and solidify at the point nearest the shaft. The lead will stick in place if, before the rotor is assembled, the inside is cleaned and coated with a little soldering paste.

Give the leather flap a good rubbing with light graphite grease on the side that comes into contact with the rotor, and coat the surface of the latter in the same way, without using too much of the lubricant. The best operating speed will have to be ascertained by experiment, and as the leather valve works itself into shape and acquires pliability, operation will be improved. Sometimes it will be found that a very light strip of wood tacked across the bottom of the leather will help somewhat. Such blowers can be made in any size, but if made with a housing much smaller than 6¼ in. in diameter, the results will be hardly worth while, although it can be made a little smaller and still do fairly good work. It is not intended for high speed; in fact, if driven too fast it will not work well. The operating speed depends largely upon the action of the leather valve, which refuses to function properly beyond a certain speed.

Steady Rest for Tapered Work

The steady rest shown in the drawing will be found a considerable improvement on the ordinary one furnished with a milling machine, which is rather limited in its use. It consists of a truss-shaped beam, mounted on end jacks as shown, and having a recess cut on the underside to fit on the center-jack head; several center jacks can be used, and the beam made long enough to suit any length of work. A V-shaped groove is cut in the top side, for round work, and the flats are used for flat work. The rest may also be used for grinding.—Henry S. Laraby, New Haven, Conn.

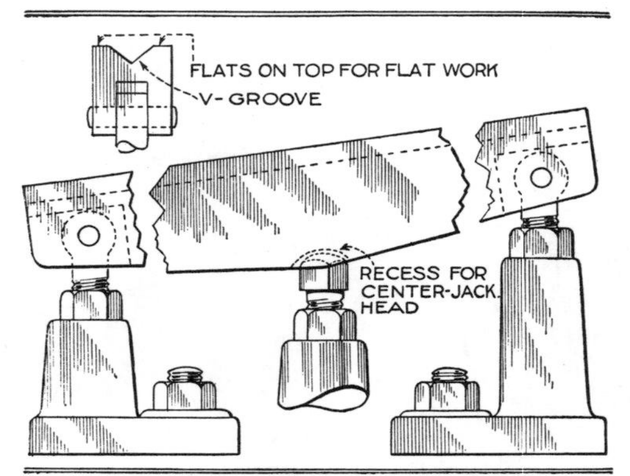

A Steady Rest on a Milling Machine That has been Found to Be of Considerable Usefulness for Tapered Work

Cheap Concrete Forms

By using tar paper to face forms for rough concrete work, a cheaper grade of wood can be used for making the forms, and the total expense of the forms considerably reduced. They are covered with a single layer of tar paper, and the concrete can be poured in without the danger of its running out through knotholes or cracks. It is also much easier to remove the forms, since the cement will not stick to them as it will to wood forms in which the joints are not tight. This method is particularly adapted to horizontal floor or sidewalk slabs.

Micrometer Attachment for Height Gauge

In checking a drill jig that had a number of holes in line with each other, I found that a quick method of discovering errors in the location of the holes was to use a micrometer attachment on a vernier height gauge. The micrometer head is fitted into a steel bracket, shaped as shown, and clamped to the gauge in place of the regular blade. When the micrometer thimble is at zero, the end of the spindle is exactly in line with the top of the gauge jaw, thus eliminating any additional calculation. A standard pin is fitted in the first hole, and the height gauge is set so that the micrometer spindle touches the top side of the pin. The reading of the thimble is carefully noted. Having the correct height established in this way, the pin is set into the next hole and the height gauge is slid along so that the micrometer spindle is located above the pin. The spindle is then turned down against the top side of the pin as before. If the reading is the same in both cases the holes are in line; if not, the amount of error is at once apparent. In this way all the holes can be carefully measured.—Alexander Malcolm, Providence, R. I.

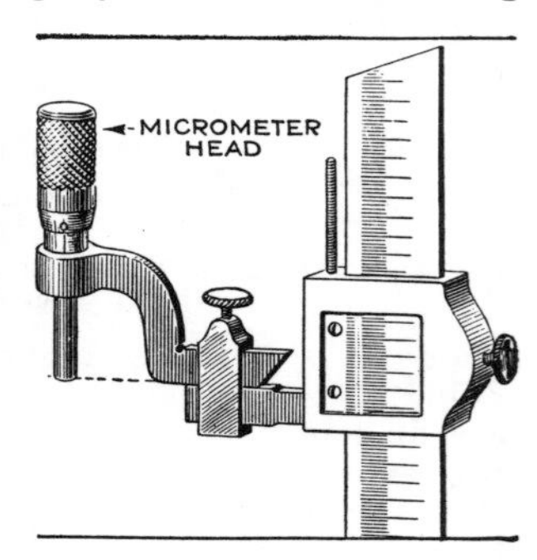

Fastening Pulley to Small Motor

A small pulley that is not subject to heavy load can be held on the motor shaft without a key or a setscrew. The entire length of the shaft outside of the motor is threaded and the pulley is fitted on the shaft between two rubber washers. These are forced tightly against the face of the pulley by means of nuts screwed on the shaft. Thin steel washers are, of course, used between the nuts and the rubber washers, and a locknut is provided, to prevent the other nuts from loosening. With this arrangement the pulley will not slip unless placed under an abnormally heavy load.

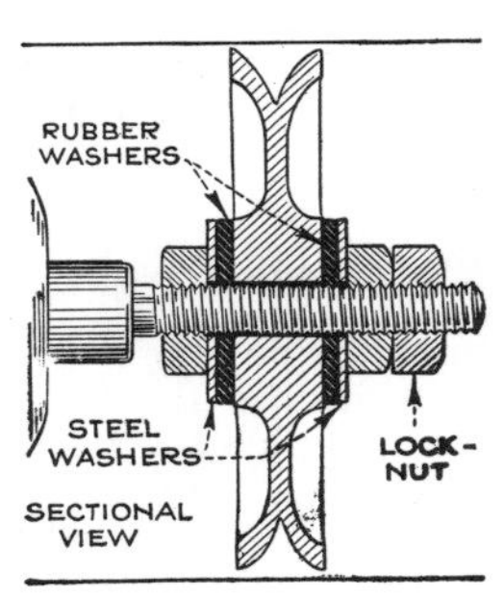

Improving Lathe Tailstock Clamp

In a popular engine lathe the tailstock is clamped to the ways by means of two bolts, which pass through the base of the tailstock and extend down through a clamping bar that bears on the lower edge of the lathe bed. As these bolts are held loosely at their upper ends, there is a decided tendency for the clamping bar to bind when the tailstock is moved along the ways, unless the bolts are loosened far enough to allow the bar to clear the lathe bed, which necessitates several part turns of the nuts.

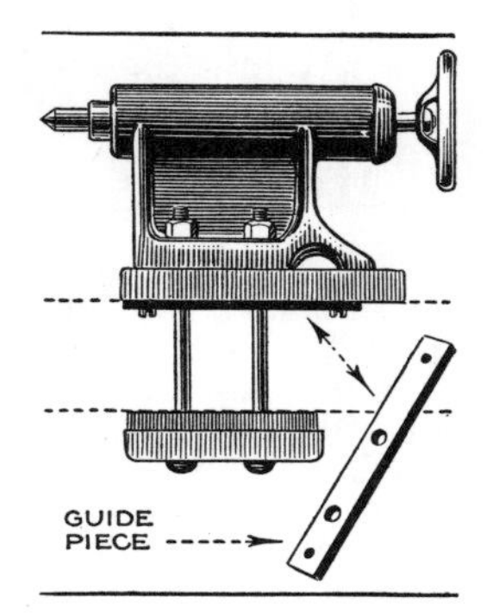

This trouble has been overcome by installing a guide piece as shown in the illustration. It consists of a flat piece of steel, 1/4 in. thick and 1 1/4 in. wide, with two small holes drilled through it to receive screws that fasten it to the base of the tailstock, and two larger holes which are a snug fit for the bolts. With the addition of this guide piece, a quarter turn on the nuts is sufficient to permit the tailstock to be moved easily.—Edwin Kilburn, Spring Valley, Minn.

Preventing Stream Erosion

Along many streams it is necessary to hold the bank back in some efficient and cheap manner, otherwise the ground will

Method of Building an Inexpensive Wall to Prevent Erosion of Streams Having Low Banks

gradually slump down into the stream, due to the washing away of the banks. An excellent method of preventing this is shown in the illustration.

A woven-wire fence is erected where the new water edge is to be made, the fence posts being driven into the bed of the stream. Brush and saplings are then deposited as indicated, the branches pointing away from the water, and the butts inserted into the fencing. Earth is thrown on the brush to make the wall solid, and in a short time the new bank is knit together by marsh grasses and rushes.

Removing Dust from Batch Hopper

During the construction of a large power house, the concrete foreman constructed a square sheet-metal hood and chimney over his batch hopper, to remove the cement dust. A 1/2-in. pipe, connected to the compressed-air supply, was arranged so that it pointed up the center of the hood, and, when the air was turned on, a strong suction was created in the chimney, which caused the dust to be drawn up. The expense of this attachment was about $10, which was more than repaid by the cleanliness of the mixing room and the increased efficiency of the men.—Aaron Evans, Rockport, Wash.

Large Homemade Pulleys

Most mechanics in out-of-the-way places find that when they need a pulley,

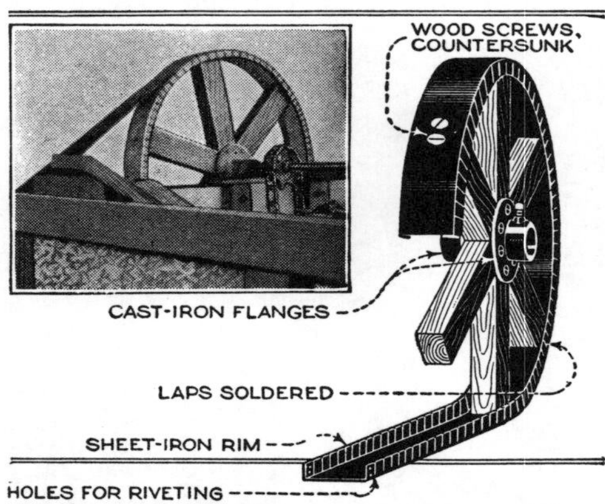

Large Pulleys That Are Light but Rigid can Readily be Made in the Out-of-the-Way Workshop

they cannot wait to have it cast, or until one can be delivered, but must have it at once. One resourceful mechanic constructs his own pulleys, when necessary, from wood and sheet metal, as shown in the illustration.

Two cast-iron flanges, specially made for this purpose, and a number of which are kept on hand, form the hub of the pulley, wooden spokes being bolted between them, and a sheet-iron rim of sufficient thickness provided on the outside. The flanges are fitted with setscrews to lock the pulley to the shaft. The spokes are beveled at the inner ends to fit together properly at the hub, and are rounded at the other end to conform to the curvature of the rim. The rim is made of a strip of sheet iron, the length being equal to the circumference of the pulley, plus 2 in. for the lap. Cuts are made along the edges by means of a hacksaw, and the strip is bent along the cuts as indicated. If the sheet metal is light, the pieces cut should be made to overlap each other when the strip is bent around the spokes, but if it is heavy, the cuts should be V-shaped, and of such size that their edges will fit closely together when bent. Solder is then run over the flange to fill the openings between the laps, making the rim rigid. If this is done neatly, and the rim given a coat of paint, the cuts cannot be seen. The ends of the rim overlap about an inch, and are riveted together. The rim is attached to the spokes by means of flat-headed wood screws, the holes being countersunk in the rim.

Most of the pulleys made in this manner have been about 2 ft. in diameter, with a 3-in. face, and for these 6-in. flanges, 2 by 3-in. spokes, and 22-gauge rims have been used. Because of their lightness and rigidity, these pulleys are much preferable to those made of cast iron or wood for slow speeds, especially when they are very large and are to be used on a light shaft.—Jonas Byberg, Silverton, Ore.

Bench Block for Straightening Rods

For straightening brass or copper rods, the bench block shown in the drawing will give excellent results. This device was used for straightening a number of ½-in. brass rods that had previously been used on tank work and were bent to a semicircular shape. It is made from a square block of steel, drilled diagonally, the hole being made a trifle larger than the diameter of the rods, and part of the block is cut away to half its thickness as shown. Holes are drilled in opposite corners for screws to hold the block to the bench. The bent rods are inserted in the hole as far as possible, then tapped down with a lead hammer and pushed through farther, until the rod passes through the hole.

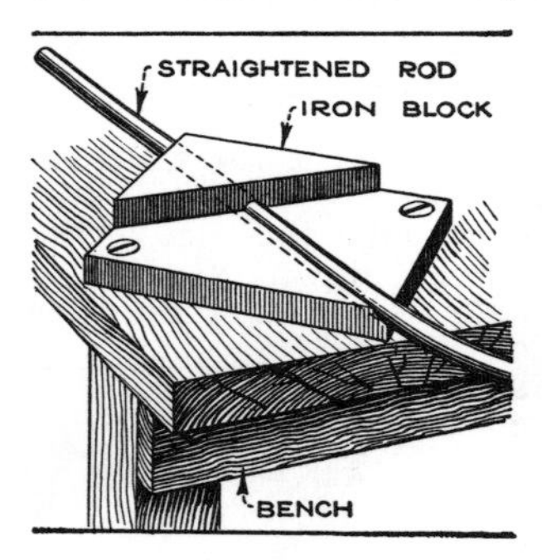

Before this form of block was made, an ordinary flat block was used, but too much time was required to get the rods straight, as they warped in different directions when struck with a hammer, and it was necessary to go over each one several times. In the case of the block shown, however, the straightened part of the rod remains straight, as it is supported in the hole, and therefore it will be quite straight after it has passed through.—Harry Moore, Montreal, Can.

Satin Finish for Goldplated Work

To satin-finish gold, the articles must first be scratch-brushed with a revolving brush made of fine steel wire, the brush being driven at high speed. The brush and work are kept wet with bran water, which is made by immersing in a gallon of boiling water a bag containing ½ lb. of bran; the bag must be well squeezed to be sure that the water is made "strong." The water is placed in a drip can suspended above the wheel, and a tin or cardboard guard is mounted above the wheel to prevent splashing. After scratch-brushing, the work will show a satin or dulled finish; it is then dipped in hot ammonia water, after which it is plated, using a rather weak current. Bicarbonate of soda and water is afterward used, on a handbrush, to clear the color of the work, which is apt to become rather foggy in the plating bath.

Homemade Jack for Erectors

Machinery erectors and other machinists frequently require jacks smaller than the average, which are often too high to be used to advantage. A set of several small jacks will make erecting and assembling work easier, and will quickly pay for the time spent in making them.

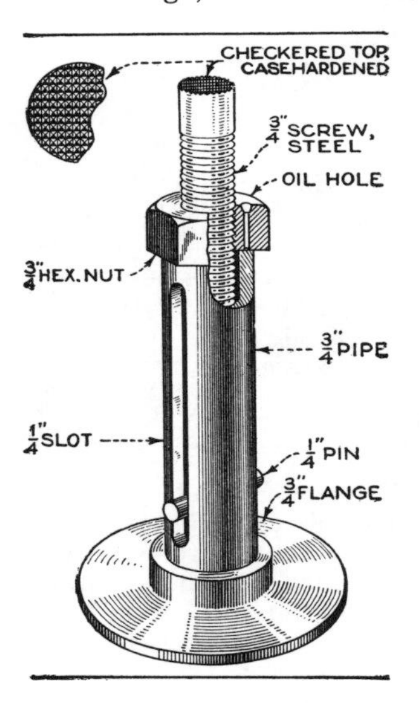

The body of the jack shown in the drawing is made from ¾-in. extra-heavy pipe, such as used for hydraulic and high-pressure purposes, fitted at the bottom with a floor flange. The pipe is screwed into the flange flush with its lower face, so as to make a firm and continuous supporting surface. The elevating screw is made from ¾-in. round steel, threaded to within an inch of the head, which is checkered and casehardened to give a good nonslipping surface; the checkering can be done before casehardening by making deep cuts at right angles to each other with a three-cornered file. The screw is drilled and fitted with a ¼-in. pin, which slides in a slot cut in opposite sides of the pipe and prevents the screw from turning. A good casehardened hexagon nut is used to raise and lower the jack.

Cutting Gear Teeth on the Shaper

Gears that had a number of broken teeth filled in by welding were machined

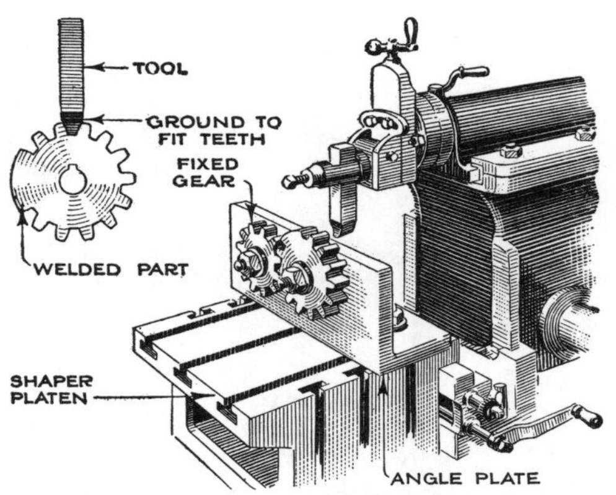

Machining New Teeth in a Damaged Gear Repaired by Welding

on a shaper by means of the method shown in the drawing.

An angle plate was set up on the table of the machine, and a cutting tool was made, using an unbroken section of the gear as a template. The welded gear was placed against the angle plate and secured by a center bolt. A pinion was then bolted to the plate, so as to mesh with the unbroken teeth of the gear to be machined, with one of the good tooth spaces of the gear at the top. The gear was then brought up to the tool to locate the correct position of the shaper table. The welded section was now set under the tool and the cutting commenced, using only the vertical feed. The small pinion meshing with the larger gear was bolted solidly to the plate and was not disturbed until the work was done. As each tooth was cut, the work was turned by detaching it and turning it one tooth, so that a fresh surface of the new metal was brought in front of the cutting tool.

Melting Sulphur

Sulphur is often used to anchor bolts in cement or stone floors, but as it catches fire so easily when melted over an open flame, its use is somewhat inconvenient. This difficulty can, however, be avoided by first melting some lead, and then partly immersing the sulphur vessel in the molten lead. The sulphur will be melted in a short time, and there it will not catch fire, unless the temperature of the lead is allowed to exceed 625° Fahrenheit.

Facing Valves on Drill Press

A novel method of refacing valves is shown in the illustration, a drill press and a hand grinder being used to do the work. A cupped emery wheel is fitted on the grinder, and the valve face is ground with the inner surface. This makes the face round, which, by many mechanics, is considered superior to a flat face, as it seats more readily and uniformly, and the smaller contact surface removes all carbon particles that become lodged on the seat.

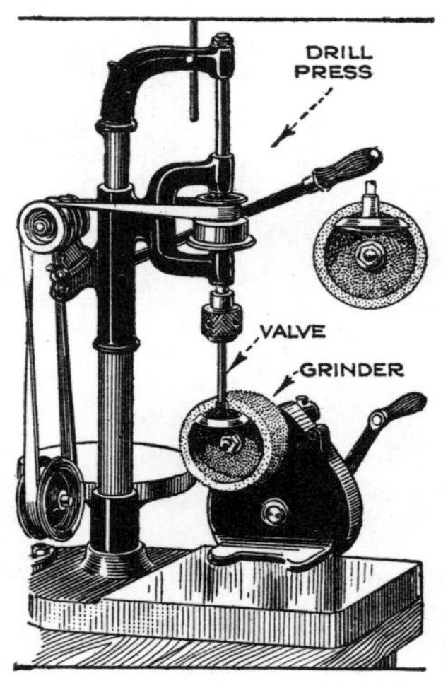

The grinder is revolved with one hand while the drill-press spindle is lifted to bring the valve face in contact with the inside surface of the emery wheel. In grinding, only the smallest possible amount of metal is removed from the valve, and therefore the valve must not be held on the wheel for any considerable length of time.

Miter Nailing "Jack"

The miter nailing "jack" shown in the illustration is used for holding the mitered end of a piece of wood while the other end is being nailed as indicated, the object of the jack being to avoid bruising the beveled edge.

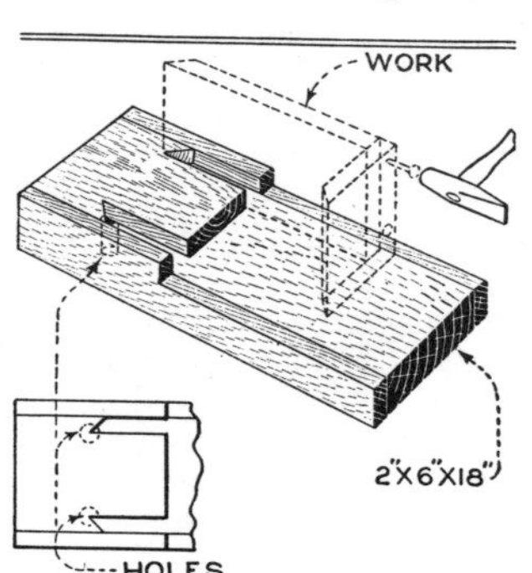

The base of the fixture is made of 2 by 6-in. wood, about 18 in. long. A piece of ⅞-in. wood is then cut with recesses for the beveled edge of the work, and this piece is nailed solidly to the base near one end, as shown. Strips are then nailed to the sides to complete the slots in which the mitered pieces are placed while nailing. Small holes, drilled through the base at the points of the slots, prevent the accumulation of sawdust and dirt in the points. The dotted lines show the position of the work when nailing.—F. M. Arthur, Bethune, S. C.

Long-Range Cotter-Pin Puller

The cotter-pin puller shown in the illustration was devised by an automobile mechanic, and has been found to be of considerable assistance in removing cotter pins from places where it is difficult or impossible to use pliers or other tools. This tool can be used without the preliminary work of straightening the ends of the cotter pins, and also without the danger of scratching and bruising the hands.

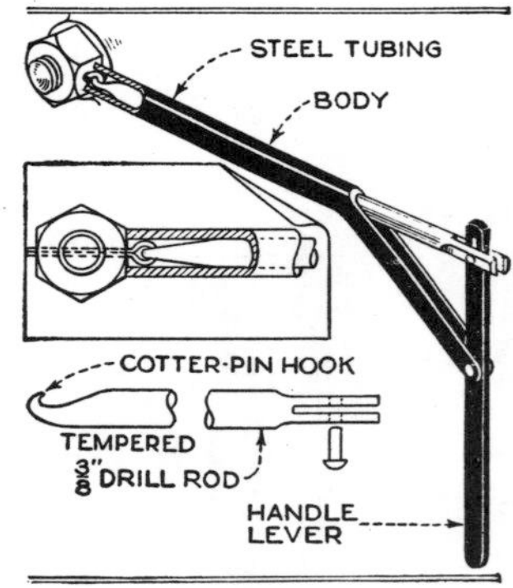

The body of the tool consists of a length of steel tubing of about ⅜-in. inside diameter. A ⅜-in. steel rod that slides freely inside of the tubing is filed or forged to a hook shape at one end, as indicated, and the other end is slotted and drilled for a small pin. One end of the tubing is cut and bent to form a support for a handle lever, which is pinned loosely to the end of the rod. The lever is also pivoted on the support extending from the tubing. In use, the body of the tool is held against the side of the nut while the rod pulls the cotter pin, the handle providing a good leverage.

Locating Squares on Shaft Ends

When cutting a square on the end of a shaft, take a square-nose tool and cut down a short length on the shaft end, in the lathe, until its diameter is equal to a side of the square. This enables the milling cutter or shaper tool to be fed down to the correct depth at once, without further measuring.

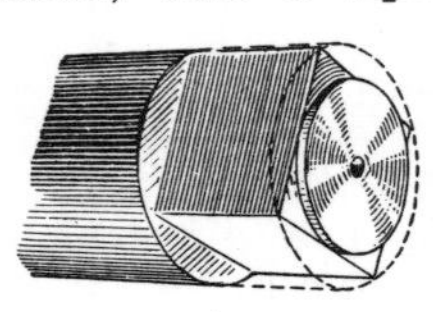

Building Concrete Retaining Walls

By A. C. Cole

THERE is nothing at all difficult about the building of retaining walls in concrete, the cost of the work is low, and the finished wall adds greatly to the appearance of the inclosed grounds.

The excavation for the wall footings must be carried below the frost line, and, where the earth is firm enough, the bank itself may be used as one side of the form, undercuts being made in the bank to form the projecting lower portions of the footings. Where the earth is not self-supporting, it is, of course, necessary to cut away the bank so that forms can be used on both sides and the wide footings poured. This, however, is not a disadvantage, as it allows a layer of loose stones, gravel, or cinders to be laid along the back of the wall before filling back the earth, and this helps the drainage.

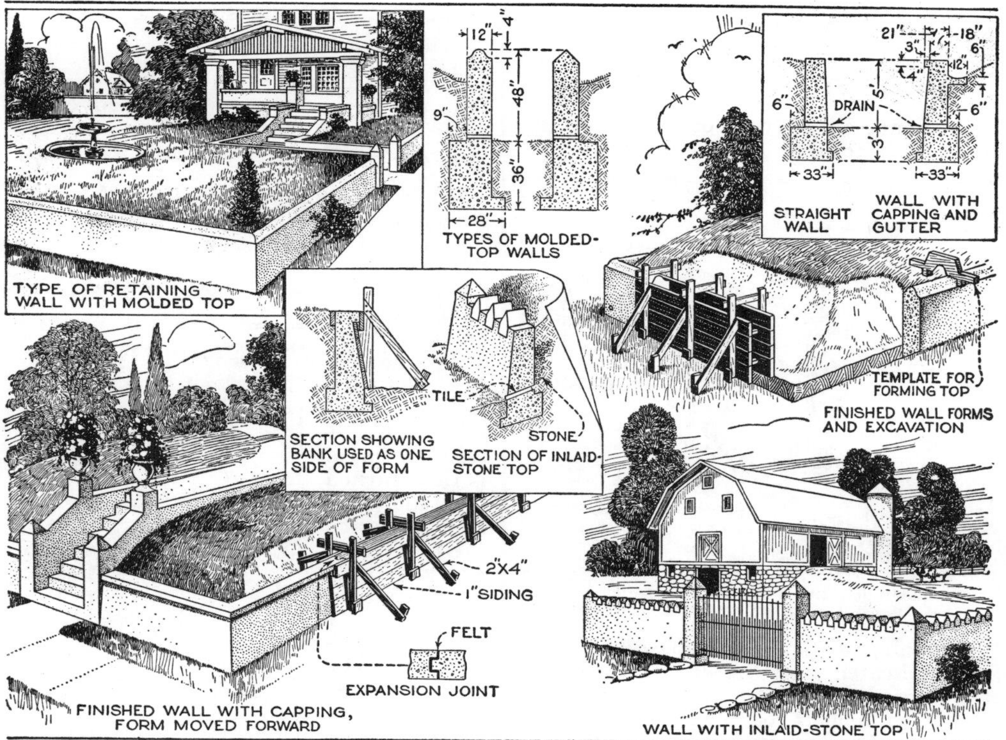

Various Forms of Easily Made Retaining Walls in Concrete: Details of Molded, Capped, and Inlaid-Stone Tops are Given in the Inserts

As may be noted in the drawings, the forms are very simple; 1-in. siding is used for the sides, with 2 by 3 or 2 by 4-in. uprights and braces. Enough uprights, braces, and struts must be used to prevent the forms from bulging, and the walls held the proper distance apart by short pieces of the material used for the uprights. The walls are held by twisted-wire ties in the usual manner, and by cross braces at the top; the spacing pieces are moved upward as the concrete is placed.

As soon as the footings have been placed, and the forms erected, a number of concrete drain tiles are placed in the forms, as indicated in the sectional drawings, to carry off water, and the remainder of the concrete is then placed. The concrete used should be mixed in the proportion of 1 part cement, 2 parts sand, and 4 of clean, broken stone, and, when pouring the concrete, a flat, sharpened stick or a spade should be used to cut down between the form and the mixture, to work the stone back from the face of the wall, rendering the surface dense and smooth.

If the wall is at all long, the work should be done in 20-ft. sections, moving the forms along as soon as the concrete in one section has set, and expansion joints, of the type shown, filled with asphaltic felt, provided between sections.

Various forms of coping are shown in the drawing. The molded top presents a very neat appearance, and is easily formed by means of a wooden template, drawn along the top of the wall while the concrete is still "green." With a little more trouble, a neat gutter may be formed on the back of the wall, the trough being shaped with a trowel. A particularly attractive top is formed by inlaying stone blocks, as shown in the lower right-hand view, although this is rather more expensive.

The forms can be removed as soon as the concrete has set enough to sustain its own weight, and the surfaces may be finished by simply rubbing with a wooden float dipped in water and sand; in this way the form marks are rubbed off, and a smooth, permanent surface obtained.

Novel Fence-Wire Stretcher

The fence-wire stretcher shown in the illustration consists of a short length of

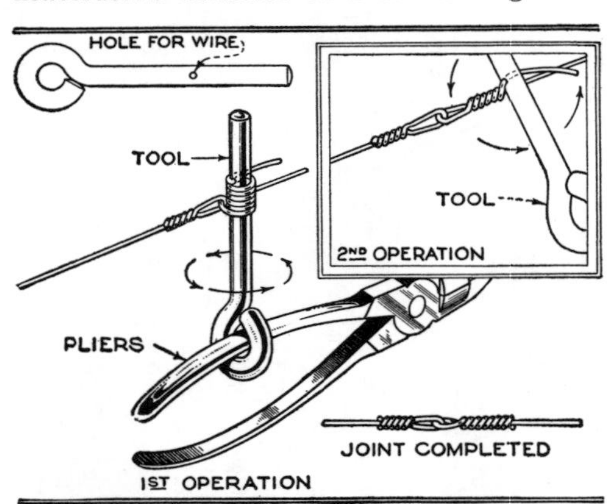

Lower Illustration Shows Method of Tightening Wire, and Insert, Method of Fastening Free End

½-in. iron rod with a hole drilled through it as indicated, and the end formed to a ring large enough to accommodate the handle of a pair of pliers. When the wire is to be tightened, it is not cut near a post, but midway between two posts. One end of the cut wire is formed into a loop, and the other end passed through the loop and through the hole in the tool. The tool is turned by means of the plier handle, as indicated, so that the wire is wound around it until sufficiently tight. The tool is then revolved around the wire several times, as shown in the upper detail, and the surplus wire clipped off.

Increasing Diameter of Small V-Pulleys

When it is desired to increase the diameter of a V-pulley, such as often found on the side of a small flywheel, a "rim" of babbitt can be cast around it, providing the increase in size is not too great.

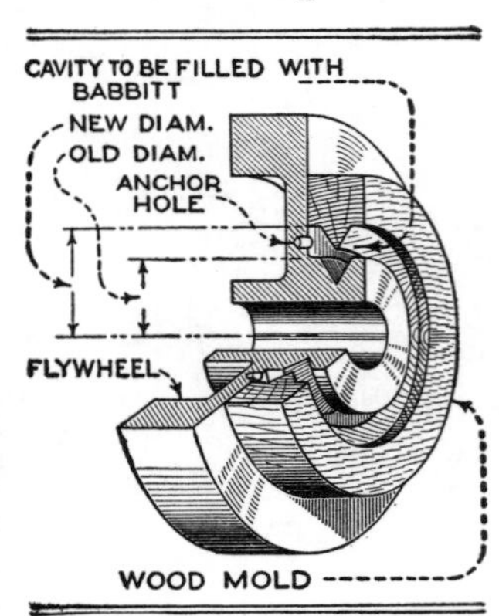

Small anchor holes are first drilled in the side of the wheel, as shown. A wooden mold is then turned out of good dry pine to the new diameter. The mold is placed around the pulley, concentric with the bore, and clamped in place, after which babbitt is poured into the open space between the mold and the old pulley. If it is desired to use the old pulley again, it is only necessary to cut off or melt the babbitt. When melting the babbitt, whittle a clean surface on the end of a pine stick and dip it repeatedly in the metal. When the stick chars, pour the babbitt.

An Efficient Paste Spreader

In offices where many papers are wrapped by hand for mailing, the paste spreader illustrated will be very useful. It eliminates the paste brush, and speeds up the work considerably.

The base is made from an ordinary 1-in. board. An upright piece of the same material is screwed to one side of the base to keep the edges of the pile of wrappers even. Heavy spikes will serve for the paste container guides, although ¼-in. iron rods are better. The container is a triangular trough with a flat bottom, in which a number of small holes are drilled to distribute the paste along the wrapper edges. Ears are left at each end of the container, and holes drilled to fit the guides, so that the container can move up and down easily. Medium-weight galvanized sheet metal is a suitable material for the container.

To use the spreader, the papers are first placed in a pile under the paste container, which is then filled with paste, mucilage, or glue, whichever is necessary. When a wrapper is drawn out from under the container, it is automatically coated with paste. If it is found that too much paste is applied to the wrappers, the container may be weighted down so that less paste will escape through the holes.—Lowell R. Butcher, Des Moines, Ia.

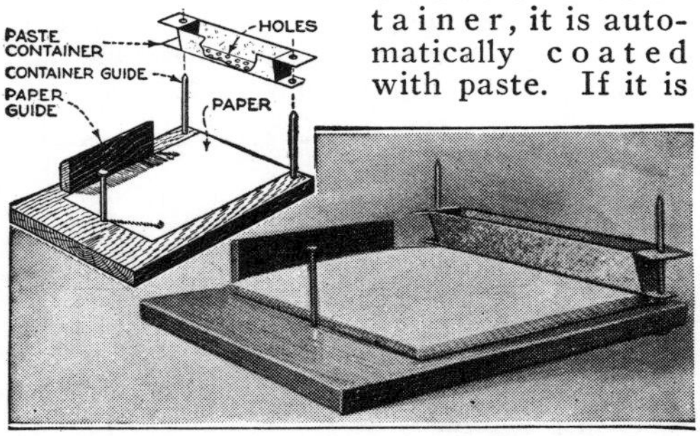

Device for Applying Paste to the Ends of Wrappers, That Speeds Up the Wrapping Process Considerably

Novel Mounting for Instruction Manual

In garages and service stations where drawings and wiring diagrams are required for reference while working on cars, it is almost impossible to keep them from being soiled, as they are continually being handled with greasy hands.

To prevent this, in one station, the sheets were glued to the inside of an ordinary roller shade, which was mounted on the wall in front of the foreman's desk. Whenever the reference prints were to be used, the shade was simply unrolled, and when the job was finished, rolled up again. Besides keeping the prints clean, this prevented them from being creased, torn, or lost.

Novel Method of Mounting Reference Prints on the Inside of an Ordinary Roller Shade

Cutting Glass Tubing

The illustration shows an excellent method of cutting glass tubing. A block of wood with a V-groove cut in it is attached to the bench; a triangular file is arranged across this, the tang of the file having an eye formed in it, which swings on a pin driven through another block attached to the bench, as shown. The other end of the file is slipped through the end of a coil spring which is fastened to a screweye driven into the bench, and draws the file downward against the tubing. The tubing is placed in the V-block, between the block and the file. Turning the tube will then cause the file to score the glass, after which a few light taps will break it cleanly.

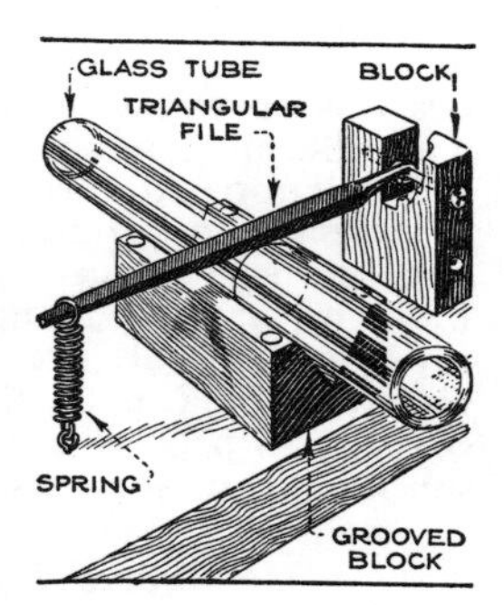

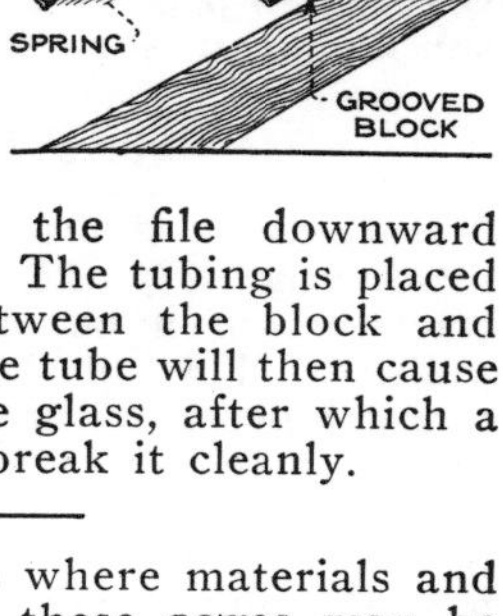

ℭInformation as to where materials and parts mentioned in these pages may be obtained will be furnished, on request, by the Bureau of Information.

Curing a Broody Hen

There are hundreds of ways advocated for curing broody hens, but most of these are not entirely effective. Simply confining the hen in a coop without nests will not cure her, unless she is kept there until completely exhausted. A positive cure, which requires only 5 or 6 days, is shown in the drawing. An ordinary elevated coop will not do the work, as the idea is to prevent warmth under the hen when she sits down, and therefore the floor should not be made of wood, but of 1-in. wire mesh. The air from underneath soon effects a cure; it has done so with the most persistent hatchers.

An Elevated Coop with Wire-Mesh Bottom Effects a Cure for Broody Hens in Five or Six Days

The coop should be elevated about 3 ft. above the ground, and it should be large enough to accommodate 6 or 8 hens. Pans or narrow troughs, on which the fowls cannot sit, are used for food and water. The top of the coop should be covered to protect the hens from the hot sun and from showers.

Machinists' Hook Gauge

Nothing is so hard to measure in the machining of work on the lathe as the thickness of hubs of wheels, gears, and pulleys. This is due to the fact that many holes are too small to allow the use of a regular hook rule, and even if one could be used, it is often too short to reach through the bore. A very serviceable hook gauge that eliminates these difficulties can be made as shown in the illustration.

The main part of the gauge consists of a suitable length of ¼-in. drill rod provided with a hook at one end. The hook is made by forging a sharp bend in the rod, and filing it to the shape shown. The straight edge of the hook is filed perfectly square with the axis of the rod, and the corner is filed out with a small round file, to prevent the accumulation of dirt, which would result in incorrect measurements. The notching out of the corner also prevents a burr on the edge of the bore from showing a false reading on the gauge.

The head of the gauge consists of two parts; an inner sleeve, bored out of center as shown, which is necessary to allow sufficient metal for the thumbscrew, and an outer sleeve, bored to a neat sliding fit over the inner one, and having a flange at one end, which is turned perfectly square with the rod. The outer sleeve moves over the inner within the limits of the thumbscrew slot. This always holds the outer sleeve square to the graduation line on the inner sleeve, and as a flat is filed on the rod, against which the screw bears, the whole gauge is kept in line.

Across the face of the outer sleeve is filed an opening, as shown, to expose the surface of the inner sleeve. Midway between the limits of travel of the outer sleeve, a graduation line is scribed on the inner one as shown, and a similar line scribed across the center of the flats on the outer sleeve. The gauge is set by keeping both graduations in alinement

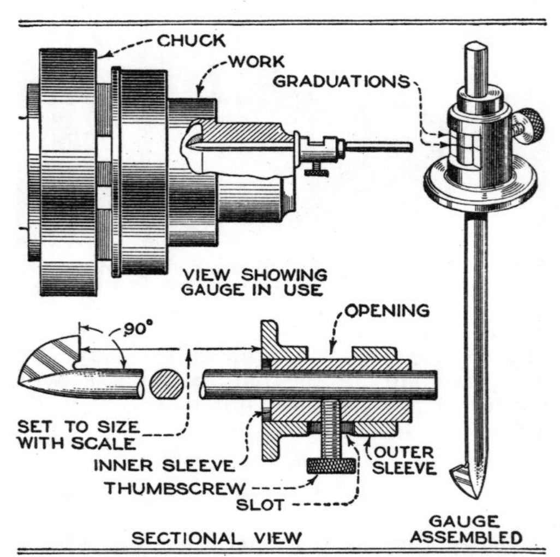

A Handy Hook Gauge for Measuring the Thickness of Hubs of Wheels, Gears, and Pulleys

while measuring between hook and outer sleeve with the scale. When set to size, the thumbscrew is tightened, and, upon applying the gauge to the work, holding the hook against the inner face of the hub and sliding the outer sleeve against the outer face, the amount to be turned off is indicated by the distance between the graduations. This gauge not only indicates when the thickness of the hub is correct, but how much it may be over or under size.

A gauge of this kind, when used for general purposes, should be made of ¼-in. rod; smaller or larger sizes can be used to suit the work. With the gauge of ¼-in. steel, holes can be measured through ½-in. bores.

Lubricating Wristpins

During winter the tractor requires considerable care, as the heavy oil that is used in tractors becomes almost a grease in zero weather, and in this condition does not lubricate the wristpin bearings properly, so that there is danger of burning out the bearings or "freezing" them.

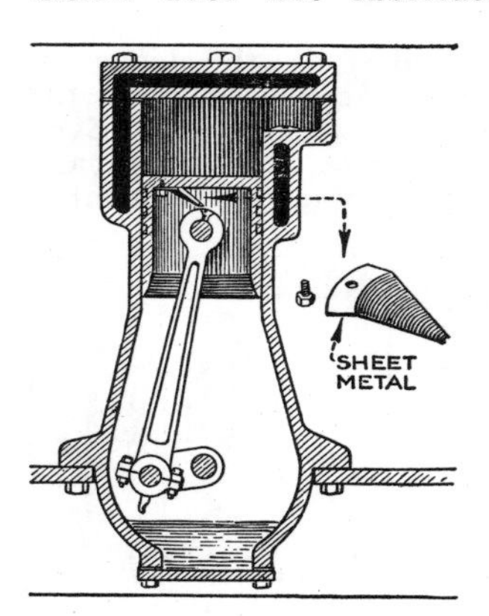

To offset this danger, I provided the auxiliary oiling device illustrated, which consists of a piece of No. 20 sheet steel, hammered to the shape shown in the detail and screwed to the underside of the piston head, so that the spout terminates directly over the oil hole in the top of the wristpin bearing. The point where the device is bolted must be opposite the point where the splash from the crank reaches the inside of the piston, so that the spout will catch some of the oil. This oil will then drop on the bearing where it is needed. The addition of this device has been found to eliminate much trouble previously experienced.—G. G. McVicker, North Bend, Neb.

A tap should never be used to clean a hole in hardened work, even if the work is soft enough to be scratched with a file.

Holder for Side-Planing Tool

The illustration shows a useful side-cutting planer-tool holder, which does work that at times cannot be done with

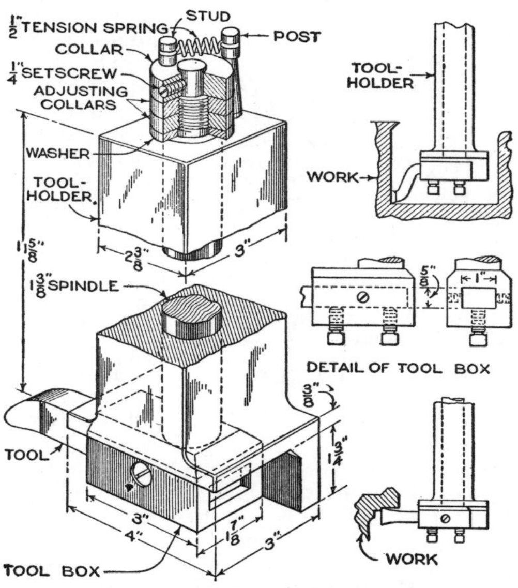

An Improved Holder for Side Planing That can be Used on Right or Left-Hand Work

the regular planer heads. It can be used on either right or left-hand work.

The tool box is machined on the lower end of the spindle, and fits against the shoulder at the rear of the body. The upper end of the spindle is threaded and fitted with a washer and two adjusting collars; over the latter is placed a collar, which is fastened to the spindle with a setscrew. A stud in the top of the collar, and a post in the body of the holder, are connected by a tension spring, which pulls the tool box back against the shoulder at the end of the return stroke. Cutters, forged with an offset large enough to allow the lowest edge of the tool to project below the heads of the setscrews in the tool box, allow cutting to the bottom of slots, as in the drawing.—R. W. Laing, Fergus, Can.

Absorbing Excess Oil on Dirt Streets

When a dirt street is oiled, the oil is usually tracked all over where it is not wanted. This was prevented, in an Iowa town, by spreading powdered stone—refuse from a stone crusher—over the road. The stone dust absorbed the excess oil, and it packed down at once.

Cement and Cloth Repair for Radiator

The soldering of a honeycomb radiator is difficult work and can be accomplished satisfactorily by an experienced repairman only. However, a repair for small leaks, that can readily be made by anyone, is shown in the illustration. It consists of packing strips of cloth, saturated with a thin mixture of Portland cement and water, into the small spaces where the leaks are found. The cement hardens and binds the cloth into a solid mass. It is not necessary to remove the radiator when making this repair, but the water should be drained out so that the cement particles in the cloth will not be washed away, and the cement should be permitted to set before refilling the radiator.

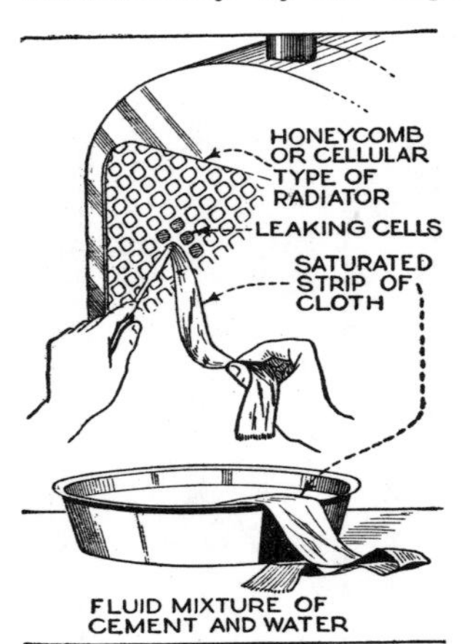

Setting Compound Rest for Tapers

For certain kinds of taper work, when the compound slide is used, swiveled around, and fed by hand or power, the taper is best found by the trial scribing of a surface plate and clamping the slide in position when the scribed angle is found to be correct. A small surface plate, or any smooth metal plate, is clamped to the lathe bed, while a surface-gauge scriber is attached to a holder clamped in the tool block, the plate being either chalked or blued, according to the accuracy required. Then the lathe carriage is run along by hand, far enough to allow the surface-gauge pointer to scribe a line along the plate; this line, of course, being parallel to the lathe bed.

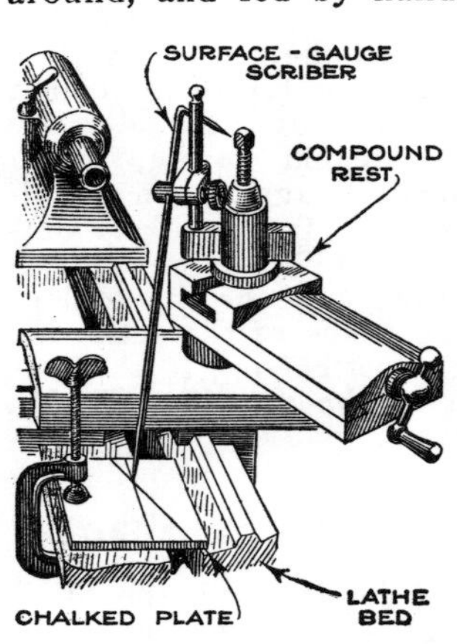

It is assumed that a template showing the correct taper is at hand, and that the exact reading of the taper angle, in degrees, is unknown, as is often the case. If the angle is known and the compound rest graduated, it can be set off at once without the necessity of the scribing process described. Using the template, another line is scribed on the surface plate to make the required angle to the line already made; then, the compound rest is swung around to approximately the right position, clamped, and the compound slide traversed. The surface-gauge pointer, being still in place, will indicate how closely the rest has been set, and the rest is swung and reset until the scriber follows accurately the line scribed from the template

Drilling Holes through Round Stock

Every mechanic has more or less difficulty in drilling holes centrally in shafting and other round stock, the degree of trouble encountered depending upon the skill of the person doing the work. Even with an accurate layout and great care, the holes are frequently drilled off center.

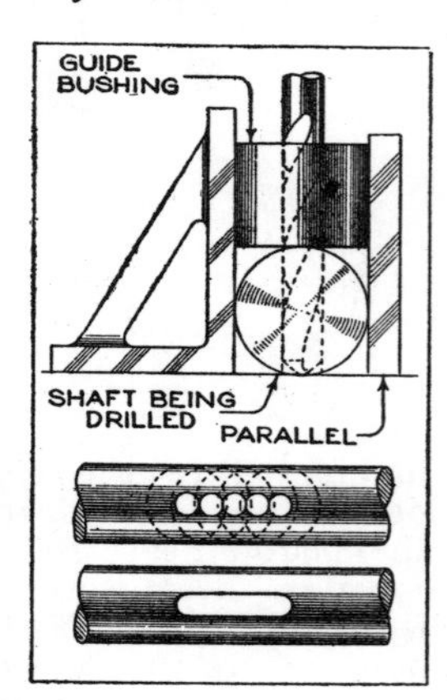

The method illustrated makes it possible to bore one hole or a succession of holes in cylindrical work with the certainty that all of them will be at right angles to the axis of the work. Also, no layout is required unless a hole has to be a certain distance from the end of the work, in which case a scale can be used, or, where accuracy is required, a depth micrometer, by merely subtracting half the diameter of the bushing from the required dimension. The bushing is turned to exactly the same diameter as the work it is to be used with, and the central hole should be the same size as the one to be drilled in the work. The bushing and the job are then clamped in a vise, or, in cases where the work is too large, between parallels.

Straightening Damaged Clincher Rims

Clincher rims sometimes become dented and must be straightened to prevent injury to the tires. The rims can be straightened by means of a large pipe wrench. The rim or wheel is removed and placed on the floor and the pipe wrench applied to the dented spot so that the head of the wrench bears against the center of the rim, and the upper jaw presses outward against the dented portion as shown. The end of the wrench handle and the side of the rim farthest away from the wrench will then rest on the floor. By standing on the rim as indicated in the drawing the dent can readily be removed.—E. T. Gunderson, Jr., Humboldt, Iowa.

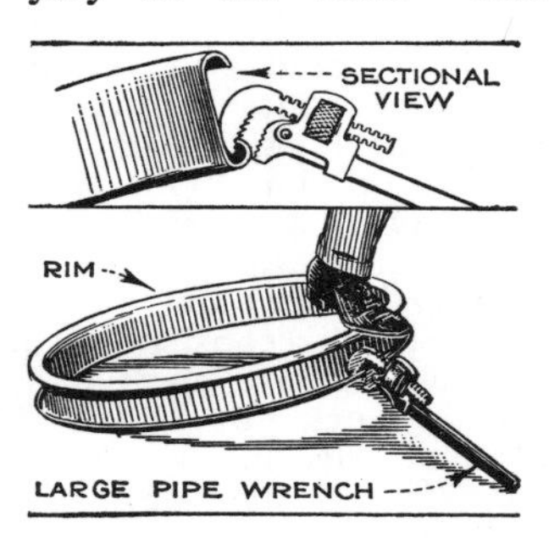

Ferrotyping Made Easy

Many commercial photographers ferrotype a great number of their prints to give them a glossy finish. This is usually done by laying the prints face downward upon the ferrotype plate and applying pressure with a hand roller, which is hard work and requires time and patience. A better method of doing this is shown in the photograph. An ordinary hand wringer, adjusted to give a slight pressure between the rollers, is used to do the work, the prints being laid face downward on the ferrotype plate and both run through the wringer. Buckling can be prevented by keeping the prints at least ⅛ in. from the edge of the plate.—J. G. Pratt, Washington, D. C.

¶When storing cement, never pile it directly on the ground, which always contains some moisture.

Simple and Useful Clamp for Stepladder

A simple and useful clamp for the stepladder, that serves as a rest for holding windows while setting the panes or painting, can be made from two pieces of oak about 2½ ft. long, with a bolt passing through the center of both as shown; a wingnut is provided on the bolt. It is not necessary to remove the wingnut to attach the clamp. Merely push the clamp over one leg of the stepladder from the inside, and then over the other leg, after which the wingnut is tightened. This tool can be used equally well on a common ladder.—Edgar Wright, Brookfield, Mass.

Handy Clamp on Stepladder for Holding Windows While Working on Them

Filling the Auto Vacuum Tank

If a funnel and small gasoline can are at hand, the simplest way to fill the automobile vacuum tank is to remove the plug at the top of the tank and pour in the gasoline. If no funnel is available, the best method of filling the tank quickly is as follows: Close the throttle and shut off the ignition, then press the starter switch. It may be necessary, with some starters, to switch on the ignition for a moment, in order that the starter gears may mesh. The action of the motor will then cause enough suction to draw the gasoline from the rear tank into the vacuum tank. The throttle must be kept closed, as otherwise the engine simply draws most of the air through the carburetor, and not enough through the vacuum tank.

Building a Floor Crane

BY J. V. ROMIG

ONE of the handiest pieces of equipment for the small machine shop, garage, or service station is a portable floor crane, which can be rolled to any part of the shop to take the heavy lifts, and, when not in use, can be shoved out of the way.

A strong and serviceable floor crane can be made in any small shop or garage, at small cost for labor and material, and it will prove a paying investment. With this crane, heavy work may be raised from the floor to the bench or the tables of the various machines, shafts can quickly and easily be placed between the centers of the lathe, and, in the garage, engines can be lifted out of chassis, and run over to the repair bench or stand; in fact, the uses that can be found for the crane are "too numerous to mention."

The lower frame or base of the crane is made from two pieces of 5-in. channel iron, upon which are mounted two columns made of pipe. On top of the columns is the hoist arm, also of channel iron, and fitted with pulleys over which runs the hoisting chain or cable. A drum and a set of winch gears, with their shafts and bearings, are bolted to the columns.

The base members are cut to a length of 62 in., laid out, and bent to the shape shown in the detail drawing; the bends are made at an angle of 45°, with the webs of the channels on the outside. The frame members are spaced apart by a piece of 3/8-in. boiler plate on the underside, and by the 4-in. pipe flanges used for the columns on top. The standard diameter of 4-in. extra-heavy pipe flanges is 10 in., so this will be the width of the length of boiler plate; the plate is cut long enough to project beyond the channels, to form a bearing for the back-caster pivot. Ball-bearing caster wheels are fitted to the three ends of the base as indicated, the caster at the back being provided with a forked handle or tongue, to enable the crane to be pulled about easily. The width of the front end of the base is 48 in., which enables it to be pushed between the wheels of an automobile of the standard 56-in. tread.

The columns are made of 4-in. extra-heavy pipe, and are fitted with flanges at both ends as shown. Both pipes should be cut and threaded so that, when the flanges are screwed home, the over-all length of the columns will be the same; they are bolted to the lower frame and hoist arm with 1/2-in. bolts, and must be perfectly square and parallel.

The arm or boom of the crane is also made of 5-in. channel irons, 48 in. long. They are spaced apart by pieces of pipe, faced on the ends perfectly square and to the same length, and held with 1/2-in. or 5/8-in. bolts. Two cable pulleys are placed within the arm at the points shown, before the arm is assembled. The pulleys run freely on plain 3/4-in. pins, held in place by heavy cotter pins, and they should be provided with oil cups, and be kept properly lubricated.

The hoisting mechanism consists of a cast-iron drum, mounted on a shaft carried in small pillow blocks on the columns. The bases of the pillow blocks should be machined to fit the curvature of the columns, or, if there is not metal enough in them for this, small plates, curved on one side to fit the columns, and flat on the other, should be used between the blocks and columns. The drum shaft carries a 12 or 14-in. gear at one end, meshing with a 3 or 4-in. gear carried on a shaft above the drum. This shaft is also carried in pillow blocks, fitted as before, and is provided with a strong crank handle. The assembly is bolted to the columns, with 1/2-in. through bolts, at a convenient operating height, the pillow blocks being spaced so that the gears will mesh with the minimum of backlash, while still running free. A bent bracket, made of 3/8-in. steel plate, is bolted to the back of one of the columns, and carries a pawl which engages with the large gear, and holds the load when hoisted.

Either a cable or chain may be used; if a cable, it should be of plow steel, not less than 3/8 in. in diameter, and if a chain is used, it should be strong enough to sustain a load of at least 800 pounds.

Most of the material for this exceedingly useful tool can be picked up at a junk dealer's for a few cents a pound; the work of cutting and assembling is quite simple, and may be done in the men's spare time, if necessary.

Cement for Auto-Top Repairs

Many autoists repair a torn top with a piece of rubberized fabric and tube cement; it is found, however, that the cement deteriorates in time under exposure to weather. By substituting shellac for the cement, the repair can be made practically permanent. The portion of the top to be covered should be cleaned thoroughly, and the shellac should be spread so that there will be no spaces under the edges.

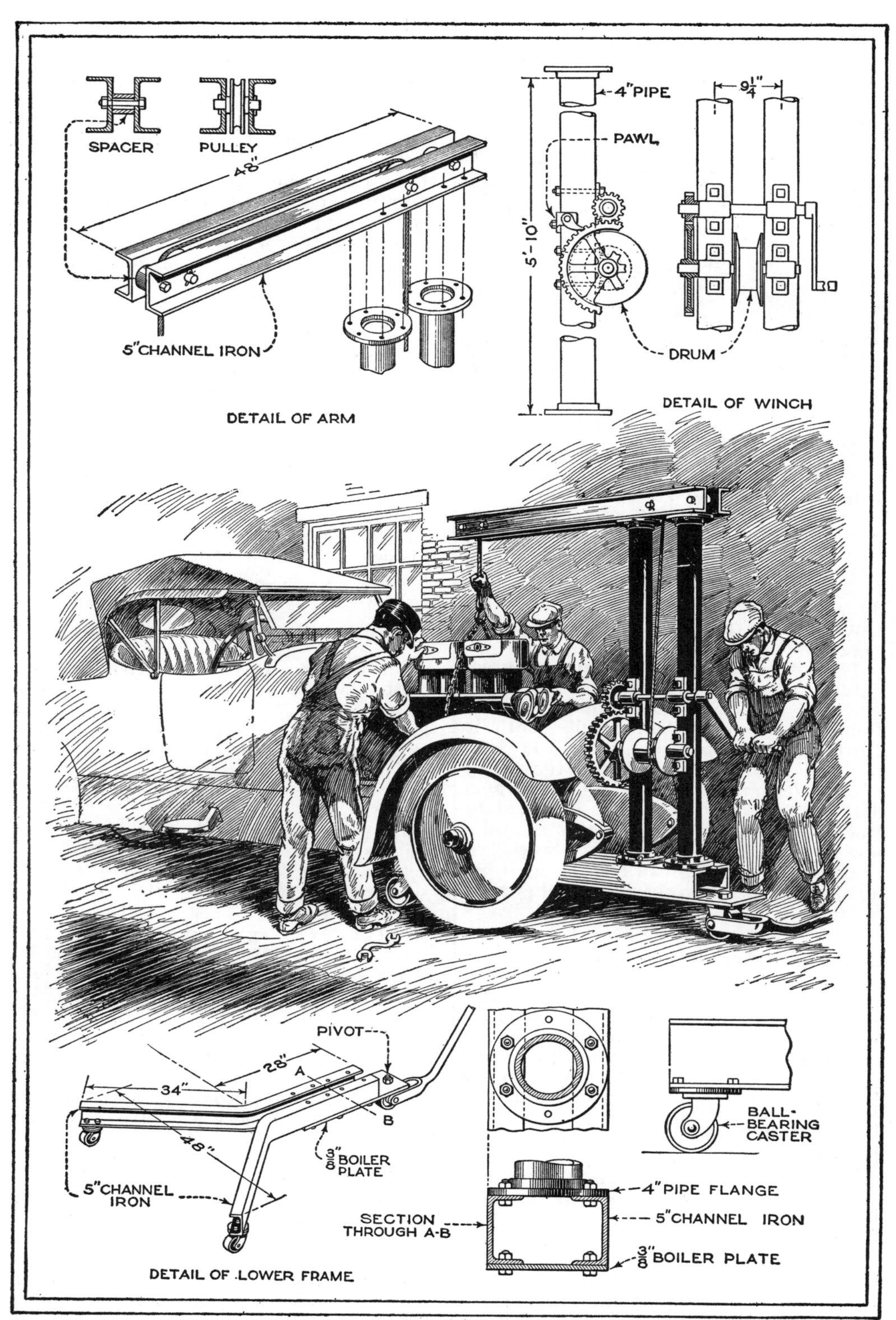

A Floor Crane That may be Constructed of Material Found in Any Junk Yard, and That will Very Quickly Pay for the Time Spent in Making It, by the Time Saved When Heavy Work must be Lifted

Turning Hard Rubber

Anyone who has had experience in turning hard rubber, ebonite, and bakelite, knows how difficult it is to keep the edges on the steel tools, and to produce a finely burnished surface. The tool dulls rapidly, and drags the surface of the material, so that the work presents a ragged appearance.

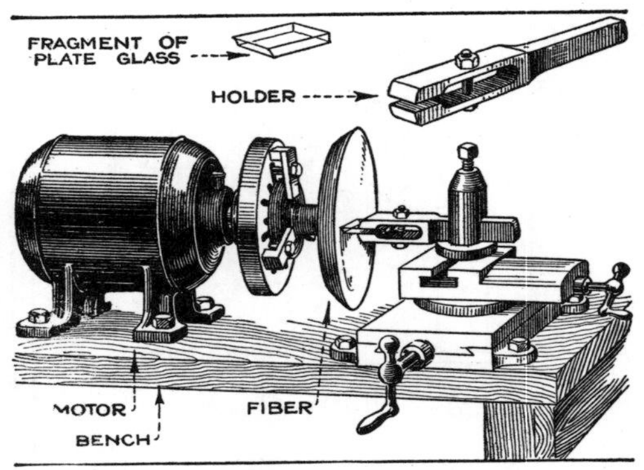

Method of Cutting and Facing Hard Rubber with Pieces of Plate Glass

The difficulty can be avoided to a great extent by using a small piece of plate glass as a cutting tool; this has been found to give excellent results, both in cutting and in surfacing the work. The piece of glass is clamped in a toolholder of the design illustrated in the upper detail. The cutting edge is obtained by fracturing the glass; when this is dull a new break is made. Pieces of heavy glass broken from bottles can also be used but cannot be held so easily in the toolholder.

Convenient Arrangement for Test Leads

There are usually two pairs of test leads on the workbench of an electric repair shop; one pair is connected in series with a lamp, and the other pair tapped directly to the line, to obtain full-line voltage when testing small motors and heating appliances. A very simple method of obtaining the same result with one pair of test leads is shown in the illustration.

A double-pole double-throw knife switch is used. One of the center terminals is connected to the positive line, and the other to the test lead. The two terminals on one side of the switch are connected to a lamp, and those on the other side are short-circuited. The other test lead is tapped directly to the negative line. By throwing in the switch on one side, the lamp is put in series with the test leads; by throwing it in on the other side, as shown in the illustration, the full-line voltage is obtained. When the switch is open, the positive lead is dead.

Marking Celluloid

A simple and effective method of marking one's name on any celluloid article, such as a draftsman's triangle, is to letter the name neatly on the surface of the celluloid with black drawing ink, and then, after inverting the triangle, to focus the sun rays with a reading glass on the written portion. After this is done the ink is washed off and a neat replica of the writing will be left on the celluloid surface.—O. S. Sawn, Worcester, Mass.

Corner Studs for Frame Houses

The large cracks appearing in the plaster at the corners of the walls of frame houses are very often due to the fact that the corners are not well made, properly braced, or strong enough.

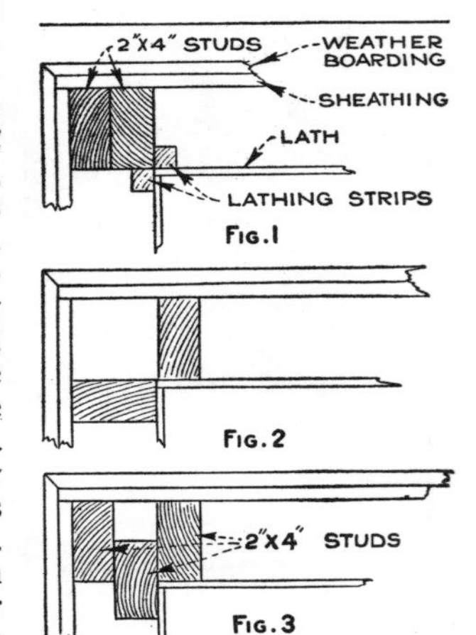

For the sake of economy it is common practice to use two 2 by 4-in. studs, arranged as shown in Fig. 1, with two small lathing strips nailed at the inside corner of the inner stud. Another poor method is shown in Fig. 2, in which the corner studs are placed so that the edges butt together with a 4 by 4-in. space in the corner between the studs and the sheathing. Fig. 3 shows a good construction of a corner, using three 2 by 4-in. studs. The center stud, spiked firmly between the other two, projects about ⅛ of its width so that the lath can be nailed to it, or a 2 by 6-in. piece of timber may be used for the center member. This construction is about twice as strong as either of the two shown in Figs. 1 and 2, and only one extra stud for each corner is required. Strength should always be insisted upon in the details of frame houses, especially when the additional cost is slight.—John N. Sioussa, Washington, D. C.

Adjustable Universal Chuck

The illustration shows how a universal chuck may be fitted to act as an independent chuck, and, within limits, as an eccentric chuck; this method may also be used as a means of adjustment for a chuck out of true. A plain cast-iron faceplate, with a heavy flange, is screwed to the spindle nose and trued in the usual manner. Holes are drilled, or, better, slots cut through it for the studs that hold the chuck; if holes are used, they are made a little larger in diameter than the bolts, to allow the chuck to be moved across the faceplate. An auxiliary faceplate is then made up, as shown, and recessed to fit the smaller one; 3 or 4 holes are drilled and tapped in the periphery, to fit safety setscrews tightening against the smaller plate. The auxiliary faceplate is also provided with a shallow boss, which is made a push fit in the chuck counterbore.

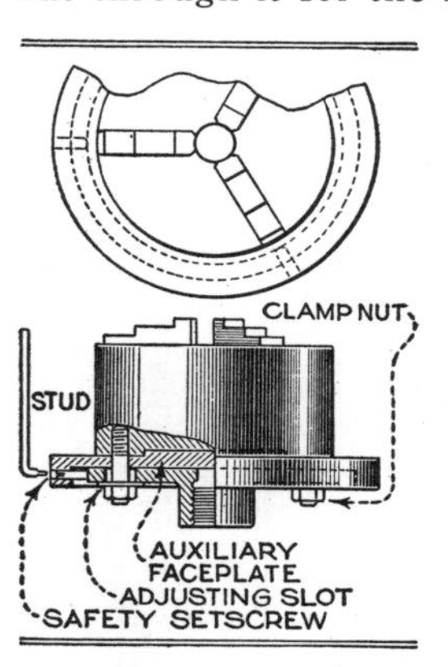

To center the work held in the chuck, or to set it eccentrically, the nuts on the studs holding the chuck and auxiliary faceplate are loosened slightly, and the setscrews adjusted until the work runs true; the nuts are then tightened. In case the lathe nose becomes inaccurate, the auxiliary plate and chuck are removed, and the smaller plate faced true; the chuck is then replaced and adjusted by means of an indicator.

¶ A good liquid tire paint is made by mixing 5 lb. whiting in 1 qt. gasoline, and, when thoroughly mixed, adding 1 qt. rubber cement. It is applied to the tire with a brush, and will not crack or chip, due to the elasticity of the rubber cement.

Working on Side of Building

The method of working on the wall of a building as shown in the illustration is used by circus-bill posters to put up their signs in places that are otherwise nearly inaccessible. Two ladders are used; one is laid on the roof, and projects a few feet beyond the edge; the other is lashed to the projecting end, and hangs vertically. One man remains on the extreme inner end of the horizontal ladder, while another climbs down the vertical ladder, the weight of the first man keeping the whole arrangement in position. The horizontal ladder should not project over the edge of the roof more than 1/4 or 1/5 of the entire length of this ladder and the man holding it down must apply his weight at the extreme inner end; he must be about equal to the other man in weight. In this way he will be able to hold the man on the ladder securely.

A Practical Application of the Lever for Working on the Side of a Building

Painting Inside of Conductor Piping

Conductor piping rusts much more rapidly than the gutters, and for this reason it should be painted on the inside, which will protect it for a long time. The painting can conveniently be done by means of a sponge drawn up through the piping on a length of rope or heavy twine. The rope should be long enough to extend up through the inside of the piping and down to the ground on the outside, so that, when the rope has once been passed through the pipe, the remainder of the work can be done from below. A large sponge is tied to the rope and a weight tied under the sponge.

Carrying Sheet Metal

Where pieces of sheet metal have to be carried for short distances by hand, the device shown in the illustration will be found useful. For a handle, a short piece of round stock is used; this is slotted at one end to take a piece of flat steel with a slot sawed in it to take the work. Both parts of the tool are held together by means of a pin. The end of the handle projecting over the slot in the flat piece is filed to the shape shown to form a cam. The handle will, when pulled upward, hold the sheet securely in the slot, and the weight of the material will also tend to tighten the grip of the holder. In use, the sheet is gripped so that the handle projects away from the workman. When carried in this manner the sheet swings slightly away from the worker's feet and clears the floor much better than if carried straight.

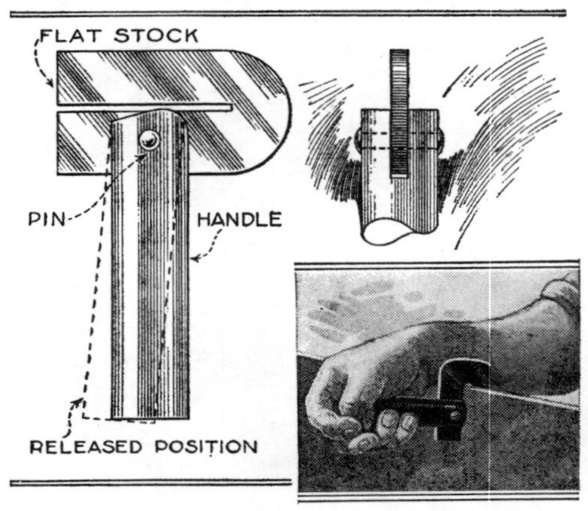

A Simple Holder That Enables Sheet Metal to be Carried with Ease

Lubricating Automobile Springs

Authorities on automobile maintenance agree that graphite is by far the best spring lubricant. Many motorists, however, refrain from using graphite because of the difficulty of getting it between the springs without taking the springs apart. A very simple and easy method of efficiently lubricating automobile springs with graphite is as follows:

Take about 2 oz. of powdered graphite and mix it in 4 oz. of ordinary commercial ether. Put the mixture into an oilcan and apply it to the springs; it will be found to flow readily between the tightest leaves. The ether evaporates quickly and leaves behind a deposit of graphite. The graphite left on the outside of the springs may be wiped off with a cloth.

Since ether is poisonous if taken internally, it should be mixed and applied to the springs out in the fresh air where there is not the slightest danger of inhaling it. It is also highly inflammable, and care should be taken to keep it away from fire.

One-Piece Chimney-Extension Cap

The drawing shows a one-piece chimney-extension cap that may be cut with little or no waste from a sheet of galvanized iron. The method of cutting is shown in the upper left-hand detail. The cylindrical part is first formed and the edges carefully seamed. The top flaps are then bent over, seamed and soldered, which completes the cap. If it is not thought necessary to have both sides exactly symmetrical, the extra allowance on the sides of the body for seaming may be omitted, and the sheet cut straight as indicated by the dotted lines. When the body is seamed, the upper curve on one side will be a little smaller than that on the other, but this is hardly noticeable, and allows the sheet to be cut with no waste at all. The cap not only forms a protection over the chimney, but also tends to increase the draft.—Francis T. Griffin, North Bend, Neb.

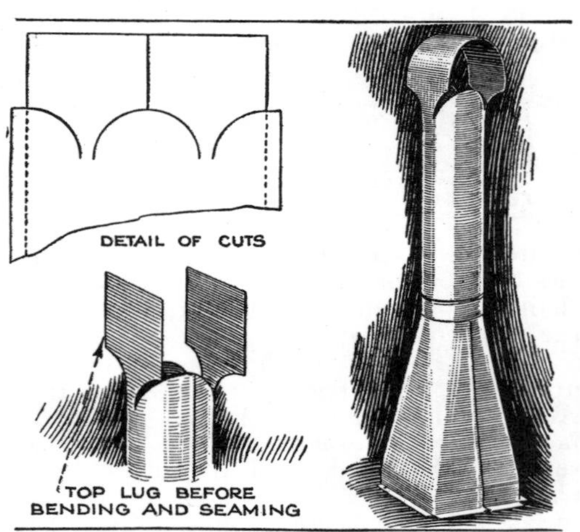

A One-Piece Chimney Extension Cap That may be Cut without Any Waste

¶When broaching, see that all chips are removed before placing a new piece of work on the broach.

A Heavy-Duty Bench Band Saw

BY FRANK N. COAKLEY

HE band saw shown in the accompanying drawing is built up mainly from the most easily obtained of materials — pipe and fittings; it will be found a most practical tool for the small shop, and one capable of heavy work.

The method of assembling the 2½-in. pipe frame is quite apparent from the drawing, so nothing need be said about this. The bearing for the bottom-pulley shaft is a babbitted cross, reamed to fit a 1½-in. cold-rolled steel shaft; an oil hole is drilled and tapped in the side of the cross, at the top, and an oil cup fitted to lubricate the shaft. The top-pulley shaft bearing is a tee, babbitted and reamed, in the same manner as the lower bearing, for a 1½-in. pin. This bearing is made adjustable, as shown in the sectional drawing, by screwing a 3-in. bar, with a long thread, into the tee outlet. The bar slides in one pair of the outlets of a 2½-in. cross, the outlets being machined to a good fit on the bar. A ½-in. pin is riveted through the cross, and fits in a slot cut through the bar; this keeps the bearing in alinement. A 5-in. circular adjusting nut, tapped to fit the bar, is run on between tee and cross before the bearing is assembled; this nut has eight ⅜-in. holes drilled around its circumference for a spanner wrench. If a bar of the proper size is not available, the sliding piece may be made of double extra-heavy pipe, turned to size. Care must be taken, when assembling the frame, to get the upper and lower bearings in line, and square with each other.

The thrust plate is made from 2-in. cold-rolled steel, turned to shape, bored to fit a ¾-in. pin, and casehardened. The pin has a groove turned in it near its end, and a ⅜-in. pin, driven through holes bored in the thrust plate, runs in the groove and keeps the plate in place. The pin is carried by a 1-in. square bar, which runs through a babbitted hole in the end tee of the frame, and is held by a ⅝-in. setscrew with a large knurled head; the ¾-in. thrust-plate pin is held by a ½-in. thumbscrew.

The table is made of 1-in. hardwood; it rests, at the front, on a pipe flange

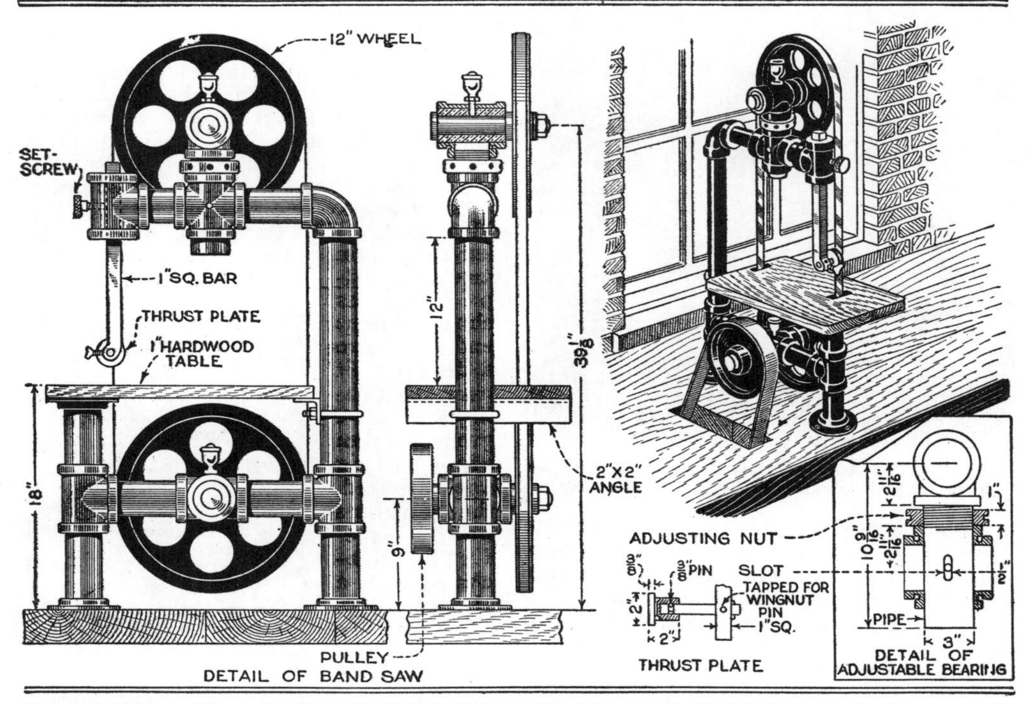

Pipe and Fittings, About the Most Easily Obtained of Materials, are Used Exclusively for the Frame of This Sturdy Bench Band Saw for the Small Shop

screwed on the frame member, and, at the rear, is screwed to a 2 by 2-in. angle iron, which is fastened to the frame by a U-bolt.

The saw pulleys should be ¾-in. face by 12-in. diameter, and should be turned and balanced to insure vibrationless running. It is advisable to cement endless rubber bands to the pulleys, to prevent the saw from slipping and heating. The driving pulley should have a 2¼-in. face, and be of such a diameter that the saw pulleys will run at 500 to 600 r. p. m. Saw pulleys up to 15 in. in diameter can be used by proportioning the frame to suit. A ⅜-in. saw will be found to be the best size for all-around woodworking. The feet of the machine are pipe flanges, and lag screws, or bolts, are used to fasten it to the bench.

Assembly Stand for Automobile Axles

To allow the workman full use of both hands in assembling the front axles of automobiles, the simple stand shown in

Stand Used for Assembling Front Axles of Automobiles That Facilitates the Work Considerably

the photograph was devised. The spring-perch holes in the axle slip over two studs on two separate stands; then the workman can perform the necessary operations, knowing that the axle is just as rigid as if it were actually fastened to the automobile.—J. H. Moore, Toronto, Canada.

Protecting Drawings

Ordinary transparent lacquer used for coating brass and other metals can also be applied to paper reference sheets, tables, drawings, etc., to protect them from being soiled by handling. The lacquer is poured into a shallow tray, and the sheets are dipped so that both sides are thoroughly coated, then hung up to dry. If desired, another coating can be applied after the first has dried. The lacquer covers the paper without affecting the printed matter, and it toughens and glazes the surface so that it will not collect dirt so quickly. It also prevents the paper from being stained or torn easily.

A Lathe Test Piece

When mounting a lathe job that is to run perfectly straight and true the alinement of the centers should be carefully checked. This is often done by running the centers together, or by using a thread gauge with male and female 60° angles, but these methods are not very accurate; it is better to use a test piece of the type illustrated. This consists of a 10-in. length of 1-in. tubing, fitting snugly into two steel endpieces, as shown. These endpieces are a driving fit over the tubing and are ground down after being assembled, the centers being carefully machined with a single-edge tool while running the test piece in the chuck and steady rest. The sides of the endpieces are also trued. As the head center rotates, it is always well to run the lathe, and to hold the test piece by hand in order to keep it from rotating. A dial indicator is brought to bear on the side of one endpiece, as shown, and after registering the position of the needle, the dial is moved over to the other end, which is similarly checked; the dial needle will check alike at both ends if the centers are in perfect line. By using a test piece of this kind, considerable guesswork will be eliminated, and the accuracy of the job assured.—J. V. Romig, Allentown, Pa.

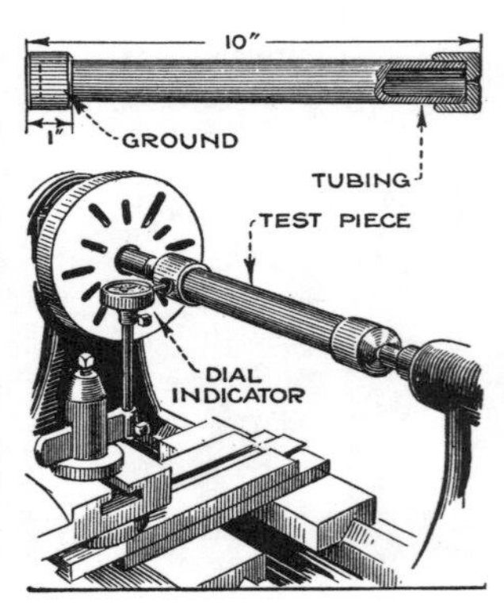

Locking Door-Knob Screws

The small setscrew used to hold a door knob in place on the lock shank often works loose and is lost. Although replacement of a few screws is not expensive, it is troublesome, and in large buildings, where this trouble happens often, it is advisable to prevent frequent recurrence by placing small lock washers under the heads of the screws.

Safety Gauge for Punch Press

It frequently happens that a punch-press operator places two blanks into the forming die instead of one, the result being that either the die or the press is broken. This accident usually occurs when blanks are stuck together with a layer of oil, and the double thickness is not readily noticed. Furthermore, piecework rates, which are usually paid for press work, are not generally conducive to giving the work close inspection.

To avoid the danger of breaking dies and presses in this way, I designed an adjustable safety gauge that is bolted on the punch-press table in a position convenient to the operator, who passes each blank between the measuring anvils before placing it in the forming die. The anvils are spaced to allow the passage of only one blank. Although the use of the gauge slows up production somewhat, not so much time is lost as when dies and presses are laid up for repairs. The elimination of repair costs also enables the firm to raise piecework rates.

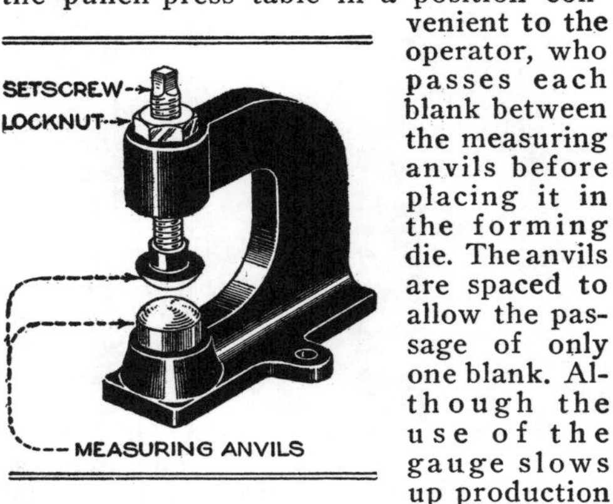

The gauge has a flat cast-iron base, with lugs for bolts. Both measuring anvils have round faces to permit the easy passage of the blanks. The anvils are made of tool steel, hardened, and the upper one is threaded and provided with a locknut.—Chas. Homewood, Ontario, California.

Wood that has been thoroughly soaked in an almost saturated solution of salt and water, and then dried, will not warp.

Tool for Handling Light Work

A piece of wire bent to a U-shape is often used to hold light tubular work for minor operations, such as dipping, tinning, etc., where the full outside surface must be exposed. The illustration shows an improvement on this type of holder. The improvement consists in the addition of two disks, each flattened on the edge and drilled in the center to fit the wire; the ends of the wire are bent, pushed through the holes, and bent again, so that the disks are free to revolve, but cannot come off. The flattened sides of the disks make a much better contact with the work than wire alone, and one tool of this kind will serve for many sizes of work, while, when using the U-shaped wire only, several different sizes must be made to handle any large variety.—Harry Moore, Montreal, Can.

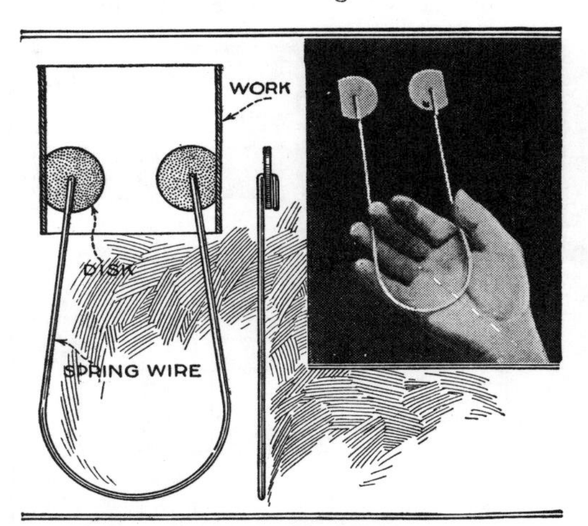

A Simple Holder for Handling Light Tubular Work for Such Operations as Dipping and Tinning

Removing Large Scrap Casings from Rims

To remove a scrap 40 by 8-in. casing from the rim in a short time, cut into the tire from the outer side, about 2 in. above the bead. Cut at an angle through the rubber and through the cords and keep on cutting all the way around the tire. The outer sidewall can then easily be pulled out to remove the inner tube and the flap, after which the casing can be taken off the rim without much trouble. This process takes about 30 minutes, while the ordinary method often takes from 2 to 5 hours.—Harold L. Fox, Atlantic City, N. J.

Tapping Round Work

It is usually more difficult to keep a tap straight and square on round work than on flat work, as there is nothing to

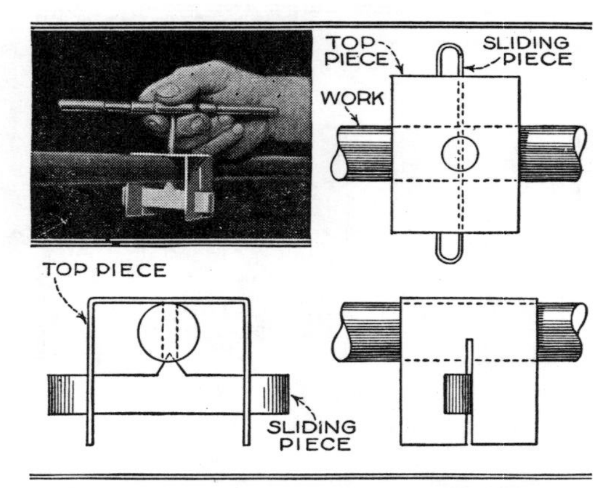

A Simple Guide Used for Tapping Round Work Square and Straight

guide the eye. The illustration shows a tap guide, made of flat stock, that aids in tapping holes straight in such work. One piece is bent at right angles on two sides, drilled with a clearance hole for the tap in the center, and a slot is sawed up each side. The second piece is made to slide up and down in the slots; the center is cut to a V-shape, and the ends are turned over to bear against the sides of the first piece so that both parts are held in line by the spring effect. To use the device as a guide it is slipped over the work and the sliding piece pushed up until the V-shaped point enters the bottom of the hole to be tapped. This movement centers the clearance hole in the top over the hole in the work, and brings the upper surface to a square position so that the tap can be guided straight with the eye. If greater accuracy is desired, a square can be used, with the stock resting on the flat upper surface of the guide.

Testing Silk

Silk fabrics are often "loaded" to give them the appearance and feel of heavy fabric, because a loaded silk is cheaper to produce than a piece of goods that is made entirely of silk and is of the same weight. The loading process generally consists in impregnating the silk with metallic salts, such as tin and lead. A chemical action is set up in the fiber by this process which weakens the goods to some extent; furthermore, when the loading materials have been removed from the fabric by washing, the garment is in many cases practically ruined. Loading also causes the silks to crack and split at folds and creases.

A simple method of detecting silks that have been treated with metallic salts is a burning test. A piece of pure silk, when burned, will shrivel up into a bunch in the same way as wool. If metallic salts are used, the silk will not shrivel up, but the ash will retain its original shape and pattern, and can often be handled without breaking, depending on the amount of loading that has been done.

Handy Fish-Wire Puller

It is a very tiresome job to pull fish wire through conduit by means of pliers, and it is not advisable to wrap it around a stick, as this is liable to ruin it. A puller of the type illustrated has therefore been found of considerable convenience; the harder one pulls on it the tighter it will grip the wire without injuring it, whether the wire is flat or round.

The handles are cut from pieces of wood about 2 in. square and 12 in. long. Part of each handle is rounded off to make a comfortable grip for the hand, and the square ends of the handles are slotted to receive a strip of flat iron, which acts as a hinge. Pieces of angle iron with slots cut across them to correspond with those cut in the handles, are fastened to the ends by means of flat-head wood screws, the sharp corners or edges of the angles being slightly rounded with a file, so that they will not cut the fish wire. A small piece of flat iron is screwed to each side of the handles to take the strain off the hinge, which is held by two stove bolts passing through the handles as shown.—W. W. Parker, Lead, S. D.

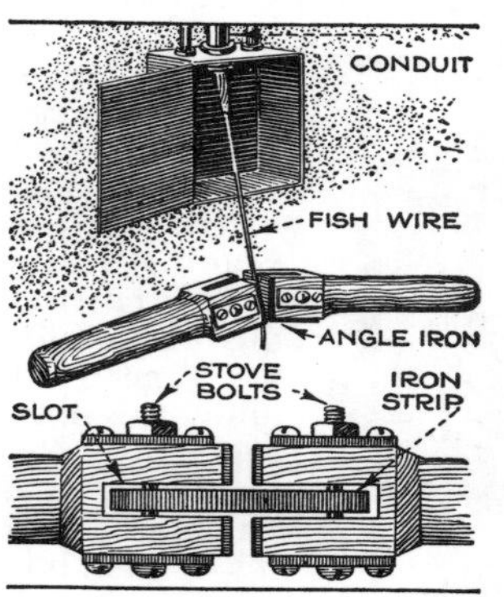

¶All open flames should be kept away from any place where there is any possibility of acetylene escaping.

A Good Wire-Fence Straightener

BY J. R. KOONTZ

EVERY farm and ranch owner, in fact anyone who has occasion to use wire fencing, knows how soon it is bent and forced out of shape by horses, hogs, and cattle tramping or crowding it down in order to get grass, etc., that may be on the opposite side. In a short time the fence becomes unsightly, and if allowed to stay without straightening will become more of a nuisance than anything else.

The wires can be straightened with the hands, but, with heavy wire it is a difficult job, and painful to the hands, and, when much of it must be done, the enforced bending posture causes a pain in the back. With a wire straightener these aches and pains may be avoided, and the fence straightened much easier, thus transforming a difficult job, and one that is put off as long as possible, into an easy one.

A straightener of the type shown in the illustration can be made at practically no cost, beyond that of the labor, from materials usually to be found in the junk heap. Two handles, taken from an old plow or cultivator, are used, or, if only a single-hook tool is desired, the handle of a discarded lawn mower will serve. The handles are cut to 30 in. long; two round braces or struts, 10 in. long, which may be taken from an old chair; two pieces of flat tire iron, 20 in. long, and two pieces of tire iron 10 in. long, are also necessary, in addition to eight wood screws and one iron rivet.

A hook is bent on one end of each of the 10-in. irons, and two screw holes are drilled in each, so that they can be fastened to the lower ends of the handles as shown. Screw holes are also drilled at the ends of the 20-in. pieces, and a hole for the rivet in the center of each. Holes are bored in the handles for the ends of the chair rails, which are then glued in place between the handles. The 20-in. cross braces may then be attached, and riveted together.

In using the tool, the hooks are placed over the line wires, the foot placed against the stay wire, and the line wire pulled back into shape without stooping.

PLOW HANDLES
WOOD
FLAT IRON

Left, Parts for the Wire-Fence Straightener; Center, Tool in Use; Right, Assembled Fence Straightener

Coloring Copper Brown and Black

Different shades on copper, ranging from a light brown to a deep black, may be obtained by using a weak solution of liver of sulphur. A half ounce of the liver of sulphur to a gallon of water is sufficient to make a solution strong enough for the brown colors. By increasing the quantity of the chemical, using the same amount of water, and bringing it to the boiling point, the same colors can be produced on brass.

To obtain the popular verd-antique finish, the work is stippled with a solution made from 4 oz. copper nitrate, 4 oz. calcium chloride, and 1 oz. bichromate of soda in 1 gal. of water. After coating the work with this solution, the high lights are rubbed down with a cloth and finely powdered pumice stone, after which lacquer or wax is applied as desired.

Drilling Hardened Steel

I have found the following method for drilling hardened steel very satisfactory. The usual pointed end of the drill is ground to a half-round shape, then made as hard as possible. The surface to be drilled is etched with dilute muriatic acid. Instead of oil, turpentine or kerosene in which a little gum camphor has been dissolved is used as a lubricant. Should the bottom of the hole become polished, so that the drill rides over it, remove the drill, etch the bottom of the hole with the acid, to roughen it, and proceed as before.
—Wm. J Edmonds, Rutland, Vt.

Auto Upholsterer's Stuffing Tool

It is common practice among automobile upholsterers, when filling pleated seat backs, to lay in a roll of wadding and

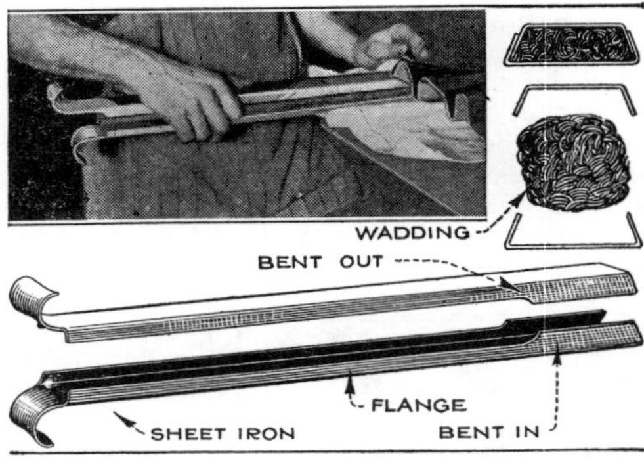

Auto Upholsterer's Stuffing Tool Permits Pleats to be Sewed First and Stuffed Afterward

sew the covering over it as they go. The process, which is a slow one, may be greatly facilitated by the simple stuffing tool illustrated, which permits the pleats to be sewed first and stuffed afterward.

The tool consists of two strips of sheet iron 31 in. in length; the width at one end is 5 in., for a length of about 2 in., and the remainder of the strip is 4 in. wide. The edges are bent over as shown to form flanges, then the flanges are cut off at one end of each piece, and the strips bent over to form handles, which are stiffened with ridges of solder. At the wide end of the tool, the flanges of one section are bent outward and those of the other section inward so that one may slide within the other. In use, the roll of stuffing is placed in the tool and slipped inside the pleat. By pulling the outer section back 2 in. the locking portions of the flanges slide clear, and the tool can be removed without difficulty.—Edwin M. Love, Alhambra, Calif.

Instructions Cast on Machines

On many machines it is necessary to attach a plate of instructions or warning so that they can be operated safely. Enameled plates are often used, but are not satisfactory because the enamel splinters. Etched and engraved brass plates give satisfactory service, but, as they are detachable, are often lost. The most permanent method of providing instructions is to cast the lettering on the frame. This is done by embossing the desired lettering on narrow aluminum strips and nailing these to the surface of the pattern. The location is determined simply by reference to the parting of the mold, so that the lettering will not be obliterated in the molding process. The finished casting is ground to even up the tops of the letters and make them conspicuous.

Identifying Scaffold Lumber

Many contractors, and others having use for scaffolds at regular intervals, use special lumber for the purpose, particularly for the footboards. The material is generally 2-in. lumber and is selected for its freedom from knots and other defects. The ends of these boards are painted a conspicuous color so that they can readily be identified in a pile of lumber, should they get misplaced, but they are usually kept in a separate pile.

Smokestack Made from Old Kitchen Boilers

When installing a new furnace it was learned that the 40-ft. smokestack which was required would cost approximately $40.00. Instead of paying this price, eight old kitchen boilers were bought for 50 cents each at a scrap yard. The ends were cut off with an acetylene torch in an hour's time and the small openings in the sides were plugged. One end of each

Left, Boiler with Ends Cut Off; Right, Erecting the Smokestack

tube was hammered down so that it would fit into the end of another section, and the sections riveted and welded to each other. The smokestack made of these boilers was heavier than one made of the usual material, not to speak of the saving in cost effected in this way.—J. E. Holstrom, Knoxville, Tenn.

Making a Beam Micrometer

The cost of a complete set of micrometer calipers prohibits the average toolmaker or machinist from owning one; a beam micrometer also, while not so expensive as a complete set, is beyond the reach of many. With the exercise of a little skill, however, accurate beam micrometers may readily be made by the workman himself.

The toolmaker, and others whose work demands an accurate tool, will find the micrometer shown in the larger drawing well worth making, as it can be made just as accurate as any of the high-priced tools on the market.

The beam or frame is made of ¼-in. steel, 9½ in. long and 5 or 6 in. wide, depending upon how high it is desired to make the spindle and anvil. This height should be either 3 or 4 in., and the width of the beam 1½ in. The inner edges of the foot and beam must be absolutely true and square with each other, if the tool is to be accurate, and great care must be taken with this part of the work. The foot is drilled for the anvil, which is of tool steel, made, as shown in the sectional detail, with a ball-shaped end and a shank smaller in diameter than the hole. This allows the inner face of the anvil to seat squarely against the surface of the foot: the ball must be a tight press fit.

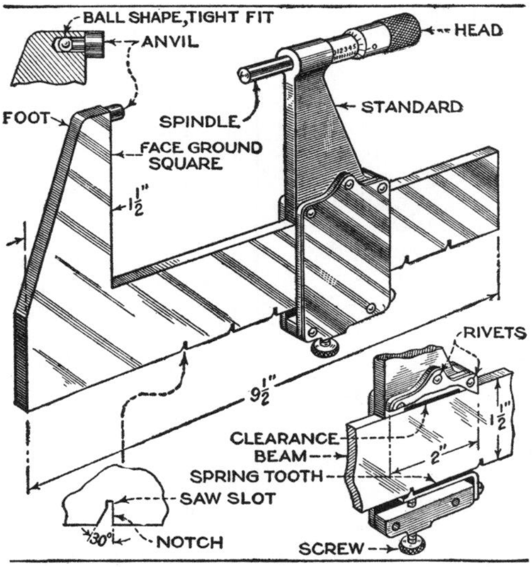

The micrometer-head standard is built up of flat steel, the upper part, carrying the head, being shaped from ½-in. stock, leaving the diameter of the eye ½ in., and the body ¼ in. thick. This is connected to the bottom piece by ⅛-in. side plates, the whole being assembled tightly by perfect-fitting rivets, neatly headed. A clearance slot is filed in the bottom surface of the upper part of the standard, so that it has a two-point bearing on the beam.

The locating spring tooth is made of tool steel, hardened and tempered, and is fastened to the bottom piece by a round-head screw. The shape of the notches in which the tooth rests should be particularly noticed. This form of notch divides the work of locating the standard and of drawing it to position When the screw is turned upward to press the tooth home, the inclined side of the notch, engaging with the corresponding side of the tooth, slides the standard until the straight sides of notch and tooth are in contact. It is only necessary to make the straight sides of the notches accurate as to location, and, as all of the wear comes on the inclined side, this accuracy is retained indefinitely. When the screw is released, the tooth will spring out of the notch with a little end pressure. The micrometer head is lightly pressed into the eye in the standard in the usual manner, and the contact surfaces of the anvil and spindle lapped true.

Beam Micrometer, Measuring from 0 to 6 Inches, That may be Made by Any Skilled Workman

Where extreme accuracy is not essential, a micrometer head, attached by means of a simple bracket, or auxiliary head, to the scale of a combination square, will serve the purpose, the head of the square being used as the anvil. It is preferable to use a square with a hardened, drop-forged steel head.

The auxiliary head is made from a piece of cast iron or steel, ½ by 1 by 4 in. in dimensions, machined all over by the size given in the smaller drawing. A hole to fit a standard micrometer head is then drilled through it, and, at right angles to this, a hole is drilled and tapped for a binding screw, the head slotted as shown, and one side of the binding-screw hole drilled out to fit the body of the screw; the screw used has a knurled head. The bottom of the head is now slotted to fit nicely on the scale, holes for two small setscrews are drilled and tapped in one side, in line with the scale groove, and the screws fitted.

To use the tool, the square head is set on a scale division, and, with the micrometer reading at zero, the auxiliary head is moved up, until the end of the spindle just touches the square head, and locked in position. The square head is then moved the desired number of divisions, locked, and the micrometer used as usual. When setting the head on the scale divisions, a magnifying glass should be used.

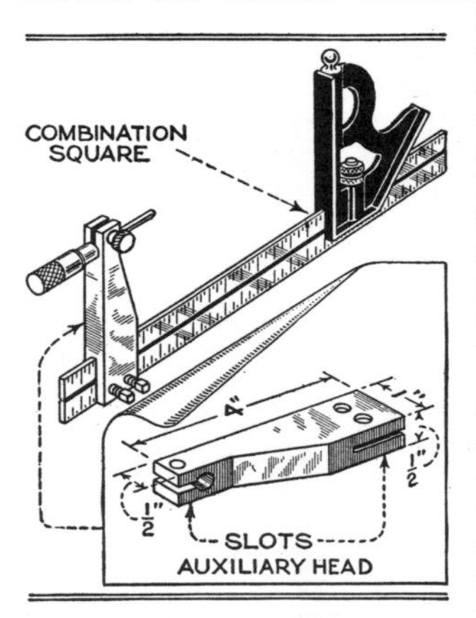

A better way to set the tool is to use a set of the micrometer standards sold by various tool companies, but where these are not available, the magnifying glass will enable the workman to set the tool as closely as the ordinary vernier caliper may be adjusted. A tool of this kind has been used for a long time, and has given splendid service.

Wire Gauge Attachment for Plates

Steel and iron plates are very seldom accurate as to thickness at their edges. Sometimes this is caused by the shear turning up the edges, by a saw, which leaves a burr, or perhaps the edges are just badly knocked. For this reason a wire gauge, when used to measure plates, is often unreliable, and the cause of many mistakes, because the actual thickness of the plate may be less than that shown by the gauge. To measure plates accurately they should be gauged at a short distance from their edges. The attachment shown in the illustration accomplishes this in a handy manner when used in conjunction with a wire gauge.

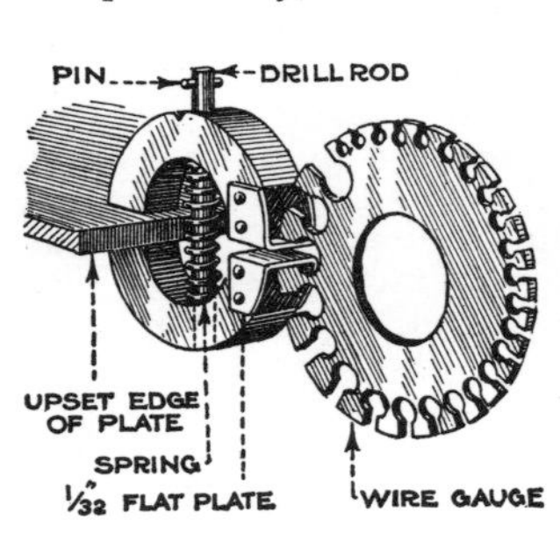

A collar, about 3/8 in. thick, makes a good body for the device. A hole, about 1/4 in. in diameter, is drilled through it, and it is then cut in two as shown. A piece of drill rod is driven tightly into the hole in one part, and made a sliding fit in the hole in the other. The faces of both halves are then brought together and filed and lapped true to each other. Two pieces of 1/32-in. sheet steel are bent over to fit the two pieces at one side, and are riveted in place by a couple of pins in each, the faces of the collar pieces at this side being cut away to clear the gauge. To keep the two parts together a small pin is driven through the drill rod, and a shallow groove is filed in the top of the collar in line with the pin, so that the pressure of a light spring around the rod keeps the pin in the groove and prevents the two parts from coming apart when not in use. Any size of plate, from 1/16 in. thick, can be measured with this device, as shown in the drawing; it is recommended that the gauge and attachment be fastened together by means of a short chain, if constantly in use.

Economizing on Cropping Blocks

It is a general practice in steel manufacturing plants to crop bars of steel before straightening them. This is done on a cast-steel cropping block, and when the edge of the block becomes rounded or chipped, which is caused by heavy cropping, the block is machined down to form a new edge.

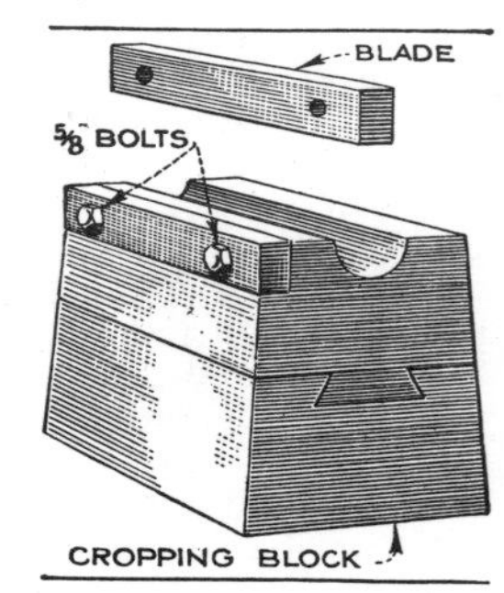

An improvement on the ordinary block is made by rabbeting the edge of the block as shown, to a depth of 2½ in. and a width of ¾ in., to form a seat for a removable tool-steel blade which is bolted to the block. The four edges of this blade can be used, and, when the last edge is worn, a new blade can be substituted for the old one. The holes in the blades and the block are drilled 2 in. from each end, and exactly on the center, so that the blade will fit the block and holes exactly in either position. The steel used for the blade should be 80-point carbon tool steel, with a Brinell hardness of 477.

¶To evaporate 1 cu. ft. of water requires the consumption of 7½ lb. of coal, or about 1 lb. of coal to 1 gal. of water.

A Practical Salt Box for Stock

BY J. R. KOONTZ

TO have healthy live stock one must see that they have plenty of salt at all times. To feed salt to hogs, cattle, and sheep, and, at the same time to keep it clean and from being trampled into dirt, has been a problem for many stock raisers and farmers. If placed in a wooden box it is no time until the box is upset, and besides, a wooden box does not last long under the rough usage it receives.

Salt boxes made of concrete are the answer to the problem. They cannot be broken, and are heavy enough to prevent the stock from upsetting them, so that the salt will remain in place until it is all used up.

The boxes should be made a little larger inside than the regular salt block, and deep enough so that about three-quarters of the block is below the edge of the box. The boxes are easily made, and cost only about 25 cents each.

First wet some sand, and from this form a block or core the same size the hole is to be in the block; saw four boards about 10 in. wide, and long enough so that, when assembled around the core as shown in the illustration, there will be a space of 3 in. between each board and the core. The boards should also extend 3 in. above the core. Place the boards around the core, driving stakes into the ground to hold them as shown; do not nail the boards, as the stakes are quite

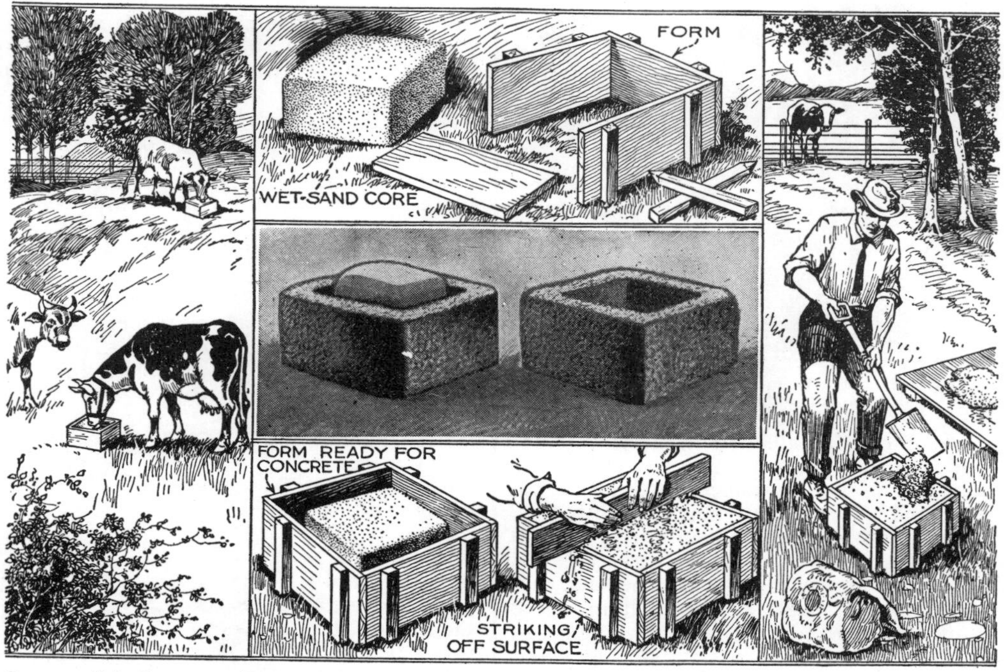

Concrete Salt Boxes are Easily Made with Improvised Forms, and will Prove of Great Help to the Stock Raiser, as They cannot be Upset and will Last for Years

sufficient to hold them firmly, and they can be taken apart easily.

Fill the space around the core with concrete mixed in the proportion of 1 part cement to 3 of clean, sharp sand, prodding the concrete down well with an iron rod to insure its filling all corners of the form. When the concrete has set, remove the form boards, turn the box over, and dig out the sand.

Place the box in a cool spot, and keep it wet for about a week, when it can be placed in service with the assurance that it will last for years.

Illuminating the Scale Beam

The difficulty in properly adjusting the weight on the beam of a scale in a small store, due to insufficient light, was remedied by providing a mirror set in the position shown, to reflect the light on the scale beam, the mirror being mounted on a triangular block. The light from the window opposite the scale was reflected so that the graduations could be seen distinctly, and at night the store lights were similarly reflected on the beam. The use of an electric light was first suggested but the mirror was found to serve the purpose just as well, and without the cost of burning an extra light.

The Dark Side of a Scale Beam Illuminated by Means of a Mirror Reflecting Light on It

Simple Whitening Process for Metals

A simple and inexpensive method of whitening small copper or brass articles, such as hooks and eyes, pins, buttons, etc., in quantities, is to immerse the articles in a solution made as follows: 2 oz. of fine silver in grain form are dissolved in a little nitric acid, and this solution mixed in 1 gal. of distilled water, after which a strong solution of salt and water is added, which will precipitate the silver in the form of chloride. This precipitate is washed thoroughly to remove all traces of acid, and the last rinse water should be tested with blue litmus paper to make sure that all the acid is removed. The chloride of silver thus formed is next mixed with an equal amount of cream of tartar (potassium bitartrate) and sufficient water to form a mass of the consistency of cream. After the articles are thoroughly cleaned, they are immersed and stirred until sufficiently white, when they are rinsed in hot water and shaken up in sawdust to dry.

Taper-Turning Tool

When a lathe has no compound slide, there is some difficulty in turning tapers that cannot be machined by moving the tailstock. A satisfactory taper-turning tool for use on such lathes is shown in the illustration. It consists of a straight, solid tool ground flat on the end, with a roller attached as indicated. The stud carrying the roller is cut away for half its diameter, so that it fits over the tool and brings the center of the roller in line with the edge of the tool. A slotted heel strap and screw complete the attachment. In use, the work is first roughed out, and the tool is then set at the correct angle to turn the required taper. Starting at the large end, the tool is fed in to cut the full width of its face. Then it is moved forward a distance about equal to its width, and it is again fed in until the roller touches the part already finished, and so on to the end of the taper.

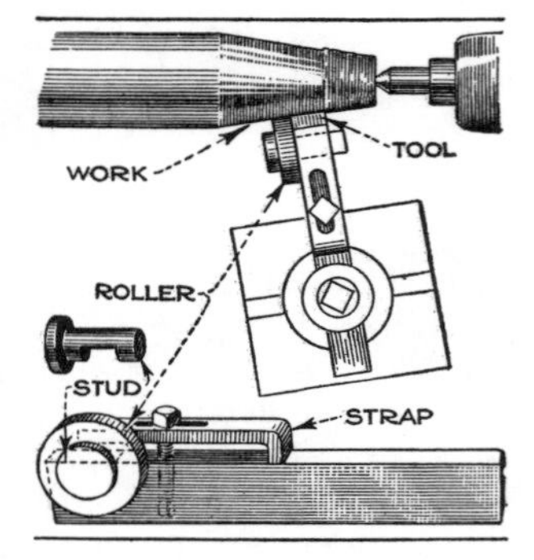

Cement for Closing Leaks in Iron Pipe

The following formula is good for making a cement for closing leaks in iron pipe: 5 lb. of coarsely powdered iron borings, 2 oz. of powdered sal ammoniac, 1 oz. of sulphur, and enough water to make a paste of a thick consistency. By leaving the sulphur out the cement will set more firmly, but will require a longer time. The cement is tamped tightly into the leak.

Keyed Mandrel Aids Production

The speed of production and accuracy of work can often be improved greatly by a little thought applied to the arrangement of machining operations. For example, the gear blank shown in the drawing was formerly chucked, faced on one side, and bored and reamed, then forced on a plain mandrel, or expansion mandrel and turned all over; after this, the blank was keyseated and the teeth cut. When turning in this manner, it was necessary to take light cuts, to prevent the blank from slipping on the arbor. When the operations were rearranged, keyseating followed the boring and reaming; the blank was then placed on the mandrel shown, and tightened by means of the taper key. This drew the bottom of the bore against the mandrel in exactly the same way as it would be drawn on its own shaft, and, in addition to permitting heavy roughing cuts to be taken, insured accuracy in the circumference. The top half of the mandrel was drawfiled to permit easy entry into the bore, and the key used had a taper of ¼ in. per foot.

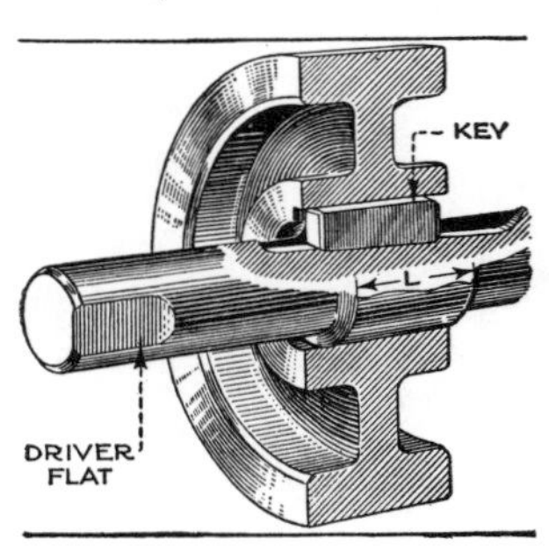

The gears turned and cut on these mandrels were much quieter than those previously made, as any possibility of eccentricity in the teeth was avoided.

When a one-piece rim is sprung, and will not go together when using a block and jack or a rim-mounting tool, put it on the wheel, tighten up the lugs, and hammer it. Many badly sprung rims can be very easily mounted in this way.

Lifting Bar for Auto Engine

Automobile engines are easily carried by means of the three-arm lifting bar shown in the drawing. It consists of three lengths of pipe screwed into a tee, and three hooks, made of ½-in. steel rods about 1 ft. long. The hooks are attached to the front end of the crankshaft and to the two rear engine brackets. Three men can readily lift the engine and carry it, as the lifting bar distributes the weight and keeps the workmen away from each other, thus preventing interference.

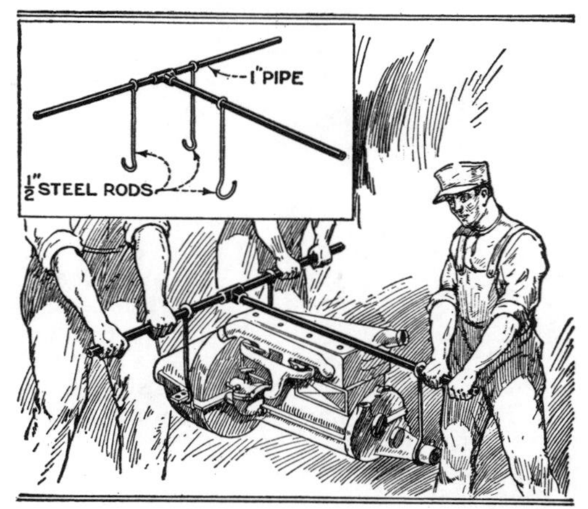

A Handy Lifting Bar with Which Automobile Engines can Easily be Lifted and Carried

Portable Drawing Board

The illustration shows a drawing board that is very convenient for traveling, as it can readily be put into a suitcase. It consists of two smooth boards each 10 by 23 in. in dimensions, and two removable wooden strips that are slightly tapered in their length and are beveled on their edges to fit snugly into dovetailed grooves cut across the back of the boards. These strips hold the two parts of the drawing board together when pushed tightly into the grooves, no nails or glue being required to hold them.—Stanley Dusdieker, Cedar Rapids, Ia.

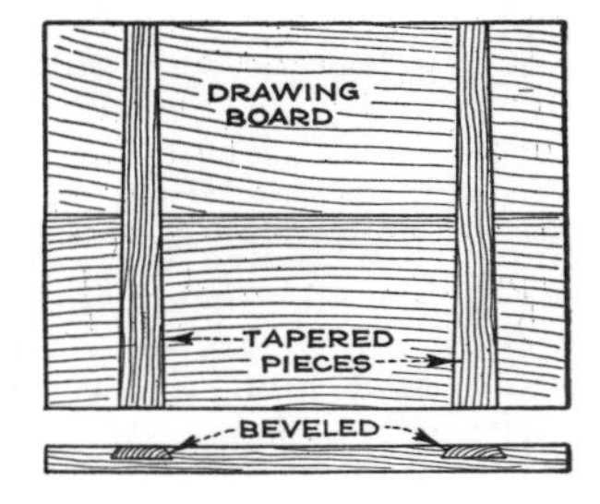

Groove in Bench Prevents Parts from Rolling Off

The usual method of preventing small parts from rolling off a workbench is to nail a strip of wood on the bench top, near the edges. However, it is not always desirable to have such a strip on the bench, as it often proves to be a hindrance in working, and therefore a V-shaped groove cut along the edges as shown in the illustration has been found much more satisfactory. The groove is about 1 in. wide and about 2 in. from the edge of the bench top. It takes only a few minutes to cut the groove by means of a carpenter's grooving plane.

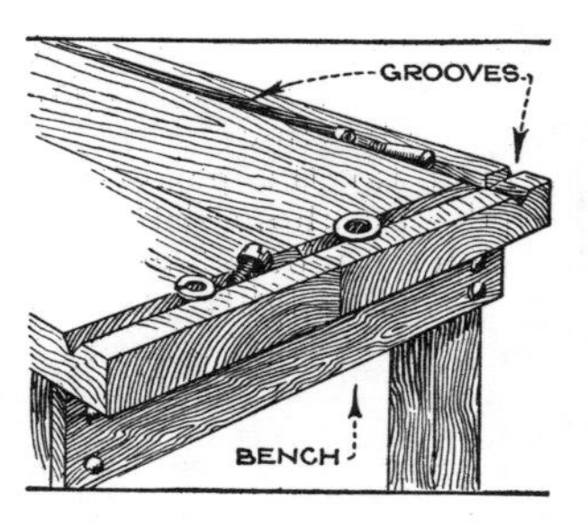

Supporting Irregular Work in Machine Vises

Ordinary parallels are not of much use as supports for irregular work held in machine vises, unless the surface of the work touching them is flat. Very often a job can be done more conveniently by using an adjustable support of the type shown in the drawing. This support consists of a length of round rod, forming a slide bar, on which two short lengths of tubing are fitted, the latter being drilled crosswise and threaded inside to receive the work-support screws. The support screws are countersunk, as shown, to receive the ends of small coil springs, which keep the parts together, prevent the screws from turning too easily, and hold the tube pieces in the position set. After assembly, both screws are turned down close to the tube, and while in this position, a mark is cut on each screw head as shown.

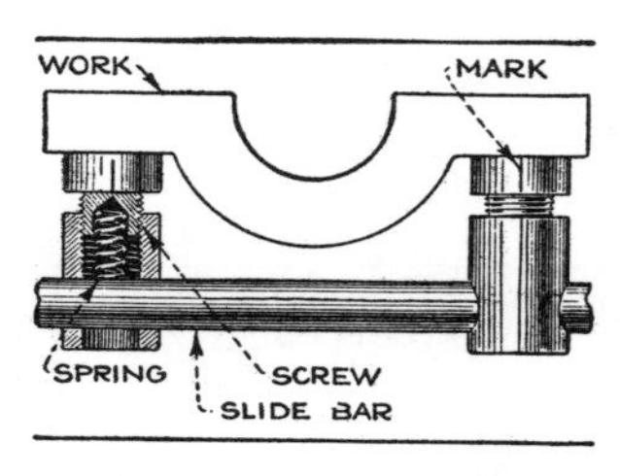

Many kinds of work can be supported by machine vises fitted with this adjustable support, the tube pieces being moved in or out to avoid irregularities in the form. The screws are used to suit work of various heights by turning them equally, using the marks as guides. By making the slide bar long enough, work extending beyond the vise jaws can be supported by means of a thin parallel resting on the vise bottom.—Harry Moore, Montreal, Can.

Filling Listed Furrows

The practice of listing out the soil was formerly confined to corn planting only, but has now become one of the principal methods of crop production, especially in dry territories. The ridges and furrows made by listing must be leveled down again and various implements have been made to do this. Of these a simple and effective one, which can readily be made on the farm, is shown in the illustration. The crosspieces, which are made of 2 by 10-in. material, should be long enough to cross five ridges from center to center. Lengths of 2 by 6-in. hard pine are attached edgewise to the crosspieces with nails and bolts in the position shown, so that the points where two adjacent pieces come together at the front will be located over the center of a ridge. The weight necessary to use on the implement depends on the hardness of the soil. In leveling the field, it is best to cover the surface twice, by half overlapping at each round. This leaves one furrow for the tractor wheel to run in, making it self-guiding, while the other wheel runs in the partly filled furrow. In this way four rows are covered at once, and at each round two rows are finished. —G. G. McVicker, North Bend, Neb.

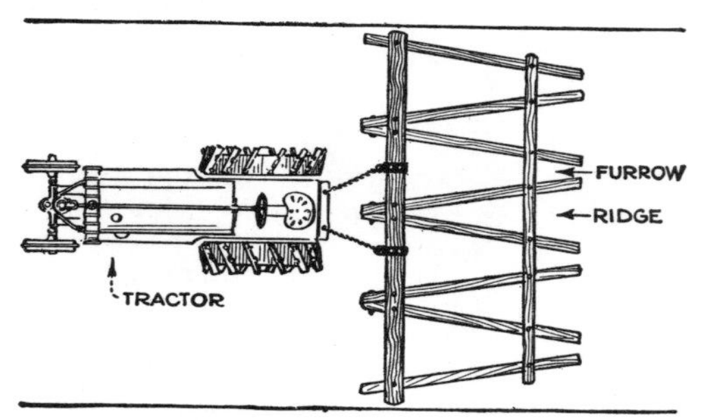

An Easily Made and Effective Drag for Leveling the Ridges and Filling the Furrows on Listed Land

¶A little kerosene added to enamel will make it easier to apply. Stir in, very thoroughly, about one tablespoonful to the gallon of enamel.

A Homemade Refrigerating Machine

BY JOHN GORRELL

THE household refrigerating machine described in this article has been in successful operation for some time, and, although a vast amount of time and experiment was necessary before the machine would work well, the problems have all been solved, and the reader who builds one is assured of a satisfactory machine.

A brief outline of the principle of operation is essential, in order that the builder may construct and operate the machine intelligently. In Fig. 1 is seen a condenser that contains a liquid gas under pressure, an expansion valve, cooling coils in the ice chamber, and a motor-driven compressor. If, when the compressor is running, the expansion valve is opened slightly, some of the liquid passes into the cooling coils, where the pressure is greatly reduced. The liquid now boils or evaporates rapidly, at a low temperature, and, in doing so, absorbs a certain amount of heat from the pipes and the surrounding air. As the gas boils off the liquid, it is drawn into the compressor, compressed and passed into the condenser, where it is robbed of the heat of compression, and liquefies again, ready to go through the cycle once more, as long as the compressor is running. Sulphur dioxide is the gas used in this case.

Photo Showing Compressor and Condenser Installed in Basement: The Ice Box Is on the Third Floor

The compressor is the most important part of the system; it is the one that costs most in time and money, wherein the greatest trouble is encountered, and that must receive the best care and workmanship. The compressor must hold the gas both when in operation and when idle, hence the difficulty. It is not possible to buy a small compressor on the market that will satisfy the requirements, as none is gastight. It is possible, of course, to build a special compressor, but this is very expensive. It is also possible to make an ordinary air compressor gastight, but a good job is almost impossible, and would cost too much.

The only successful method for the experimenter is to inclose the whole compressor, and provide an oil-sealed, oil-displacement stuffing box. Fig. 4 shows the pattern for the compressor-inclosing tank or casing; this is quite large enough for a 1⅝ by 2-in. vertical garage air compressor, which is the type used; a larger compressor is not advisable.

The lumber used for the pattern is ½ by 16-in. material, and about 8 ft. will be required, both sides to be planed. The pattern may be fairly roughly made, and still serve the requirements, but care should be taken to allow ½ in. of draft. The flange is ⅝-in. thick, to allow for machining. The inside corners should be filleted, and the pattern sandpapered smooth all over and shellacked. While the shellac is drying, the top cover can be made. This cover is shown in Fig. 5; it is simply a flat piece of material, cut to dimensions, and with an extra piece nailed to it where the shaft of the compressor comes through. This piece is also filleted. Don't forget that the casting will be about ⅛ in. per foot smaller than the pattern; use a shrink rule if possible.

The casting is made in gray iron, and will cost about $7.00. The flange and part of the plain side of the cover are planed true and smooth, and the compressor may then be placed in the casing and holes marked for the bolts to hold it in place. After drilling, the compressor is shimmed up until the shaft is at right angles with the machined flange, then bolted in place, using leather washers and gaskets, well covered with a paste made of litharge and glycerin, under the nuts and washers.

On the right-hand side of the casing two holes are drilled and tapped for gauge-glass fittings, and care should be taken to get these in line, or it will be difficult to fit the glass without breaking. If a street elbow is used in each hole, any mistakes can be easily corrected. There is a hole drilled and tapped for ⅜-in. pipe on either side of the casting, as shown in Fig. 6. The right-hand one merely leads inside the casing, and is the intake. That on the right is the outlet, and is fitted with a tee; the pipes leaving the casting have a long thread, so that a leather washer, coated with paste, can be tightened against the casting on each side with locknuts.

Two gauges are needed; one reads to 100 lb. per sq. in., and is used on the high-pressure side; the other reads to 100 lb., and also to 30-in. vacuum.

Careful measurements will show where the shaft will pass through the cover plate. At this point, a hole is bored and tapped for a 2-in. pipe. The stuffing box, which may be of iron or brass, is then made as in Fig. 7, the outside being threaded 8 threads per inch to fit the casting. A ring and nut are also made to the dimensions given, and the stuffing box screwed home, and packed with a good 1/4-in. graphite packing.

When the compressor is in the box, the cover bolted on, using a good gasket material for the joint, and all joints tight, the casing is filled with enough paraffin oil to bring the level 1 in. higher than the shaft.

The compressor should have an 18-in. pulley, and the motor a 2 1/2-in.; a 1-in. belt is used, and the motor should not be placed too near the compressor. A 1/4-hp. motor, operating at 1,750 r.p.m. is satisfactory, unless of the split-phase type, in which case a larger one will be found necessary to make the machine self-starting.

The condenser shown in Fig. 1 has been found to answer all requirements. It consists merely of two 10-ft. lengths of 1 1/2-in. galvanized-iron pipe, connected by two elbows and a 12-in. nipple. If space is available, it would be desirable to make the pipes 15 ft. long, especially if the box is very large, or more than 50 ft. from the condenser. All threads in the condenser should be coated with plenty of the litharge and glycerin paste, and the joints made up at once. This paste should not be used more than half an hour after it is made, even should it still appear fairly soft, and must not be softened with glycerin, when once hard.

To insure proper drainage of the liquid the pipes should slant 10° or more as shown. Notice that the fittings do not form pockets that retain the liquid. If space is limited the condenser may be made of shorter lengths, but using more of them, and keeping the cooling surface the same.

The condenser may be placed anywhere, but the basement is usually a good place, as the temperature there is lower than anywhere else. In the installation shown in the photo, the compressor and condenser are in the basement and the ice box on the third floor.

As there is a liquid under high pressure on one side, and a gas under low pressure on the other, the expansion valve must be capable of fine adjustment. A good 1/4-in. or 3/8-in. brass needle valve will serve the purpose, or a regular expansion valve may be obtained. It should be connected so that the liquid will pass up against and around the point when leaving the condenser. If this is done, there will be less chance of the gas leaking around the stem. When installing or making adjustments, the point must never be screwed down too hard on the seat, as both are easily ruined. The author has found it advisable to place an ordinary steam valve, with a composition seat, between the condenser and the needle valve, about 6 in. from the latter. This makes it unnecessary to touch the expansion valve except to adjust it, as the steam valve can be closed when there is any reason for shutting off the liquid.

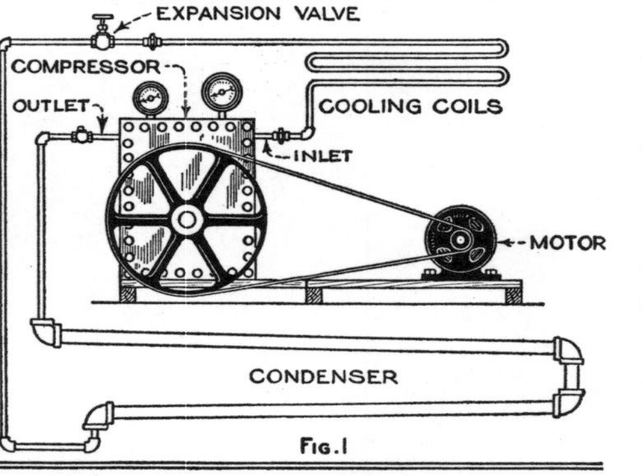

Diagram to Illustrate the Action of the Homemade Refrigerating Plant

As refrigeration starts on the low-pressure or suction side of the expansion valve, this valve is best placed just inside the chamber that holds the refrigerating coil. This coil is made of from 30 to 50 ft. of lead pipe, of 1/2-in. inside diameter. The pipe can be placed in any desired manner, but a vertical helix, 10 to 15 in. in diameter, with the adjacent turns held slightly apart, has been found satisfactory. The needle valve is placed at the top and the suction pipe consequently goes at the bottom. This is known as the "downfeed" method, and prevents

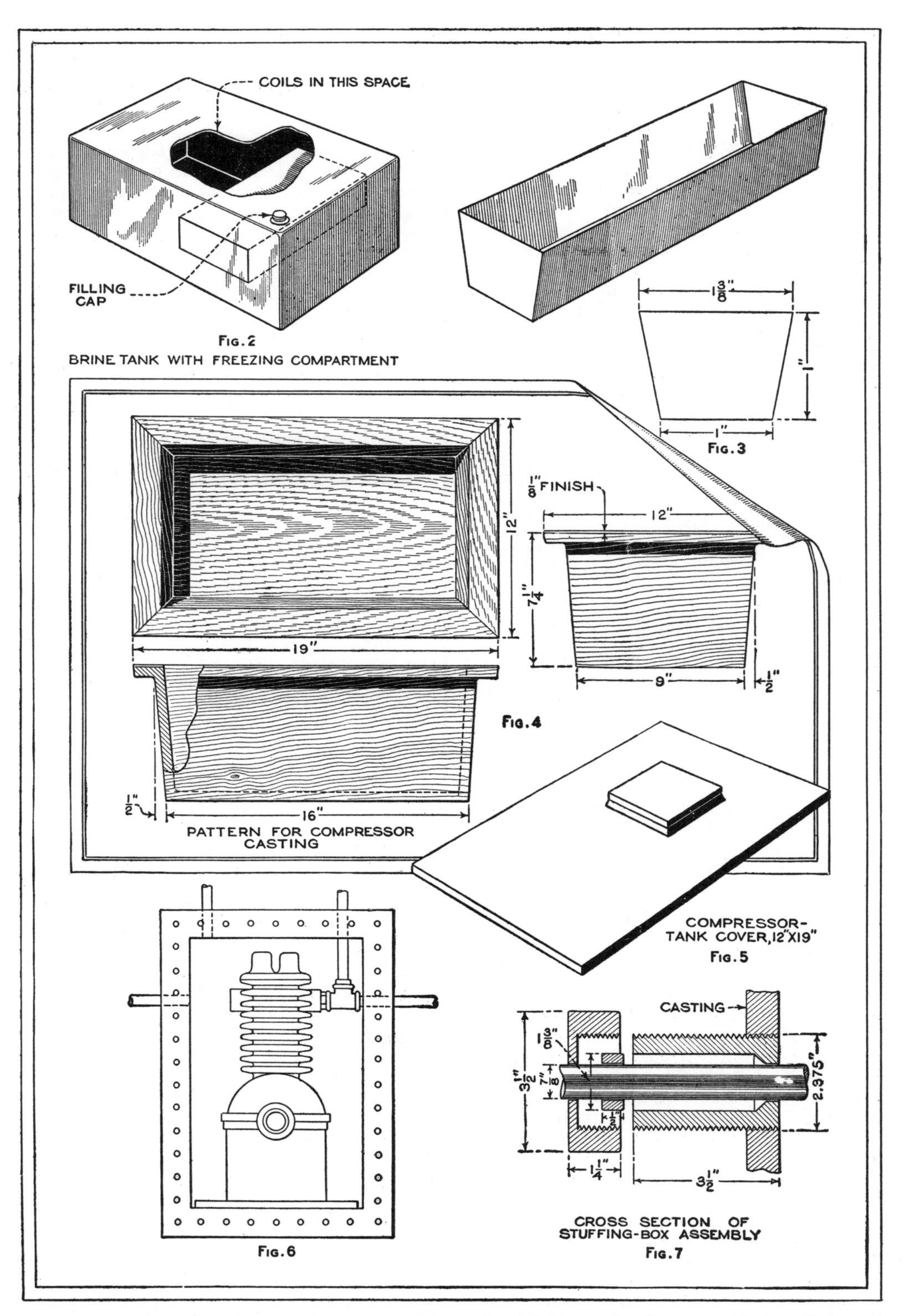

Figures 2 and 3, Brine Tank and Water Tray; Figures 4 and 5, Pattern for Compressor Tank or Casing and Tank Cover; Figure 6, Assembly of Compressor in Casing; Figure 7, Method of Making Stuffing Box

flooding of the system. On each end of the pipe a ¼-in. galvanized nipple is placed, by simply screwing it into the pipe, and allowing the nipple to cut its own threads. When into the pipe about 1½ in., nipple and pipe should be soldered together. On each nipple a union is placed; ordinary gasket unions are unsuitable, and only those known to the trade as railroad unions can be used. These have an iron projection that fits into a brass recess, and a gastight joint is

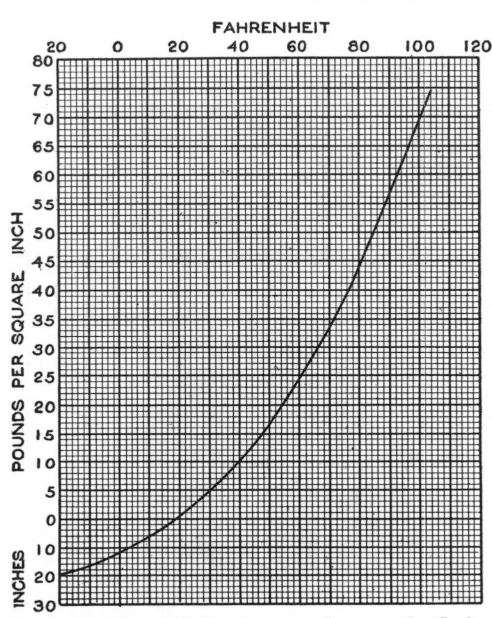

Graph Showing Relation between Pressure in Casing and Temperature in Ice Chamber

easily obtained by simply tightening the union firmly.

There has always been discussion as to whether the direct system of refrigeration, or the indirect, is the better. The former is the one described above, and the latter is the same, except that the cooling coils are placed in brine. The brine is cooled by the coils, and, in turn, cools the air in the ice chamber.

The direct system takes up less space, weighs less, costs less to install, and is easier to build. On the other hand, it does not keep the ice box at nearly as even a temperature, starts and stops frequently, requires thermostatic control, and is not completely satisfactory, as, when the machine is not running, the ice and snow on the coils melt, and the water is objectionable, and finally, if for any reason the machine stops work, the temperature in the ice box rises rapidly. The brine system occupies more space, is heavier, adds about $12.00 to the cost, and is supposed to be a few per cent less efficient than the direct. However, it requires little attention, starts and stops but once or twice a day, does not require a thermostat, and the brine acts as a reservoir of cold. If the electricity were off, or it were impossible to operate the machine, the brine would probably keep the contents of the box from spoiling for a day or more; so, for our purposes, the indirect system is the better.

The brine tank is made of heavy galvanized sheet iron, and fits inside the ice chamber, with a space of 3 in. between it and the walls. The lead pipe is placed within it, the ends being brought through holes drilled to receive them. A small opening is made at the top of the tank and fitted with a screw cover, for filling with brine. The brine is made by dissolving calcium chloride, which can be obtained from any ice plant or chemical-supply house, in water.

Enough clean, soft water is used almost to fill the tank; the water is boiled, and then the calcium is mixed with it in the proportion of 3.3 lb. to the gallon, if the calcium is anhydrous (water free), or 4.2 lb. to the gallon if the calcium contains water. A scum will come to the top; this is removed, and the brine allowed to cool before pouring into the tank. Do not use salt brine, as it will eat the galvanized-iron tank.

If it is desired to freeze water for table use, a rectangular tube is soldered horizontally through the tank, as in Fig. 2. The back end is closed, and a small door made for the front. If sherbets, ices, etc., are not to be frozen, a number of shelves can be put in this space, to carry the water trays shown in Fig. 2. When the water freezes in these trays it is forced up and does not burst them, as it would if the sides were straight. The length of the trays is optional and partitions may be soldered across them, to make the ice in small cubes. When frozen, the trays are inverted, and hot water poured over the bottom, loosening the ice.

The sulphur dioxide can be purchased in 6-lb. cylinders for about $5.00, and in many cases the cylinder can be returned for refilling. The gas is admitted through a valve, tee, and nipple placed on the suction side, near the compressor, after the air has been driven out of the system as completely as possible. When all the gas has been drawn from the cylinder by running the compressor, the valve is closed, and the system is charged, as the compressor has placed the gas in the condenser. With the compressor still running, the expansion valve is opened until the pressure in the casing is about zero. By adjusting the expansion valve to keep this pressure constant, the temperature in the brine tank will become about 14° above 0° F. The accompanying graph will give enough information to enable the user to regulate the temperature of the brine tank.

When the machine is idle, and the expansion valve left open, the pressure in the casing will be the same as that in the condenser. There will be very little oil displacement if the stuffing box is properly made, and all that is necessary to restart is to turn on the motor. If the machine is run several hours a day, to run the temperature well down, there is no need for any thermostatic control.

If all the work has been carefully done, the machine will operate with complete success, and give much better service than ice. The food chamber will be drier, and thus the possibility of molding and spoiling is lessened. The cost of operation is dependent upon the cost of power, size of motor, insulating qualities of the box, and the difference in temperature between the ice box and the outside air.

The only attention required is the oiling of the motor, replacing of oil in the casing, and occasional recharging. A material list, exclusive of pipe, fittings, oil, belting, etc., is given below.

MATERIAL LIST

Item	Cost	Item	Cost
Condenser	$ 6.00 to $12.00	Compressor	$25.00 to $35.00
Lead pipe	4.00 to 8.00	Gauges	3.00 up
Brine tank	6.00 to 8.00	Castings	5.00 to 7.50
Calcium chloride, per lb.	.04 to .10	Machining castings	15.00 to 30.00
Expansion valve	2.00 to 4.00	Motor	18.00 to 30.00
Steam valve	1.00 to 1.50	Gauge glass	1.50 to 2.00

Improving Tripods

The tripods used by contractors, surveyors, and photographers can be greatly improved, and the risk of slipping almost eliminated by the application of the idea shown in the drawing. This consists in nothing more than bending the metal points at the end of the legs toward the center so that the weight of the tripod and instrument will push the points down vertically instead of outwardly. This will effectively prevent the tendency to slip, which is more pronounced when the legs are spread far apart.

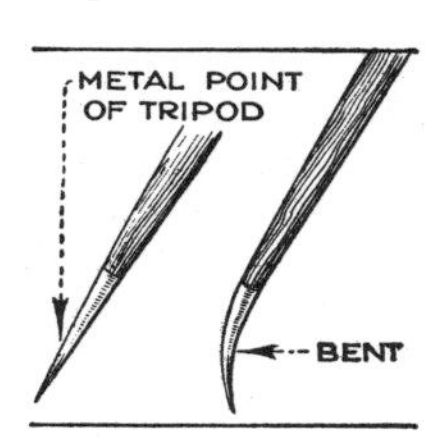

Underslung Wheelbarrow for Carrying Milk Cans

Anyone who has tried to carry a large filled milk can or to push it in an ordinary wheelbarrow, will appreciate the usefulness of the underslung wheelbarrow shown in the drawing.

The frame of an ordinary wheelbarrow is used, but the regular body is removed. A platform is suspended under the frame, by means of flat brackets, so that it comes to within a few inches of the ground. The rear brackets are made in two pieces, and slotted as indicated, so that the platform can be adjusted to suit the height of the user. The platform itself is made of 1-in. boards held on each side by lengths of angle iron. The center of gravity is so low that the load can be easily balanced to prevent spilling.

An Underslung Wheelbarrow That Enables Filled Milk Cans to be Transported Easily

Homemade Preheater for Small Castings

The efficient furnace shown in the drawing was built to enable small shock-absorber parts to be preheated quickly for welding.

A 15-in. length of 3½-in. iron pipe is

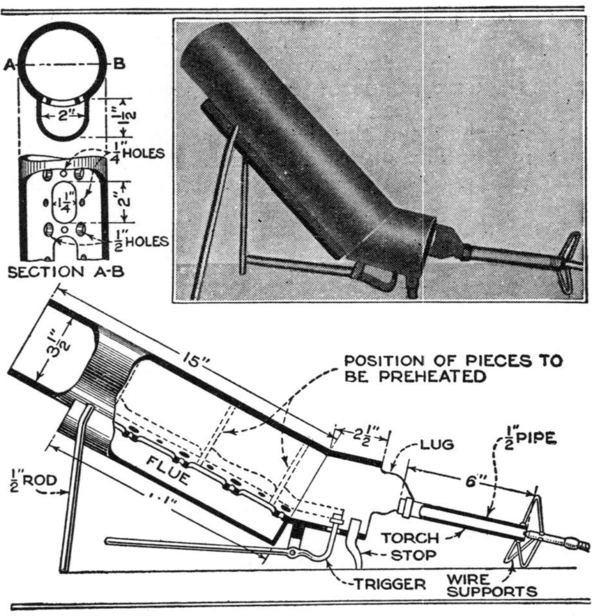

A Preheating Furnace for Small Parts That Is Easy to Make and Efficient in Operation

cut at one end at a slight angle, and a short piece welded on to form an elbow. At one side of the short piece, near the top, a lug is formed, to which the burner is attached by means of a ring. The burner consists of a 6-in. length of ½-in. pipe forming the mixing chamber, and a tip made from ⅛-in. pipe, swaged down at one end to 1/16-in. opening. To permit proper adjustment of the tip relative to the mixing chamber, the tip is attached to the latter by means of three heavy-wire supports, welded to chamber and tip; these support the tip central with the chamber, and at the proper distance from the end.

As the castings fitted rather closely within the 3½-in. pipe, a metal troughlike flue, 1¾ in. wide by 11½ in. long, was welded under the pipe, after vent holes had been cut in the latter to allow the heat to reach the parts, as illustrated, and a pair of legs, made of heavy rod, welded on.

A stop is filled in the lower end of the elbow, and a trigger provided to lift the end of the castings over the stop when it is desired to remove them.

In practice, the parts are fed into the top of the preheater and the burner lit. While the lowest casting is quickly raised to the desired temperature, those above are gradually warmed by the heat supplied through the flue, so that, as quickly as one part is welded another is heated ready for welding.

While this particular design is especially suitable for the parts treated, a modification of shape would allow it to be adapted to many varieties of work; moreover, it is also useful as an annealing furnace.—E. M. Love, Alhambra, Calif.

Working Aluminum

Apart from its light weight, which is, roughly speaking, about one-third that of copper, brass, or steel, aluminum possesses an outstanding property in its resistance to chemical action; practically the only substances that attack it appreciably are caustic alkalies, the halogens, and certain salts of mercury. Exposed to moisture, it oxidizes very gradually and regularly, and the thin film of oxide, when formed, protects the surface from further oxidation. This film is the cause of the comparative immunity of the metal from attack by chemicals, and explains why it can be used for the manufacture and storage of highly corrosive liquids, such as concentrated nitric acid. Like many other metals it is hardened by cold working and softened by annealing. It is usually supplied in five different grades of temper, and the correct temper to be used in any particular case depends on the amount of work which will be done upon it, and the degree of hardness required in the final product. Hardening under working does not take place with the same rapidity as with brass, and if the finished article is to be dead-hard, it is generally necessary to start with a medium temper, unless the final shape is very complicated. The softest tempers are used for deep press drawing, but medium-soft or even medium-hard tempers give the best results for shallow stamping. A similar range of temper is used for spinning, and for a spun cup with a diameter not less than two-thirds of the depth, a medium-soft temper gives an excellent finished hardness. Dead-soft tempers are, however, often used for deep spinning. Intermediate annealing is rarely needed, and even in drawing a very deep shell, annealing is unnecessary, unless more than six or seven redrawing operations are needed. Another method of working to which aluminum lends itself, is that in which flat sheets are worked up into the desired shapes by heating, with a mallet upon a leather sandbag. In this way contours which are impossible in steel, or can be obtained only by making a number of shaped sections and welding them together, are readily formed in one piece. For jointing aluminum sheets four methods are available—seaming, riveting, soldering, and welding, and many different surface finishes can be obtained by polishing, frosting, burnishing, scratch-brushing, plating, coloring by chemical action, and the application of paint or enamel.

Joining Shingles to Corrugated-Iron Roofing

It is seemingly a difficult matter to make a weatherproof joint when shingles and corrugated-iron roofing meet. However, the work is more simple than it appears. Lengths of valley tin are forced under the shingles and over the metal roof, the tin being securely nailed under the shingles to the roof boards. Then by means of an iron forming iron the portion of tin extending over the metal roofing is pounded down into the grooves, the forming iron being placed on the tin and blows applied with a common hammer. If desirable the tin can also be sweated on the metal roofing, thus making it impossible for water to enter the seam. The best results are obtained with roofing having narrow corrugations. The forming iron is made from a length of iron bar that fits snugly in the corrugations; one end is bent upward as shown in the drawing and the remainder is slightly curved, so that it may be grasped without the knuckles being bruised while hammering. —Louis Schneider, Clinton, Mo.

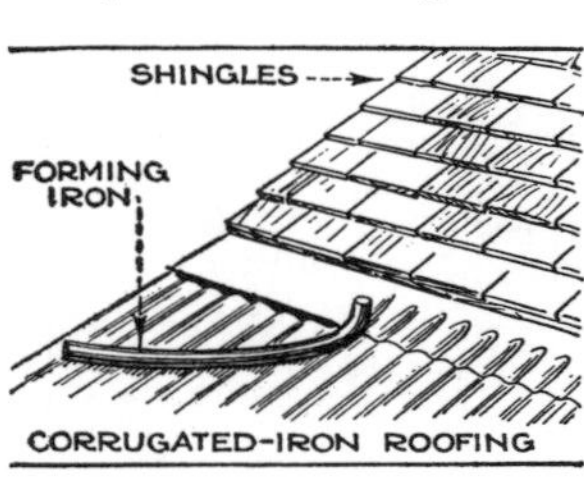

Bench Trough for Washing Automobile Parts

A practical method of washing automobile parts is shown in the drawing. A large 5-gal. bread or dish pan is inserted in a circular hole cut in the top of the workbench. The pan is not fastened down, but is simply held by its rim, which rests on the edge of the opening. A wire basket that fits in the pan nicely is used to hold the parts to be cleaned; two wire handles are provided on the basket so that it can be lowered into or raised from the pan. A wooden lid, hinged to the bench top and closing over the pan, is also desirable to prevent tools from falling into the liquid.

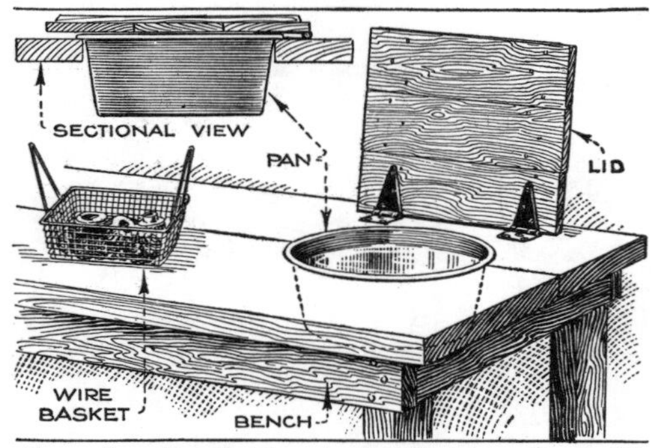

Convenient Bench Trough for Washing Automobile Parts, Which are Held in a Wire Basket

Relief Valve Prevents Water Hammer

A simple method of making a relief valve to prevent water hammer in pipes is shown in the drawing. The side outlet of a tee is turned down and threaded to fit the length of ¾-in. pipe that forms the body of the valve, and a seat is turned in the outlet for the poppet valve, which is made of hard brass. In the lower end of the pipe, a ¾-in. plug is fitted; this is drilled for the valve stem, and with four ⅛-in. holes. The thread in the lower end is cut twice as long as the plug, so that the 3/32-in. brass-wire spring that holds the valve on its seat may be compressed to provide the necessary pressure. The valve can be set to release at any pressure, and practically eliminates water hammer.

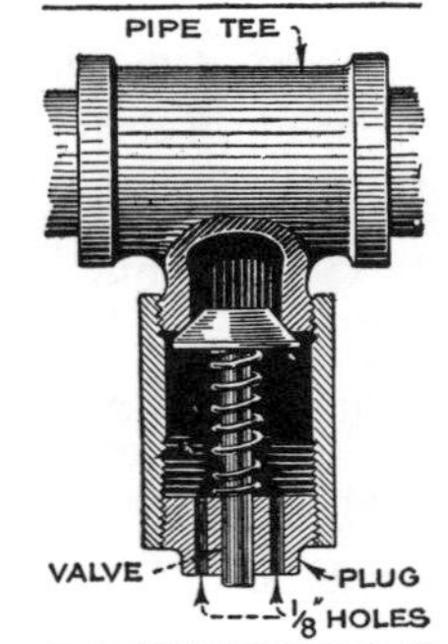

Rack for Handling Heavy Barrels

The rack illustrated has been found to be a time and labor-saving device for moving heavy barrels and casks. It is made of 1-in. pipe and fittings, with the

A Time and Labor-Saving Device for Conveniently Handling Heavy Barrels and Casks

exception of the windlass, which is made of 3/4-in. pipe. Two stout ropes are suspended from the windlass as shown, hooks being provided at the lower ends to engage with the barrel. By revolving the crank the ropes wind on the windlass, which raises the barrel a few inches above the floor, permitting it to be moved to any desired location, this being facilitated by casters that are provided under the legs of the rack. A short rope or chain with a ring at the end is fastened to the frame, to keep the crank from unwinding when under the strain of the load.—G. E. Hendrickson, Argyle, Wis.

Satin-Finishing Aluminum

To satin-finish aluminum, buff the article if necessary in order to obtain a good surface, and clean off the grease in benzine. Then dip it in a scalding solution of hot potash, not too strong, until the surface is dull and white. Rinse in cold water and soak for 5 or 6 minutes in a 5-per-cent solution of hydrofluoric acid to soften the surface. Then rinse again and dip into a mixture of equal parts of nitric acid and sulphuric acid to remove the discoloration. After this rinse again in cold water and in clean hot water; dirty water will leave stains on the surface. Dry the article in sawdust of good quality and which is free from pitch or gum. Boxwood or birch sawdust should be used if possible. Care must be taken not to touch the aluminum at this stage with the bare hands, as this makes stains.

The frosting is accomplished with a fine, soft, steel-wire scratchbrush, about 6 in. in diameter, and running 2,500 revolutions per minute. New brushes should be broken in on coarse work or by running them against a file.

A Durable Floor Paint

A durable floor paint is made by adding a quantity of cement to the paint, and using benzine instead of turpentine, with some raw oil and driers. Never use boiled oil in a floor paint. Yellow ocher is very good to use for a base, as it is harder than lead. Zinc is also added in sufficient quantities to make the paint full bodied.

Setting Machines to Conserve Space

In order to conserve space without setting a number of bar-stock machines obliquely as is common practice, one concern has placed them at right angles to the wall and between the windows, the heads being next to the wall so that the operator gets the best possible light. This was accomplished by drilling the factory wall and supporting suitable lengths of pipe on standards on the outside; the pipes contained the bar stock, which was loaded through the headstocks from the inside. The pipes projected outside into space that would otherwise not be used. The same idea could be adapted to similar machines on an upper floor by supporting the pipes on the outside of the building by knee braces or suitable brackets. Aside from the economy of space effected, the shafts that drive the machines all run at right angles.

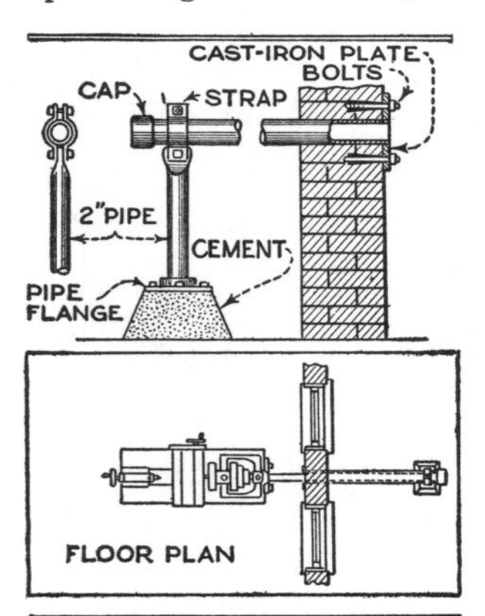

A High-Pressure Grease Machine

BY J. C. DE PUE

THE object of this device is to supply grease, under a pressure of several thousand pounds per square inch, to all grease connections on an automobile, by means of a flexible hose equipped with various adapters.

The drawing clearly shows the various parts, and their relation to each other. It will be noted that no detailed dimensions are given; this is because the original machine was constructed from odd pieces of material found around the shop, and machined to fit each other, and so no record was made of individual sizes. However, in the following description, approximate dimensions of the more important parts will be given, so that anyone wishing to duplicate the machine will have no difficulty in securing the necessary material; and in laying out the work to suit the shop facilities.

A 30-in. piece of 6-in. pipe, threaded at both ends, and two caps to fit, were obtained for the outer cylinder or container. One cap was screwed firmly on the lower end, and the cylinder mounted on the three-wheeled truck shown, by means of a clamping band, three braces, and three studs. The bottom cap was drilled and tapped for the threaded inner ends of the studs; the outer ends are also threaded, and extend through the truck-frame members, where they are fastened by the nuts that also hold the lower ends of the braces. The upper ends of the braces are fastened to a band clamped around the cylinder; this detail is not shown in the drawing, as it is a simple one, and it is desired to leave the sectional view free from complication. The truck shown was one formerly used to carry oil barrels, but one can be made from flat iron.

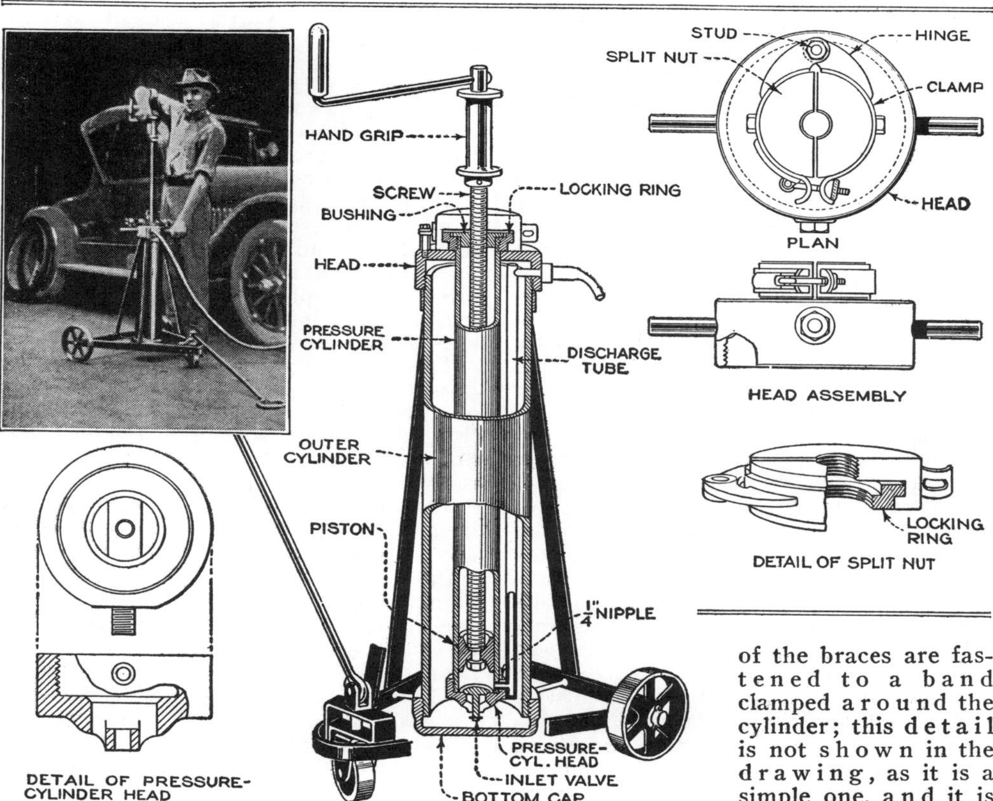

A Homemade Grease Machine for the Garage and Service Station: Insert, Filling the Pressure Cylinder with Grease

The upper cap was then turned smooth on the outside, and bored out and threaded for the pressure cylinder, also drilled and tapped for the outlet for the hose connection, handles, and hinge stud.

For the pressure cylinder, a piece of brass tubing was used; this had an inside diameter of 2 in., a wall thickness of 3⁄16 in., and was cut long enough to extend from 1⁄2 in. above the top cap to within 1 1⁄2 in. of the bottom of the outer cylinder. The tube was threaded 3⁄4 in. at each end, 14 threads per inch, one end being screwed into the upper cap. A locking ring was turned from a piece of bushing bronze, and threaded to fit the pressure cylinder; this locks the cylinder to the head, and has a flange that fits the split nut, thus when the nut is closed it is locked directly to the cylinder. The bushing for the upper end of the cylinder, which guides the screw, was also made of bronze, and is a push fit in the cylinder; it has a small flange that acts as a stop, the locking ring being machined out to clear it.

The screw was made of 1-in. cold-rolled steel, and, except for a length of 7 in. at the upper end, was threaded 8 threads per inch; the lower end was turned down to 3⁄4-in. diameter and threaded to fit the nut that holds the piston. The piston was also turned from a piece of cold-rolled steel, and made a good sliding fit in the cylinder, without rings or packing of any kind. The bore of the cylinder being true and smooth, the piston was found to work with practically no leakage, and, after six months' continuous use, scarcely allows enough grease to leak past to lubricate the screw.

The pressure-cylinder head was made of bronze; after being turned to size it was bored and threaded to fit the cylinder, then bored for the valve seat, inlet opening, and valve stem; two segment-shaped pieces were next cut out with a hacksaw, leaving an inlet opening on each side of the valve-stem guide. This part was then screwed onto the cylinder, and the outlet opening drilled through both head and cylinder, tapped, and fitted with a 1⁄4-in. nipple for connection to the discharge tube. The latter is a length of extra-heavy steel tubing, welded shut at each end, and drilled and tapped about 1 in. from the lower end for the 1⁄4-in. nipple; at the upper end it is tapped to fit a 9⁄16-in. S. A. E. capscrew; this forms the hose connection, and is drilled through and tapped 1⁄8-in. pipe-thread size to fit the hose. The hose, being a standard part of a well-known lubricating system, was purchased locally, and three adapters, to enable the machine to be used on other systems, were made to fit the outlet end of the hose.

The split nut was made from a piece of brass, bored out to fit the locking ring and threaded to fit the screw; the clamping band, of flat iron, was then bent around it, and fastened in place with two 3⁄8-in. capscrews. The two halves of the ring were then welded in place on the band, after which the nut was sawed in two, placed in position on the head, and secured by means of the hinge stud. The drawing shows clearly the method used to clamp the halves of the nut together; there are only two operating positions, locked on the screw, and wide open.

The photograph gives a good idea of the method of filling the pressure cylinder. The split nut is opened to clear the screw and the screw drawn upward, filling the cylinder with grease through the inlet valve; which, by the way, is merely a large auto-engine valve. When the top of the stroke is reached the split nut is locked on the screw, and the screw turned down by means of the crank; the downward pressure closes the inlet valve and forces the grease out through the hose.

With the old method, using a small hand compressor, it required about 3⁄4 hour to fill all the grease connections on a car, and more than this on a car fitted with spring covers. With this machine, the job can be done in 15 minutes, and done more thoroughly.

The pressure cylinder and its mechanism can be adapted to fit onto the head of a standard grease container, if desired, thus dispensing with the outer cylinder, and eliminating even the short time required to fill it.

This machine has been in constant use in a shop employing 20 men, and, to date, has handled over 500 lb. of grease, without any attention other than refilling, except for the replacement of one hose, which was broken from excessive pressure. A test gauge was attached, and it was found that a slight turn of the crank developed a pressure of 4,000 lb. per sq. in., and, as the hose is guaranteed only to stand 2,000 lb., it was necessary to caution the men to "go easy on the hard ones." With this reasonable precaution no further trouble has been experienced.

The total cost of the material purchased was $12.00, the remainder being picked up around the shop; about $20.00 covered the labor cost, as the machine was made in spare time. It will be noted that considerable bronze was used in the construction; cast iron could just as readily have been used, but, as the bronze was on hand, it was cheaper to use it than to hunt for cast iron.

Carrying a Rail on Handcar

A long iron rail is by no means an easy thing to handle, especially on a handcar. The work of transporting one is best accomplished by attaching the rail to the handcar in an underslung fashion, the rail being suspended from the handcar by means of two rail tongs, fastened to the rail and to the handcar. This method can only be used where there are no switches as there is not sufficient clearance between a switch and the rail to permit the latter to pass over it. Three men can easily do the work, one acting as a counterweight to balance the handcar while the other two are lifting the rail.—Willard A. Francis, Bowerston, Ohio.

Clamp for Soft Materials

The illustration shows a serviceable clamp for cutting by hand soft materials such as leather and felt. It consists of a length of round steel rod, bent to the shape shown and held on a board by means of screweyes. The distance between the ends of the rod and between the screweyes is such that the clamp can be released from the screweyes by pulling it to one side as indicated by the dotted lines. By using long screweyes the ends will protrude above the board and will support the clamping rod when the knife is pressed against it. The screweyes may be turned to adjust the clamp to various thicknesses of material.

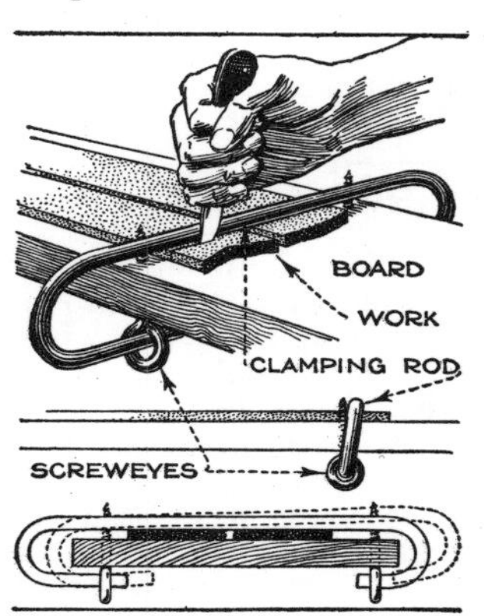

Auto-Driven Tumbling Barrel

A satisfactory tumbling barrel for cleaning and shining up auto and machine parts can be made by attaching a small wooden box to the rear wheel of an automobile. The box should have a hinged cover at one end and be provided with an additional board that projects about an inch beyond the ends. The box is clamped to the spokes between two adapter blocks and two steel plates, both faced with leather to prevent marring the spokes. Two ½-in. bolts at each end hold the box securely on the spokes.

In use the wheel is jacked up from the floor and run at a very slow speed. The box, when loaded, can easily be emptied by simply turning the wheel. For cleaning parts or for rolling small castings, shot or sand can be used as an abrasive, and for polishing, sawdust or scraps of leather will do the work.

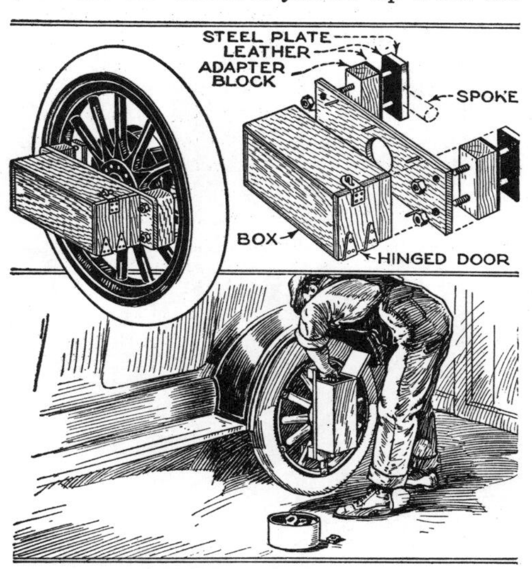

A Small Box Attached to the Rear Wheel of an Automobile Makes an Effective Tumbling Barrel

Using Blowtorch on Windy Days

On windy days considerable difficulty is encountered in using a blowtorch, as the wind keeps the head too cool to make a blue flame. To prevent this an effective windshield can be made from an ordinary tin can, cut out as shown, and slipped over the head of the torch. This shield is also of assistance in preheating the torch as it concentrates the flame around the head.—Andrew Fischer, Jr., Chicago Illinois.

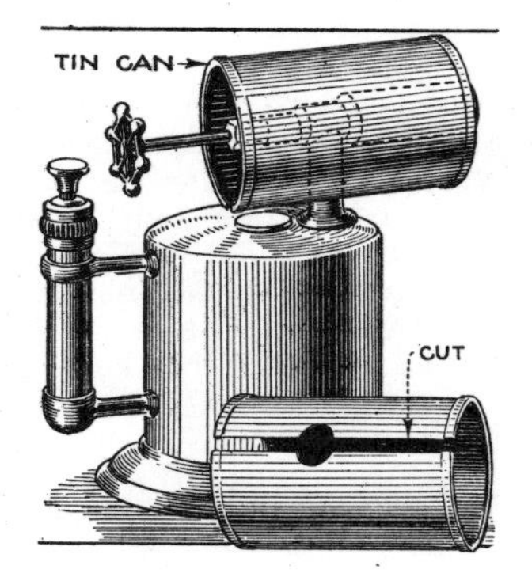

Automatic Accelerator for Sawing Outfit

On circular saws it is often necessary to speed up the engine in order to cut heavy wood, but it is, of course, not

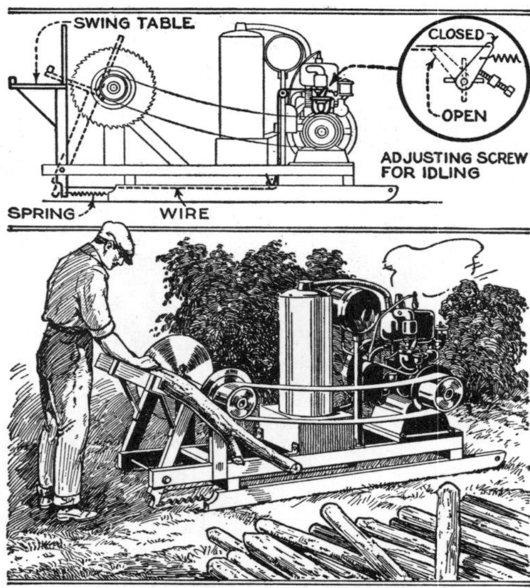

Automatic Accelerator Which Speeds Up the Engine When the Table is Moved toward the Saw

necessary to have the engine running so fast while no wood is being cut. To take care of the speed variation, an automatic accelerator can be improvised to work in connection with the swing table; when the latter is swung forward the speed of the engine is increased considerably, and when brought back again the engine will idle down. The accelerator consists of a length of flexible wire, one end of which is attached to the leg of the swing table and the other end to the arm of the throttle valve on the carburetor. A large coil spring is connected to the leg of the swing table and the end of the skid so that the table will be pulled back as soon as pressure against it is released. A small coil spring is also used to pull the throttle valve back to the closed position when the wire is released. The throttle valve is not closed entirely but kept open a trifle by the idling screw.—C. M. Wilcox, Torrington, Conn.

When melting scrap gold, the jeweler always examines it carefully to make sure that no iron, steel, or solder, or other foreign material is mixed with it. Do not use filings, or the joints of articles, but save these for the refiner.

Rack Aids in Filing Forms

Railroad and insurance offices, and many other places where a great deal of classification of printed forms is necessary in preparation for permanent filing, will find the device illustrated of considerable value.

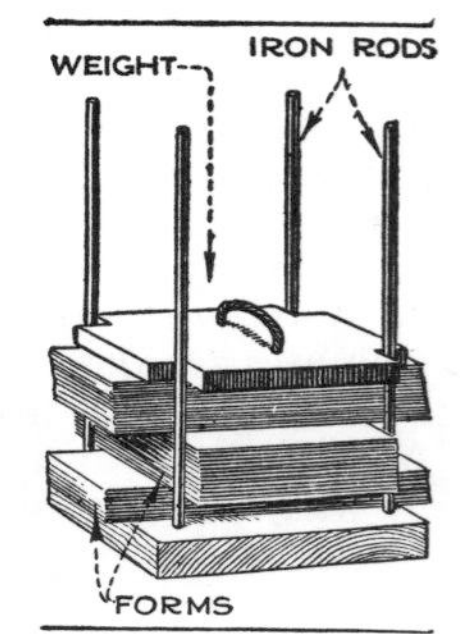

A heavy wooden block, of any suitable size, is provided with four iron rods, properly spaced to suit the forms, as shown. An iron or heavy wooden block, with the corners cut out to clear the rods, and provided with a handle, completes the fixture. When the forms have been sorted and arranged in their proper piles, they are placed in the rack at right angles to each other, with the assurance that they will not be upset, or blown away.

Any individual pile can be removed in an instant, and a piece of colored cardboard inserted in its place, to keep the piles from becoming mixed.

Alinement Gauge for Lathe

A useful gauge for centering work strapped to the saddle of a lathe is shown in the drawing, and can be made without much trouble. The usual method of measuring from the center is tedious, to say the least, but with a gauge of this type all parts of the bore can be measured quite easily.

The cylindrical part is bored out to fit the tailstock spindle, slotted at the front to the width of the caliper arms, and drilled and tapped for the knurled tightening screw, as shown in the lower detail. The caliper arms are made as indicated and drilled to make a neat fit on the small diameter of the tightening screw. A light spring between the two arms completes the instrument.

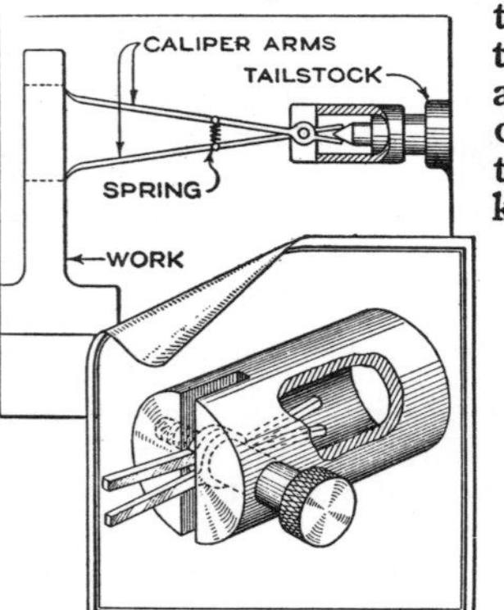

To use the gauge, with a casting on the lathe saddle, the hollow cylindrical part is slipped over the tailstock spindle, with the tightening screw loose. The cylindrical sleeve is pushed back against the tailstock center, which causes the ends of the caliper arms to slide up on the center. The opposite ends of the arms are set by this means to the required diameter of the hole, and the screw is tightened. The gauge can then be revolved by hand around the tailstock spindle, showing at once when the work has been correctly set up.

Concrete Washbowl for Garage

The drawing shows a concrete washbowl for use in garages. The bowl is built in a corner, as shown, so that it will not take any floor space. A number of holes are made in the wall at the point where the bowl is to be made, so that the concrete will be anchored securely. A wooden form is made as shown in the right-hand detail, two holes being drilled in it for the two pipes that are brought through the bowl as indicated; one of these is the water pipe, and is fitted at the top with two elbows, a nipple, and a valve; the other pipe is the drain pipe, which runs under the floor to the sewer. An ordinary tin wash pan is used as a form for the bowl. Several coats of heavy oil paint and two coats of white enamel

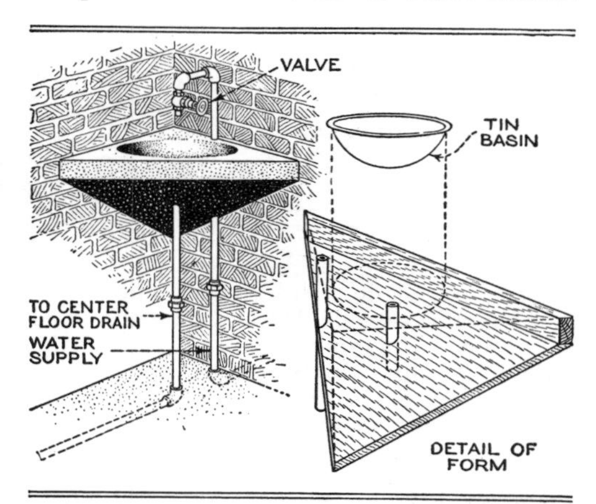

A Concrete Washbowl for the Garage can be Readily Made and does Not Take Any Floor Space

are applied to the inside and top of the bowl, to waterproof it and make it smooth.

⊏After a rain, do not put the auto top down until it is thoroughly dry.

Computing Chart for Spring Scales

A handy and helpful attachment for a spring scale is a computing chart of the kind shown in the illustration. It is made of tin, painted white and screwed to the

A Handy Computing Chart on Which the Price of Any Number of Pounds can be Seen at a Glance

face of the scale. Lines are ruled across the tin horizontally in line with the pound graduations, and columns are ruled vertically under various articles listed. The number of columns, of course, varies considerably in different cases, the butcher's chart showing various kinds of meat, the poultry dealer's chart chickens, ducks, geese, etc., and the junk dealer's chart iron, brass, copper, lead, etc. It is a good idea to prepare several blank charts so that a new one can be filled out at once when prices change. The chart shows at once the price of any number of pounds of each article, up to the capacity of the scale.

Turning Long Babbitt Bearings

In making some long babbitt bearings difficulty was experienced in holding the babbitt in the lathe securely and turning it. However, this trouble was overcome by filling a piece of pipe with babbitt, placing the pipe in the lathe and turning the pipe and babbitt at the same time. This made it easy to turn as well as to hold it firmly in the chuck.

Grinding Washers

Standard washers are often too big on their outside diameters for some particular job, and must therefore be ground down to the required size. When quantities of washers have to be ground down in this way, the work can be done quickly by using a holder of the kind shown in the drawing. It consists of a short shaft and a handle. The shaft is split lengthwise as shown and drilled at one end for a pin, which must fit tightly in one piece of the split shaft and loosely in the other. The latter piece is drilled and tapped in the center for a headless screw. The holder is used by turning the screw back a little and slipping the washers on, six on each side of the screw. When the screw is tightened the shaft binds all the washers but not the handle, as the holes in it are slightly larger. To grind the washers the handle is held by the left hand on the tool rest of the emery wheel while the washers are turned around by the pin on the end of the shaft.

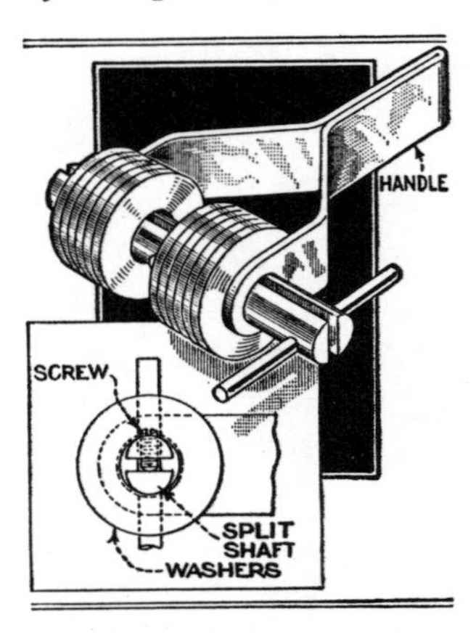

Holding Lathe Faceplate Securely

It is often desirable to reverse the lathe, especially when threading, but there is always present the danger of having the faceplate fly off. The illustration shows a simple way of eliminating this danger. Fasten a small cold-rolled steel strap to the lathe spindle with two small screws, as indicated. Drill a hole through the other end of the strap, and into the hub of the faceplate, and ream this out to fit a heavy taper pin.

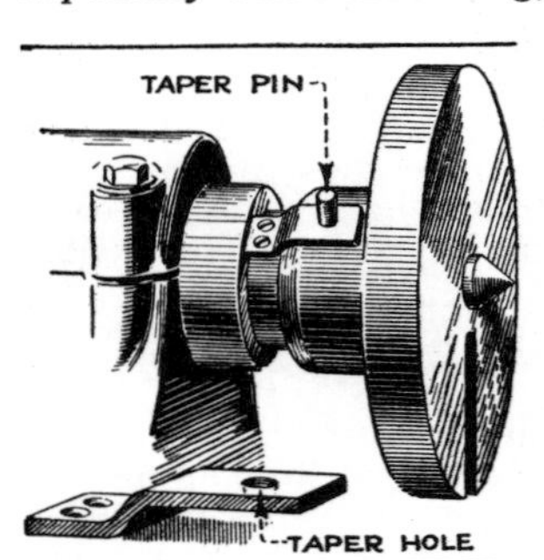

"Ball-Bearing" Trestles

To facilitate the sliding of sheet metal over a wooden trestle, where the material is being fed into or taken away from a punch press or other machine, groove the top of the trestle to receive steel balls ½ in. or larger in diameter. The groove should be so deep that only about a third of each ball bearing projects above the surface. The balls themselves do not revolve, but their smooth surface, which comes in contact with the material, allows it to pass over with very little friction.—W. E. Rausch, Milan, Mich.

A Homemade Router

A router can be purchased in tool stores, but many workers, both amateur and professional, prefer to make their own. The one shown in the drawing is simple and easy to make, and answers the purpose perfectly. The block is made of beech or maple, the latter being the easier obtained, and it is usually desirable to have three sizes: 1 by 2¼ by 4 in., as in the drawing, 1⅛ by 3 by 6 in., and 1¼ by 3½ by 8 in. A throat is cut out of the block, so that the worker can see the work, tapered to prevent clogging, and recessed to fit the cutter bar. Three sizes of these are used, to suit the various blocks: 3/16 by ¼ in., ¼ by ½ in., and ¼ by ¾ in., bent and ground as shown, and made a sliding fit in the block. The block is also drilled and counterbored to receive the shank and head of the clamping bolt, which can be made from a length of brass bar, or a brass casting, and provided with a wingnut. Below the wingnut, a brass plate is countersunk and screwed to the block; if desired, a plain washer can be used, but the brass plate makes the better job.—M. E. Duggan, Kenosha, Wis.

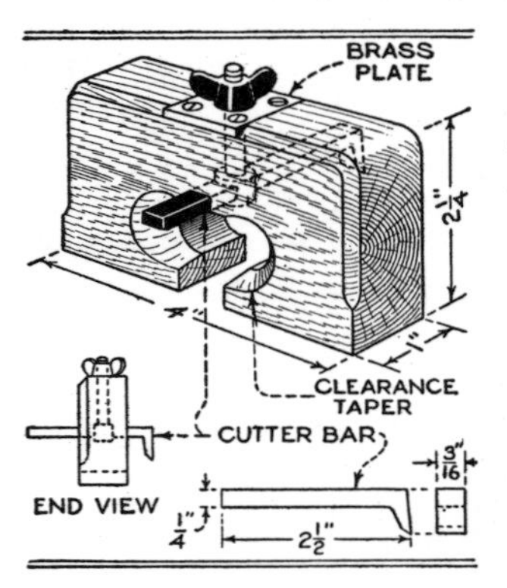

¶If any difficulty is experienced in obtaining materials mentioned in these pages, write to the Bureau of Information.

Making a Bench Hacksaw

By J. V. Romig

THE bench hacksaw described in this article will prove a valuable addition to the small workshop; it is easily built from material obtainable everywhere, and the design is such that very little machine work is necessary.

The base is a piece of wrought-iron or steel plate, drilled and tapped for the ¾-in. standards, drilled for holding-down bolts, and slotted for the vise bolts. The standards are ¾-in. cold-rolled steel, threaded at one end, and drilled and tapped for capscrews at the other.

The saw, which should be of the heaviest hand pattern obtainable, is fastened to a piece of cold-rolled steel with round-head screws, as shown, and spaced away from it with ½-in. washers or collars. This machine-steel slide works in a bearing arrangement made from angle brackets of brass screwed to a machine-steel bar, and this, in turn, is screwed to vertical slide members, made of flat stock, bent, and drilled and reamed to fit the standards. They must be perfectly square with the standards, and should be a close, but free fit.

To the top of the standards is screwed a piece of flat stock, to stiffen them and hold them rigid. A latch is attached to

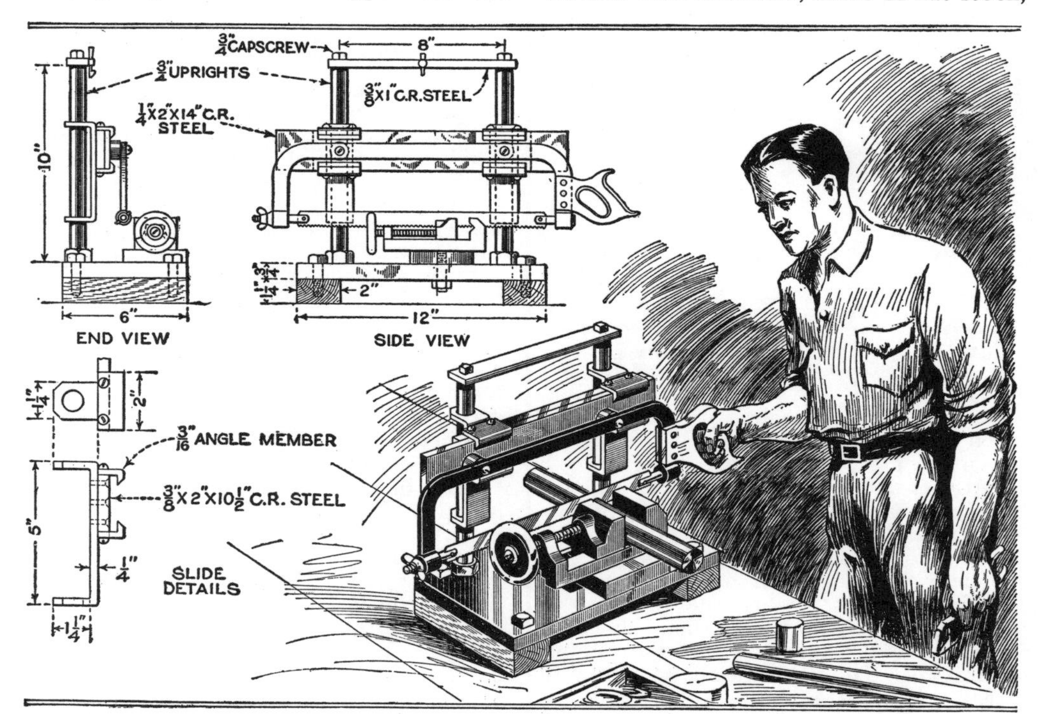

An Easily Made Bench Hacksaw That Will Prove Invaluable in the Small Workshop: No Castings Are Used and Little Machine Work Is Necessary

this bar, hooking over a pin on the back of the slide, to hold the saw in its highest position while the stock is placed in the vise for sawing. By mounting the base above the bench on two pieces of wood, the vise nut and nuts for clamp bolts are easily turned. The vise can be removed and work clamped to the base, when necessary.

A wooden handle of the carpenter's-saw type should be used on the hacksaw, as it will not tire the hand as the round type does.

The vise is of the type used on small drill presses, and can be purchased from the makers of such machines.

Much better and quicker work can be done with a tool of this type than with a handsaw, and blade breakage is greatly reduced.

Centering Drill Rod Accurately

When machinists or toolmakers are required to make taps, reamers, counterbores, or similar tools out of drill rod, the centering must be done accurately.

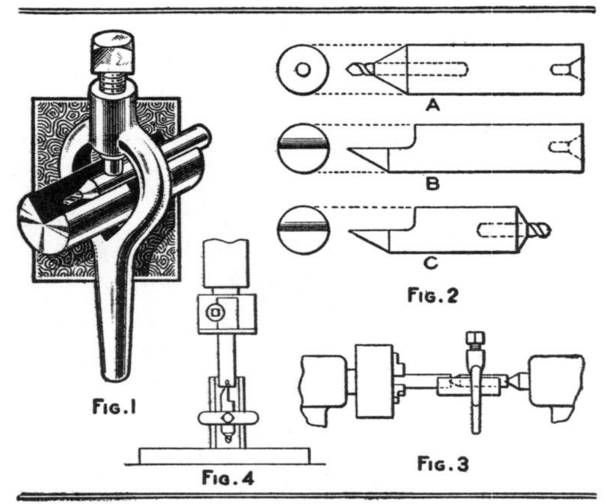

Simple Centering Tool for Use in Making Taps, Reamers, Counterbores, Etc., of Drill Rod

The simple toolholder illustrated has been found to give very good results. It consists of a round block, made from a length of steel rod, grooved as shown, finished smooth with a file or by grinding, casehardened, and used with the centering tools shown in Fig. 2.

The tools shown in details A and B of Fig. 2 are used when the centering is done on the lathe, tool A being used to drill the center hole and tool B to countersink it. Tool C is used on the drill press; it gives better results than the other tools in regard to speed, as there is no changing of centering tool, the block being turned upside down for countersinking. The length of this tool must be at least 3/8 or 1/2 in. shorter than the block, and its shank diameter the same as the diameter of the work. Tool A need not be shorter than the block, but its diameter must also be the same as the rod to be centered. The tool B should be made from .005 to .02 in. smaller than the work, to allow a certain amount of pressure against the sides of the groove in the block. Fig. 1 shows one of the tools in position in the block, held in place by means of a lathe dog. Care should be taken that there are no burrs on the rod ends when centering, otherwise the work will not be true. Figs. 3 and 4 show the tool in position for use on a lathe and drill press.

Convenient Punch and Chisel Set

A variable-sized punch and chisel set takes up very little space in the tool kit and is much lighter in weight than a whole set of solid tools. It can readily be made by any mechanic. The holder consists of two pieces, the handle and the tightening sleeve, which screws on the slitted end of the handle as shown, to clamp the shanks of the tools in the holder. The handle is knurled to facilitate holding it, particularly when using small chisels in confined places and corners.

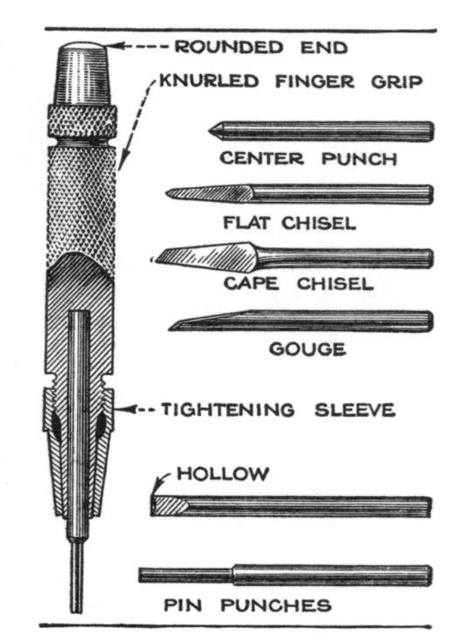

As many separate tools can be made as desired, to suit the needs of the user. The pin punches are made of various diameters at the nose, each just a little smaller than the pin it is to drive. All points or working faces should be hollow or concave, which will prevent the spreading of the pin, due to upsetting. Center punches, pin punches, chisels, and gouges are made out of tool steel or drill rod forged to shape, and ground after hardening and drawing the temper. The tools used for driving purposes should be made of tool steel, carefully hardened, and drawn to a dark-brown or purple color, which makes them tough, and lessens the danger of breaking them.

Safety Cut in Studs and Bolts

Studs and bolts used for attaching cylinder heads and plates on engines are frequently twisted off and the break often occurs inside of the hole, which makes it a difficult matter to remove the broken piece. This, however, can be prevented by making a V-cut, slightly deeper than the thread, around the stud or bolt above the surface, so that, if it breaks at all, it will break off at the groove, and can then be easily removed with a small pipe wrench.

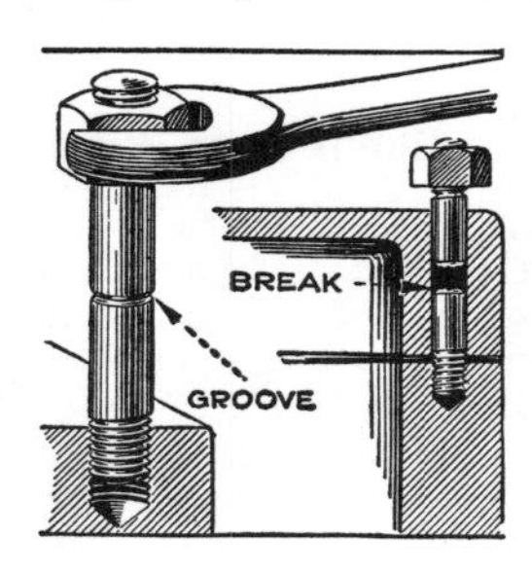

Machining Angle Plates on the Lathe

The machining of angle plates is usually done on the shaper or planer, but it can also be done on the lathe, when the former machines are not available. The angle plate is swung between the lathe centers as shown in the illustration, and it is then an easy matter to finish the faces. After the faces are finished, and have been tested for squareness, the sides are finished by mounting the angle plate with one edge against the faceplate, using washers or pieces of tin under each corner to true the plate perfectly square with the faceplate. The angle plate is then attached to the faceplate by clamps, resting on the brace.

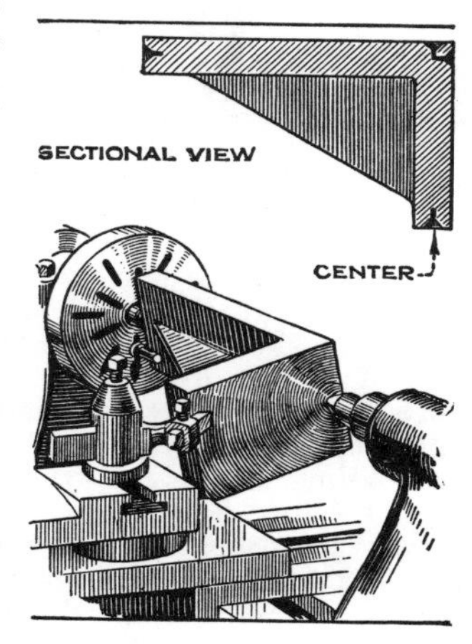

Holder for Drafting Scale and Triangles

The holder for drafting scale and triangles, shown in the illustration, was designed to meet conditions in a drafting room of a technical school, where

Holder for Drafting Scale and Triangles in a Schoolroom Prevents "Losing" or Exchanging Them

four classes used the same instruments alternately. The holder eliminates the necessity of returning the rules and triangles to the instructor at the end of each class period, as these articles can be easily seen on the desks and checked up. Any interchanging of triangles between desks is prevented by stamping the desk number on each. The upper detail shows the size and shape of the holder, and the drawing below shows how it is mounted on the desk.—E. G. Asku, Sarnia, Can.

Mirror for Ironing Machine

On some types of ironing machines the work cannot be seen when it passes between the rollers, and the result is that it often comes out wrinkled. This trouble can be prevented by mounting a mirror on the frame of the machine as shown in the drawing, to enable the operator to look between the rollers. In case the work becomes doubled up or twisted, the machine is promptly shut off and reversed.

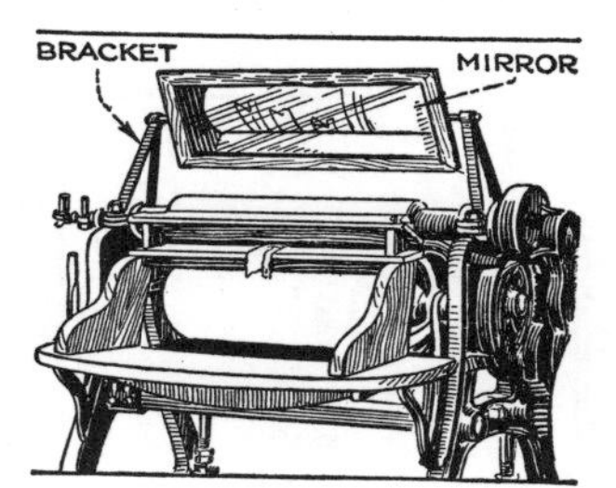

Storing Extension Lamp

An extension lamp with a 25-ft. cord is a very serviceable accessory for any motorist, but difficulty is usually encountered in handling the cord. Frequently it is placed in the tool box, but the objection to this, aside from the danger of tools cutting the cord, is that the tools must be removed when the cord is needed.

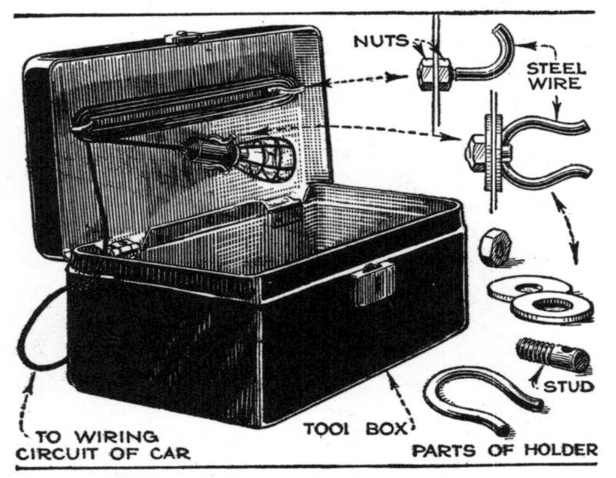

Auto Extension Lamp Conveniently Stored under the Tool-Box Lid to Avoid Damage from Tools

A much better place to store the cord is under the lid of the tool box, as shown in the drawing. The cord is wound on two hooks made from ¼-in. rod, and the lamp is held by a spring holder, shown in the upper details. The cord is led through a hole drilled in the side of the box and is permanently connected with the wiring circuit of the car, so that the lamp is ready for use at all times.

Repairing a Cracked Jig

In repairing a cracked drill jig for a large marine-motor crankcase, it was found impossible to use clamps to pull it together and therefore the repair was accomplished in the following way: The crack was first cleaned thoroughly, which was done by flooding it with gasoline and blowing it out with compressed air. After obtaining a piece of cold-rolled steel, ⅜-in. thick, just as wide as the jig was thick, and about 10 in. long, two screw holes were drilled near the ends and just inside of them two dowel-pin holes as shown. The surface of the jig was laid off and drilled to correspond, allowing 1/16 in. additional space between the holes to allow for the crack. Holes were then drilled and tapped in the jig to correspond to the screw holes in the plate. The plate was heated until it had expanded so that its holes were directly in line with the holes in the jig, and the pins and screws then driven in. As the plate cooled, its shrinkage closed the crack so tightly that it could hardly be seen.

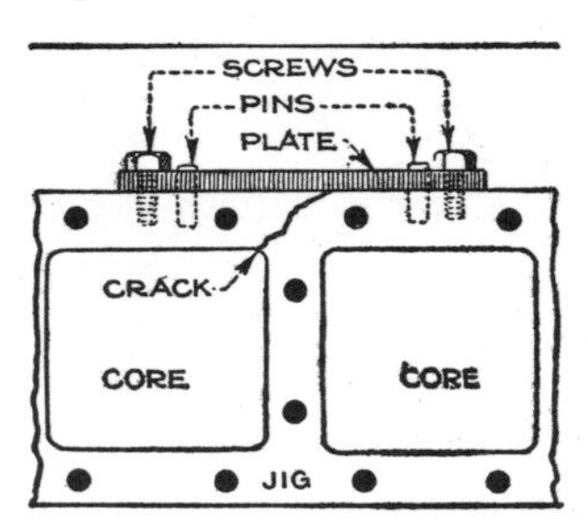

Preventing Waste of Compressed Air

In shops using compressed air to clean machinery, dies and molds, or manufactured articles, there is always a great tendency to waste the air. The 1/16-in. or ⅛-in. hole in the nozzle of the air "gun" looks too small to the average workman; he therefore tries to improve it by reaming it out to a larger size, and this, of course, allows a greater volume of air to escape. In a large eastern plant this practice became very annoying and made it nearly impossible to keep up the air pressure, so that it was necessary to take preventive measures. All air pipes to machines and benches were of ⅜-in. pipe, terminating in a regulation ⅜-in. cock, bushed down to ⅛ in. A thin copper disk, with a 1/16-in. hole, drilled in the center, was placed between the bushing and the cock, at the bottom of the thread, as shown in the drawing. At 80 lb. pressure the plate allowed just enough air to pass to work the air gun properly. For the ⅛-in. size of gun, the disk is drilled with a ⅛-in. hole.

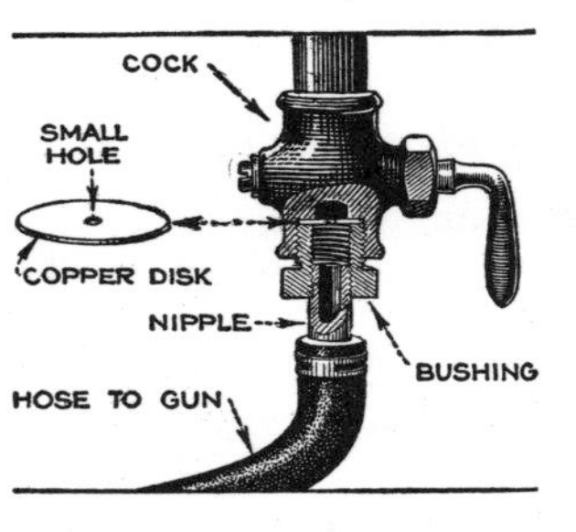

Another practice among a certain class of workmen is to blow their clothes with the compressed air, which is not only wasteful, but dangerous, as air at high pressure entering any openings of the body is liable to cause severe injuries. Furthermore, the dust on the clothes is not blown off but is blown through the clothes to the skin, defeating the very purpose of using the air.—A. S. Jamieson, Springfield, Mass.

Removing Paint from Tile

Spots and splashes of paint on tiled floors present a very unsightly effect and should therefore be removed. This can readily be done by washing with a solution of caustic soda, which will remove the paint without the necessity of using an after wash of acid to destroy the effects of the alkali, plain water only being required. If the tile is likely to stain with the soda, a rinse of diluted ammonia will remove the spots, and the ammonia can then be washed off with clean water.

Breaking Off Iron Plate

A favorite method of separating a piece of iron plate from the main stock is to chip a groove along a line drawn to the required shape, and afterward to break the piece off by wrenching it or striking it with a hammer. This, however, often results in bending the piece, which makes it necessary to flatten it out again before it can be used.

In one shop where a great deal of this kind of work was done, the method shown in the illustration was found to be very convenient and to save considerable time,

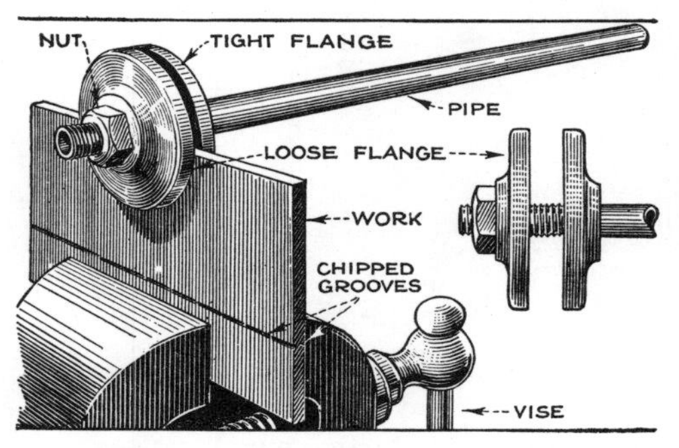

A Handy and Time-Saving Tool for Breaking Off Pieces of Iron Plate without Bending Them

as with it, plates could be broken off without bending. The tool consists of a length of iron pipe threaded at one end, two pipe flanges, and a nut. One flange is screwed on the threaded end until it is tight, and the other is screwed on until the work is gripped fairly closely, the nut then being used to lock it. With the plate securely gripped in the vise, pressure is applied to the handle as the tool is rolled along the edge of the plate.

¶ In making drawings, do not dimension from the rough edge of a casting, but from a finished surface.

Holder for Filling Coal Bags

In the larger cities where the houses are so close together that a coal chute cannot be used to discharge the coal

A Handy Stand That Saves Considerable Time When Filling Coal Bags

from the wagon into the basement, it is common practice to use heavy canvas bags, which are filled at the coal yards. To facilitate the work of filling the bags the holder shown in the illustration was devised. It is made of heavy lumber and has hooks under the chute to hold the bag while it is being filled.—E. M. Scott, Chicago, Ill.

Using a Broken Bit

An auger or bit with a broken or badly damaged screw is usually discarded; it can be made serviceable, however, in a very simple manner. A short piece of tubing, equal in diameter to a smaller bit, is slipped over the broken or damaged screw point as shown, and filled with solder, any openings between the bottom of the tube and the bit being first filled with laundry soap. To use the tool, a hole is first drilled with the small bit the size of the tube, then the larger one can be used in the usual manner, without danger of running off, as the tube forms an excellent guide.

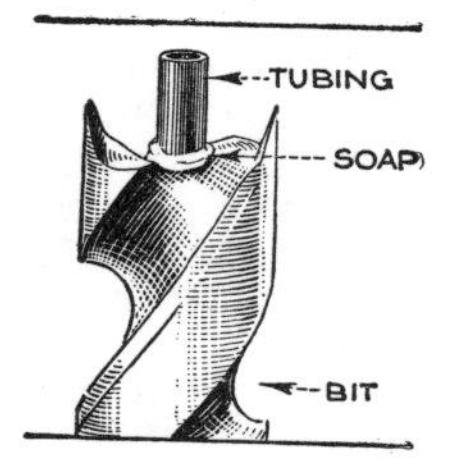

Making a Clover-Seed Huller and Scarifier

BY IRA D. MULLINAX

THE machine for hulling and scarifying sweet-clover seed described in this article was made by the boys in an Illinois High School. The machine was designed by the farm crops and agricultural engineering sections of Iowa State College, patented, and given to the people, so that anyone is at liberty to make and use it. It is in use by seed companies and farmers for scratching the seed coats of clovers and alfalfa so that the seeds may absorb moisture readily, thereby increasing greatly the prospects of obtaining a good "stand" from costly seed.

The machine may be built at home by any farmer possessing a kit of carpenter's tools, and who has average skill in their use. Most of the material needed for constructing the huller may be obtained from the local lumber and hardware dealers, as may be seen from the bill of material at the end of the article. The machine shown in the photograph measures approximately 5 ft. long, 2 ft. wide, and 4 ft. high, but the relative dimensions may be varied to a considerable extent without impairing the efficiency of the machine.

Hulling and Scarifying Machine Built by High-School Boys That Has Proved Profitable to Them and to Local Farmers

The sweet-clover seed is poured into the feed hopper and runs downward through a gate into a chute leading into the open side of a blast fan. The fan is driven by a ¼-hp. electric motor, although it can be belted to a countershaft mounted on the end of the huller, and driven by a gasoline engine or tractor, if necessary. The outlet of the fan is connected to the scarifying chamber or tube. The inner surface of the outer side of this tube is covered, from the point marked A, in the side view, to B, with emery cloth, sandpaper, or garnet paper.

The garnet paper, or whatever abrasive is used, should not extend below point B, as it is not desirable that the seeds be thrown directly against this surface. As the seeds are delivered into the fan casing by the feed chute they are struck sharply and forcibly by the fan blades. They are then carried by the strong airblast from the fan out through the throat and thrown against the hard, smooth surface of the lower end of the scarifying tube, and thence upward. When passing from B to A, the seeds are held in close contact with the rough surface of the garnet paper, and their hard coats are cracked, punctured, scratched, and otherwise softened, making it possible for them to absorb the ground moisture readily.

The seeds are delivered by the upper end of the scarifying tube into a compartment with a sloping tin-lined bottom, as indicated in the side and perspective views. In this compartment the force of the air is considerably reduced, and it makes its exit, carrying with it a portion of the chaff and waste. The seeds are stopped by an adjustable baffle board, which causes them to fall to the floor and run into the chute that delivers them to a bag or measure. Behind the first baffle, a second is fitted; this may be a canvas curtain, as shown, or a board similar to the first.

When building the machine, good white pine, or its equivalent, free from knots and checks, should be used; this is easily worked, and makes a light machine, which can easily be handled. The legs, braces, and other parts of the frame are made of 2 by 4-in. stock, surfaced on four sides. The sides, ends, top, partitions, etc., should be of good boards, surfaced and matched so as to make tight-fitting joints. The seeds are small and often high-priced, hence cracks in boards and

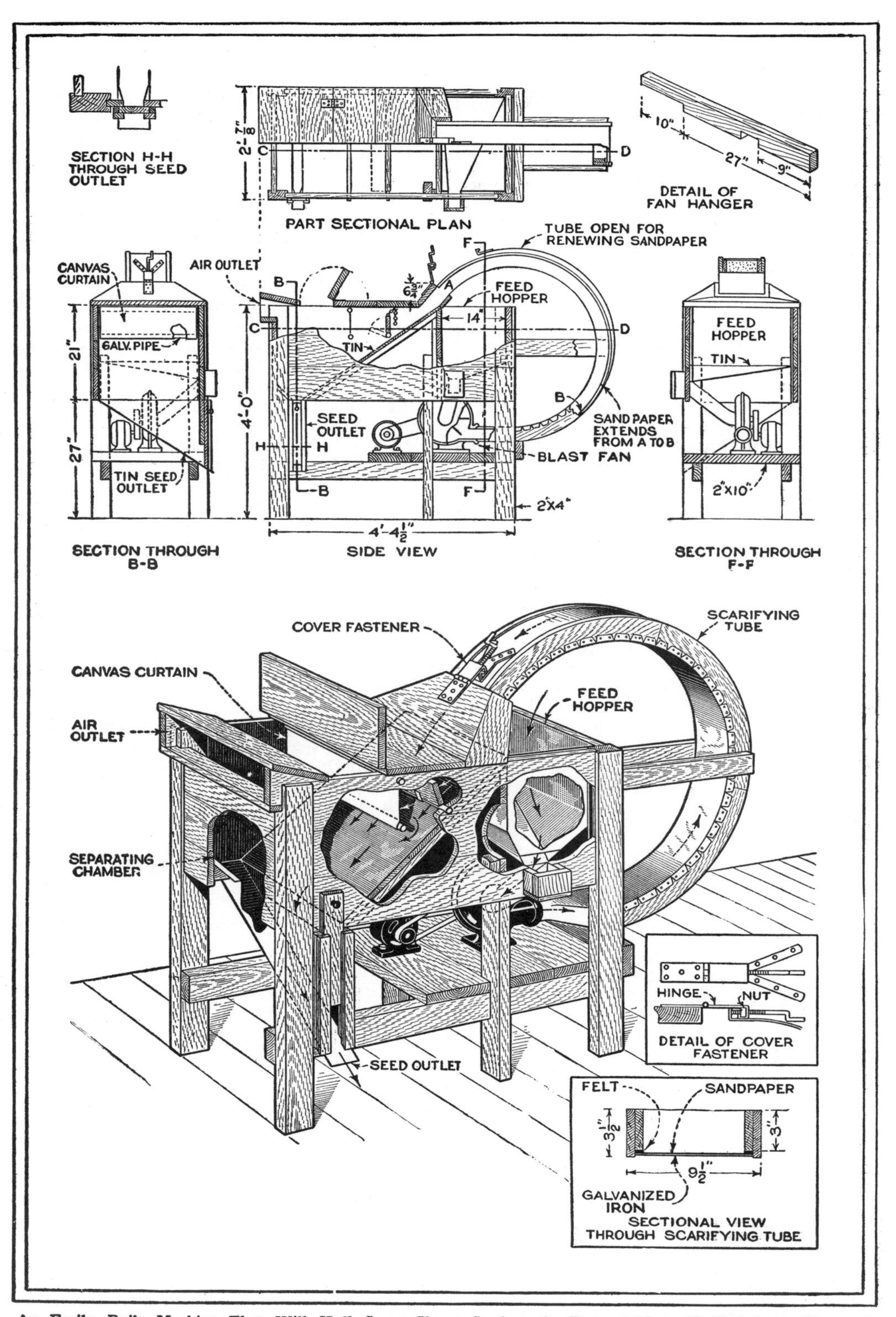

An Easily Built Machine That Will Hull Sweet-Clover Seed at the Rate of 10 to 12 Bushels an Hour: It Is Not Difficult to Operate and Will Pay for Itself in a Short Time

open joints may prove costly. The sides or panels are set into continuous mortises in the legs, as shown in section H-H, and glued and nailed in place. Strengthening all corners with metal braces is advisable, and the braces should be screwed to the wood. The baffle board is pivoted on long screws driven through the side panels into the lower ends of the board, and the upper end is adjusted by means of a chain hooked over a screw hook driven into the underside of the top. The board may be pivoted on a piece of pump rod running from side to side, if desired, simple tin straps bent around the rod and tacked to the board being used as bearings, as shown in the perspective view. The canvas curtain is of 6 to 10-oz. material, with a hem at top and bottom. The upper hem slips over a length of 3/8-in. iron rod, or pump rod, and the curtain is weighted with a length of galvanized-iron pipe, slipped into the lower hem. The size of this pipe depends upon the speed of the fan, and a little experimenting may be necessary in order to determine the proper weight.

The outer side of the scarifying tube is made of galvanized iron, cut and hinged about point B, and fastened at the top by a clamp made from a strap hinge, screw, and nut, as shown in the detail. The upper end of the galvanized iron is strengthened by a flat-iron spreader, riveted in place; the screw bears against the upturned end of this and draws the cover tightly around the tube frame, against the strip-felt packing shown in the tube detail.

The motor should be of a speed that will drive the blower at from 2,800 to 3,000 r.p.m., with the proper pulleys. The speed must be reduced for seeds that are softer than sweet-clover seed, or a portion of the abrasive may be removed from the scarifying tube, thus regulating the treatment so that only a small percentage of the seeds will be injured. With correct speeds and length of abrasive surface, not more than 2 per cent of the seeds will be broken. One application of garnet paper will usually treat 50 bu. or more.

The boys run their sweet-clover seed once through the machine to hull it, and then run it through a second time, when it is scarified. From one-half to four-fifths of the seed is hulled the first time, depending upon the quality and condition of the seed.

Students in the school have organized an agricultural club, which last year hulled and scarified 12,000 lb. of clean, salable seed for 25 farmers, some of the seed being sent 50 miles to the school. This year even more seed is being treated, and letters have been received from seven or eight states inquiring for prices on treated seed. The club has been charging local growers 1 cent per pound, on the basis of clean seed.

In 1922, ten times as much sweet clover was grown in this territory as in 1921, and this year the acreage will be greatly increased, a result much desired by agricultural research workers. The scarifier built by the boys has been a large factor in attaining this gratifying state of affairs, as it has provided the farmers with a service that they were unable to obtain elsewhere. Farmers in other communities can benefit greatly by following their example.

MATERIAL LIST

2 pieces 2 by 4 in. by 18 ft. white pine.
1 piece 1 by 4 in. by 12 ft. white pine.
3 pieces 2 by 10 in. by 2 ft. oak or birch.
60 board ft. 6, 8, or 10-in. matched white pine.
2 sheets 28-gauge galvanized iron.
1 blast fan.
1 1/4-hp. motor.
1 pair 5-in. strap hinges.
1 piece 3/16 by 2 by 8-in. wrought iron.
1 large hasp.
2 pulleys (size depending upon motor speed).
1 half-gal. can mixed paint.
Nails, screws, bolts, felt, etc.

Refilling Barometers

Barometers that have developed air bubbles can be cleaned in the following way: Pour the mercury into a porcelain dish and cover it. Prepare a solution of 1 part of sulphuric acid and 20 parts of water. Pour the acid into the water slowly, with constant stirring, never the water into the acid. When the solution has cooled, the barometer tube is washed with it, and then with clean water. Place the tube in a warm place to dry, with the open end up so that the vapor may pass off more easily. Next clean the mercury by forcing it through a piece of chamois skin, allowing the liquid to fall into a clean porcelain dish. This operation should be repeated several times.

To refill the tube, pour a small amount

of mercury into the widened end, holding the tube downward at an angle and tapping it lightly to force the mercury down to the closed end. Air bubbles that may be formed while pouring in the mercury are removed by tapping the tube with a stick of soft wood, holding the tube down slightly while doing so, and tapping with considerable care to avoid breaking the tube.

When the process has been completed, close the wide end of the tube with a cork or wadding. This sealing must not make the tube air-tight. If any mercury has been lost, add enough to make up for the deficiency, comparing the height of the mercury with that of another barometer of the same make.

Simple Screw Holder

Although there are a number of tools for starting screws in places that are nearly inaccessible, the tool shown in the illustration would be hard to beat for simplicity, and can easily be made, in a few minutes, from a length of heavy galvanized wire and a washer. The wire is doubled as shown in the lower detail, the ends bent over to fit the screw head, and the washer slipped over the doubled end, after which this end is widened to prevent the washer from coming off again. In use the ends are slipped onto the screw head, and the washer moved down to clamp the screw.

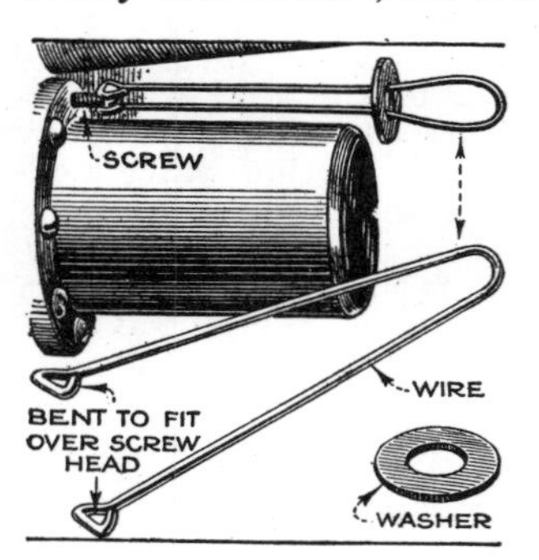

Handy Gauge for Machinists

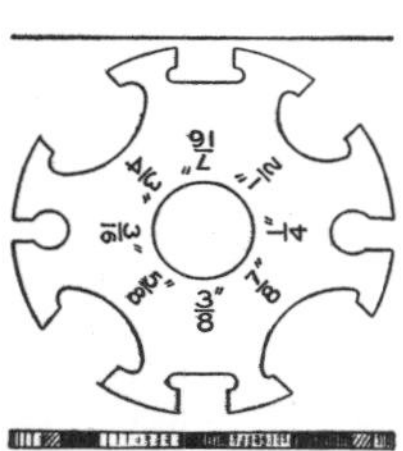

A great deal of time is wasted by machinists in using calipers and micrometers to measure small work approximately. A gauge made similar to the common wire gauge, as shown in the drawing, has been found to be a valuable tool, as with it measurements can be made in a fraction of the time otherwise consumed.

Crimping Tool for Pipe

Anyone who has attempted to join two lengths of galvanized-iron pipe, when the end of one length is not crimped, will appreciate the homemade crimping tool shown in the illustration. A pair of ordinary long-handled flat-nosed pliers was heated and the jaws forged to a V-shape, as shown in the detail. In use the crimper is simply pressed over the metal around the end of the pipe, which reduces the diameter, so that it can be pushed into the end of the other length of pipe.—G. A. Luers, Washington, D. C.

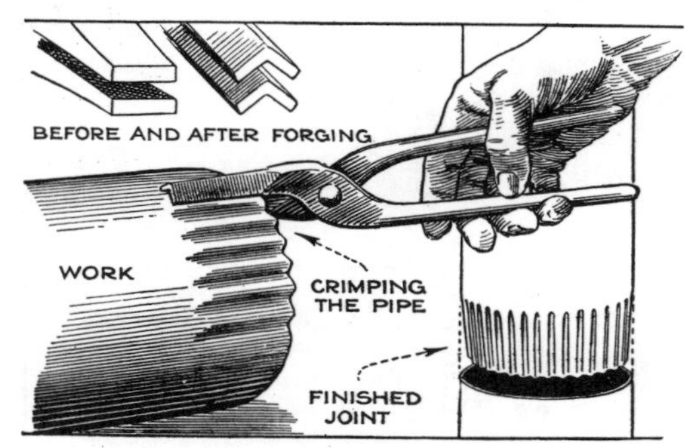

Homemade Pliers for Crimping Galvanized-Iron Pipe, Made from Ordinary Flat-Nosed Pliers

Guard for Mangle Rolls

After a laundry worker had caught her fingers between the rolls of an old-style mangle, the machine was equipped with a safety guard, which made it impossible for similar accidents to occur. The guard consists of a length of ½-in. pipe supported at the end by a flat iron bracket screwed to the table as shown in the drawing. There is about ¼-in. space between the pipe and the table so that the work can be fed in between the rollers, but the fingers of the operator cannot pass the guard.—A. C. Cole, Chicago, Ill.

¶If oxygen or acetylene valves become frozen, thaw them out with hot water.

Combination Punch, Shear, and Riveter

Punch, shear, and riveter for heavy-duty work are tools that should be found in every mechanic's shop, but the cost

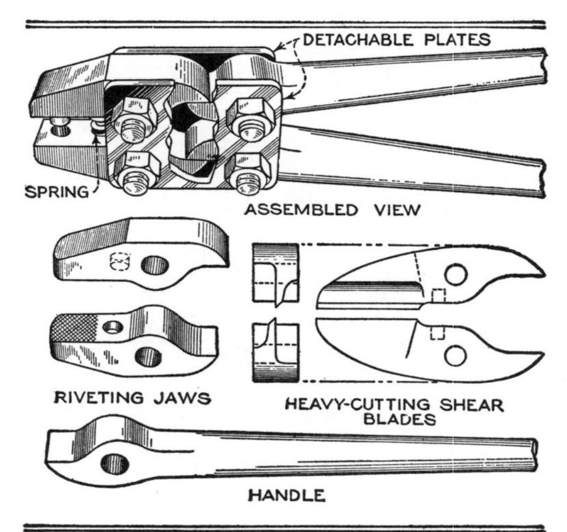

A Combination Punch, Shear, and Riveting Tool for Heavy Work That Can Be Made by Any Mechanic

of these makes a combination tool preferable. Such a tool is shown in the illustration. It consists of two handles and interchangeable shear blades, riveting and punching jaws, attached to the handles by means of two detachable plates and four heavy bolts as indicated in the upper figure, which shows the tool assembled. The handles and end members are made of square bar steel, which makes machining unnecessary except drilling, as the parts can be formed to shape by grinding. The side plates are made of ordinary steel plate. A small coil spring is provided between the jaws to facilitate using the tool. Several pairs of handles of various lengths should be provided to obtain different leverages.

Cementing Glass to Metal

For cementing glass to metal a mixture of sodium silicate and quartz meal, baking 12 to 24 hours to set hard, is recommended. If the color is unimportant a useful preparation may be obtained by soaking leather scrap glue in water, melting it by heat and then mixing it with 11 lb. of pitch, 4½ lb. of asphaltum and 4½ lb. of resin to each 1¾ lb. of glue solution. The mass may be loaded with powdered slate, etc., without losing its adhesive properties. An equally good cement is prepared by dissolving equal parts of russian glue and shellac, and adding levigated chalk. Casein cement, for immediate use, is made by mixing fresh curd with one-fourth its weight of powdered chalk; while a second preparation, which will keep, consists of a solution of casein in ammonia, or of a solution of the same material in a 5-percent solution of caustic soda or borax, with the addition of a very small proportion of hexamethylene-tetramine. This cement is impervious to water.

Resin adhesives are also used, the "amber" cement employed by jewelers being composed of three parts of mastic and two to four parts of shellac, dissolved to a "sirup" in 90-per-cent alcohol.

Oiling Automobile Springs

Old crankcase oil can be used to advantage for lubricating automobile and motor-truck springs and other parts of the chassis, the work being quickly and thoroughly accomplished by means of a small hand sprayer of the kind used for spraying orchard trees. The nozzle is equipped with a quick-acting valve and with it a fine stream of oil can be thrown in almost a straight line for about 10 ft. This method of oiling is a time and labor saver for garages as well as for private owners.—G. C. Douglas, Raleigh, North Carolina.

An Easily Made Pin Setter

The drawing shows a handy tool for setting pins in places where the fingers cannot reach comfortably. The dimensions of the tool depend, of course, on the diameter and length of the pin to be driven in, the one illustrated being made of 3/16-in. round stock, bent to the shape shown, and drilled in the end to take a pin. It is also drilled through for a stop pin, which fits tightly in one side and loosely in the other. In use, a pin is slipped in the hole at the end, until it touches the stop pin. Then by grasping the holder in the hand as shown, the pin can be pushed in place.

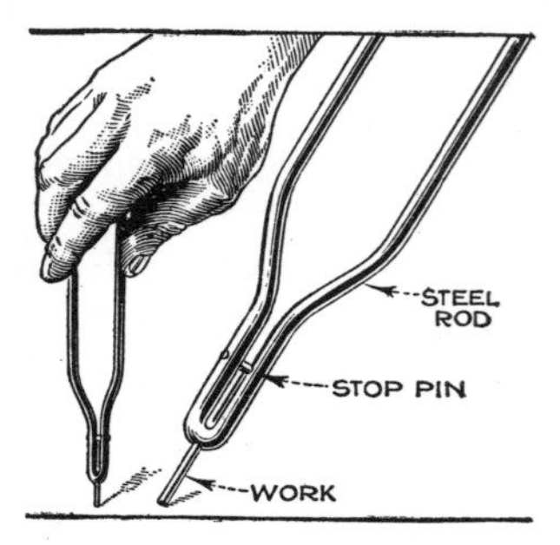

A Novel Dairy Barn

Milking and feeding go together, and therefore provision should be made to milk and feed at the same time. A novel dairy barn, which is arranged to permit this, is shown in the drawing.

The hay manger is located above the heads of the cows so that they have to reach up a trifle to pull the hay out; the bottom has a row of ½-in. iron bars to allow this. A hay manger of this type has the advantage of containing enough hay to last the cows for a number of days. The trap door of the hay manger hangs outward on chains and can be pushed back into vertical position whenever necessary, as in cold or stormy weather.

The grain manger is of the ordinary type, except that it is much larger and also lower. Both mangers can be filled from the outside, from a wagon or truck, the surplus hay being temporarily stored on the roof, ready to be raked into the manger when needed.

Another interesting feature of this dairy barn is the chain cow tie, which is an improvement on the stanchions usually used, as the cows have greater freedom to move their heads around, the bars permitting the chain to be moved up and down, but preventing the cows from moving backward.—Herbert A. Shearer, Eagle Rock, Calif.

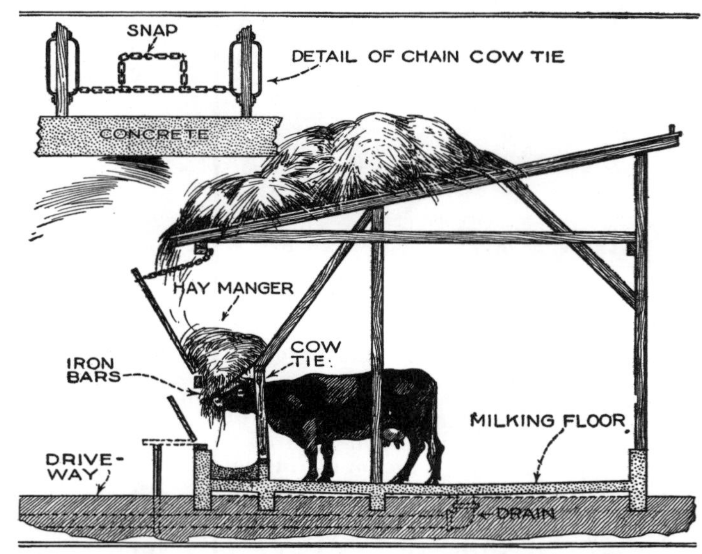

Novel Dairy Barn with a Self-Feeding Hay Manger and a Large Grain Manger: It Also Has Chain Cow Ties, and a Concrete Milking Floor

Removing a Counterbored Screw

Having occasion to remove a screw that was set in a counterbore about an inch deep, and that had become "frozen" in and began to break up when the screwdriver was forced, I hit upon the idea of soldering the tip of the screwdriver to the screw and found it successful. By playing the flame of a blowtorch on the screwdriver as illustrated, the screw and the tip of the screwdriver were heated sufficiently to cause a drop of solder to melt and bind both together.—John F. Dwiggins, Petersburg, Tenn.

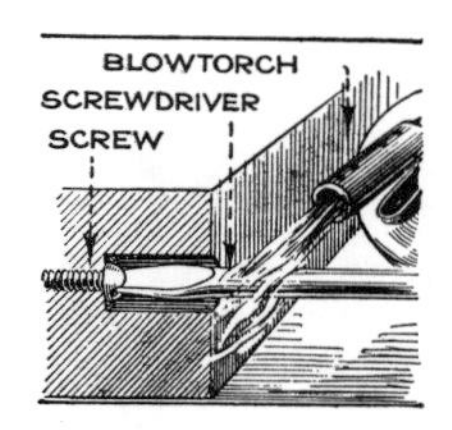

ℂAsk the Bureau of Information where to obtain parts and materials mentioned in Shop Notes and Amateur Mechanics.

Lamps Indicate Blown Fuses

In places where fuses are often blown, it will be found convenient to shunt a carbon lamp around each fuse so that the lamp will burn when the fuse is blown. The lamps will not burn otherwise because the current can pass through the fuse much more easily than through the lamp, as the latter has a much greater resistance. The diagram plainly shows the method of connecting the carbon lamps.

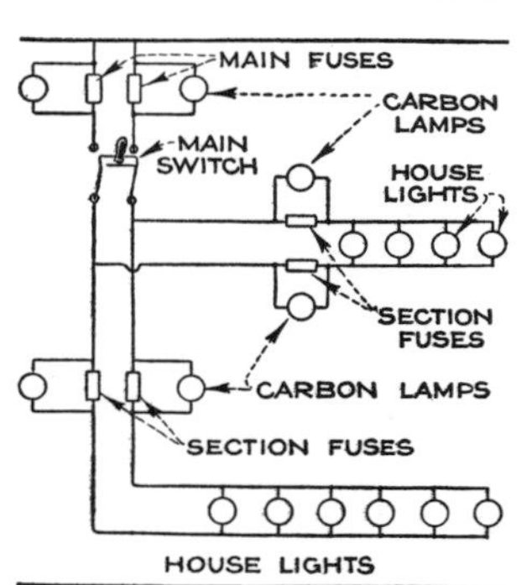

Handy Chute for Unloading Hogs

A Convenient Chute for Unloading Hogs from Wagons to the Pens at the Shipping Yards

The chute shown in the photo is in constant use for unloading hogs in a shipping yard at North Vernon, Ind. It pivots on the corner of a building, and the outside legs are fitted with small wheels, so that it can be pulled around easily. In use the chute is swung with one end against the back end of the wagon box, and the hogs driven through the chute into the pen. When not in use the chute is swung back against the building, closing the opening, and serving as part of the fence.—J. C. Allen, West Lafayette, Ind.

Bevel-Cutting Tool for Bar Stock

A handy and speedy tool for pointing, beveling, or turning radii on the ends of round stock, can easily be made and used on any type of lathe, combining in the smallest possible amount of metal a tool holder and guide for the stock. The cutting tools are made from power-hacksaw blades that have been broken or worn out, the holder being made from tool steel, drilled and reamed out to fit the stock being worked. A diagonal slit is then sawed with a hacksaw blade that has had the set of the teeth ground off to the thickness of the blade section. In use, the cutting edge of the tool is turned down, causing the chips to drop and prevent clogging. The inclination of the slot serves the double purpose of permitting an easy clamping action of the holder in the turret, and at the same time presenting the tool at an easy cutting angle. The holder should be hardened to prevent undue wear on the guide section.

SLIT
CUTTER BLADE
5/8"
1/4" CHIP HOLE
SECTIONAL SIDE VIEW
TOP VIEW
HARDENED STEEL
HOLE DRILLED AND REAMED TO FIT STOCK
30° BEVEL
60° BEVEL
1/4" RADIUS
RADIUS & BEVEL
VARIOUS SHAPES OF CUTTERS MADE OF HACKSAW BLADES

Blades of various shapes for different classes of work are easily ground from pieces of power-hacksaw blades on a fine-grained wheel.

On speed-lathe work, it has been found best to hold the tool in the chuck of the headstock spindle and allow it to run continuously, holding the work in a drill chuck in the tailstock spindle.

Stand for Light Testing Work

White paper makes an excellent background for testing work by the light method. In the illustration a stand is shown that was made especially for this purpose. This stand holds the paper so that it can be slid up and down to suit the operator, and also be turned around to any position to reflect the light. The base of the support is a slab of round stock, in the center of which is driven a length of 1/8-in. wire, sharpened at one end and bent over as shown, to eliminate the chances of an accidental scratch. When using squares, center gauges, straightedges, or similar tools used for testing the shape of work this stand will be found to be of considerable assistance, as it does away with the necessity of setting the paper up against different objects to obtain the correct light.

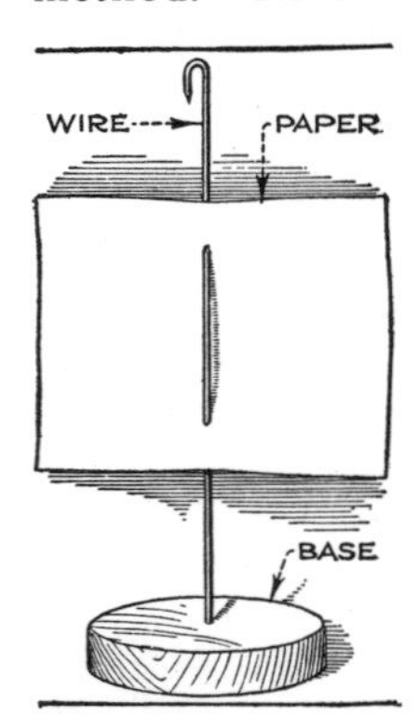

¶Steam rising from water at the boiling point has a pressure equal to the atmosphere, 14.7 lb. per square inch.

Drilling Fiber

A small shop order called for the drilling of a large number of soft fiber sheets. The holes were laid off and prick-punched in the usual way, but trouble arose during the drilling in that a ragged burr was formed on both sides of the holes and attempts to remove it merely resulted in a much worse looking hole.

To overcome the trouble, a fixture of the kind illustrated was attached to the drill press. It consists of a piece of flat iron, a collar, and two bushings, one threaded and the other plain. The plain bushing is a tight fit in the hole in the center of the drill-press table, and the threaded bushing screws into a tapped hole in the flat iron, which is bent to the shape shown, and clamped to the drill-press spindle by a collar and setscrew. Thus the entire surface of the table is clear of any obstruction and the work can be moved around as freely as if no fixture were used.

In operation, the flat-iron bracket is held about 1 in. above the surface of the work; then with the drill revolving in the hole of the threaded bushing, the spindle is brought down until the drill point enters the punch mark. The threaded bushing is then screwed down tightly on the work and the hole is drilled. With the work thus held tightly between the two bushings, a clean-cut hole can be drilled. The threaded bushing is turned back only a couple of threads when changing the position of the work—just enough to allow the operator to see when the drill point enters the punch mark, so that operation of the device does not by any means slow up the work.

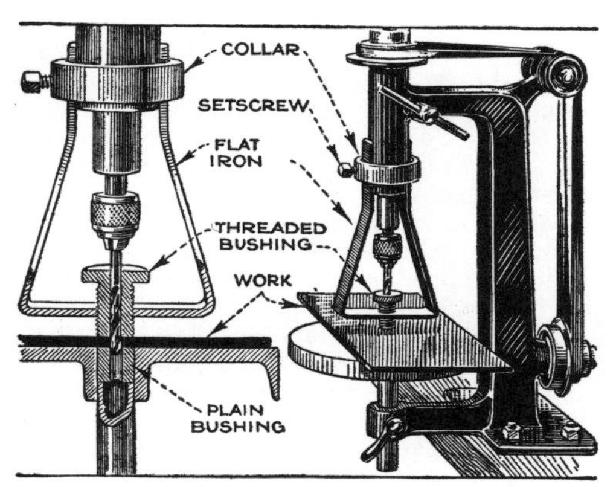

Fixture on the Drill Press for Drilling Holes Through Soft Fiber without Burrs

Roller for Handling Lumber

The roller support for handling lumber shown in the drawing is of considerable assistance in many places, as it can be placed in a door, window, between girders and studdings, or on a truck. It has the advantages of being both simple and adjustable, and can be used without any stays or props.

A Simple and Adjustable Roller Which Is of Great Assistance in Handling Lumber

The upper detail shows its construction and gives the dimensions. It consists of a jack fitted with a revolving sleeve on which the lumber is rolled. The jack is made of a screw, threading into a length of strong 2-in. pipe, and is fitted with a pipe cap and a handle for turning the screw. The revolving sleeve is a shorter length of pipe or steel tubing, and fits loosely between two collars tightened on the jack.

When a wooden post or brace is to be set on a smooth concrete floor, it often becomes a problem how to make it stand securely without the danger of slipping. If two or three ½-in. holes are chiseled in the concrete and nails driven into the bottom of the post, until about ½ in. of the head end is exposed and in such a position that they will project into the holes in the concrete, the post will not slip.

CHIPPED-GLASS WORK

BY J. S. HAGANS

MOST of us, at some time or another, have seen some examples of chipped-glass work, and wondered how the fanciful designs were made on the glass. The process is a simple one, although demanding just the right combination of temperature and materials, if the desired richness of effect is to be obtained.

A brief description of the whole process at this point will enable the reader to understand the purpose of each of the various steps in the work later on. First, the glass is roughened on the side to be chipped, then coated with thick, warm glue, and laid away to dry. When dry, it is put into a closed chamber and subjected to a fairly high degree of heat; when heated, the difference in the expansion of the glue and glass causes the former to chip off, bringing with it fragments of glass. The result is a pattern, of wonderful design, chipped into the surface of the glass.

It is absolutely necessary that the surface of the glass to be worked upon be roughened, to afford a "foothold" for the glue; smooth glass cannot be chipped, because the glue cannot obtain a grip, and flakes off without affecting the surface of the glass in the least. The quickest and most thorough way to roughen the glass is by means of the sandblast, as shown in Fig. 1. Sandblast apparatus of various forms, suitable for this work, was described on page 464 of the March, 1923, issue of this magazine. If compressed air is not available, or the amount of work is small, the glass may be roughened with sand and water, applied by means of a block, as shown in Fig. 2. This part of the work need not be done with any particular care, because scratches, unless very deep, will be obliterated in the finished work.

The next step is to apply the glue. A good grade of glue is soaked overnight, and melted in the morning to make a rather thick liquid. This is applied to the rough surface of the work with a broad brush, as in Fig. 3, so that every part of the surface is covered with a layer of glue about 1/16 in. thick. This done, the glass is laid away on a level surface and allowed to dry at room temperature. The consistency of the glue used must be found by test, but only the best glue obtainable should be used, and a thick solution applied to the work.

In some cases, the glue will begin to chip and fly off at room temperature, and the process can be expedited by playing the breeze from an electric fan over the sheet. If the glue dries out thoroughly without showing any signs of chipping, the process can be started by the application of heat. The glass is placed on edge in an oven, and the temperature run up as high as necessary to start the chipping, being careful, of course, to guard against fire through overheating. If the glass is too large for any oven available, a simple sheet-metal oven for containing the glass can be built to be set on a stove. It might be noted here that double-strength glass should be used in this process, as the lighter single-strength glass is apt to be broken by the tension created, especially in large sheets.

Assuming that the result has been satisfactory, the sheet now bears the appearance shown in Fig. 4, and is known as "single-process" chipped glass. If a finer pattern is desired, the "double process" can be used; this consists in applying another coat of glue to the glass, and treating exactly as before.

So far, the process is simple, and a solid-chipped sheet of glass is produced, such as might be used in an office door, or for some similar purpose. A little more care and work are necessary when an advertising sign, such as shown in Fig. 6, or any similar job, is to be made.

In the example shown, the letters and the scroll are chipped, the rest of the panel remaining clear; for this particular job, good plate glass should be used.

The glass is slightly warmed, and given a thin coating of beeswax; then, still keeping the glass warm, a sheet of lead foil, or even thin, tough brown paper, is rubbed down into close contact with the waxed surface of the glass. The design

Various Steps in the Making of Chipped Glass, Both Simple Sheet and Ornamental Work: The Process Is Simple, and the Work May Be Done in a Small Shop

is then drawn on the foil, as shown in Fig. 7, and the outline gone over with a sharp knife. The foil covering the parts to be chipped is then stripped off as indicated in Fig. 8, and the work is sandblasted through the stencil, as in Fig. 9. Next, the work, with the stencil still in position, is coated with glue, Fig. 10, after which the remainder of the stencil is stripped off. From this point on the treatment is exactly the same as for the plain sheet.

Signs of this kind are usually backed with gold or silver leaf, to make the letters stand out to the best advantage, and they have an unusually rich and striking appearance because of the refraction of the light striking the bright metal leaf through the rough surface of the glass.

The plain part of the glass can be coated on the back with some free-flowing paint that contrasts with the leaf; green and red are the colors usually chosen for this work.

Very fine results can be obtained by a combination of sandblasting, as described in the issue previously referred to, and chipping. This method requires two separate stencils, and the sandblasted part of the design is done first. This part is protected by the second stencil, which exposes only the parts to be chipped.

Stamping Tags Quickly and Neatly

A shipping clerk in a small factory, who had a large quantity of shipping tags to stamp with an ordinary rubber stamp, found the work quite tedious on account of the difficulty of holding each tag so that the printing could be stamped squarely on it. To simplify the work, he constructed the attachment shown in the drawing, and found that its use effected a considerable saving of time.

A Convenient and Time-Saving Attachment on a Bench Top for Stamping Large Quantities of Cards

A small block, the same length as the stamp, was fastened on the bench top, and two 6-in. iron straps were drilled at the ends and screwed loosely to the block and to the stamp, so that it could be swung back and forth from the ink pad at one side to the tag at the other side. Tacks, partly driven into the bench top, were used as stop pins to locate the tags quickly in the proper position for stamping.—G. E. Hendrickson, Argyle, Wis.

Adjustable Pinch Bar Pulls Gib Keys

The illustration shows an adjustable pinch bar for pulling gib keys. When using an ordinary puller it is necessary to put a block behind the head as soon as the key is pulled out a short distance, but, with the puller shown, the use of a block is eliminated. The attachment consists of a tapered piece, with teeth or serrations engaging with similar teeth on the back of the pinch bar. A sliding collar holds both parts together securely, and prevents either from moving when in use. The collar is slid toward the handle when the parts must be set for another "bite."

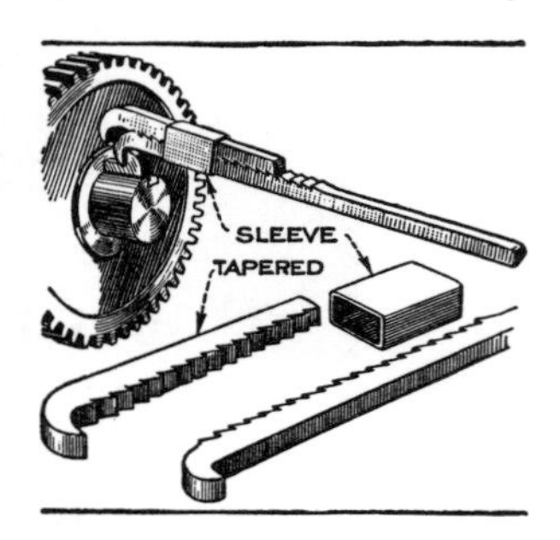

Pattern Color Denotes Material

A simple and practical method of indicating, for the information of the foundryman, the materials from which parts are to be made is to have the different materials indicated by the color of the patterns, a color chart being provided for reference. With this method it is possible to avoid mistakes and to prevent the delay necessary to trace the pattern back to the original drawing. A color scheme of this kind, which was found to be of considerable assistance in a foundry, is as follows: Black for cast iron, gray for steel, yellow for brass, red for copper, and white for aluminum. The color used on the pattern was as close to the natural color of the metal as possible.

Improving Carpenters' Compasses

Carpenters are often annoyed by the loss of the screw that clamps the adjustable point of their compasses. A simple method of eliminating this trouble is as follows: Just above the screw slot make two hacksaw cuts ⅛ in. apart and ⅛ in. deep, and another cut about ⅛ in. from the end of the leg. Bend the cut portions downward and slip through these loops an 8-penny nail, from which the head has been removed, and with the point sharpened. On many forms of work an ordinary carpenters' pencil can be substituted for the round-pointed pencil, with the advantage that the lead does not wear so quickly.

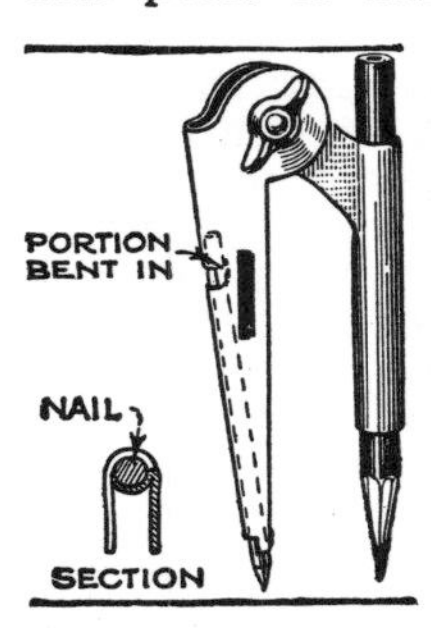

Protector for Cadmium Sticks

In making storage-battery tests with the aid of cadmium, it is usually necessary to have a jar of water handy in which to immerse the cadmium, as it does not deteriorate as quickly in water as it does in air. Rather than carry a separate jar around with the voltmeter, it has been found convenient to attach a test tube to the side of the voltmeter as shown in the illustration. The cadmium stick is fitted with a rubber cork so that the water in the test tube will not be spilled while carrying the voltmeter around.—J. B. Burnett, Vinita, Okla.

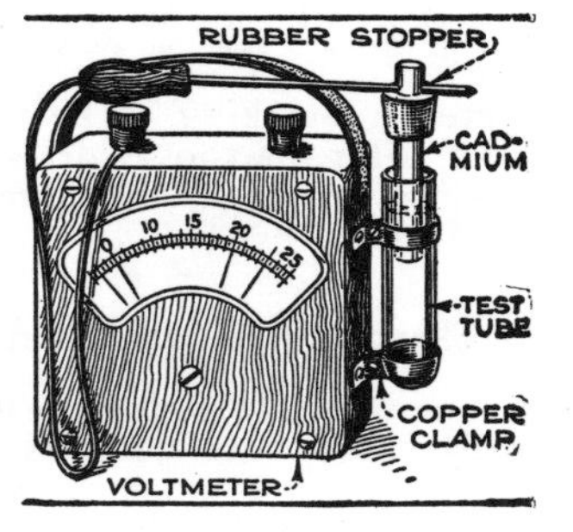

Guard over Door Prevents Danger from Icicles

Many instances have been recorded where workmen in factories have been injured by icicles falling from eaves over doors that they were obliged to use frequently. At a factory in Three Rivers, Mich., safety guards have been installed over all doors to various buildings throughout the plant, and have proved effective in preventing the formation of icicles of any size. The guard consists merely of two pieces of 4 by 4-in. timber, placed in the shape of an inverted V, and nailed to the roof directly over the entrance or door. A strip of roofing paper is nailed to the roof and against the upper side edge of the V-frame, forming a flashing to deflect the drippings to either side of the doorway. During warm weather, when there is no ice or snow, the guard serves as an eaves trough, deflecting the rain away from the doorway.

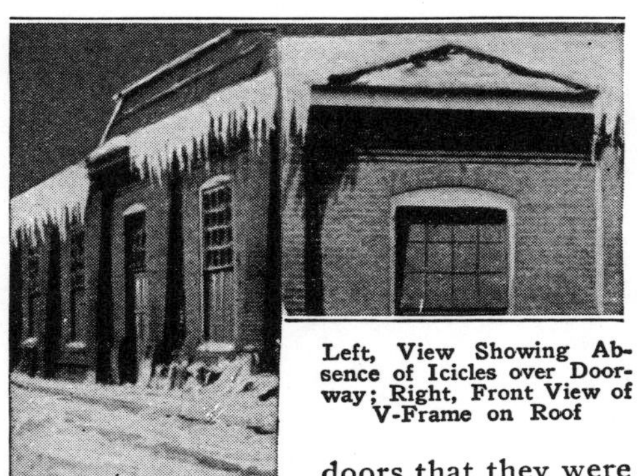

Left, View Showing Absence of Icicles over Doorway; Right, Front View of V-Frame on Roof

How to Clean Tools

To keep tools clean and bright rub a little mercurial ointment over them, which will form a moisture-resisting coating. Mecurial ointment is also known as blue butter. It is somewhat poisonous, so should be handled carefully. Another good mixture to keep tools from rusting is made by taking six parts of lard and one part of resin. Heat these together slowly until the resin is all melted. The mixture should be heated in the open air in case of fire, and benzine added in about the proportion of one pint of benzine to half a pound of the mixture. When cool, the mixture can be rubbed lightly over the bright-steel articles. Tools thus treated will resist the corrosive action even of salt water.

Pulling Stumps

In pulling stumps I find that a team and one or two long chains will do the work effectively if arranged correctly.

An Effective Method of Pulling Stumps by Means of a Heavy Chain and a Team of Horses

The greater the distance the stumps are apart, the easier they can be pulled.

When two stumps are situated close together, loop the chain around each stump and hook it. Twist it by means of a lever to get it as tight as possible, and hook the team on as shown. In case there is no other stump to hitch to, dig down so as to expose the main root, and, after fastening one end of the chain, wind it around the stump, and under the root, providing a loop large enough for a 10-in. pole. This pole should be about 20 ft. long and the team is hitched at one end as indicated in the left-hand detail.—E. R. Booth, Edwardsville, N. Y.

"Oxidizing" Copper and Brass

The antique finish so much admired in fixtures, hinges, trays, etc., known also as "oxidized" work, is produced on both copper and brass in exactly the same way. The process is cheap and simple. A strong solution of potash and lye, using about two tablespoons to a quart of water, is first made. A second solution consisting of about 2 oz. of sulphide of potash and two quarts of water, is then prepared. After fastening a short piece of wire to the article, to serve as a handle, the article is dipped into the first solution to remove all the grease and dirt. It is then rinsed in hot water and dipped into the sulphide solution until it has a good, sharp-black color in the case of a copper article, and a grayish black in case of a brass article. It is again rinsed in hot water and hung up to dry. When thoroughly dry, it is buffed all over lightly on a soft cloth buffing wheel, then buffed so that the copper will show through in spots to produce the desired effect. A little practice will enable one to buff a piece so that it will look as well as if done by an expert.—E. R. Haan, Chicago, Illinois.

Trimming Spreader for Upholsterers

Automobile upholstery of the better grade is trimmed with tape that rolls back on itself, after tacking, to conceal the tacks. As it is rather difficult to hold the trimming flat while nailing, the spreading tool shown in the photograph has been found useful for this purpose.

A piece of galvanized iron about 4 in. long and 3 in. wide is cut to the shape shown in the lower right-hand detail. The narrow tongue is curved to form a handle and the tapering projections bent to form cones. In use the tape is fed into the large ends of the cones and is drawn out through the narrow ends, causing the edges to roll apart, thus exposing the center for tacking. The trimming closes again after the tool is drawn a few inches further.—Edwin M. Love, Alhambra, California.

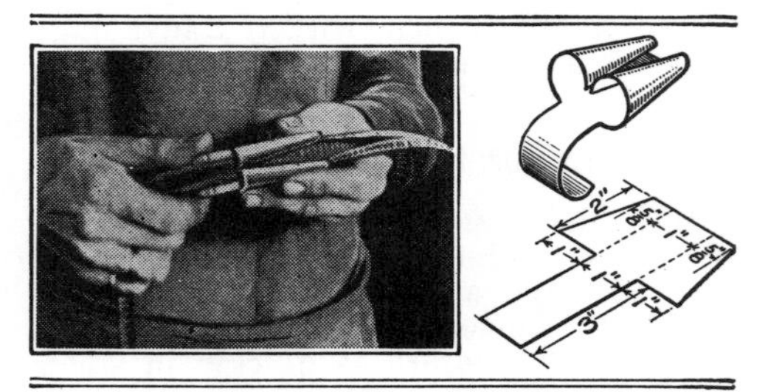

A Tool for Spreading the Trimming Tape Used on the Better Grades of Automobile Upholstery

Restoring Overexposed Blueprints

A simple method of restoring overexposed blueprints consists in taking the print from the washing-tank and laying it face upward, while still wet, on the table, then placing an unexposed dry piece of blueprint paper of the same size over the wet one, and rubbing it with a piece of cloth or with the hands. This brings the two surfaces into intimate con-

tact, and when separated, it will be found that the overexposed print is perfectly clear and of a rich blue color. The color obtained in this way is better than that obtained by the ordinary exposure and development, but there is, of course, the objection that a piece of blueprint paper is wasted for each print made.

Keeping Dirt from Boots When Excavating

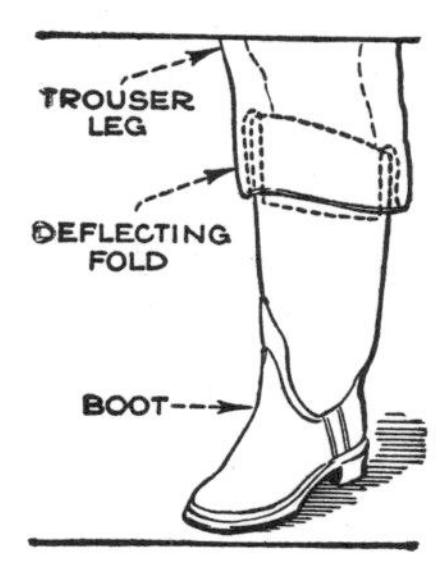

When excavating trenches, the worker's boots collect loose dirt and stones, which makes it very uncomfortable for him and makes it necessary to remove the boots frequently. This trouble may be prevented by folding the trouser leg over the boot so as to overlap about 3 or 4 in. as shown This lap prevents the passage of dirt into the boot.—Louis Schneider, Clinton, Mo.

Planing Deep Grooves

Every machinist and toolmaker knows what a tedious job it is to machine a deep rectangular groove in metals, particularly in brass or steel, with the ordinary tool holders on the planer or shaper. These tool holders carry the tool bit at an angle that gives the nose a positive rake, which is very good on plain work, but in grooving work, where a wide, square-nosed tool is used, it tends to dig in and break off. By reversing the tool holder—that is, by using it backwards — the bit is given a negative rake. Of course, the bit must be re-ground so that the nose has a good cutting lip, and it will then do good work, taking a fairly heavy cut, and tending to spring away from the work, rather than to dig into it.—George A. Volz, Redford, Mich.

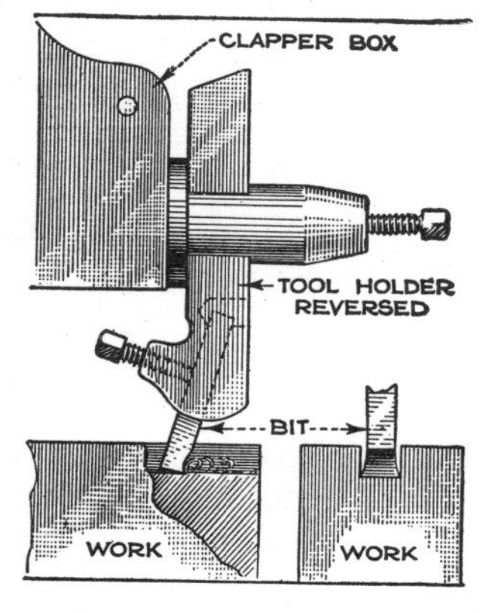

Useful Clamp for the Woodwork Bench

The drawing shows a simple homemade clamp that is of considerable usefulness to woodworkers. It consists of a wooden block, securely screwed to the benchtop in the position shown, and faced on one side with 1/16-in. sheet iron. This forms the permanent jaw. A 2 by 4-in. lever, also faced at one end with sheet iron, and slotted at the other end as shown, is arranged to pivot on a strap hinge that is screwed to the benchtop and bolted to the lever at the point indicated. The upper end of the lever forms the movable jaw. The vise is tightened by means of a 2 by 4-in. cam, attached to the bench leg with a butt hinge, the narrow part of the cam fitting in the slot of the lever and extending outward about 6 in. so that it can be operated by the foot. Forcing the cam lever downward brings the vise jaws together, clamping the work between them. If the object is too small to be held between the jaws, one or two small wooden blocks are put between it and the jaws.

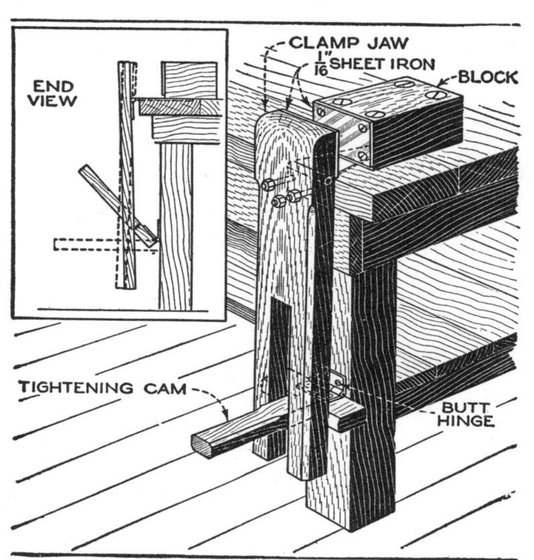

A Simple Foot-Operated Bench Clamp of Considerable Usefulness to the Woodworker

Cleaning an Oil-Soaked Belt

To clean an oil-soaked belt, coil the belt loosely in a box or tub and fill the box with whiting, being sure to get the whiting between the surfaces for the entire length. Let it remain thus overnight, and the whiting will absorb the oil and leave the belt clean.

A Lesson for Patternmakers

By M. E. Duggan

When I say that a pattern was molded in green sand, with a dry-sand core, and that the core was made without the aid of a corebox, the patternmaker who has had foundry training readily understands, but the patternmaker whose training was received in a shop far from the foundry looks at me with astonishment, and wonders how it was done. The young patternmaker will therefore appreciate a clear description of this detail of patternmaking and foundry practice.

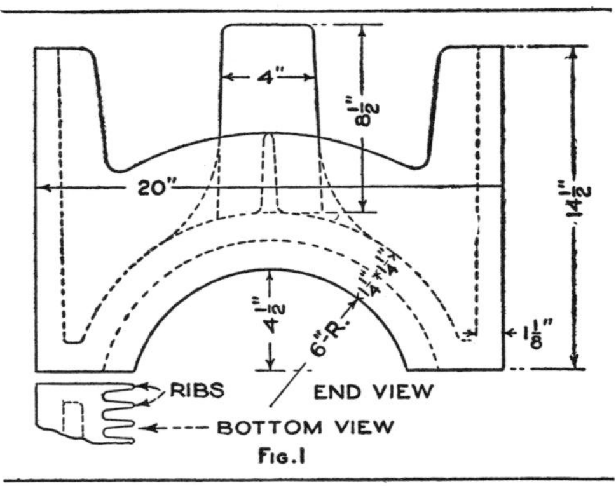

Piece That Was Cast in Green-Sand and Dry-Sand Core without Corebox

The pattern selected for illustration was made by a worker who had a number of years' experience; he constructed it for green-sand molding, which, by the way, was impracticable in this case. When the casting was made, and the patternmaker was told that the job was done "in green-sand and dry-sand core" he thought that there was something wrong with the foundry, as he was positive that no corebox had been made for the job.

A side view of the work is shown in Fig. 1; it was made with ribs ⅜ in. thick at the bottom, tapering to ¼ in. at the edge, and 1¼ in. deep. A section through the center is shown in Fig. 2. The pattern was molded with the ribs up; the piece could not be molded in green sand because the sand could not be made secure and would drop when the cope was being closed down on the drag, and the thin ridges of sand forming the spaces between the ribs would be "washed" away in the closing of the mold. For these reasons the molder decided to use a dry-sand core.

With the pattern inverted, core sand was rammed in between the ribs, the pattern was then turned "right side up" on a core drying plate, and core sand filled in below and around it as indicated in Fig. 2; the pattern was then lifted from the sand core and the core baked.

Pieces of bent wire were imbedded in the core before baking, and, after baking, the sand above these wires was cut away to allow other wires to be passed under them. Then the core was taken to the molding floor and the core and pattern put back in the position shown in Fig. 2, except that a bottom or molding board was used instead of the iron core-drying plate. Drag flasks were then put in place and green sand filled in as shown, completing the drag.

The drag, with the pattern, core, and bottom board was then rolled over to receive the cope flask, in this case what is known as a "flat back"; this molding method makes it possible to use almost any flat cope flask.

When the rolling was done, the bottom board was removed, and the cope flask placed in position. Two wooden battens were placed across the cope flask, as shown in Fig. 3, and the core tightly drawn against the cope by means of wires passed under the wires in the core, and around the battens.

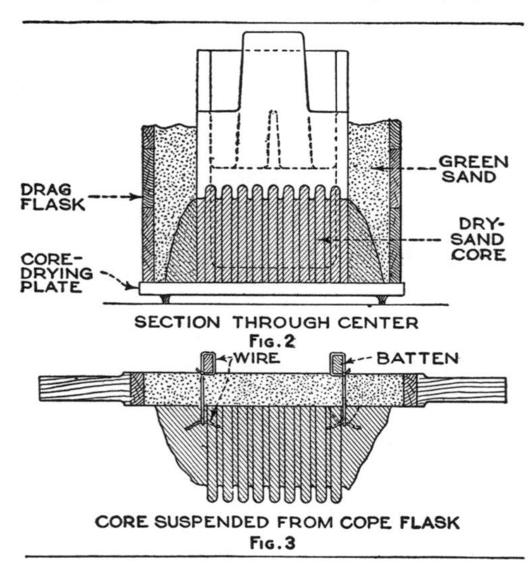

Above, Preparation of Drag; Below, Dry-Sand Core Forming Cope

The cope, with the core attached, was then lifted, the pattern removed from the drag, the cope replaced and clamped, and the mold was ready for the iron.

INDEX TO VOLUME XX

SHOP NOTES FOR 1924

NOTES

NOTES

NOTES

NOTES

NOTES

NOTES

NOTES

NOTES

NOTES

NOTES

NOTES

NOTES